THE ANATOMY OF MATHEMATICS

By

R. B. KERSHNER

APPLIED PHYSICS LABORATORY
THE JOHNS HOPKINS UNIVERSITY

L. R. WILCOX

ASSOCIATE PROFESSOR OF MATHEMATICS
ILLINOIS INSTITUTE OF TECHNOLOGY

THE RONALD PRESS COMPANY · NEW YORK

PRINTED IN THE UNITED STATES OF AMERICA

PARADOX

Not truth, nor certainty. These I forswore
In my novitiate, as young men called
To holy orders must abjure the world.
"If . . ., then . . .," this only I assert;
And my successes are but pretty chains
Linking twin doubts, for it is vain to ask
If what I postulate be justified,
Or what I prove possess the stamp of fact.

Yet bridges stand, and men no longer crawl
In two dimensions. And such triumphs stem
In no small measure from the power this game,
Played with the thrice-attenuated shades
Of things, has over their originals.
How frail the wand, but how profound the spell!

CLARENCE R. WYLIE, JR.

PREFACE

A need has long existed for a treatise on the axiomatic method. Such a book is needed to serve as a text in a course in the subject designed to free mathematics students from the attitude that mathematics is primarily pencil-pushing and to introduce them to the ideas and methods pervading modern mathematical research. Moreover, a reference source has been lacking for workers in those sciences which are employing to an increasing degree the results and techniques of abstract mathematics.

Accordingly, this work has been produced in the hope that students may be aided in bridging the gap between classical and modern approaches, and that the terminologies and points of view which the axiomatic method entails may become more readily accessible to those who suddenly find themselves in need of becoming familiar with them.

No attempt is made to glamorize or oversimplify the subject in order to attract as many readers as possible. In view of the diffidence of the layman when confronted with the word *mathematics*, it is expected that this book will prove of greatest service to teachers or prospective teachers of mathematics or science in the high schools and colleges and to science majors and graduate students. However it is hoped that at least a few so-called laymen will take advantage of the opportunity, here provided, to learn what modern mathematics is like, without being expected to bring an elaborate technical education to lay upon the altar. The only prerequisites for reading this book are the desire to start and the perseverance to finish. The reader does not even need to know the sum of 7 and 5; incidentally, if he does not know this sum, he will not learn it from this book.

The axiomatic method is presented primarily by example, because of our strong conviction that no conception whatever of the nature of mathematics or of rigorous deductive reasoning can be created by descriptive talk; and that only by close contact and hard work can a reader gain a thorough understanding and appreciation of the subject.

While undoubtedly much inspiration for this work has been provided at the subconscious level by various colleagues, teachers and mathematical experiences, the existence of Landau's *Grundlagen der Analysis* probably exerted the greatest single influence. In fact, the spirit of the *Grundlagen* approximates that of the present work more closely than does that of any other work known to us. The chief difference between the *Grundlagen* and the present treatment, aside from content, lies in the completeness with which we have proved certain things which Landau feels are very simple. Indeed, we believe that some of our work with positive integers has disclosed problems and subtleties comparable in interest and difficulty to those met in much more "advanced" subjects.

The order in which our names appear is purely alphabetical; neither of us claims to have contributed more than the other. Initially the work on the set-theoretic matters, inductive definition, the principle of choice was due to Wilcox, while the treatments of the rational and real number systems and the one-dimensional continuum are fundamentally due to Kershner.

The poem *Paradox*, by Clarence R. Wylie, Jr., appeared in the July, 1948 issue of *Scientific Monthly*, and is used with the permission of the *Scientific Monthly*.

Much insight into pedagogical aspects of the subject has been gained through the opportunity which one of us has twice had to present the material in a course for third and fourth year college students.

We are most indebted to Mrs. L. R. Wilcox, who typed most of the manuscript and who offered many invaluable criticisms concerning its content.

R. B. K.
L. R. W.

CONTENTS

CHAPTER 1

INTRODUCTION

CHAPTER 2

LANGUAGE

CHAPTER 3

THE DEVELOPMENT OF MATHEMATICS

CHAPTER 4

THE PRIMITIVE MATERIALS OF MATHEMATICS

CHAPTER 5

FURTHER MATERIALS OF MATHEMATICS

CHAPTER 6

THE POSTULATIONAL METHOD

CHAPTER 7

GROUPS

CHAPTER 8

THE POSITIVE INTEGERS

CHAPTER 9

FUNDAMENTAL RELATIONS ON THE POSITIVE INTEGERS

CHAPTER 10

FINITE SETS

CHAPTER 11

INDUCTIVE DEFINITION AND THE PRINCIPLE OF CHOICE

CHAPTER 12

EXTENDED OPERATIONS AND APPLICATIONS

CHAPTER 13

INFINITE SETS

CHAPTER 14

ISOMORPHISM AND CATEGORICAL SYSTEMS OF AXIOMS

CHAPTER 15

EQUIVALENCE AND ORDER RELATIONS

CHAPTER 16

THE POSITIVE RATIONAL NUMBERS

CHAPTER 17

ONE–DIMENSIONAL CONTINUA

CHAPTER 18

THE POSITIVE REAL NUMBERS

CHAPTER 19

THE REAL NUMBERS

CHAPTER 20

FIELDS

CHAPTER 21

CONCLUSION

APPENDIX

THE ANATOMY OF MATHEMATICS

Chapter 1

INTRODUCTION

1.1. Objective. Almost from its beginnings mathematics has played a triple role. At the very earliest it was, apparently, closely allied to religion and hence, like primitive religions, was compounded equally of down-to-earth pragmatism and far-flung mysticism. Early Egyptian mathematics was indispensable to the surveyor and the astrologer alike. The third aspect of mathematics was added in the sixth or fifth century B.C., when it was discovered that mathematical results are amenable to logical analysis and demonstration. Then mathematics became, for many of its practitioners, a pure mental discipline, with its significances, both practical and occult, considered as by-products.

With the mystic significance of mathematics we shall not be concerned here. We remark only that the astrologers and numerologists are legion, and there seems, unfortunately, little hope that the mystic aspects of mathematics will suffer from a lack of publicity.

The practical use of mathematics has an importance which it would be foolish to deny. Without mathematics such amenities of modern civilization as elevators, automatic cigarette vending machines and atomic bombs could not have been developed. In short, mathematics is an indispensable ingredient of modern science and technology, and so, for good or ill, it has marked our lives. But this aspect of mathematics is too obviously important to need further accolade here. And there has been, in recent years, a positive spate of books dedicated to the glorification of mathematics considered as the handmaiden of the sciences.

And so this book will be concerned with the third role of mathematics, the mental discipline. The study of mathematics as the prototype of logical thought does enjoy a current vogue among the professional practitioners, but no more than a hint of this fact has distilled over into the classrooms.

True, a certain lip service is paid to the "axiomatic method" in many high school courses in euclidean geometry, but the standards of rigor are out-of-date by well over twenty centuries! Actually the small gesture toward the recognition of the value of careful thought, represented by the usual high school geometry course, almost certainly does more harm than good. The critical student is inclined to feel that a "logic" which includes the parroting of such abracadabra as, "The whole is equal to the sum of its parts," or "A point is that which is without length, breadth or thickness" (*exasperation* qualifies aptly) is not for him. The trouble is simply that euclidean geometry is one of the more difficult branches of mathematics to treat axiomatically; for example, it is too difficult to include in this book.

In subsequent mathematics courses, in high school and college, the major emphasis is quite frankly placed on the tool aspect of mathematics. The criterion of achievement is problem-solving ability. The most successful texts are those with the most numerous and varied problems.

One cannot quarrel with this utilitarian view as long as it is applied to the education of engineers, physicists, chemists, and others who will need the ability to use mathematical methods of problem-solving. But one may seriously question how a physician, lawyer, advertising man or business executive is benefited by having, or by having once had, the ability to find out how old Ann is, from a collection of unlikely data.

On the other hand, a lawyer, business executive or anyone else would be aided by an ability to distinguish between the specious and the specific, between wishful and careful thinking. And the physicist or engineer who wants to use the tool of mathematics without cutting himself would be particularly aided by learning a little of the "why," along with the necessary vast amount of "how."

Now it must be admitted that an understanding of abstract reasoning, as exemplified by modern standards of rigor in mathematics, does not automatically make for clear and careful thinking on all subjects. It is even admitted, reluctantly, that there may be mathematicians with a considerable aptitude in exacting fields of thought, who are as opinionated politically, bigoted ecclesiastically, and intolerant generally, as anyone you are likely to find. In addition to an understanding of the nature of a proof, there are needed also the desire to transfer that understanding into other fields, and the open-mindedness to permit the transfer to be made. But certain it is that the transfer is impossible if there is nothing to transfer. With a firm conviction that logic can be of great value to any open-minded man, this book will be devoted to an exemplification of modern standards of logical thought, as applied to the simplest branches of mathematics.

In the succeeding chapters we shall attempt to describe the ultimate and intimate logical structure—in short, the anatomy—of mathematics. Chapters 2 and 3 will consist of necessary preparations, the sharpening and sterilization of the scalpel and the general measurement of the corpus. Chapters 4 and 5 will cover bone and tissue chemistry, the analysis of the materials of which our subject is composed. Chapters 6 and 7 describe the skeleton or framework which underlies any mathematical subject. Finally specific body forms begin to appear in Chapter 7 and the remainder of the book.

1.2. Format. A few words about the format of the book are in order. Each chapter is divided into a number of sections. Items, such as statements, figures, and the like, to which importance is attached are displayed in conjunction with a reference mark usually placed at the left margin. In almost all cases the reference mark consists of three numbers separated by periods in the following manner:

(1.2.1) Statement.

The three separate numbers indicate the chapter, the section, and the individual number of the displayed item. For example, (11.4.15) would be in Chapter 11, Section 4, and would be the 15th numbered item in that section. Complete sections will be referred to by a pair of numbers of which the first is the chapter number, so that (11.4) means Chapter 11, Section 4.

Statements in the body of a mathematical theory, which form a portion of the theory and require proof, are called *theorems*. The terms *corollary* and *lemma* also occur. A *corollary* is a theorem which is an immediate or easy consequence of a preceding theorem or definition. A *lemma* is a theorem which is proved mainly as an aid in establishing a subsequent theorem.

Sections and sometimes whole chapters dealing with specific mathematical subject matter are so designated by a display of the appropriate information in square brackets immediately following the heading.

The underlying hypotheses of a branch of mathematics will always be referred to as *axioms*, rather than postulates. This word choice is entirely arbitrary and is not intended to have any significance.

It will be discovered that a typical mathematical theory builds a rather elaborate superstructure on a compact foundation. Therefore, in the development of a theory, it is necessary to make frequent use of definitions and assertions stated earlier. For this reason the pages of the book are rather liberally sprinkled with phrases such as "by (15.3.7), it is seen that . . .," or "it follows from (14.1.7) and (14.1.8), in view of (10.2.2.b), that. . . ." A back reference is given whenever a reasonable possibility exists that the reader may not recall the pertinent assertions or definitions. If the reader can follow the demonstration or argument presented without turning back to ascertain what (14.1.7) or (10.2.2.b) states, he should by all means read on. If he finds that it is usually necessary to track down the back references before the argument becomes clear, then he might be aided by preparing a cumulative list of items to which frequent reference is made, in order to minimize the time spent in leafing through the book.

Beginning in Chapter 4 a number of *projects* appear at the ends of sections. These projects are designed to enable the reader to gauge his absorption of the textual material and to help him increase his mastery of the subject by applying and extending the methods and theories presented. An appendix containing solutions or hints pertaining to the projects is included. Of course, the projects will be of greatest value to the reader if he uses the appendix as sparingly as possible, preferably only for verification of his own solutions. In this connection, it is worth observing that a solution to a project may differ radically from that in the appendix and still be quite correct.

Chapter 2

LANGUAGE

2.1. Confusion from Language. It is a rather unfortunate fact that ideas can be conveyed from one person to another only through the medium of language. The recognition of this fact, and of the difficulties implied by it, is a prerequisite to a careful presentation of a precise subject. Thus we are led immediately to a discussion of language, because the degree of lucidity that we achieve may depend on what attitude we adopt toward language, and on the tenacity with which we adhere to the program dictated by our attitude. In order to bring the problem into focus, let us consider a few examples of human communication.

According to principles of etiquette, when we leave a dinner party we should say, "Thank you so much; good night." Our hostess might then reply, "It was nice to see you again," or "I'm so glad you could come." Here is a case of almost the least meaningful use of language. Any of hundreds of similar phrases would serve the purpose equally well, the exact words selected being quite immaterial. The reason for such latitude is, of course, that what is said has little or no relation to what is meant, if indeed anything at all is meant beyond a desire to conform with the "rules." Uses of language such as this are referred to as "presymbolic," because of obvious similarity to the meaningless utterances of early man. In presymbolism one meets few language problems indeed!

Political speeches, the writings of music critics, and so on, illustrate slightly less presymbolic uses of language. When a politician cries, "The present administration has destroyed human liberty and must not be returned to power," he certainly does not mean what he says; often he does not even believe it himself or expect his listeners to do so. He might mean simply that he dislikes, or hates, the present administration, and that he *hopes* for its defeat. A music critic might write, "The tones were projected on the screen of consciousness to form there a dynamic pattern of such depth of perspective that one could not help feeling the presence of a third dimension." Interpreted "literally" this is sheer nonsense. Of course, the critic is merely trying to create a mood, to share with his readers some sort of emotional experience. In these circumlocutions again, the exact choice of words within obvious limitations is relatively unimportant, so far as communication of *ideas* is concerned.

Everyday discourse exemplifies a use of language in which the degree of precision required lies somewhere between the utter lack of it in pre-symbolism and the high degree demanded by science or mathematics. Despite our exaggerations, understatements and slight ambiguities, most of us manage to get along reasonably well.

A further stage of specialization in the use of language is that illustrated by insurance policies, legal documents, government forms, and the like. Here the ideas to be conveyed are not exceptionally difficult, but the importance of lack of ambiguity is greater than in everyday discourse. Correspondingly, elaborate phraseology is introduced to guard against misinterpretations that might otherwise be possible.

The reader could easily supply further examples of more or less specialized forms of communication. And it would become apparent that the more specific the concepts are in a field of discussion, the more serious is the confusion due to the unqualified use of everyday language. It is not surprising, then, that in mathematics we shall find that language troubles are as perplexing as they can be anywhere. We must therefore make a powerful attack on them and render them as harmless as possible.

In preparation for an analysis of language difficulties, it is convenient to distinguish between two ways in which communication can fail, according as the end result is *incomprehension* or *misunderstanding*. Incomprehension results when *no* idea is communicated, misunderstanding when an unintended idea is communicated. Incomprehension arises from a number of sources, among which may be mentioned unfamiliarity of the words used, elaborate phraseology and, occasionally, inherent complexity of the idea it is desired to convey. Misunderstanding arises most commonly from the familiarity, and consequent multiplicity of meanings, of the words used.

Of the two ways in which verbal communication can fail, incomprehension leads to far less dangerous results. Often no actual harm comes from a *complete* failure to be understood. For incomprehension is generally recognized at the receiving end to be a communication failure; therefore a lack of understanding simply preserves the status quo. Misunderstanding, however, is dangerous because the recipient of the communicated idea proceeds with the calm but erroneous conviction that he knows what was intended.

The two extremes of ambiguity and unintelligibility are the Scylla and Charybdis of verbal presentation. In order to avoid the possibility of misinterpretation, one may be forced to use unfamiliar phraseology and thus reduce the clarity. Again, the examples of legal documents and government forms indicate to what extent lucidity may be decreased by the elaborations of language required to insure that statements are unequivocal.

In the next section, we begin our analysis of the language problem. The aim is to reach some understandings with the reader, which will enable us to avoid, as well as may be, both equivoque and obscurity.

2.2. Definitions. It should now quite naturally occur to the reader that in any use of language other than presymbolism, misunderstandings might be minimized by effecting agreement on definitions of dubious terms. The need for agreement is generally admitted; who, indeed, has not heard the demand, "Define your terms!" in an intelligent discussion? Yet reaching agreement on meanings is not a simple task, as we shall see.

It is easy enough to decide that you must define dubious terms. But what do you mean by a definition? If by a definition you mean the sort of thing that is found in dictionaries, then defining your terms is very little help at all.

Consider the statement, "She was fair." Suppose there is some doubt in your mind as to what the term *fair* means. You look in the dictionary and find something like this:

> fair (adj.) [AS. *faeger*, beautiful] 1, pleasing to the sight; handsome; beautiful; 2, not dark in color or complexion; blond; 3, without blemish; spotless; clean; 4, favorable; giving promise; 5, moderately satisfactory; pretty good; 6, impartial; just; 7, according to regulations; 8, allowing lawful pursuit; 9, distinct; unobstructed.

This leaves you in considerable doubt as to whether she was beautiful, clean, impartial and otherwise wholly admirable; just moderately satisfactory; or simply an unobstructed blonde not above allowing pursuit, provided it is according to regulations.

In a discussion in which it is important to be understood *independently of context*, such a multiplicity of possible meanings is intolerable. Thus we are led to one quality our definitions must have if they are to be helpful: *They must be unambiguous.* A word which is defined must be given a single meaning which invariably applies.

But multiplicity of meanings is really only one of our worries. If a definition—even an unambiguous one—is to be helpful, it must give the meaning of the new word in terms of words which are previously agreed upon as understood. Most readers are probably not familiar with the special heraldic meaning of *fret*, but it is to be doubted that they are enlightened by the dictionary definition:

> fret (*Her.*): Two bendlets in saltire interlaced with a mascle

Let the dubious words in this definition be investigated.

> bendlet: A diminutive of the bend one half its width;
> in saltire: In the manner of a saltire;
> saltire: An ordinary consisting of a bend dexter and a bend sinister crossing;
> mascle: A lozenge voided.

The reader may be pardoned a feeling that he is not getting anywhere. Of course, there is still hope that patience would be rewarded and that one would eventually reach recognizable terms by continuing to look up the unknown words.

Still there is not always hope. Suppose you wish to learn the value of the Austrian coin, the krone. A dictionary gives:

> krone: The former monetary unit of Austria-Hungary (1892–1925); also the corresponding coin, equivalent to 100 heller.
>
> heller: In Austria, up to 1925, a small copper coin equivalent to $\frac{1}{100}$ krone.

Here you have come to a dead end. Or better, here you are driving madly around an unrecognizable circle with no side turnings. Clearly, then, a helpful definition should give the unknown word in terms of known words. You cannot learn Russian from a Russian dictionary, be you ever so clever.

Now we have arrived at the heart of the trouble. The inescapable fact is that the dictionary must willy-nilly lead you into a mad circle:

> A krone is 100 hellers; a heller is $\frac{1}{100}$ krone;

or, as Gertrude Stein more beautifully expressed the same "thought," a rose is a rose is a rose. The circle may, and usually does, contain far more words; nevertheless, if you chase the definitions through, sooner or later you find the same old words whirling by again and again. This must happen simply because the dictionary is trying to do the impossible. *It is trying to define all words.*

The fact that it is impossible to define all words can be seen quite easily. We have already mentioned that a helpful definition must give the defined word in terms of previously known words. From this it follows that a truly defined word does not actually have to be used. In any discussion, the defined word could be avoided by using its defining phrase instead. In other words, since a defining phrase has the same meaning as the word it defines, the phrase can replace the word. Hence a defined word is an unnecessary word. Now we see the difficulty clearly. If all words were defined, no words would be needed. The impossibility of this conclusion suggests that there must be some words that are not to be defined.

Before commenting on a solution to our fiendish problem, we pause briefly to see how mad the process of defining words in terms of themselves really can be.

2.3. The Evils of Cyclic Definition. Thus far we have seen that the use of circular or cyclic definitions is futile if all the words in the circle are unknown. We shall see presently that riding the merry-go-round is not only a silly pastime, but that serious dizzy spells can result. The definition of words in terms of themselves is responsible for some of the familiar logical paradoxes.

Let us consider first the well-known barber paradox, in which the Barber of Seville is defined by this statement:

> He shaves all those men of Seville and only those men of Seville who do not shave themselves.

It is assumed, of course, that the terms appearing in the definition are all understood. We ask now, "Who shaves the Barber of Seville?" Since every man whom he shaves, according to the definition, does not shave himself, it is impossible that the Barber shave himself. But if he does not shave himself, then according to the definition, he is one of those men whom he shaves. The consequence of these considerations may be stated thus:

> If the Barber shaves himself, then he does not shave himself; if he does not, then he does.

Another form would be this:

> It is neither true nor false that the Barber shaves himself.

The problem posed by the barber paradox caused quite understandable concern when it was first noted, because the definition of the Barber seemed quite parallel to the sort of definitions used in mathematics. Actually, the *source* of the difficulty is easy to locate. (The *reason why* the paradox occurs is another matter, which will not be discussed.) The definition of the Barber involves the men of Seville. If the Barber is to be considered as one of the men of Seville, then the definition is cyclic. That is, the Barber is defined, in part, in terms of himself, and trouble may be expected. As we shall see later, cyclic definitions will be dealt with by ostracizing them; hence the definition of the Barber will be regarded as inadmissible, or as no definition at all. Of course, if the Barber is regarded, not as a man of Seville, but as some completely new creature introduced by his definition, the paradox disappears, and the definition is admissible. In this case, he may shave himself or not as he chooses, since the definition specifies his actions only with respect to the men of Seville, *of whom he is then not one.*

Another famous paradox, introduced by Bertrand Russell, is based on the same general idea. Let us call an adjective *self-descriptive* if it describes itself; otherwise it is called *non-self-descriptive.* A self-descriptive adjective is thus one which, if inserted into each of the blanks, makes a true statement of the following:

——— is a(n) ——— word.

The adjectives *polysyllabic* and *English* are among the few good examples available. Another example is *mispelled.* Most adjectives make the required statement obviously false (*long, German*), or nonsensical (*hairless, thankful*).

Now let us consider the adjective *non-self-descriptive* and raise the question as to whether or not it is self-descriptive. If we assume it to be self-descriptive, then a true statement results when we insert it into the blanks. Thus it is non-self-descriptive by the statement itself. On the other hand, if we assume it to be non-self-descriptive, the assumption coincides with the statement with the blanks replaced by *non-self-descriptive.* Therefore it is self-descriptive by definition. To sum up,

> if *non-self-descriptive* is self-descriptive, then it is non-self-descriptive; if it is non-self-descriptive, then it is self-descriptive.

Again, the paradox arises since the term *non-self-descriptive* is defined in terms of all adjectives and is at the same time considered an adjective itself. The definition is admissible if *non-self-descriptive* is considered as some variety of word not covered by the term *adjective*; otherwise it is inadmissible.

When we are in a position to do so [(5.4)], we shall again comment on these paradoxes and show their relation to mathematical definitions and conceptions. For the present we shall not need them further, since they have served our purpose of emphasizing the need for a complete elimination of cyclic definitions. We proceed to show how this elimination can be accomplished.

2.4. The Language Basis. In (2.1) we discussed the confusion resulting from a lack of clear, unambiguous definitions. Then, in (2.2), we saw how the standard source of definitions, the dictionary, even if we could imagine it devoid of ambiguities, necessarily leads to circularity; and we saw in (2.3) that dependence on cyclic definitions not only gets us nowhere, but introduces deep-seated logical difficulties. Perhaps all this seems chaotic and destined to remain so.

But a hint that a solution exists lies in the fact that the dictionary *is* often of value to us. True, if we look up a word, and are led through a chain of unfamiliar synonyms back to the original word, the dictionary has not helped. But if just one of the synonyms is known, then automatically they all become known. Definitions can be helpful, then, if they always give meanings ultimately in terms of a list of known words.

We have already indicated that not all words can be defined. There should then be a basic list of words that we forego defining; these words are learned by the elaborate means by which one learns to speak in childhood. Once the basic list has been decided upon and agreement on the meanings of these words has been reached, all remaining (defined) words become meaningful by virtue of the elaborate network of paths connecting them with the basic words.

It is now seen that if we were to construct a language systematically, we should introduce first a *language basis*, consisting of words and phrases, upon which all agree, and about which there is no argument. The remainder of the language would then be built by definitions introduced in some specific order, and having the property that new words would be defined always in terms only of words of the basis or previously defined words.

The need to recognize the existence of an undefined basis cannot be overemphasized. The discussions to which we have referred, in which someone has cried, "Define your terms!" probably suffered less from lack of definitions than from lack of agreement on the undefined basis or even realization that a basis was necessary. The authors cannot recall having heard a discussion in which some bewildered participant has made the really pertinent and prerequisite demand, "State your undefined terms."

Indeed, the need for a language basis is so little recognized that, so far as we are aware, no one has attempted the task of choosing one. It might be mentioned, however, that a so-called "Basic English" exists, and, although its construction was motivated by entirely different considerations, it probably is an approximation to a language basis. Basic English is intended to be a minimum vocabulary with which one can convey ideas. Accordingly, it consists largely of those words whose use one cannot avoid, and thus of words that one would probably place in the language basis. However, Basic English is almost certainly not a complete language basis for English.

Though we shall not attempt here to carry out the prodigious task of constructing explicitly a language basis, all that we do throughout the book will be influenced by the *existence* of a basis and its general nature rather than by its precise content. We turn, then, to a brief and necessarily superficial examination of a language basis.

First, it should be observed that the undefined words which lie in a basis ought naturally to be the most primitive ones in the language. These words would probably be "hardest to define" in the popular sense, and hence would reasonably be included in the basis, which is to consist of words admittedly undefinable. Thus, probably the best answer to the question of Pontius Pilate, "What is Truth?" is the statement, "Truth is a word lying in the language basis; hence it is not to be defined."

It is, of course, important not to confuse "undefined" with "meaningless." On the contrary, the undefined basic words are verbal symbols for primitive *meaningful* concepts; defined words have meaning only second hand, as it were, being shorthand for phrases of words from the undefined basis. What, then, is the source of the "meaning" of the undefined basic words? This question is indeed deep-lying and perhaps not completely answerable. An example might, however, help to throw some light on the matter.

At some time during a child's life, a moving object, which has four legs and makes a clattering noise, comes down the street. Simultaneously, Mother, who is standing near him, uses the word *horse.* The coincidence of the new object and the new word impresses him, and he assumes the word to refer to the object which he saw and heard. Some time later another object passes. This one is different: the first was white while this one is brown; the first one was running while this one is walking. Yet Mother again uses the word *horse,* and reasonably so, since the two objects do resemble each other.

After this situation has arisen a number of times, the child feels that he knows what qualities are allowed to be different and what must be the same, in order that the word *horse* be applicable. Then comes the happy day when an object comes down the street, and, although he has never seen this particular object before—this one is gray—he points triumphantly at it and says, "*Horsie!*" Mother agrees and beams. At this point *horse,* or its variant *horsie,* is a meaningful word to the child.

Yet no one would argue that *horse* means the same to the child and his mother. A visit to the zoo might prove otherwise: the child might use the word in reference to striped animals which his mother calls *zebras* and not *horses.* Yet, gradually, as his experience broadens, the child will find fewer and fewer conflicts between his terminology and that of his mother. Eventually one might say that the child and his mother have "essentially" the same meaning of *horse.*

The process of acquiring a meaning for even such a concrete word as *horse* is elaborate and does not lead to quite the same understanding on the part of all people. Clearly the meaning to any one person depends on the totality of his particular experiences. With abstract terms like *truth, beauty,* and so on, the situation is the same, except that meanings differ much more from one individual to another. There is certainly no general agreement on the applicability of the term *beauty* in any particular instance. Indeed, agreement here is so poor that the term is unusable in logical discussions.

Our conception of a language basis has now been clarified to this extent, that, although the words in it are not defined, each of us has acquired his own meaning for them by an elaborate psychological process of noticing and "integrating" correlations. Our individual meanings differ since they depend on the particular correlations we happen to have noticed, our particular experiences with the words, our varying abilities in effecting the necessary integrations, and probably a host of other things. Meanings of some (usually concrete) terms agree so closely that no serious disagreements result; other (usually abstract) terms can boast of virtually no agreement in meaning. These extremes correspond to what are commonly referred to as "objective" and "subjective" meanings, respectively. Of course, many words, for example, *truth*, lie between the extremes.

We might now elaborate the answer to the question of Pontius Pilate thus:

> *Truth* is a word in the undefined language basis. It is a word for which you must already have acquired a meaning. You acquired this meaning by hearing the word used many times, noticing the situations to which it applied, and extrapolating to further situations to which it would presumably apply. Your meaning would probably differ somewhat from mine, since we have had different experiences. However, if you have no meaning of your own, there is nothing that I can do to help you, since any attempt to define the word would require the use of terms less clear, less intuitive, less likely to be understood, less *basic* than the word *truth*.

It is important to observe that in our discussion the words *horse*, *beauty*, *truth*, appear to belong to the basis, but that they were placed there only for the purpose of illustration. Perhaps more primitive terms could be found, in which case these latter would be regarded as basic instead. Indeed, there might be considerable choice as to which words are considered most basic or most likely to be known.

Let us now assume that a basis has been found, and that a logical language has been constructed, at least as far as ordinary discourse is concerned. Our omission of the details will necessitate that we, the authors, exercise considerable care in our exposition. We must limit our use of basic words as much as possible to those near the "objective" extreme. And we must be certain that the words which are not basic are not too far removed from the basis and that their definitions in terms of basic words are well known. That this sort of care should be exercised in any precise discussion is, of course, quite evident.

Our scrutiny of language closes with specific comments on logic and the terms connected with it, and on technical mathematical terms.

2.5. How Logic and Mathematics Relate to the Language Basis. Presumably, if we are to do what we promised in Chapter 1, we shall become entangled with logic, logical processes, logical reasoning and a few logical ideas. As might be expected, the word *logic* will be regarded as belonging to the language basis. That there is good reason for this appears when one attempts to formulate a definition. For example:

> Logic is a specific mental process causing one to assert with conviction that a certain collection of circumstances necessarily entail a particular consequence under any imaginable concomitant conditions. It is based on the ability to recognize an analogy (agreement of essential factors) between the given circumstances and other circumstances where the outcome is known from experience.

Such a definition does, we admit, say some things about logic which we accept, but we object to its vagueness and particularly to its incompleteness. The words *analogy*, *mental process*, *conviction*, and so on, are just as difficult to understand, just as basic, as is *logic*. Moreover, exactly what specific mental process is involved is far from clear. *False analogy*, for example, could be described by the definition; yet we do not admit false analogy as logic.

If *logic* is to be a member of the basis, its meaning is to be acquired in a manner similar to that described in (2.4) in connection with *horse*. One comes to understand *logic* by observing that which is considered to be logical. Unfortunately, the term *logic* is not concrete—what must be observed is more difficult to observe than horses; and *logic* cannot be said to lie very close to the objective end of the basis. The general semanticists would no doubt insist that *logic* is meaningless unless unambiguously qualified, as, for example, "logic as understood by James Smythe, IV, on January 14, 1946, 3:00 P.M. EST." This seems extreme to us, but we do feel the need to qualify thus: "logic as understood by the majority of living mathematicians." Instead of attempting to explain further what *logic* means to mathematicians, or in particular to us, we shall say merely that *logic is like what we do in this book.* We sincerely hope that we shall provide a reasonably complete illustration of the sort of reasoning that is considered logical by modern standards.

In our qualification, the adjective *living* suggests what is actually the case, that logic is by no means static. In fact, logic has undergone almost unbelievable changes since the time of Euclid; it has experienced a long and thorough purification by fire. What remains has established its validity by leading to correct (usable) results for many centuries without a misstep. Certainly mathematicians have given it a hard workout and have had the greatest opportunity to catch it in malfeasance. Incidentally, should the reader question the relation between logic and usefulness, let us remind him that scientific progress during the Golden Age of Greece resulted from the application of logic to the investigation of natural phenomena; that during the dark ages, scientific progress went into reverse because of the substitution of belief in authority for logic; and that the current scientific age, starting with the Renaissance and continuing to the present, followed upon the re-establishment of logic as a basic tool of scientific investigation.

In all fairness, we must admit that not all mathematicians are content to consider *logic* as basic. Considerable effort has been expended, particularly in this century, in analyzing the principles of logic and formulating a number of them in terms of something considered to be more primitive or elementary. Of course, in any such analysis, some portion of the concept of logic must be assumed to lie in the language basis. Like most fields that have attracted any considerable amount of attention, the subject of analysis of logic has grown to such proportions, both in quantity of material and in intricacy of details, that its study is a task in itself, quite independent of, and comparable in magnitude to, our aims. For this reason and others it has been considered more suitable to accept the whole of logic, rather than some fraction of it, as a fundamental undefined notion. "Logic is logic. That's all I say."

In connection with logical processes we shall meet certain terms, such as *there exists*, *implies*, and others like them. These belong to the logical basis and are best discussed when they are first employed [(4.9)]. Other terms, like *set*, *function*, are to be referred to as mathematical terms; these will be discussed fully in Chapters 4 and 5. Still other mathematical terms, such as *number*, *point*, *line*, *plus*, *times*, may also occur. Since these will not belong to the language basis, it is important to emphasize a few matters concerning them.

Whenever nonbasic mathematical words are introduced, they will, of course, be explicitly defined. Whenever technical use is made of these words, the reader must carefully eliminate any preconceptions concerning their meaning and think only of their definitions. This will be difficult, but it is absolutely necessary. Unless *all* suggestions conveyed by these words from past association are persistently ignored, a multiplicity of meanings may arise.

Our mathematical definitions will be unambiguous and complete. It will be apparent that on any technical occurrence of a mathematical term that has been defined, that term can be erased and its defining phrase substituted, without affecting the meaning of the sentence involved. Our attitude is similar to that expressed by Humpty-Dumpty:

> HUMPTY-DUMPTY: When I use a word, it means just what I choose it to mean—neither more nor less.
>
> ALICE: The question is whether you can make words mean so many different things.
>
> HUMPTY-DUMPTY: The question is which is to be master—that's all.

Of course, many mathematical words have a variety of nonmathematical meanings which are assumed known and with which we shall not interfere. Thus we might say,

> at this "point" we wish to "add" a "number" of arguments along the same general "line."

But any use of these terms as mathematical words will be reserved until they have been explicitly introduced by definitions. And whenever a technical word is used in a popular or intuitive sense, the fact that a nontechnical meaning is intended will be indicated by enclosing the word in quotation marks; at least, this will be done when any doubt could exist as to what usage is intended.

It is regrettable that mathematical words should have other meanings as well, since a nonmathematical meaning tends to influence understanding of the mathematical meaning. Thus, *set, function, relation,* and *operation* have mathematical meanings that are entirely, or almost entirely, divorced from their everyday meanings. The reader should not expect *real numbers* to be any more real, or any less imaginary, than *imaginary numbers.* There is nothing even remotely irrational about *irrational numbers.* These are all equally straightforward mathematical entities which happen to be unfortunately named. For the rather gratuitous confusion introduced by this adoption of new meanings for old words we apologize, although the fault is not ours; in fact, it is not even of our generation.

Chapter 3

THE DEVELOPMENT OF MATHEMATICS

3.1. Introduction. In the preceding chapter it was mentioned that many words in common usage have meanings which are, at best, dubious, and that many words will be used in this book in a somewhat unusual sense. One of the words of which both these remarks are true is the word *mathematics* itself. This word and its foreign equivalents have been applied through the centuries to a vast variety of facts and fictions. At the present time, the word mathematics means quite different things to the layman, the scientist, and the professional mathematician. The layman is apt to confuse mathematics with arithmetic, or at least advanced arithmetic. The scientist considers mathematics as one of the sister sciences, while many professional mathematicians are inclined to regard it as more closely allied to the fine arts. This is explained by the fact that during the course of its development, mathematics has been all these things, and, to some extent, it still is all these things.

3.2. The Science of Number. Although the primary object of this book is to discuss the question where mathematics has got to and not the problem of how it got there, a brief, somewhat fanciful discussion of the development of mathematics will serve to provide perspective. One of the most common descriptions of mathematics is as the "science of number." While this description of mathematics is far from being valid at the present time, it has excellent historical justification, since there is indeed a science of number, and since it was to this science that the name mathematics was first applied.

Let us envisage a tribal chieftain surrounded by his warriors. Like most rulers, he is unhappy, and his life can be made tolerable only by conquering the rulers of several neighboring tribes. Unfortunately, his fellow sovereigns also have many warriors. If the gentleman we are imagining lived sufficiently early in history, the word *many* meant to him "more than two," that is, a chieftain might have one warrior, two warriors, or "many" warriors. All chieftains with "many" warriors were presumably on an equal footing until an actual conflict decided the question of superiority. This was the stage of pre-scientific experiment.

Some might say that this was the stage of empirical science, since empirical science is often thought of as simply trying things. Actually this is an unfair description. It would be almost better to think of empirical science as a scheme for minimizing the necessity of trying things. Thus the object of any empirical science is to organize the essential phenomena of its subject matter, so that the results of a few experiments permit the prediction of the results of many other experiments.

To return to our chieftain whom we left contemplating territorial expansion, it is clear that he would be greatly benefited by an empirical science which would enable him to decide the result of a conflict with one of his neighboring rulers, without the risk involved in an actual attempt. Thus there was a necessity for distinguishing, if possible, between his "many" warriors and the "many" warriors of his rivals. Experience in battle showed that these "manys" were not equivalent. In fact, when two armies met and the warriors paired off in hand-to-hand combat, one of the kings was likely to have some warriors remaining without individual opponents. These extra fighters were able to dash around unopposed and work all manner of unmentionable havoc on the exposed backs of their occupied adversaries. It was soon observed that the king who had these extra warriors was generally victorious. This was (or could have been) the origin of the notion "more" and the question "how many?" It will be seen later [see, for example, Chapter 10] that the most precise modern definition of the word *more* is based on exactly this origin, so that collection A has "more" than collection B if each of the things in B can be matched with one of the things in A without exhausting A.

Deep reflection on the concept "more" might have suggested to the chieftain a method for predicting a probable result of conflict without staking his existence on the outcome. He and his rival might, in the manner of more modern nations, hold a peace conference, and, at some stage in the festivities, each of his warriors might embrace a prospective opponent to swear undying friendship. If the chieftain observed that some of his warriors had no embracees, he might contemplate with confidence provoking an appropriate incident. If, however, all his warriors were busily occupied in oaths of fealty, then he could only hope that his neighboring monarch was an honorable man and would not break his vows.

The system described above for deciding the question of *more*, while reasonably effective, was certainly cumbersome, and some substitute was earnestly sought. It was soon discovered that it was perfectly accurate and very convenient to introduce intermediate comparing devices. Thus a chief could compare his army with the spears of an opposing force rather than with its members. Better still, a spy could hide by the trail and break off a small twig to represent each member of the enemy's forces as they filed by. This method must have been practiced for countless centuries, one twig being broken as each man filed past, and the breaking of each twig being accompanied by a little grunt of satisfaction. In due course of time, these grunts became formalized into a chant,

$$\text{uh, ooh, eeh, } \cdots,$$

or, as we should say,

$$\text{one, two, three, } \cdots.$$

Finally, some genius observed that the twigs were unnecessary since the grunts themselves would serve the purpose adequately.

Thus we evolved the means of answering the question "how many?" The final grunt achieved in performing the counting process described above came to be a symbol for the "how many-ness" of any collection of objects. It is these symbols of "many-ness" which came to be called numbers. By a *number* then, until further notice, we shall mean one of a particular collection of grunts (differing with the language) associated with the ritual of counting.

After counting was well established, certain interconnections began to be noticed. Thus a man might observe,

(3.2.1) I placed three stones on a pile of seven stones. The resulting pile had ten stones.

This statement is a very simple observation of fact and has no connection with science or mathematics. Repetition of the experiment described quickly leads one to a generalization, namely,

(3.2.2) if you place three stones on a pile containing seven stones, the resulting pile will contain ten stones.

This statement is a scientific remark, that is, it predicts the results of an unperformed experiment. It shares with all results of science the quality of being unprovable. This remark may sound surprising but reflection should show that no one could possibly have a right to be *absolutely certain* of the results of an unperformed experiment. Thus a modern scientist says that if a kettle of water is placed on a fire, then it is *overwhelmingly probable* that the water will become warmer; he does not say *certain* except in undergraduate courses. Such absence of absolute certainty, which is a characterizing feature of all statements of science, in no way nullifies the value of the subject. In fact, overwhelming probability is all that anyone has any right to expect with regard to knowledge of the future in this world, and is a great deal more than one usually gets.

The next stage in the process of abstraction or generalization beyond that expressed by (3.2.2) is made when it is observed that the statement is clearly true not only of stones, but of sticks, people, or anything else. Thus one may say,

(3.2.3) if three objects are placed on a pile of seven objects, the resulting pile contains ten objects.

This shows that the essential fact expressed by the statement (3.2.2) concerns many-ness or number, and nothing else. A great many statements such as (3.2.3) were discovered experimentally early in the history of the counting process. The collection of such statements might be called the science of number, or arithmetic, and it was to this science that the name *mathematics* was first applied.

There is an exceedingly important difference between the statements (3.2.2) and (3.2.3), which hints at the distinction which we regard as existing between mathematics and the natural sciences. The first statement, while *not strictly* provable, at least suggests an experiment which one could perform to partially verify its truth. One is reasonably confident of his knowledge of the meaning of *stones*. The statement (3.2.3) is not quite so simple, in that the word *object* is somewhat vague. The way in which one understands the statement is as a sort of abbreviation for a vast variety of concrete remarks of the nature of (3.2.2), which can be obtained by inserting various specific choices for the "object" mentioned in (3.2.3).

A further stage in generalization is achieved as follows: Let us for the moment define a *three* as any collection containing three objects, and similarly for a *seven* and a *ten*. A three is thus what is commonly called a threesome. Then (3.2.3) can be abbreviated by the statement,

(3.2.4) a three placed with a seven yields a ten.

This statement illustrates the stage of generalization in which the essential features (in this case, the three-ness, seven-ness or ten-ness) are isolated, given names and discussed as if they were entities.

Our four displayed statements illustrate the beginning of a process of generalization which is characteristic of the history of mathematics. At the stage of development represented by (3.2.2), there is no distinction between science and mathematics, except possibly in the particular collection of experiments discussed. However, mathematics now introduces a new feature that distinguishes it from the sciences. It is with this distinguishing feature that this book will be largely concerned. This feature, briefly, is the elimination of the necessity for performing experiments at all, by the substitution of logic.

We might indicate how a man can convince himself of the truth of the last of our displayed statements (3.2.4) without having recourse to any experiments whatsoever. (Actually, he will perform what might be called "mental experiments"; it is largely these which constitute what we call logic.) First *eight* is, by definition, the next grunt after *seven*. Hence, if he has a pile of seven and places one more object, he will have a collection characterized by the next grunt, that is, he will have an eight. Mentally placing still another object on his collection, he has, on the one hand, two more than seven, and on the other hand, one more than eight, or (by definition) *nine*. One more object mentally added gives, on the one hand, three more than seven, and on the other, the successor of nine, which is *ten*. Thus, without any physical manipulation, and without even deciding what objects are being considered, a man can convince himself that a three together with a seven yields a ten.

Incidentally, anyone who is unable to appreciate the profound advance in human development required to inaugurate an abstract argument like the above, should be reminded that there still exist, in the present world, primitive tribes who have not reached this level of sophistication.

3.3. The Science of Measurement. Another popular description of mathematics is "mathematics is the science of measurement." While this description, like "mathematics is the science of number," is no longer valid, it too has an excellent historical justification. After the grunts called numbers were invented to answer the question "how many?" the primitive equivalent of a mathematician turned his attention to providing an answer to the more vexing questions "how long?" "how tall?" "how far?" The method adopted for answering these questions was by a device which is typical of the breed of mathematicians even to the present day.

Some years ago, a little problem which was supposed to ferret out incipient mathematicians became rather popular. The victim was asked to imagine a kitchen containing a gas stove with one burner lit, and a kettle of water placed on the floor. He was then asked how he would proceed if he wished to heat the water in the kettle. He usually answered quite reasonably that he would place the kettle on the fire. Then he was asked to solve a second problem identical to the first, except that now the kettle was on a table. If he responded in an equally reasonable manner, he was supposed to have no chance of becoming a mathematician. For a real mathematician would *transfer the kettle to the floor*, thus reducing the second problem to the first, which had already been solved.

The primitive mathematician, faced with the problem of providing an answer to the question "how tall?" proved his right to the title mathematician by reducing the problem to one previously solved, namely, the question "how many?" A present-day housewife is supposed to have ordered wallpaper for a room two brooms high and five brooms long. A modern farmer, when asked the question, "How tall is that horse?" might well respond, "Fifteen hands." If he had said, "Sixty inches," or "Five feet," the point would be no different. The question "how tall?" is still answered by telling how many somethings the height would contain. All that is required is that you and your auditor both be familiar with the something. The particular something used is called your *unit of measurement.*

The answer provided was not perfect. For example, one might find that a certain horse was more than fifteen hands tall but not so much as sixteen hands. The most convenient measuring device was a stick, and special sticks called rules were invented early for the purpose of measuring. If sticks, rather than hands, were being used as measuring devices, and a certain height was more than fifteen sticks but not so much as sixteen sticks, a more precise measure could be obtained by breaking the stick into smaller pieces, and telling how many of these smaller parts were required to bridge the gap. This led to the introduction of *broken,* that is, fractured, or *fractional* numbers. The Greek mathematicians discovered that not even these fractional numbers were enough to answer the question, "how long?" precisely in all cases. This by no means obvious fact, and the still less obvious method taken to overcome this difficulty, will be discussed later in the book [in Chapters 17, 18].

Of course, having invented fractional numbers, mathematicians could not rest until they had learned rules for manipulating them, similar to the "three and seven gives ten" rule for the counting numbers. Thus the arithmetic of fractions is a part of the science of measurement.

3.4. The Science of Space. The description just given may indicate how mathematicians came to playing with straight sticks. They soon began to notice some rather remarkable facts about these sticks. For example, some unknown genius discovered that if three sticks, which were respectively three, four and five units long, were joined at the ends to form a triangle, then the two shorter sticks would be perpendicular. Observations of this type were the beginnings of another science to which the name *geometry* was given.

The science of geometry was, in its early stages, as unlike the science of number as possible, and it is somewhat mystifying how these totally different subjects came to be included under the common heading of mathematics. One answer seems to be that it was the measurers, that is, the mathematicians, who had available the leisure, the inclination and the straight sticks necessary to discover geometric facts.

The process of abstraction described in connection with numbers soon came to be applied to the geometric facts discovered. Here again, the salient properties, this time the straightness and length, were abstracted from the numerous objects which possessed them, and were embodied in a somewhat mysterious, intuitive object that possessed only straightness and length; this object was called a *line segment.*

Again, as in the case of numbers, the mathematicians objected to the necessity of performing experiments to verify a fact about line segments. In this case, the possibility of avoiding experiments, that is, of substituting purely mental experiments, was not nearly so obvious. However, in the third century B.C., advanced thinkers began to show that many of the physical facts concerning line segments were purely logical consequences of a very few of them.

Historically, the science of space, that is geometry, was the first field in which the use of logic as a substitute for experiment was pursued with anything like a systematic effort. But once convinced of the feasibility of the scheme, the Greek geometers developed this approach with so much vigor that Euclid was able to give a presentation of the subject in which all major geometric facts were derived, in what was considered to be a purely logical manner, from a small number of initial premises, or axioms.

It must be admitted that by modern standards there were, in Euclid's geometry, a vast number of loose arguments, implicit appeals to intuition or picturization, and other misdeeds that are to be expected in a first attempt at a very difficult task. Indeed, a presentation of euclidean geometry which satisfies modern standards of rigor was not achieved until quite recently (1904). However, the attempt of the Greek geometers was sufficiently impressive to be universally conceded as one of the great landmarks of intellectual progress. The euclidean treatment is still taught in high school, as a pattern of logical thought; and a Twentieth Century poet has proclaimed, "Euclid alone has looked on beauty bare." Finally, the euclidean axiomatic method set the pattern for all modern developments of mathematics, although, as we hope to show in this book, present-day mathematicians have gone far beyond Euclid in the matter of careful analysis of their thought processes.

3.5. The Science of Axiomatics. The great success of the axiomatic method as applied to geometry did not at once, or indeed for a long time, win for it an absolute victory in the remaining development of mathematics. The traditional doctrines of algebra, trigonometry, analytic geometry and calculus were developed with no attempt to reduce the fundamentals to a simple collection of axioms; a mixture of logic and intuition was the accepted means of developing theorems.

By the middle of the Nineteenth Century, the appeals to intuition and the lack of a firmly established foundation for the traditional branches of mathematics had aroused considerable confusion, and even distrust of the validity of the results. This attitude was particularly marked and particularly justified in the case of the calculus. Because of this mistrust, a group of Nineteenth Century mathematicians inaugurated an attempt to establish a solid foundation, and to eliminate intuition from the methods of proof in the calculus. The success of this attempt led to a new belief in the axiomatic approach as the only completely satisfactory means of treating any branch of mathematics. The Twentieth Century has seen the almost complete triumph of the axiomatic method, with careful axiomatic bases established for all branches of mathematics. There has also been considerable study and refinement of the method itself. As we mentioned earlier, the euclidean presentation of Greek geometry is now considered as a remarkable but certainly far from precise attempt at axiomatics, rather than the model of care and perfection it is often represented to be.

The major improvement in the modern viewpoint on axiomatics has been directed toward the elimination of intuition from proofs. It has been found that the only safe way to avoid intuition is to make its use impossible. This is accomplished by conscientiously refusing to know anything at all about the entities with which you are dealing, be they called numbers, points, lines or what you will, beyond what is stated explicitly about them in the axioms. Thus the entities with which a branch of mathematics is concerned enter, in the first instance, as completely abstract, formless objects. Then a collection of axioms stating certain facts about these abstract objects is announced as the basis of the mathematical structure. These axioms are to be considered not as hints or clues as to the nature of the abstract objects with which you are concerned, but rather as the complete statement of *all* you know about them. It will be shown later in the book that this open-minded attitude toward the basic entities of mathematics has other and perhaps greater virtues than that of preventing the use of intuition in proofs. It was in the hope of encouraging this open-minded attitude on the part of the reader that we entered a plea in (2.5) that he discard any preconceived notions about the meaning of mathematical terms.

Should the reader feel that our discussion of axiomatics fails to convey clearly exactly what is meant, let us hasten to remind him that our method of thorough explanation of these basic matters is by examples, the subject matter of the later chapters. Understanding and appreciation of axiomatics are not to be expected until the axiomatic procedure has been observed in action. The present discussion is part of the program notes that may mean little until the music has been heard.

The modern view, that mathematics deals with completely abstract entities, is simply the fulfillment of the process of abstraction illustrated by the successive statements (3.2.1), (3.2.2), (3.2.3), (3.2.4). An entity which has only the properties essential to a subject (those stated by the axioms) is created mentally, given a name and discussed as if it were a concrete object. There is no departure from mathematical tradition in this modern view but only the culmination of a process of abstraction which has been characteristic of mathematics from its beginning.

The emergence of the abstract viewpoint adopted in the Twentieth Century by a large number of mathematicians led finally to a feeling that the subject matter of mathematics was not the study of numbers or space or any elaborations thereon, but simply the determination of consequences of systems of axioms. From this standpoint any system of axioms whatsoever is fair material for investigation. Thus mathematics has come to be, at least in the eyes of many practitioners of the art, something which can be loosely described as the science of axiomatics.

Chapter 4

THE PRIMITIVE MATERIALS OF MATHEMATICS

4.1. Introduction. It is time now to begin directing our general talk into more specific channels, to turn our attention to those matters which will have special significance for us in our main project. In our survey of the language basis, we mentioned, without attempt at distinction, two types of terms, mathematical and logical. These roughly correspond, respectively, to the subject matter of mathematics, and to what is said about the subject matter.

Admittedly, any basic term is to be undefined, as we have seen. To achieve understanding of such terms, one must observe them in use. Yet, in order that the reader be as well prepared as possible for the observation process, that is, for the reading of subsequent chapters, we shall here take considerable pains to describe and illustrate what the mathematical terms have come to mean to mathematicians (or at least to the authors). The present chapter deals with the basic terms and a few closely associated with them; others are deferred until the next. Logical terms are briefly treated in (4.9).

What we say in this chapter may seem pointless to many. The authors are actually among these, in that to them the terms to be described are more fundamental, more basic, than the words used in the description. But this may not be the case with all readers. If a familiar note is struck now and then, some progress will have been achieved for these readers toward making the terms meaningful.

4.2. Elements. In the last chapter, it appeared that the discourse of mathematics concerns completely abstract and formless entities. In the statement,

if three objects are placed on a pile, . . .,

it is completely unessential to have any definite picture of the "objects" involved, or any knowledge of their precise nature. They could be, in particular, stones, pencils, statues, animals, or a host of other things. But in spite of the generality of the word, there are many things that the reader would probably not consider to be included by "objects." Thus many people would not regard mental attitudes, odors, thunderstorms, acts of kindness or the second line of "Carry Me Back to Old Virginny" as "objects." Moreover, a dozen marbles, a pair of shoes, a herd of cattle and the Marx Brothers might also not be included.

For mathematical work, it is necessary that the entities of our discourse possess such generality that all the terms mentioned are subsumed, whether the items are concrete or abstract, whether they are singular or plural. Accordingly, the word *element* is introduced to replace "object," "entity" or similar words, with the intention that *element* should be understood in the broadest possible sense. Probably the nearest nonmathematical synonym for *element* is "conceptual entity"; it should be emphasized, however, that any specializing restriction that the reader is inclined to place on the nature of a "conceptual entity" should not apply to *element*.

If there seems to be cause for discontent occasioned by the high degree of abstractness associated with *elements*, there should be compensating cause for rejoicing that there is no need to fix concrete meanings early, but that such meanings may be decided upon at any time during or after the development of a theory. An element is a blank into which may be read or inserted any specific meaning. It may help the reader at first to think "object" when he sees the word *element*; but it must not distress him if some element should be specialized to mean, for example, "a pile of four objects."

4.3. Sets of Elements. In dealing with elements, it will be found unsatisfactory—perhaps the reader has already found it so—to allow them to wander through our imagination altogether unchaperoned. It is logically untidy and even chaotic to permit them too much leeway. True, they must not be subjected to qualitative restriction; but it is necessary to restrict them, in any discussion, in a quantitative way. Speaking of "all elements" would represent the extreme violation of the restriction we have in mind. Lesser violations exist, and all may lead to paradoxes such as those described in (2.3).

To be specific, we propose to limit our discourse in any given discussion or theory to certain particular elements, which we imagine to be before us throughout the theory. These elements may lead us by definitions to other elements, but no difficulties are to be feared from these occurrences, since talk about the entities introduced in this way can be interpreted as talk about the original elements. In any discussion, then, there are to be no stray elements, no orphans. All elements appearing are thought of as belonging to a family which is fixed and invariable throughout the theory. Such a family is called a *set*, and the elements comprising it are said to *belong to*, or to *be members of*, the set. Hence elements may be said to come only in sets. We never work with elements, except when we have a set of them in which to work.

Since the presence of elements implies that of sets, and vice versa, the terms *element* and *set* need not be considered separately. They are always used together in the phrase *set of elements*. Still, within such a set of elements lie the individual elements, and this fact must be recognized and understood, since many of our dealings will be with the individuals. It will be seen that there are sets, each of which consists of exactly one element; these sets could be used to effect a rather artificial elimination of the term *element* from the basis, so that only *set* would remain. It is unimportant whether or not this is done; we are interested only in achieving some understanding of the basic concept *set of elements*.

Now the word *set* is probably sufficiently familiar to the reader in such occurrences as "a set of chessmen," "a set of dishes," and the like. The mathematical use of the word differs from the ordinary use in that the elements of a mathematical set cannot be expected to resemble one another in any way (except in that they are elements). For elements have been shorn of all features by means of which comparisons might be made. Even when specific meanings are ascribed to the elements, resemblances are not to be expected. Thus we shall feel free to consider a set consisting of the Eiffel Tower, the earth and a certain dog named Rover.

We wish to make certain that the word *set* will be interpreted in the broadest possible sense, namely, in a sense suggested by any of the terms "class," "aggregate," "collection," "conglomeration," "flock," "herd," "school," "family," and the like. Thus one might speak of the set of all people who were president of the United States in 1939, a set consisting of but one element (member). One might also speak of the set of all possible positions of an elevator in its shaft, a set so large that its elements could not conceivably be counted or listed.

We hasten to mention that many mathematicians and logicians have not been satisfied to resign themselves to an acceptance of the concept of "arbitrary set of arbitrary elements." Nevertheless, we feel dissatisfied with all attempts to define this concept or to analyze it in terms of more fundamental notions. Moreover, it is questionable whether such attempts, if successful, could have a serious effect on the bulk of mathematical theories constructed on a foundation which accepts the concept intuitively. We propose, therefore, a wholehearted acceptance of "set of elements" as an undefined concept, but one about which we have sufficient intuition to enable us to act toward it in a manner which seems intelligent to us.

It is necessary to make a few comments on the restriction that we have placed on elements, namely, that they must appear in any theory in exactly one fixed set. Upon reflection, one is led to the surmise that there should be no objection to allowing two or more fixed sets to be before us in a single theory. The surmise is justified; in fact, it is easy to see that this possibility is implicitly allowed in either of two ways. One may argue that since the elements of a given set are *arbitrary*, they may themselves be sets of (other) elements. Or one may say that, if several sets are before us, all the elements involved may be regarded as constituting a further set, which may then be thought of as the basic, given set.

An example would be this. Consider a set of speedometers. For each of these there is a set of all positions of its indicator. Let us refer to this *set of positions* as the "range" of the speedometer. We thus have under consideration a set of ranges, each range being a set of indicator positions. We could then regard the set of ranges as fundamental; the elements of this set would be sets of indicator positions. Or we could imagine the (much larger) set of all possible indicator positions of all the speedometers as the one fundamental set.

Whatever point of view is adopted, this type of situation is regarded as admissible. Indeed, it will be the basis for discussion in some of the work that we shall do. Further elaboration of the idea leads to a "set of sets of sets" and so on. To worry about how far this process can be continued would be tampering with the language basis, and so is out of place here. It should be said, however, that the concept "set of *all* sets" leads to paradoxes as does the concept "set of all elements" and is definitely inadmissible.

4.4. Notation. Let the reader imagine how difficult life would be, if objects, people, emotions, and other items of discourse had no names. Not only would such pleasures as neighborhood gossip be forced into nonexistence, but almost all forms of useful communication would cease.

Since sets and their elements are (so far) exactly those entities about which we wish to talk, it should be clear that we shall be forced to introduce symbols or labels for these conceptual objects. For the most part, it will be convenient to use letters (Roman, German or Greek) for our labels, although other printers' marks will occur occasionally. Thus we speak of "an element a" of a set, meaning an element to which for purposes of future reference (usually in the sentence or paragraph at hand) the name or label a has been given. Sets, which are also objects of our discourse, will receive the same treatment. Thus we speak of "a set A," meaning that A is a symbol which is to stand for, or represent, the set.

Of course, phrases such as "the element a" are not to be interpreted literally. For "a" is not really the element itself, but the symbol or label selected to represent the element in what is being said. The usage is parallel to that in "the man Caesar" or in other cases where, for convenience in language, an object and its name are treated as though they were indistinguishable.

It is natural now to ask what can be said of elements and sets—how they are interrelated. If there is but one set under discussion, then all elements that appear must belong to the set, and very little else of significance can be said. But, if there are at least two sets available for discourse, then the situation is different. If A, B are two such sets, then a given element a might belong to A, or it might not belong to A (that is, it might belong to B, and would be compelled to belong to B if there were no further sets under consideration). The basic logical word *not* in the last sentence is to be so understood that exactly one of the two statements, "a belongs to A," and "a does not belong to A," must be true. For the two possible statements we introduce notations. We write

$$a \in A \text{ if } a \text{ is a member of } A, \qquad a \in' A \text{ if } a \text{ is not a member of } A. \tag{4.4.1}$$

The two statements in (4.4.1) are called *negations* of each other.

The statement $a \in A$ may be read, "a is an element of A," "a is in A," "a in A," "a be in A," and so on, according to the grammatical needs of the sentence in which it occurs. Thus, "let $a \in A$" would be read, "let a be an element of A."

The notation $a_1, a_2 \in A$ is used to mean $a_1 \in A$ *and* $a_2 \in A$; $a_1, a_2, a_3 \in A$ means that all three elements a_1, a_2 and a_3 are in A; and so on. The subscripts 1, 2, 3 have no other significance than to aid in distinguishing the symbols for the elements mentioned. Their use will often help us to avoid the necessity for introducing many different letters.

When a set consists of a few specific elements, abstract or identified partially or completely, the set is denoted by displaying the labels of all its elements within square brackets. Thus we write

$$[a, b, c, d]$$

for the set consisting of the elements a, b, c, d.

An example or two are now in order. If A is the set consisting of the Eiffel Tower, the earth and the dog Rover, then A is the set

[the Eiffel Tower, the earth, the dog Rover].

If B is the set of all indicator positions of a speedometer, then B does not lend itself to the bracket notation. If a is the dog Rover, and if b is the indicator position of the speedometer corresponding to a reading of sixty miles per hour, then we have

$$a \in A, \qquad a \in' B, \qquad b \in B, \qquad b \in' A.$$

In fact, the same four statements would be true if a were the Eiffel Tower, or if a were the earth, or if b were any other indicator position of the range of the speedometer. Simple though these examples are, they should be thoroughly checked and rechecked by the reader, until he is convinced beyond a doubt that he understands them, and that he feels absolutely at home with the notations.

4.5. Equality. The statement $a \epsilon A$ says something about an element a and a set A. There is a type of statement which involves two elements or two sets, or for that matter, two conceptual entities of any conceivable kind to which we have given labels. The statement we have in mind is one that will occur so often that we shall soon be taking it for granted. Let a, b be elements of any kind. (They may, in particular, be sets.) We say that "a is *equal* to b," and write "$a = b$," if a and b are *the same element.* Thus

$a = b$ means "a and b are two labels for the *same* object."

If it is false that $a = b$, then we write $a \neq b$ (read "a is different from b," "a and b are distinct," or "a is not equal to b").

Thus, in the sense in which we use the word *equal,* all men are created unequal. The only situation in which mathematical equality can be used regarding men is that in which one man has two names, as in

Mark Twain = Samuel Clemens.

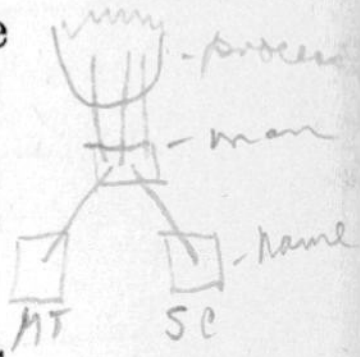

In mathematics, *equals* means the same as *alias.*

From this discussion, it appears that such a statement as "equals may be substituted for equals" means, if anything at all, that changing the name of an object does not change the object. ("A rose by any other name would smell as sweet.") We hope that the reader's meaning of "label" or "name" is such that the truth of this statement is too evident to require further comment.

It might be wondered why it should be necessary to recognize the possibility of one element's having two different names. Would it not be possible to insist on using only one name for each element? The answer is that, in mathematics, one frequently wishes to introduce a name for a specific element without having at hand sufficient information to decide whether or not this same element has been previously named. And the eventual discovery that an element a did actually occur earlier with a different label b (that is, $a = b$) may be of great importance; indeed, most mathematical results can be regarded as arising in this way.

To illustrate that statements of equality may have content, consider the following example. Let A be the set of all presidents of the United States during the period of hostilities of World War I, and let B be the set consisting of Woodrow Wilson. Then $A = B$ is a true statement.

Moreover, this statement conveys the information that Woodrow Wilson served as president throughout the World War I hostilities.

It should be noticed that in the example we defined B as the *set* consisting of Woodrow Wilson, rather than simply Woodrow Wilson. This is essential, since it is necessary to distinguish conceptually between an element and the set consisting of that element. Thus

$$[a] \neq a.$$

However, two single element sets are equal precisely when the elements are the same, that is,

$$[a] = [b] \text{ precisely when } a = b.$$

In general, it follows from our concept of equality that two sets are equal precisely when each consists of the same elements as the other. For example,

$$[a, b] = [b, a].$$

The mathematical use of the word *equal* differs from the common usage as found in "all men are created equal," in that the common use really has the force of "equal in certain respects." Thus, in common parlance one might speak of two "equal" stacks of coins, meaning not that they are really the same stack (mathematically equal), but that they are "equal in number." This last means that the "number" of coins in the first stack is equal (the *same* as) the "number" in the second stack.

It might be argued that abstract elements are so lacking in qualities that they are indistinguishable from one another, and therefore should be regarded as "equal." We therefore emphasize that whatever properties they lack, they do possess identity. There will be occasion later [in (15.2)] to introduce various ways in which elements may *resemble* one another, similar to the way in which men may be regarded as being "equal." When this occurs, we shall use the term *equivalent* rather than *equal*. Elements will then be equivalent in certain respects or for certain purposes. Further clarification of this idea is not possible at this point.

4.6. Subsets. If it appears to the reader from the preceding sections that conversation about one given set and its abstract elements must be bleak and uninteresting, we admit that we have so far given no indications to the contrary. It has even been mentioned that, if only one set A is before us, and if a is one of its elements, then all that can be said is $a \in A$. In the present section, we shall see that things are not really what they seem, and that under the apparent void lies untold wealth.

Let us suppose that a set A is before us, where

(4.6.1) $$A = [a, b, c],$$

a, b, c being abstract elements such that $a \neq b$, $b \neq c$, $c \neq a$. A very little reflection will show that A is by no means the only set before us. In fact, once A has been admitted to our consideration, we are automatically forced to recognize that six other sets have also been admitted. These are

(4.6.2) $$[a, b], [b, c], [a, c], [a], [b], [c].$$

Each of these new sets is clearly obtained from A by ignoring, or discarding, a certain element or certain elements, and recognizing only what remains.

The process of selecting sets, each one of which is a "part" of the given set, is generally applicable, that is, the process is not limited to sets which can be denoted by means of the brackets as in (4.6.1). Any set resulting from the process is called a *subset* of the original set. Thus, in the example, $[b, c]$ is a subset of A. A description of *subset* can thus be formulated:

(4.6.3) A set B is a *subset* of a set A whenever all the elements of B are elements of A.

If B is a subset of A, we write $B \subset A$ (read "B is contained in A") or $A \supset B$ (read "A contains B"). The three statements,

$$A \supset B, \quad B \subset A, \quad B \text{ is a subset of } A,$$

all mean the same thing. The negation of the statement $A \subset B$ $(B \supset A)$ is written $A \not\subset B$ $(B \not\supset A)$. Thus $A \not\subset B$ means that A is not a subset of B, that is, that there exists an element of A which is not an element of B.

If A is the set of all animals, and if B is the set of all dogs, then $A \supset B$. Another example is given by

$$[b, d, e] \subset [a, b, c, d, e].$$

Still another is the following. Let A be the range of a speedometer [as in (4.3)]; let B consist of all elements of the range corresponding to all speeds of 30 miles per hour and under; and let C consist of the single indicator position corresponding to the reading 0. Then $B \subset A$ and $C \subset A$; also $C \subset B$. This example serves to give some hint of the importance of subsets. Thus B might be intimately connected with the legal speeds of operation under certain conditions, and C would describe a state of no motion. That $C \subset B$ means that a state of rest is a legal speed.

If A is any set, then it is convenient to say that $A \subset A$, that is, that A is a subset of itself. To do this is merely to effect agreement on an arbitrary convention, which turns out to be useful. If B is a subset of

A which is different from A ($B \neq A$), it will be said that B is a *proper subset* of A. A notation for this is $B \subsetneqq A$.

It is essential to remark that, if for two sets A, B it should occur that $A \subset B$ and $B \subset A$, then A and B must be equal, that is,

(4.6.4) if $A \subset B$ and $B \subset A$, then $A = B$.

The reader should convince himself of the truth of this statement; a little reflection should show that it is inherent in the very meaning of equality of sets.

A special convention which deserves mention is the following. If A, B, C are sets, the "continued statement" $A \subset B \subset C$ means $A \subset B$ *and* $B \subset C$. Generally speaking, when two or more statements are elided in this way, the meaning will always be the conjunction of the several statements. Varied and frequent uses of this convention will occur throughout the book. Thus, if a, b, c are elements of a set A, then $a = b = c$ means $a = b$ and $b = c$.

A specific subset of a set A may be determined by telling exactly what its elements are to be, or, in other words, by stating what properties they (and only they) should have, or what restrictions they (and only they) should satisfy. [See the examples above.] We shall use the notation

(4.6.5) $[a \in A; \cdot \cdot \cdot]$

to represent the subset of A consisting of exactly those elements satisfying the restriction to be inserted to the right of the semicolon. The brackets abbreviate "the set of all," and the semicolon stands for "such that," or "for which." If A is the set of all books, then

$$B = [a \in A;\ a \text{ is green}]$$

is the set including every element a in A such that a is green (and including no others). More simply, B is the set of all green books. When it is clearly understood in what set a is considered to lie, then "$\in A$" is sometimes omitted from the notation. Then we write simply $[a; \cdot \cdot \cdot]$.

An interesting possibility arises from the use of the bracket notation just described. In all innocence, we might write a symbol $[a \in A; \cdot \cdot \cdot]$, in which the restrictions are so stringent that they are satisfied by no elements of A. For example, if A is again the set of all books, we might write

[$a \in A$; a was written by Zane Grey and a was written in 400 B.C.],

particularly if we did not know who Zane Grey was. One might be inclined to say that in such a case, $[a \in A; \cdot \cdot \cdot]$ is not a set at all.

Since, however, much effort might have to be expended in ascertaining whether any element a exists satisfying the restriction, it is more convenient to adopt the convention that the notation does represent a subset. Having no elements, this subset is said to be *empty*. The letter Θ is always reserved for the empty subset of whatever set is under consideration. Thus $S = \Theta$ (read "S is empty") means that S has no elements, while $S \neq \Theta$ (read "S is non-empty") means that there is at least one element in S.

The recognition of the empty subset of any set under consideration implies that the list (4.6.2) of subsets of the set A in (4.6.1) is incomplete. The empty subset Θ is an additional subset which must be included. In conformity with the bracket notation used in (4.6.2), we might denote the empty set by $[\ ]$, with no elements displayed. However, the notation Θ will be used in deference to custom.

It is worth remarking that the empty set arises only as a rather accidental subset of some non-empty *fundamental* set. Every fundamental set in a discussion will always be understood to have at least one element. We hope that we are offending no one by insisting that, when we talk we should have something to talk about!

4.7. The Algebra of Sets. The previous section has given a glimpse of what may be expected within a given set. Although we cannot offer in this book an exhaustive treatment of subsets of a set, we must investigate the theory a bit further so that portions of it may be used later.

Let us assume that two sets A and B are simultaneously under discussion. As has been suggested in (4.3), A and B may be regarded as subsets of a single set; whether or not this is done is quite immaterial. In either case, we may now conceive of "lumping together" the elements of A with those of B to form a new set. The new set then consists of all elements which are *either* in A *or* in B. Our name for the set thus obtained is the *set-theoretic sum* of A and B, and our notation for it will be $A + B$. If A and B are subsets of another set C, then $A + B$ is also a subset of C. Of course, A and B are both subsets of $A + B$ by the very definition of set-theoretic sum. We have

(4.7.1) $$\begin{aligned} A + B &= \text{set-theoretic sum of } A \text{ and } B \\ &= [\text{all elements of } A \text{ together with all elements of } B]; \end{aligned}$$

and, if $A \subset C, B \subset C$,

(4.7.2) $$A + B = [c \in C;\ c \in A \text{ or } c \in B].$$

(It is interesting to note that, even though A and B are not initially thought of as subsets of another set, they are in reality always such; namely, they are subsets of $A + B$.)

For example, suppose A and B are given thus:

(4.7.3) A = [the planet Venus, the earth, the planet Mars, the dog Rover],

(4.7.4) B = [the Eiffel Tower, the earth, the dog Rover].

Then

$A + B$ = [Venus, the earth, Mars, the Eiffel Tower, Rover].

Similarly, if F is the set of all fathers, and if M is the set of all mothers, then $F + M$ is the set of all parents.

A few general comments remain to be made. First, since A involves no preferential position over B in the definition of $A + B$, there is no reason why we should write A first. The two sets really enter on an equal footing; if we write $B + A$, we arrive at the same end result. It is therefore to be concluded that $A + B = B + A$. A detailed discussion of the matter of preferential position or precedence is to be found in the next section.

Suppose that $A \subset B$. If it is attempted to put the elements of A together with those of B, it should be seen that, since all the elements of A are already present in B, the set-theoretic sum should be B itself. Thus, whenever $A \subset B$, it follows that $A + B = B$. In particular, we have $A \subset A$, so that $A + A = A$.

We turn now to a second way in which two sets determine another. If A and B are before us, it may happen that they have elements (or possibly just one element) in common. For example, the sets in (4.7.3) and (4.7.4) have the earth and Rover in common. *All* common elements are then regarded as comprising a new set which is called the *set-theoretic product* of A and B. The notation for this new set is $A \cdot B$ (or $B \cdot A$ might be used for the same reasons adduced in connection with the discussion of $A + B$). We have then

(4.7.5) $A \cdot B = B \cdot A$ = set-theoretic product of A and B
= [all elements which are members of both A and B]
$= [a \in A; a \in B] = [a \in B; a \in A]$
$= [a \in A + B; a \in A \text{ and } a \in B]$.

The reader should convince himself of the truth of all the equalities. If $C \subset A$ and $C \subset B$, that is, if C is a subset of A and of B, then $C \subset A \cdot B$. For every element of C must lie in A and in B (since $C \subset A$ and $C \subset B$); hence every such element is a common element of A and B and therefore a member of $A \cdot B$.

It can happen, and often does, that two given sets A and B have no elements in common. The notation $A \cdot B$ is used in this case to mean what one would naturally expect, namely the empty set Θ. Thus

$A \cdot B = \Theta$ means that A and B have no common elements, while $A \cdot B \neq \Theta$ means that A and B have at least one element in common. When $A \cdot B = \Theta$, we say that A and B are *disjoint*.

An immediate fact inherent in the description of $A \cdot B$ is that it is a subset of each of A and B (even if $A \cdot B = \Theta$). We leave it to the reader to convince himself that, if $A \subset B$, then $A \cdot B = A$, and that, in particular, $A \cdot A = A$.

A still further way in which a third set is obtained from two given sets is as follows. Again let A, B be the given sets. The third set is to be the subset of A consisting of all those elements of A which are not elements of B. It is called the *set-theoretic difference* of A and B, and is denoted by $A - B$. Thus

(4.7.6) $$A - B = [a \in A;\, a \in' B].$$

In the example of (4.7.3) and (4.7.4),

$$A - B = [\text{Venus, Mars}].$$

Similarly, in the same example,

$$B - A = [\text{the Eiffel Tower}].$$

From this it may be inferred that $A - B$ and $B - A$ cannot be expected to be equal. Of course, if $A = B$, then $A - B$ and $B - A$ are both empty and hence equal; but the fact is that they cannot be equal in any other case, as is easily shown.

A few special cases deserve consideration. Suppose first that $A \cdot B = \Theta$. Then every element in A is not in B, so that $A - B = A$; similarly, $B - A = B$. Next, suppose that $A \subset B$. Then there is no element in A which is also not in B, that is, there is no element in $A - B$. Therefore $A - B = \Theta$. If $A = \Theta$, naturally $A \subset B$, so that again $A - B = \Theta$. It is left for the reader to verify that, in all cases,

$$A - B = A - (A \cdot B).$$

In the last statement, parentheses are used in a way in which we shall often employ them. The right side of the statement of equality is the set $A - C$, where $C = A \cdot B$; thus the parentheses serve to indicate that $A \cdot B$ is to be "formed" first, and then that the result is to be used with A in "forming" the set-theoretic difference.

Suppose now that $A \supset B$. Then $A - B$ has a special significance. In (4.6) it was stated that a subset B of A is obtained by ignoring or deleting certain elements of A, considering B to consist of what is left. The elements ignored certainly themselves constitute a subset of A; this subset is exactly $A - B$. In this case, $A - B$ is called the *complement of B in A*. Note that, if $B = A$, the statement that $A - B = \Theta$ means what is clear anyway, that in passing from A to B we delete no elements. It is instructive now to verify that, in all cases for which $A \supset B$,

$$B + (A - B) = A, \quad B \cdot (A - B) = \Theta.$$

It is important to realize that the set-theoretic complement is a special case of the set-theoretic difference. The difference $A - B$ is a general concept, applicable to any sets A, B; the complement $A - B$ is identical to the difference, but the term *complement* applies only when $B \subset A$.

The three processes discussed may now be summarized:

> the set-theoretic sum $A + B$ consists of all elements in A *or* in B;
>
> the set-theoretic product $A \cdot B$ consists of all elements in A *and* in B;
>
> the set-theoretic difference $A - B$ consists of all elements in A *and not* in B.

The material in the present section is merely the beginning of a subject known as the algebra of sets, a subject which is quite highly developed. We have refrained from giving a really systematic exposition, since such would actually be an account of a complex mathematical theory for which we are not at this stage prepared. Only those items that are essential for our subsequent use have been included. Inasmuch as arbitrary sets of arbitrary elements are the things about which mathematics talks—the stuff that the dreams of mathematics are made of—the importance of the topics discussed cannot be overemphasized. A feeling of security with respect to all the concepts introduced must be attained, if one wishes to appreciate fully the subsequent development.

(4.7.7) PROJECT: If A, B are defined as in (4.7.3), (4.7.4), list the sets C which are such that $C \subset A$ and $C \subset B$, and verify that, for every such set, $C \subset A \cdot B$.

(4.7.8) PROJECT: Let A, B be sets. Show that,
(a) if $A \subset B$, then $A \cdot B = A$;
(b) if $A \cdot B = A$, then $A \subset B$;
(c) if $A + B = B$, then $A \subset B$.
Also show that if C is a set, then $C \cdot C = C$.

(4.7.9) PROJECT: Let A, B be sets. Show that, if $A \neq B$, then $A - B \neq B - A$.

(4.7.10) PROJECT: Let A, B be sets. Show that $A - B = A - (A \cdot B)$.

(4.7.11) PROJECT: Let A, B be sets, $A \supset B$. Show that $B + (A - B) = A$, $B \cdot (A - B) = \Theta$.

4.8. Ordered Pairs. A language basis should, without doubt, be as small as possible. But it is conceivable that, when certain words are defined instead of being placed in the basis, their definitions may become awkward, artificial and conceptually difficult. In fact, the definitions may be less satisfactory than the original intuitions connected with the use of the words. Such is the situation with which we are now confronted. It is possible at this point to describe all further mathematical words in terms of sets of elements only. Yet we reject such a program because of the certain confusion that would result; rather, we shall introduce one further mathematical concept that is to be regarded as basic. It will then be relatively easy to *define* the other terms which are *nearly* basic in the next chapter.

The term to be introduced is *ordered pair*. In describing it, we might begin with the notion of "pair." In ordinary language the term "pair" is usually thought of as referring to a set consisting of two elements, that is, a set of the form $[a, b]$, where $a \neq b$, as for example, [father, son]. An *ordered pair* is more than this, however. It is a pair together with an "order" for the elements, that is, a specification as to which element "comes first" and which "comes second." It is clear that the set $[a, b]$ has nothing whatever to do with the order of the elements, since $[a, b] = [b, a]$.

Now a simple ordering of two elements should be familiar from experience. For example, in the sentence, "Howard Jones and Frank Jones are father and son, respectively," it is evident that the order in which the words "father" and "son" appear is essential to the meaning. The statement, "train leaves for Philadelphia and Baltimore," might well be interpreted differently from "train leaves for Baltimore and Philadelphia." Even the phrases, "husband and wife," and "wife and husband," convey different impressions.

Let a and b be two elements of some set. Suppose that we specify an order for a and b by saying that a should come first and b second. The set consisting of a and b, together with the specified order is called the *ordered pair* a, b; the notation for this is (a, b). As a matter of convenience, we allow the concept ordered pair to apply even if $a = b$. In this case, of course, order plays no role, since (a, a) is unchanged if the two symbols a and a are interchanged. Otherwise, the ordered pairs (a, b) and (b, a) are different.

If (a, b) and (c, d) are ordered pairs, then it is clear from the general concept of equality that

$$(a, b) = (c, d) \text{ only when } a = c \text{ and } b = d.$$

Examples of ordered pairs are numerous indeed. We list a few that come to mind readily:

(4.8.1) married couples, the male being named first;
(4.8.2) pairs of people who have played bridge as partners, naming the younger first;
(4.8.3) pairs of shoes, naming the left first;
(4.8.4) a knife and a fork, in that order;
(4.8.5) any partnership of two participants, naming the senior or dominant partner first (assuming such exists);
(4.8.6) the sets A, B in the expression $A + B$ or $A - B$.

In (4.8.1), monogamy is not implied, since it is (mathematically) immaterial in how many ordered pairs a specific element (person) appears. In (4.8.2) or (4.8.5), it is possible that some element (person) would appear as first entry in one ordered pair and as second entry in another. In (4.8.6), the order of A, B in $A + B$ is neutralized by the fact that $A + B = B + A$; but it is essential in $A - B$, as we have seen [(4.7)].

It is now necessary to perform a somewhat more difficult feat of imagination than any yet encountered. Let us suppose that a set A and a set B are under consideration. If $a \in A$ and $b \in B$, there is determined the ordered pair (a, b). This ordered pair is now to be considered as a single object. But we have already demanded that objects, or elements, should be found only in sets. Hence we are led to envisage a set in which (a, b) lies, regardless of how we may have initially selected $a \in A$ and $b \in B$. Such a set would then be the set of *all* ordered pairs whose first entry is an element of A and whose second entry is an element of B. The name of this august set is *the cartesian product of A and B*, and its notation is $A \times B$. Thus

(4.8.7) $$A \times B = \text{the cartesian product of } A \text{ and } B = [(a, b); a \in A, b \in B].$$

For example, if M is the set of all men who have ever lived, and if W is the set of all women who have ever lived, then $M \times W$ consists of all ordered pairs composed of a man and woman. The pair (Mark Antony, Joan of Arc) is one of the many elements of $M \times W$. Let P and Q be two abstract sets as follows:

(4.8.8) $$P = [p_1, p_2, p_3], \quad Q = [q_1, q_2],$$

where $p_1 \neq p_2$, $p_2 \neq p_3$, $p_3 \neq p_1$, $q_1 \neq q_2$. Then we have

$$P \times Q = [(p_1, q_1), \ (p_1, q_2), \ (p_2, q_1), \ (p_2, q_2), \ (p_3, q_1), \ (p_3, q_2)].$$

It should be observed that nothing has been said that would prevent the sets A and B in (4.8.7) from having elements in common, or even from being equal. Thus, if Q is the set in (4.8.8), then

$$Q \times Q = [(q_1, q_1), (q_1, q_2), (q_2, q_1), (q_2, q_2)].$$

(4.8.9) PROJECT: If P, Q are the sets defined in (4.8.8), and if $R = [p_1, p_2, q_1]$, display the sets $Q \times R$, $P \times R$.

4.9. Summary. Let us pause momentarily to take inventory of the materials so far encountered. Two basic terms have appeared, namely, *set of elements* and *ordered pair*. But there have been introduced many more concepts, such as set-theoretic sum, product and difference, subset and cartesian product. What sort of terms are these, and how were they introduced? It should be evident that these terms were defined, and that a good deal of "ordinary" language was used in effecting the definitions. Now if one were to strip away the unessentials, one would find that the auxiliary concepts are defined in terms of the basic ones, with the help of a few additional terms, the basic *logical* terms.

The basic logical words or phrases met thus far are these:

1. "is a member of" or "ϵ," as in (4.4) and (4.4.1) in particular;
2. "not," as symbolized by the prime in ϵ', used often, in (4.4.1) in particular; also as symbolized by the diagonal in $\neq$;
3. "all" or "every," as in "the set of all · · ·" in (4.6.5), or as in (4.6.3);
4. "such that," as in (4.6.5);
5. "there exists" or "there is," as in the third from the last paragraph of (4.6);
6. "if · · · then," as in the discussion following (4.7.5);
7. "or," as in (4.7.2);
8. "and," as in (4.7.5).

These phrases are all to be understood as in ordinary language and so will require no further attention here. In Chapter 6 some of them will be examined and illustrated more fully.

In order to facilitate future reference, the concepts and symbols treated in the present chapter are listed together with brief descriptions.

Basic terms:

element: abstract entity admitting any concrete interpretation;
set: class, collection, aggregate; composed of elements;
ordered pair: two elements (not necessarily different) with an order of occurrence.

Special notations (A is a set):

$a \epsilon A$: a is an element of A;
$a \epsilon' A$: a is not an element of A;
$[a, b, c]$: set consisting of elements a, b, c;
$[a \epsilon A; \cdots]$: set of all elements $a \epsilon A$ such that $\cdots$;
(a, b): the ordered pair a, b;

$a = b$: a is equal to b: a and b are labels for the same element;
$a \neq b$: a is not equal to b.

Defined concepts and their notations (A, B are sets):

$A \subset B$: A is a subset of B: if $a \in A$, then $a \in B$;
$A \not\subset B$: A is not a subset of B: there is an element $a \in A$ such that $a \in' B$;
$A \supset B$: $B \subset A$;
$A \not\supset B$: $B \not\subset A$;
$A \subsetneqq B$: A is a proper subset of B: $A \subset B$ and $A \neq B$;
$A + B$: set-theoretic sum of A and B: set of all $a \in A$ together with all $b \in B$;
$A \cdot B$: set-theoretic product of A and B: $[a \in A; a \in B]$;
$A - B$: set-theoretic difference of A and B: $[a \in A; a \in' B]$; also the complement of B in A, provided $B \subset A$;
$A \times B$: cartesian product of A and B: $[(a, b); a \in A, b \in B]$.

Chapter 5

FURTHER MATERIALS OF MATHEMATICS

5.1. Introduction. It will be recalled that objections to dictionary definitions were raised in Chapter 2 on the grounds that words are defined in terms of themselves. In order to avoid such a source of difficulties including logical paradoxes, the need for a language basis was stressed. Chapter 4 contains a description of the language basis for mathematics. With this basis available to us, we may now construct a legitimate dictionary, in which further mathematical concepts may be defined strictly in terms of the basic ones, namely, *set* and *cartesian product*, together with their elements and subsets.

The present chapter is devoted to the introduction through definitions of the mathematical terms *relation, function, operation* and *one-to-one correspondence* and various concepts subordinate to these. Let us emphasize again that the sole purpose of defining these terms is to avoid the long and cumbersome phraseology that would result were we forced at every stage to employ only basic terms in our discourse.

5.2. Relations. It is a curious fact that of the concepts *relation, function, operation,* only the first has a meaning close to that ascribed to it in ordinary usage. Let us first consider a few examples of everyday occurrences of the word *relation,* in the hope that such a consideration will lead us to a precise definition.

"The relation of father to son," "the relation of marriage," and "the relation of being younger than," are excellent examples familiar to us all. The first point to notice is that whenever one of these "relations" is used in discourse, it occurs in connection with two objects (or people). The second point is that a "relation" signifies some sort of bond between the two objects. Thus a statement like

George and Tim are in the father-son relation

says something about the pair George, Tim, and implies that a certain tie exists between them. It is clear that the pair occurring is really an ordered pair, since an interchange of George and Tim would alter the meaning. What can be said about the "tie" or "bond" that the relation implies? Despite first impressions, we are led to recognize only one essential feature of the "bond," namely, that it furnishes a property that (George, Tim) has in common with certain other pairs (the father-son pairs), but fails to share with all others.

A "relation" is thus a method for distinguishing some ordered pairs from others; it is a scheme for singling out certain pairs from all of them. This view is quite in harmony with a simple way of deciding whether or not two given objects are "related." For example, if it is desired to ascertain whether two people are married, one way, although not necessarily the most practical, is to consult the list of all married pairs. If the given couple appears in the list, the answer to the question is "yes," and otherwise "no." Any "relation" determines such a list, at least conceptually, of all ordered pairs in the "relation"; the relation is fully known if the list is known, and vice versa. Hence we may as well agree to regard the relation as *identical* with the list. The mathematical definition of *relation* is now in order.

(5.2.1) DEFINITION: Let A and B be sets. Then a *relation on* $A \times B$ is a subset of $A \times B$.

Thus, if A is the set of all men and B is the set of all women, $A \times B$ is the set of all possible ordered pairs of (first) a man and (second) a woman. The subset of $A \times B$ consisting of all *married* pairs is exactly that subset whose elements appear in the list of married couples. Hence this subset *is* the relation of marriage. The reader should check the applicability of (5.2.1) to the other examples of "relations." One might be tempted to object to (5.2.1) on the grounds that not every subset of $A \times B$ ought to be called a relation. Thus one can conceive of many bizarre lists of ordered pairs whose component elements bear no (intuitive) relation to each other. A little thought will show, however, that such an objection is really spurious, resulting from the fact that certain lists of ordered pairs merely *appear* to be bizarre because of our lack of familiarity with them. At any rate, no natural basis exists for differentiating between those subsets of $A \times B$ which "should be" called relations and those (if any) which should not. Therefore (5.2.1) will stand, and *every* subset of $A \times B$ will be called a relation on $A \times B$.

Let us suppose now that R is a relation on $A \times B$, that is, $R \subset A \times B$. The statement that the pair (a, b), where $a \in A$, $b \in B$, is "in the relation R" is of course written $(a, b) \in R$. This obviously states that (a, b) is to be found in the "list" constituting the relation. However, in order to suggest the intuitive flavor of relations, the somewhat shorter and more picturesque notation $a\,R\,b$ will be used. Hence

(5.2.2) $$a\,R\,b \text{ means } (a, b) \in R;$$

the statement $a\,R\,b$ may be read, "a is in the R-relation to b." Thus, if A is the set of all people and $B = A$, we may define a relation $<$

(read "less than") on $A \times B$ as the set of all $(a, b) \in A \times B$ such that a is younger than b; or symbolically,

$$(5.2.3) \qquad < \equiv [(a, b) \in (A \times B);\ a \text{ is younger than } b];$$

then "$(a, b) \in <$," "$a < b$" and "a is younger than b" all say the same thing. This example is seen to be the third of the three illustrations of intuitive relations given at the beginning of this section.

REMARK: The symbol $\equiv$ will be used to replace $=$ when the statement of equality is to be considered as the *definition* of the symbol on the left. Thus

$$a \equiv \cdot \cdot \cdot$$

means "define (the new symbol) a to be $\cdot \cdot \cdot$."

A convenient pictorial device for displaying a relation, when the sets A and B have only a few elements, is illustrated by a table such as is shown in any one of the figures (5.2.4)–(5.2.7). Here a dot in a particular (horizontal) row and (vertical) column indicates that the ordered pair consisting of the element at the bottom of the column and the element

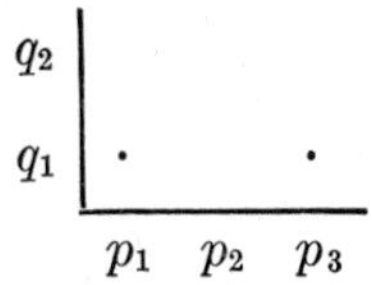

(5.2.4) FIGURE

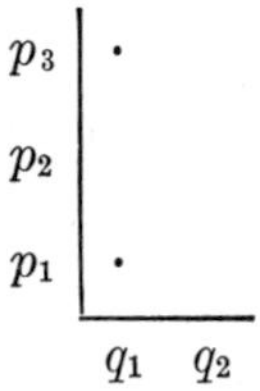

(5.2.5) FIGURE

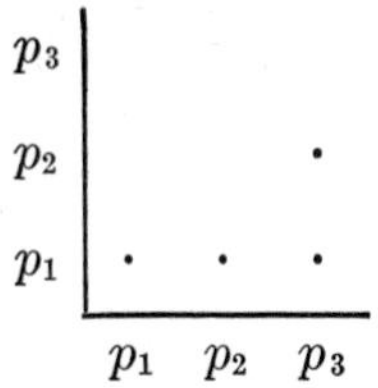

(5.2.6) FIGURE

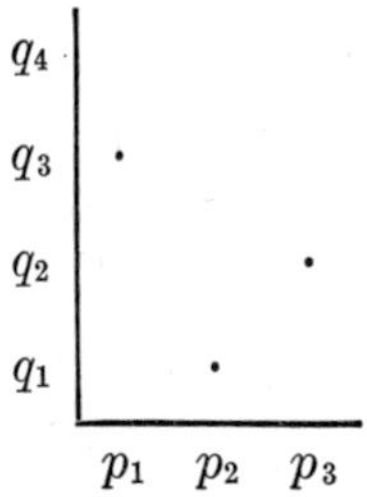

(5.2.7) FIGURE

at the left of the row (in that order) is a pair in the required relation. Such a table is effective in specifying a relation, since it tells exactly what pairs are to constitute the subset of $A \times B$ which is the relation. The table is actually a highly abbreviated way of expressing a list. Incidentally, the sets A, B are also specified by the table. For example, in (5.2.4), the fundamental sets A and B are

$$A = [p_1, p_2, p_3], \quad B = [q_1, q_2],$$

and the relation on $A \times B$ exhibited is the subset

$$[(p_1, q_1), (p_3, q_1)] \subset A \times B.$$

(5.2.8) Project: Give the sets A, B, and list the pairs constituting the relation represented by each of the figures (5.2.5), (5.2.6), (5.2.7).

5.3. The Algebra of Relations. Since relations on $A \times B$ are subsets of $A \times B$, they are subject to all the remarks made generally about subsets of a set in Chapter 4, particularly in (4.6) and (4.7). Thus, if R and S are two relations, $R \subset S$ means that, whenever $a\,R\,b$, then $a\,S\,b$; $R + S$ is the set of all (a, b) such that either $a\,R\,b$ or $a\,S\,b$; and $R \cdot S$ is the set of all (a, b) such that $a\,R\,b$ and $a\,S\,b$. The subjects of these set-theoretic ideas as applied to relations have much general interest but will not be discussed here. We shall devote this section to a detailed consideration of complements and to a few other concepts associated with relations.

Let A and B be two given sets, and let R be a relation on $A \times B$. Hence R consists of certain ordered pairs of $A \times B$. The pairs not included in R constitute, according to (4.7.6), the set-theoretic difference $(A \times B) - R$. When no ambiguity can arise we write simply $-R$ for $(A \times B) - R$. Since $R \subset A \times B$, we may also call $-R$ the complement of R in $A \times B$, as was done in (4.7). A more detailed terminology, and one that we shall adopt, is to call $-R$ the *negative* of R; the notation R' will also be used for $-R$. Thus the following statements all have the same meaning:

(5.3.1) $a\,R'\,b$, $a\,(-R)\,b$, $(a, b) \in R'$, $(a, b) \in' R$, $(a, b) \in (-R)$, $a\,R\,b$ is false.

For certain special symbols, the negative is denoted by superimposing the vertical bar: if $<$ is a relation, the negative is $\nless$.

For example, if A is the set of all people and $B = A$, and if R is the relation of marriage, then $a\,R'\,b$ would mean simply that a and b are not married. Except in a polygamous society, it is to be expected that

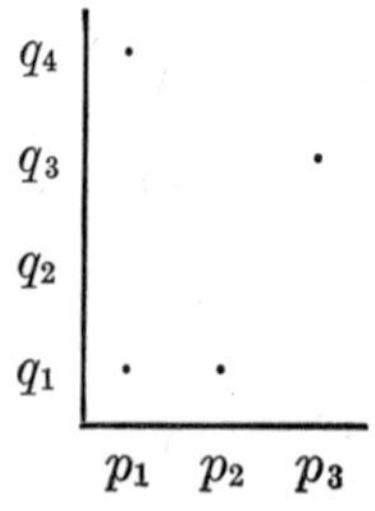

(5.3.2) Figure

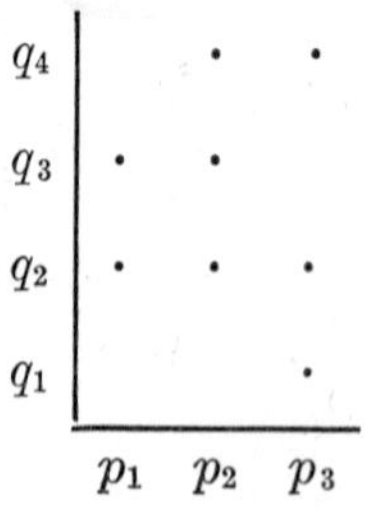

(5.3.3) Figure

R is a much smaller set than R', that is, R has "fewer" elements, since there are fewer married pairs than unmarried pairs. If A and B are the same as above, but R is the relation "is younger than," then $a\,R'\,b$

means that a is not younger than b, so that either a is older than b or they are of the same age. If the pictorial device is used to display a relation R, then R' is obtained by filling the blank spaces with dots and erasing those dots which were present originally. Hence, if (5.3.2) represents a relation R, then (5.3.3) represents R'. The reader should convince himself of the truth of the following simple statements, which hold for all relations:

$$(R')' = R, \quad R + R' = A \times B, \quad R \cdot R' = \Theta.$$

Three special relations deserve attention. If A and B are arbitrary sets, then $A \times B$ is itself a subset of $A \times B$ and therefore a relation. It may be called the *universal relation* on $A \times B$, since it consists of all pairs (a, b). Thus, for every $a \in A$ and every $b \in B$,

$$a\ (A \times B)\ b.$$

If the universal relation is represented pictorially, then a dot occupies each space.

The second special relation is the empty subset Θ of $A \times B$. It is called the absurd relation, since it consists of no pairs whatever. In other words, if $a \in A$ and $b \in B$, then the statement $a\,\Theta\,b$ is false. The pictorial representation of the absurd relation displays no dots. It should be clear that the negative of the universal relation is the absurd relation and vice versa, that is,

$$(A \times B)' = \Theta, \quad \Theta' = A \times B.$$

The convenience of including the absurd relation among relations is based on the considerations which led in (4.6) to our inclusion of the empty set among the subsets of any set.

Finally, if $A = B$, a relation E is defined thus:

$$E \equiv [(a, b) \in (A \times A);\ a = b] = [(a, a) \in (A \times A);\ a \in A].$$

This E is called the identity relation, since $a\,E\,b$ means the same thing as $a = b$; that is, $a\,E\,b$ means that a and b are identical. Correspondingly, $a\,E'\,b$ means the same as $a \neq b$. For example, if $A = B = [p_1, p_2, p_3]$, then (5.3.4) and (5.3.5) represent E and E', respectively.

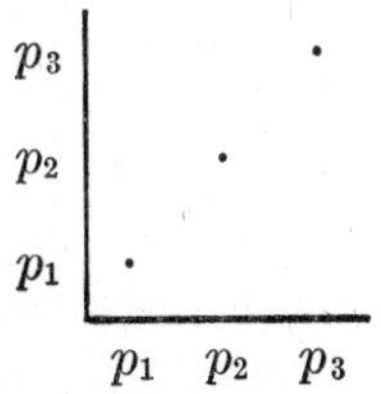

(5.3.4) FIGURE

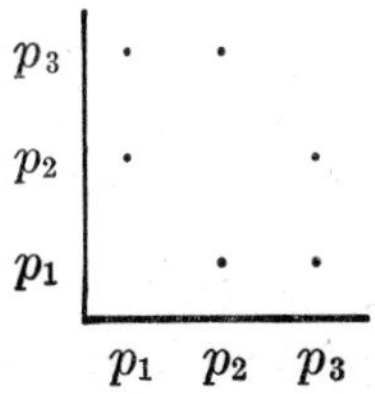

(5.3.5) FIGURE

Suppose now that R is a relation on $A \times B$. The subset of $B \times A$, consisting of those pairs (b, a) for which $a\,R\,b$, is a relation on $B \times A$. It is called the *transpose* of R and is denoted by R^*. Thus $b\,R^*\,a$ means the same as $a\,R\,b$, and

$$R^* = [(b, a) \in (B \times A);\, a\,R\,b].$$

For example, if A and B are the set of all male persons, and R is the relation "is the father of," that is, if

$$R = [(a, b) \in (A \times B);\, a \text{ is the father of } b],$$

then R^* is the relation "is a son of," since "a is the father of b" means the same as "b is a son of a." Again, if R is the relation displayed in (5.3.2), then R^* is represented by (5.3.6). The reader should verify

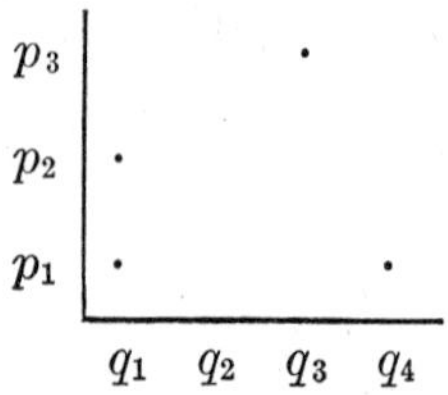

(5.3.6) FIGURE

that, in general, if $R = A \times B$ (universal on $A \times B$), then $R^* = B \times A$ (universal on $B \times A$); that if $R = \Theta$ (absurd on $A \times B$), then $R^* = \Theta$ (absurd on $B \times A$); and that if $R = E$ (identity on $A \times A$), then $R^* = R$. Since R and R^* are sometimes equal and sometimes different, these two possibilities are distinguished by calling a relation R *symmetric* in case $R = R^*$. Identity and absurd relations illustrate symmetric relations; the relation "is a son of" mentioned above is not symmetric; the relation "is married to" is symmetric.

We come now to two highly useful concepts associated with the idea of relation. Let A and B be arbitrary sets, and let R be any relation on $A \times B$. Suppose we focus attention on some given element $a \in A$, and raise the question whether there is some "mate" $b \in B$, such that $a\,R\,b$. If this question has an affirmative answer, the element a has a distinguishing property. For example, if R is the relation "is the father of," then an element a has a "mate" b such that $a\,R\,b$ exactly when a is a father of some son. Generally, the set of all elements $a \in A$ which are so distinguished is called the *domain* of the relation R. Symbolically, the domain of R is the set

$$[a \in A;\, \text{there exists (at least one element) } b \in B \text{ such that } a\,R\,b].$$

To turn things around, the set

$$[b \in B;\, \text{there exists } a \in A \text{ such that } a\,R\,b]$$

is of similar importance; it is called the *range* of the relation R. We see then that, in terms of the list of all pairs (a, b) comprising the relation R, the domain of R is the set of all "first" elements a appearing anywhere in the list, while the range of R is the set of "second" elements b appearing anywhere. It is important to observe that the domain of R is therefore the range of R^*, and, similarly, the range of R is the domain of R^*. These definitions are formalized in the following:

(5.3.7) DEFINITION: Let A and B be sets and R a relation on $A \times B$. Then

$$\text{domain of } R \equiv [a \in A;\ \text{there exists } b \in B \text{ such that } a\,R\,b];$$
$$\text{range of } R \equiv [b \in B;\ \text{there exists } a \in A \text{ such that } a\,R\,b].$$

It has already been indicated that if A and B are the set of all male persons, and if R is the relation "is the father of," that is,

$$R = [(a, b) \in (A \times B);\ a \text{ is the father of } b],$$

then the domain of R is the set of all fathers of male children. The range of R is clearly the set of all males which have (male) fathers, that is, the set of all sons. Whether this range is equal to A or not is a biologico-historical, or perhaps theological, question. The reader might look back at the various relations that have been displayed pictorially and read off the domain and range of each one. For example, in (5.2.6) the domain is $[p_1, p_2, p_3]$, and the range is $[p_1, p_2]$; clearly the domain is obtained at a glance as consisting of those elements appearing along the bottom, having dots anywhere directly above them, and the range is the set of those elements along the side, having dots to their right and on their level. In general, the universal relation on $A \times B$ has A and B for its domain and range respectively; the absurd relation has empty domain and range. The identity relation on $A \times A$ has A for both domain and range.

Admittedly, we have again merely scratched the surface in our presentation of the theory of relations. As can be seen from even our brief survey, there must be many types of relations, for example, symmetric and nonsymmetric; relations on $A \times B$ whose domain is A and those whose domain is a proper subset of A; relations on $A \times A$ which (as sets) contain the identity E (these are called *reflexive*); and so on. It would be a gigantic task in itself to classify relations into various categories and study the interconnections between the categories; such a task is beyond our scope. There are, however, several special types of relation whose study we cannot avoid. The first of these, *function*, is treated in the next section.

(5.3.8) PROJECT: If A, B are sets and R is a relation on $A \times B$, then show that
(a) $R + R' = A \times B$;
(b) $R \cdot R' = \Theta$;
(c) $(R')' = R$.

(5.3.9) PROJECT: If A, B are sets, and Θ is the absurd relation on $A \times B$, show that $(A \times B)^* = B \times A$, $\Theta^* = \Theta$. If A is a set, show that $E^* = E$ (E being the identity relation on $A \times A$).

(5.3.10) PROJECT: If A, B are sets, and R is a relation on $A \times B$, show that $(R^*)^* = R$.

(5.3.11) PROJECT: Let A, B be sets and R a relation on $A \times B$. Show that
(a) domain of R = range of R^*;
(b) range of R = domain of R^*;
(c) domain of $A \times B = A$, range of $A \times B = B$;
(d) domain of $\Theta = \Theta$, range of $\Theta = \Theta$.

(5.3.12) PROJECT: Show that, if A is a set and E the identity relation on $A \times A$, then

$$\text{domain of } E = \text{range of } E = A.$$

(5.3.13) PROJECT: Let $A = [p_1, p_2]$ $(p_1 \neq p_2)$. Find the following:
(a) all relations on $A \times A$;
(b) all symmetric relations on $A \times A$;
(c) all reflexive relations on $A \times A$;
(d) all relations on $A \times A$ which are symmetric *and* reflexive.

5.4. Functions. There is a feature which some, but by no means all, relations exhibit, a feature according to which relations might be classified. If we look, for example, at (5.2.4) or (5.2.7), we find that in any vertical column no more than one dot occurs. This means that in any vertical column rising above an element of the domain, *exactly* one dot is to be found. A glance at (5.2.5) and (5.2.6) shows that this property is not possessed by all relations. Let us then formulate the condition in general terms, introducing the name *function* for those relations which satisfy it.

(5.4.1) DEFINITION: Let A and B be sets and R a relation on $A \times B$. Then R is a *function* provided that
(a) for every $a \in$ domain of R there exists exactly one $b \in B$ such that $a\,R\,b$.

If domain of $R = A$, then the function R is said to be *on A to B*.

Another formulation of (5.4.1.a) is this:

(5.4.2) if $b_1, b_2 \in B$ such that there exists $a \in A$ with the property $a\,R\,b_1$ and $a\,R\,b_2$, then $b_1 = b_2$.

A still further formulation is this:

(5.4.3) for every $a \in$ domain of R, the set $[b \in B;\, a\,R\,b]$ consists of just one element.

Note that, if R is on A to B, it is required only that domain of $R = A$; the range of R may be B or a subset of B.

There are numerous examples of functions in addition to those which can be easily represented pictorially, like (5.2.4) and (5.2.7). The identity E on $A \times A$ is a function, since, if in (5.4.1) a is any element of A, and if we take b to be a, then $a\,E\,b$; moreover, if for some $b' \in B$, $a\,E\,b'$, then $b' = a = b$, so that $b' = b$, and (5.4.1) is verified. If M is the set of all male persons, then the relation "is a son of" on $M \times M$ is a function. For let a be in the domain, that is, let a be a son of some father. If we ask how many elements $b \in M$ exist such that a is the son of b, the answer is obviously exactly one, since a man (who has some father) has just one father. On the other hand, the transpose, namely, "is the father of," is not a function, since a man can have more than one son. We agree to call absurd relations functions, although their domains are empty; the reason is to be found in (7.4). However, universal relations fail to be functions, unless the second set B has just one element.

The word *function* was introduced quite early into mathematical literature, in a sense completely different from its usual nonmathematical meanings, to indicate roughly a "dependence" between two "quantities," which quantities were usually numbers (in the intuitive sense). With the introduction of the modern viewpoint, this notion was naturally extended to mean a "dependence" between elements of arbitrary sets. A function was then thought of as a device whereby, for each element a of a set A (or a subset of A), there is "determined" a single "corresponding" element b of B. For us such a more or less vague description is unnecessary, since our more precise description of a function achieves the same end. Thus a relation satisfying (5.4.1) is itself a method of associating with each a in its domain a single corresponding b, namely, the b such that $a\,R\,b$. Furthermore, if a device is given which associates with every a a corresponding b, the set of all associated pairs (a, b) is a relation satisfying (5.4.1).

Some writers use the word "function" to mean something close to what we call a relation; they distinguish the present concept by calling it a "single-valued function." Our terminology seems a bit more compact and agrees with the most widely accepted usage.

We are led now to make a definition of a type that will occur so frequently that a brief discussion of the logic involved is necessary. Let B be a set, and let C be a subset of B. If it is known that C has exactly one element, which state may be described thus:

$$C \neq \Theta; \quad \text{if } b_1, b_2 \in C, \text{ then } b_1 = b_2,$$

then we should be permitted to introduce *by definition* a notation, say c, for "the" single element of C. As a matter of general interest, it should be observed that the use of the article "the" is legitimate only in the situation we have described. Thus, before we may apply "the" to an element of a set C, we must first establish that C has one element—no more and no fewer. Then, after the use of "the" has been legalized, we may define a symbol or name as a label for "the" element.

Before proceeding with our discussion of functions, let us return briefly to the barber paradox described in (2.3). It will be recalled that a name "the Barber of Seville" was introduced for a (presumably) specific person. To be acceptable, the definition should have proceeded as follows. First, let B be the set of all men of Seville; then define C as the set

$$[b \in B; \ b \text{ shaves all elements and only those elements of } B \text{ who do not shave themselves}].$$

Then it would be necessary to establish that C has exactly one element, after which the Barber could be defined as that single element. The joker is, of course, that the set C is really empty! Indeed, the discussion in (2.3) shows exactly this. No one can doubt that it is illegitimate to apply "the" to something that isn't there, and hence that the definition of the Barber is inadmissible. Many paradoxes, including the other discussed in (2.3), can be treated in this same way.

To return to functions, let R be a relation on $A \times B$ which is a function. Suppose that we focus attention for a moment on some element a in the domain of R. Next, let C be the set

$$[b \in B; \ a \, R \, b] \subset B.$$

According to (5.4.3), C has exactly one element. This single element may now be given a name by virtue of the general principle just outlined. The notation which we choose is $R(a)$ (read "R of a"). Hence $R(a)$ is the element of B "corresponding" to a by means of the relation R; in other words,

$$[R(a)] = [b \in B; \ a \, R \, b].$$

It follows that the statement $a \, R \, b$ means the same as $b = R(a)$. The symbol $R(a)$, when a is any element of the domain of R, is often called the *R-correspondent of a*, or the *correspondent of a under R*.

In (5.2.4), it is clear that $q_1 = R(p_1)$ and $q_1 = R(p_3)$; the notation $R(p_2)$ is meaningless, since p_2 is not in the domain. Similarly, in (5.2.7), $q_3 = R(p_1)$, $q_1 = R(p_2)$, $q_2 = R(p_3)$. If E is the identity on $A \times A$, then, for every $a \in A$, $a = E(a)$. If M is the set of all male persons, and if R is the relation "is a son of," then, for every a in the domain of R, $R(a)$ is the father of a.

It is important to realize that a function F is completely defined by the specification of

(a) the sets A, B;
(b) the domain of F (a subset of A);
(c) for each a in the domain, the element $F(a)$ of B which is to be the F-correspondent of a.

This method of introducing specific functions is practically simpler than listing, or showing how to list, all the pairs comprising F. Functions to be introduced in subsequent work will commonly be defined by this method.

A simpler tabular representation is possible for functions than for other relations, since it is sufficient to list all elements of the domain, say along a horizontal line, showing for each the F-correspondent directly below it. Hence (5.2.4), (5.2.7) and (5.3.4) may be replaced by (5.4.4), (5.4.5) and (5.4.6) respectively. The simplified type of table suggests the

a:	p_1	p_3
$F(a)$:	q_1	q_1

(5.4.4) FIGURE

a:	p_1	p_2	p_3
$F(a)$:	q_3	q_1	q_2

(5.4.5) FIGURE

a:	p_1	p_2	p_3
$F(a)$:	p_1	p_2	p_3

(5.4.6) FIGURE

intuitive flavor of the word *function* a little better, perhaps, than our actual definition. The possibility of this representation and the idea behind it lead us to speak of a function *on* A *to* B rather than on $A \times B$ [see (5.4.1)], in case the set A is actually the domain of the function. Thus a function on A to B actually carries every element of A into some element of B; it "operates" or "works" on elements of A, producing for each of them an element of B.

Since functions are relations, and relations are sets (of pairs), the concept of equality of functions is a special case of the concept of equality of sets. Hence, if F and G are functions on $A \times B$, $F = G$ means that

F and G are identical subsets of $A \times B$. The reader should convince himself that $F = G$ means the same as that F and G have the same domain, and, for every a in this domain, $F(a) = G(a)$. We are led to the following:

(5.4.7) CRITERION: *Two functions F and G are equal exactly when*
(a) *domain of F = domain of G,*
and
(b) *for each $a \in$ domain of F, $F(a) = G(a)$.*

A simple extension of the notation $F(a)$ to represent the F-correspondent of a is embodied in the use of the symbol $F(S)$ when S is not an element of the domain of F, but rather a set of such elements. Then $F(S)$ represents naturally the set of all F-correspondents of all the elements a of S. More precisely, $F(S)$ is the set of all elements b such that there exists $a \in S$ for which $b = F(a)$. Hence we have the definition:

(5.4.8) DEFINITION: Let A, B be sets, F a function on A to B, and $S \subset A$. Then

$$\begin{aligned} F(S) &\equiv [b \in B; \text{ there exists } a \in S \text{ such that } b = F(a)] \\ &= [F(a); a \in S]. \end{aligned}$$

The notation we have described for functions F and F-correspondents is by no means the only one in use. Of several alternate designations, there is one which we shall find useful. Let us suppose that F is a function on A to B. Since every $a \in A$ determines a single $b \in B$ which is the F-correspondent of a, it is natural to denote this b by the symbol b_a (read "b sub a" or "b dependent on a"). Thus

$$b_a = F(a).$$

If this notation is to be used, it will be necessary to have a symbol in terms of it for the function F itself. Hence we introduce the notation $(b_a; a \in A)$ as synonymous with F, so that

$$(5.4.9) \qquad F = (b_a;\ a \in A) = [(a, b_a); a \in A].$$

This notation for functions is quite similar to the bracket notation for sets; since the concepts are manifestly different, extreme care must be exercised to prevent confusion of the notations. Square brackets will always refer to sets, and parentheses to functions. One sees easily from (5.4.8), (5.3.7) that $F(A) = [b_a; a \in A]$ is the *range* of the function $F = (b_a; a \in A)$.

Although the two notations for functions are equivalent and may be used interchangeably, it should be noted that they reflect somewhat different psychological approaches. The notations F, $F(a)$ suggest that one thinks first of the function as an entity, and then of the F-correspondents. With the symbols b_a, $(b_a; a \epsilon A)$, on the other hand, one has the feeling that initial emphasis is on the correspondents b_a, the function being subsequently defined with their help. That this latter view is a practical one has already been indicated: After its domain is specified, a function may be defined by telling for each a how to find b_a. It should be observed that the alternate notation (5.4.9) for a function is quite suggestive of the pictorial representation.

It may happen that a function F is to be defined on A to B so that the specification of the correspondents of elements lying in various subsets of its domain cannot be readily effected by means of a single universal descriptive statement. For example, suppose that A is to be the domain of F and that A_1, A_2 are subsets of A such that $A_1 \cdot A_2 = \Theta$. One may wish to specify that the correspondent for every $a_1 \epsilon A_1$ should be the unique element (in B) having one property, and that the correspondent of every $a_2 \epsilon A_2$ should be the unique element having another property. In such a case, we use the following form: Define F on A to B so that, for every $a \epsilon A$,

$$F(a) = \begin{cases} \text{the unique element such that} \cdots \text{if } a \epsilon A_1 \\ \text{the unique element such that} \cdots \text{if } a \epsilon A_2. \end{cases}$$

A similar form applies if the elements b_a are to be introduced first: For $a \epsilon A$, define

$$b_a \equiv \begin{cases} \cdots \text{if } a \epsilon A_1 \\ \cdots \text{if } a \epsilon A_2. \end{cases}$$

Note the necessity of assuming $A_1 \cdot A_2 = \Theta$. Without this assumption, if $a \epsilon A_1 \cdot A_2$, two requirements are made of $F(a)$, and these might conflict.

It remains for us to consider briefly each of two particular kinds of function; the following two sections are devoted to these specializations.

(5.4.10) PROJECT: Let $A = [p_1, p_2]$, $B = [q_1, q_2]$, where $p_1 \neq p_2$, $q_1 \neq q_2$. Find all functions on A to B and determine the range of each. What additional relations on $A \times B$ exist which are functions?

(5.4.11) PROJECT: Prove (5.4.7).

5.5. One-to-One Correspondences. Let F be a function on A to B, where A and B are, as usual, given sets. Since F is a relation on $A \times B$, the transpose F^* of F is a relation on $B \times A$. It is natural to ask whether F^* is necessarily, or may be, a function too. In order to answer these questions decisively, it suffices to consider a few simple examples. Let A be the set $[p_1, p_2, p_3]$, and B the set $[q_1, q_2, q_3]$. Then (5.5.1) and (5.5.2) picture two relations F and G respectively, which are obviously functions on A to B. It is evident that F^* is not a function, since otherwise at most one dot would appear in every horizontal line of the table (5.5.1). Moreover, it is equally clear that G^* is a function. These

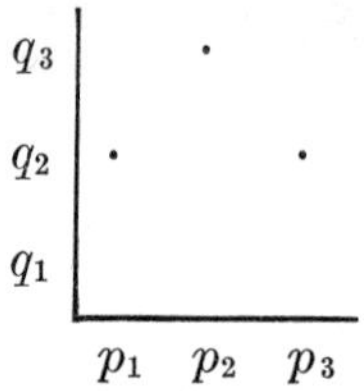

(5.5.1) FIGURE

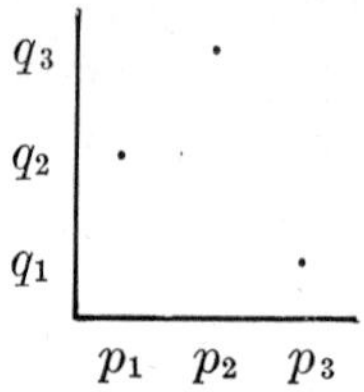

(5.5.2) FIGURE

examples serve to show that the transpose of a function *can* be a function, but *need not* be. These considerations lead to a definition.

(5.5.3) DEFINITION: Let A and B be sets and F a function on $A \times B$. Then F is a *one-to-one correspondence between A and B* if

(a) domain of $F = A$;
(b) range of $F = B$;
(c) F^* is a function.

Clearly, if F is a one-to-one correspondence between A and B, then F^* is a one-to-one correspondence between B and A; F^* is then called the *inverse* of F.

It is an important fact that not every pair of sets A, B admits the existence of even one one-to-one correspondence between A and B. For example, if $A = [p_1, p_2, p_3]$ and $B = [q_1, q_2]$, then no one-to-one correspondence between A and B exists. Later we shall see that the possibility of finding a one-to-one correspondence between A and B occurs exactly when A and B have the "same number" of elements in a precise sense to be introduced [(10.4.4.b)].

In contrast to the fact that different sets A and B may admit the existence of no one-to-one correspondence between them, *equal* sets behave quite differently. For, if $B = A$, the identity E on $A \times B$ is a one-to-one correspondence between A and B; this is true because $E^* = E$, whence E^* is a function along with E, and because the domain and range of E are both A, as was stated in (5.3). Moreover, if A has more than one element, then, as will be seen later, there is always at least one one-to-one correspondence between A and A which is different from E.

(5.5.4) PROJECT: Let $A = [p_1, p_2, p_3]$, where $p_1 \neq p_2$, $p_2 \neq p_3$, $p_3 \neq p_1$. Find all one-to-one correspondences between A and A.

(5.5.5) PROJECT: Let $A = [p_1, p_2, p_3]$, $B = [q_1, q_2]$, where $p_1 \neq p_2$, $p_2 \neq p_3$, $p_3 \neq p_1$, $q_1 \neq q_2$. Find all six functions F with domain A and range B, and for every such F show that F^* is not a function.

5.6. Binary Operations. In the general theory of functions on $A \times B$, or on A to B, A is an arbitrary set. A somewhat special case happens to arise so often that a special terminology and notations for it are desirable. The case we have in mind is that in which A is the cartesian product of two (arbitrary) sets A_1 and A_2.

(5.6.1) DEFINITION: If F is a function on $A_1 \times A_2$ to B, then F is called a *binary operation*, or simply an *operation*.

The elements of the domain of F are of course the pairs (a_1, a_2) with $a_1 \in A_1$, $a_2 \in A_2$. The F-correspondent of (a_1, a_2) is an element $b \in B$; hence

$$b = F((a_1, a_2)),$$

in accordance with our usual notation. Since the double parentheses are cumbersome, it is conventional to write more simply

(5.6.2) $$b = F(a_1, a_2).$$

Another notation is often used to mean the same as (5.6.2), namely,

(5.6.3) $$b = a_1 \, F \, a_2;$$

the notation in (5.6.3) is suggested by mathematical custom, and should become familiar to the reader if he replaces F by some other symbol, such as $+$. It should be observed that (5.6.3) will not conflict with the relation notation, since F is not a relation on $A_1 \times A_2$, but rather one on $(A_1 \times A_2) \times B$. In fact, $b = a_1 \, F \, a_2$ means the same as $(a_1, a_2) \, F \, b$.

The tabular representation for functions introduced in (5.4) naturally applies to binary operations. Thus, for example, (5.6.4) represents a

(a_1, a_2):	(p_1, t_1)	(p_1, t_2)	(p_2, t_1)	(p_2, t_2)
$F(a_1, a_2)$:	q_3	q_1	q_2	q_2

(5.6.4) FIGURE

function on $A_1 \times A_2$ to B, where

$$A_1 = [p_1, p_2], \quad A_2 = [t_1, t_2], \quad B = [q_1, q_2, q_3].$$

However, the peculiar nature of a binary operation makes possible a much more compact tabular representation. For example, (5.6.5) pic-

	p_1	p_2
t_1	q_3	q_2
t_2	q_1	q_2

(5.6.5) FIGURE

tures the same function as does (5.6.4), in the following sense. The correspondent of any pair is found in the column of the first element (in the pair) and the row of the second element. Thus the correspondent of (p_2, t_1) is found in the column under p_2 and the row opposite t_1; it is q_2.

It goes without saying that the sets A_1, A_2 and B need not be distinct, and if distinct, need not have empty intersections. All conceivable ways in which they may be interrelated are admissible. A common type of operation is one on $A \times A$ to A; it is this type that will later lead us to descriptions of such processes as addition and multiplication of numbers. Indeed, the reader may well have been reminded of the traditional multiplication table by our second type of tabular representation.

It may happen that a function has for its domain a proper subset S of $A_1 \times A_2$, rather than the entire cartesian product as would be required if the function is on $A_1 \times A_2$ to B. In this case we still use the term "binary operation" to describe the function; we refer to it as an operation on S to B. It should be noted that in this case the domain S is really a relation on $A_1 \times A_2$, in accordance with our usual terminology.

Our discussion of operations concludes with two examples. Let

$$A_1 \equiv [\text{all male persons}], \quad A_2 \equiv [\text{all female persons}], \quad B \equiv A_1,$$
$$S \equiv [(m, w) \in A_1 \times A_2;\, m \text{ and } w \text{ have had together at least one son}].$$

An operation $\circ$ is now defined by specifying its domain as S and the $\circ$-correspondent of each $(m, w) \in S$ to be the oldest son of m and w. Since such an oldest son is an element of B, $\circ$ is an operation on S to B. Either symbol $\circ(m, w)$ or $m \circ w$ thus denotes the oldest son of m and w. Let us consider some pair $(m, w) \in S$, and let

$$s = m \circ w.$$

Now it might happen that there exists $w' \in A_2$ such that $(s, w') \in S$. Then $s \circ w'$ (the oldest son of s and w'), which may also be denoted by $(m \circ w) \circ w'$, is a grandson of m and w. In the notation $(m \circ w) \circ w'$, the parentheses are used as heretofore, to show that the first $\circ$ is to be "performed" first; without them, we might be tempted to interpret the notation as $m \circ (w \circ w')$, although, in this particular case, the alternate reading would be meaningless.

Our second example illustrates an operation on $A \times A$ to A. Let $A = [p_1, p_2]$; such an operation $\circ$ might be represented by (5.6.6). In

	p_1	p_2
p_1	p_2	p_1
p_2	p_2	p_1

(5.6.6) FIGURE

connection with this operation, a good exercise might be to verify that

$$(p_1 \circ p_2) \circ p_2 = p_2 \circ p_2 = p_1,$$

while

$$p_1 \circ (p_2 \circ p_2) = p_1 \circ p_1 = p_2;$$

and that

$$p_1 \circ p_2 = p_2,$$

while

$$p_2 \circ p_1 = p_1.$$

The significance of such observations as these will become apparent in Chapter 7.

(5.6.7) PROJECT: Let $A = [p_1, p_2]$, $B = [q_1, q_2]$, where $p_1 \neq p_2$, $q_1 \neq q_2$. Find all operations on $A \times A$ to B. Specify the range of each.

5.7. Summary. The present chapter has *defined* certain nonbasic, but nearly basic, terms with the help of the basic concepts, set and cartesian product. A list of concepts and notations now available to us follows:

relation on $A \times B$ (if A, B are sets): any subset of $A \times B$;
$a\,R\,b$: notation for $(a, b) \in R \subset A \times B$, read "$a$ is in the R relation to b";
R': negative relation to R, complement of R in $A \times B$; $'$ replaced by $|$ for some symbols;
R^*: transpose relation to R: $[(b, a); a\,R\,b]$;
E: identity relation on $A \times A$; $a\,E\,b$ means $a = b$;
domain of R (on $A \times B$): $[a$; there exists b such that $a\,R\,b]$;
range of R: $[b$; there exists a such that $a\,R\,b] =$ domain of R^*;
function on A to B (A, B sets): a relation F on $A \times B$ with domain A, such that $a\,F\,b$, $a\,F\,c$ implies $b = c$;
$F(a)$ (F a function on A to B): the F-correspondent of a, that is, the one $b \in$ range of F such that $a\,F\,b$;
$F(S)$: $[F(a); a \in S]$ if $S \subset A$;
b_a: $F(a)$;
$(F(a); a \in A)$ or $(b_a; a \in A)$: F;
one-to-one correspondence between A and B (A, B sets): a function F with domain A, range B, such that F^* is a function;
binary operation: a function $\circ$ on $S \subset A \times B$ to C; "c is the $\circ$-correspondent of (a, b)" is expressed thus: $c = a \circ b$, $c = \circ(a, b)$, $(a, b) \circ c$, $((a, b), c) \in \circ$.

Warning: The notation $a\,R\,b$ has two uses. If $a \in A$, $b \in B$, and R is a relation on $A \times B$, then $a\,R\,b$ is a statement about a, b. If $(a, b) \in S \subset A \times B$ and R is an operation on S to C, then $a\,R\,b$ is an *element* of C.

If it helps the reader to remember the notions *relation*, *function*, *one-to-one correspondence* and *operation* in terms of their appropriate tabular representations, he is of course at liberty to do so. Indeed, we shall find these pictures exceedingly useful devices. However, a little reflection on the breadth of our conception of set should show that it is not always possible to construct such tables. If A is the set of positions of an elevator in its shaft, then it would be quite impossible to represent a function on A to B by our pictorial method. Moreover, even if tables are used to represent relations, it should be remembered that the relations are not the tables themselves, but rather the sets of pairs which the tables indicate.

Chapter 6

THE POSTULATIONAL METHOD

6.1. Introduction. In the preceding chapters we have described the materials of mathematics. It has been indicated that mathematics consists of a certain type of discourse about various conceptual entities known as sets, relations, functions, operations, and the like. In this chapter we shall discuss in some detail the nature of the discourse.

At the beginning of any mathematical theory there appears a set or a collection of sets, which remains unchanged throughout the theory. In addition, there may appear certain functions, relations, operations, sets of functions, and the like, which also remain unchanged. These entities are referred to as the *basis* or basic situation of the mathematical theory. They are the objects about which the theory talks.

The *theory* itself consists of a number of statements (generally called theorems), all of which could be written in the same form, namely,

(6.1.1) if so and so is true of the basis, then such and such must also be true as a logical consequence.

Of course, alternate phraseology may be used, for example,

so and so logically entails such and such,

or, most briefly,

so and so implies such and such.

The essential point is that a *theorem* does not state that something is true about the basis; it merely says that, *if* one thing is true, then another thing *must* also be true.

Generally the statement of implication that constitutes a mathematical theorem is not at all obvious at first sight. Hence, in order to persuade people that it is a valid implication, a *proof* must be provided. The proof consists of a chain of statements, each of which is obvious (immediately acceptable on logical grounds), and which taken together demonstrate the validity of the implication stated by the theorem. More specifically, a theorem will be an assertion, usually not obvious, to the effect that

$$A \text{ implies } B,$$

where A, B are statements about the basis. The proof might consist of a number of assertions, such as

$$A \text{ implies } C,$$
$$C \text{ implies } D,$$
$$D \text{ implies } E,$$
$$E \text{ implies } B,$$

where each of these individual assertions is clearly true. Taken together, these statements validate the original implication. In short, a proof is the provision of stepping stones across a gulf that is too broad for the mind to leap in a single effort.

In a particular theory, it is generally the case that a certain number of the "ifs" of each theorem, a certain number of assumptions, are common to all theorems. These universal assumptions are not repeated in the suppositive clause of each theorem, but are stated once for all at the outset, and are understood to be assumed throughout the theory. They are referred to as the *axioms* or *postulates* of the theory. The basis and axioms together are known as the *foundation* of the theory.

It is seen, then, that a mathematical theory is a collection of statements to the effect that the axioms, and, perhaps, additional assumed facts about the basis, can be true only if certain other facts are also true in consequence. From this one may get the impression that mathematics (in our view) is nothing more than an elaboration of logic; a study of logical implication. If so, and if this impression is substantiated by the material to follow, we shall have accomplished one of our aims.

The usefulness of mathematics usually arises from the existence of instances or exemplifications of a theory. An *instance* of a mathematical system is a specific interpretation of the sets, relations, operations, and so on, of the basis, for which interpretation the axioms are true. The most common and most important examples, in the past, have been instances in which the sets, relations, and so on, of the basis have been interpreted as various physical entities or concepts, as for example, the notions of position and distance, the relation of betweenness, and so on. As soon as an instance of a certain theory is discovered, that is, as soon as it is determined that the axioms are true of a particular interpretation of the basis, then all the theorems of the given theory become demonstrated truths concerning the instance.

Of course, historically, the instance has usually come first. Until quite recently at least, the foundation of any particular mathematical theory was chosen for study precisely because that foundation represented the most significant features of some concrete instance. And, in fact, there was no serious effort to distinguish between the abstract basis and the particular instance which led to the investigation of that basis. More recently, the discovery of theories which have a large number of quite different and equally important instances has shown the wisdom of making a careful distinction between a general theory and an instance or exemplification of the theory.

Because the following chapters and sections deal with a variety of theories pertaining to different foundations, we shall place at the beginning of each section a notation identifying the basis and axioms to be assumed throughout that section. Exceptions occur when the section serves to introduce a new basis and axioms, when various systems are discussed in one section, and when the systems treated are such that the full foundations may be stated in each theorem. When no basis is assumed throughout a section, the notation [No Basis.] occurs. When one foundation applies throughout an entire chapter, the foundation is stated only at the outset of the chapter. These notations occur initially in Chapter 7.

6.2. Implications. We have said that a mathematical theorem will be an assertion

(6.2.1) A implies B,

where A and B are statements. The statements A and B are called, respectively, the *hypothesis* and *conclusion* of the implication. In the next section we shall discuss in some detail the possible nature of the statements A and B. Before we proceed to this, however, it will be instructive to consider a few of the changes that can be made in the form of the assertion (6.2.1).

First, the statement "A implies B" means that B must be true whenever A is true. Thus it is impossible for B to be false and A true. In still other words, whenever B is false, A must also be false. But this last assertion may be stated as "not B implies not A." Hence we see that the statement

(6.2.1) A implies B

has as a consequence

(6.2.2) not B implies not A.

It is easily seen not only that (6.2.2) is a consequence of (6.2.1), but also that (6.2.1) is a consequence of (6.2.2). For, if (6.2.2) is valid, then, whenever B is false, A is false. Thus it is impossible for A to be true and B false. Hence, when A is true, B also is true. But this means that A implies B.

From the above, it is seen that the two statements (6.2.1) and (6.2.2) are really two different ways of asserting the same thing. They are valid or invalid together. If one has been proved, the other may be asserted without further proof. Each of these two ways of stating the same implication is called a *contrapositive* of the other.

As an example, consider the following:

(6.2.3) if a person is clean-shaven, then he has no beard.

A *contrapositive* of this statement may be written as follows:

(6.2.4) if a person has a beard, then he is not clean-shaven.

The reader will readily recognize that (6.2.3) and (6.2.4) both express the same fact.

Next, consider the two assertions:

(6.2.5) A implies B

and

(6.2.6) B implies A.

Each of these two statements is called a *converse* of the other. It is easy to see that converses do *not* express the same fact and, indeed, that a converse of a valid implication may be invalid, and vice versa. For example, a *converse* of (6.2.3) is the following:

(6.2.7) if a person has no beard, then he is clean-shaven.

This last statement is false (he may be a child or have a mustache), while (6.2.3) is true. A simpler example is the following pair of converses:

if an animal is a lion, then it is a mammal;
if an animal is a mammal, then it is a lion.

Clearly, the first of these is true while its converse is false.

We have seen that the converse of a valid implication need not be valid. However, for some statements A and B, it does happen that both "A implies B" and the converse "B implies A" are valid. In such a case the fact that both implications hold may be expressed in any of the following ways:

A and B are *equivalent*;
A is *equivalent* to B;
A (is true) *if and only if* B (is true).

So far we have considered only certain variations of the statement "A implies B" in which the statements A and B were treated as "single thoughts." However, in most cases the statement A is really the conjunction of a number of statements. We may indicate such a possibility as follows:

(6.2.8) if A_1 and A_2 and A_3 (are all true), then B (is true),

or

(6.2.9) A_1, A_2, A_3 implies B.

A *contrapositive* of (6.2.8) might be written,

(6.2.10) if not B (is true), then not all of A_1, A_2, A_3 (are true).

It should be noticed that *not all* of a number of things are true if one of them fails to be true. Hence (6.2.10) may also be written,

(6.2.11) if not B, then not A_1 *or* not A_2 *or* not A_3.

A *converse* of (6.2.8) would be

(6.2.12) if B (is true), then A_1 and A_2 and A_3 (are all true).

So far no new feature is introduced by the consideration of the possibility that A is a conjunction of statements (hypotheses). However a new feature is introduced by regarding (6.2.8) as a "conditional implication." Specifically, (6.2.8) may be written as follows:

(6.2.13) if A_1 and A_2 are accepted, then A_3 implies B.

Here, instead of treating all of A_1, A_2, A_3 as on a par, we think of two of them as "underlying hypotheses." When an implication appears as in (6.2.13), its *contrapositive* would usually be written as follows:

(6.2.14) if A_1 and A_2 are accepted, then not B implies not A_3.

Similarly, the statement,

(6.2.15) if A_1 and A_2 are accepted, then B implies A_3,

would be considered a *converse* of (6.2.13).

From the above, it appears that there is no single contrapositive or converse of an implication such as (6.2.8). There are a number of different contrapositives and converses, depending on how the "compound hypothesis" is divided into "underlying hypothesis" and "explicit hypothesis."

We have already mentioned that, in a mathematical theory, a certain number of assertions are common to the hypothesis of all theorems. These common "assumptions" are called the *axioms* of the theory. They are announced at the outset; they are not displayed in the separate theorems but simply understood to form a part of the hypothesis of every theorem. This portion of the hypothesis is, of course, always treated as an "underlying hypothesis" when contrapositives and converses are stated. Thus the statement of a theorem in the body of a mathematical theory may be indicated as follows:

(6.2.16) THEOREM: *(If the axioms and) if A, then B,*

where the parenthetical phrase does not actually appear but is simply understood. Accordingly, a contrapositive and converse might be the following:

(6.2.17) CONTRAPOSITIVE: *(If the axioms and) if not B, then not A.*

(6.2.18) CONVERSE: *(If the axioms and) if B, then A.*

In some theorems in a mathematical theory, the axioms constitute the entire hypothesis. Such a theorem has the form

(6.2.19) THEOREM: *(If the axioms, then) B.*

In such a case one does not speak of a converse or contrapositive of the implication.

Since the axioms are not explicitly displayed in the statement of a theorem, an implication such as (6.2.19) would appear simply as an assertion

B is true.

Hence, in such a ase, the statement of the theorem does not look like an implication. For this reason we emphasize the remark made earlier, that all mathematical theorems are fundamentally assertions of implication, whether or not they appear to be such.

6.3. Statements. In this section we shall describe, so far as possible, the kinds of statements that appear in the hypothesis (including the axioms) or conclusion of a mathematical theorem. Because of the extreme generality of a mathematical system, the types of statements that are made are quite limited. Actually, it is found that all statements in theorems can be phrased either as statements of *existence* or as statements of *generality.*

Suppose that two sets A and B are in the domain of discourse. Then the statement that A and B have common element(s), $A \cdot B \neq \Theta$, can be written as a statement of existence, namely,

(6.3.1) there exists an element of A which is also an element of B.

The statement that B is a subset of A, $B \subset A$, can be written as a statement of generality, thus,

(6.3.2) every element of B is also an element of A.

Roughly, a statement of existence is an assertion that there *exists* an element of some specific set which has particular properties; a statement of generality is an assertion that every element of some specific set has particular properties. Of course, these two types of statements abound in common parlance:

Every dog has his day.
Every cloud has a silver lining.
Into each life some rain must fall.

There is a fountain filled with blood.
There are more things in heaven and earth, Horatio,
  Than are dreamt of in your philosophy.
Many brave hearts lie asleep in the deep.
Great fleas have little fleas upon their backs to bite 'em.

Frequently statements of existence or of generality involve more than just one element. For example, the following assertions might occur:

there exist $a \in A$ and $b \in B$ such that $\cdots$;
for every $a \in A$, $b \in B$, it is true that $\cdots$.

These might be rewritten,

there exists $a \in A$ such that
  there exists $b \in B$ such that $\cdots$;
for every $a \in A$, it is true that,
  for every $b \in B$, it is true that $\cdots$.

We have thus arrived at statements of the form already described. Clearly this process may be continued to three, four, or any specific number of elements.

We are thus led to a general observation. Nothing prevents a particularizing phrase in a statement of existence or generality from again involving existence or generality assertions. One case of this situation requires special mention, since for such sentences, the interpretation in ordinary language is ambiguous, and a special rule has been adopted in mathematical language to remove the ambiguity. Consider the following statements:

(6.3.3) there is a day of judgment for all men,

and

(6.3.4) for all men there is a day of judgment.

In ordinary speech these two sentences would very commonly be used interchangeably and to mean either of two quite distinct things. They indicate either that there is a single, definite Day of Judgment, on which day all men are judged; or that for each man there is an individual day of judgment, possibly different for different men. In the one case, the day may "depend on" the man; in the other case, the day is unambiguously determined once for all. In mathematical language, it is essential to distinguish between these two possibilities. Accordingly, it is agreed that one of these meanings is assigned to each of the alternate phraseologies represented by (6.3.3) and (6.3.4). The statement (6.3.3), in which the existence of a day of judgment is asserted *before* mention of the men, is interpreted to mean that there is a Day of Judgment which is valid for all men. The statement (6.3.4), in which the existence is stated *after* mention of the men, is interpreted to allow (but not insist on) different days for different men. The rule is that objects whose existence is asserted *may* "depend on" previously mentioned objects, but not on objects mentioned subsequently. The difference in the precise interpretation of sentences such as (6.3.3) and (6.3.4) is exceedingly important to remember, since such statements occur very frequently in mathematics. Incidentally, it should be noticed that, with this precise interpretation, (6.3.4) is a consequence of (6.3.3), but not necessarily vice versa. If there is one for all, then for each there is certainly one (namely, that valid for all); but if for each there is one, there need not be one which is valid for all.

In our remark to the effect that the statements of theorems in mathematics can always be written as statements of existence or statements of generality, the reader may feel that we have overlooked the possibility of *negative* statements, such as,

(6.3.5) there does not exist an element of A such that so and so;

or

(6.3.6) it is not true that for all elements of A, so and so is true.

This possibility was not overlooked, and our previous remarks are valid, since these statements can be rephrased so as again to become statements of the original two forms. Actually, the negation of a statement of existence is a statement of generality, and vice versa. For example, (6.3.5) may be written,

(6.3.7) for every element of A it is false that so and so;

and (6.3.6) is synonymous with

(6.3.8) there exists an element of A such that so and so is false.

More specifically, the negation of (6.3.1) may be phrased,

(6.3.9) every element of A fails to be an element of B;

and the negation of (6.3.2) is

(6.3.10) there exists an element of B which is not an element of A.

Even for statements like (6.3.3) and (6.3.4) which involve both "there exists" and "for every" (or equivalent phrases), the negation may be written by replacing "for every" by "there exists" and "there exists" by "for every," and also negating the particularizing phrases. Thus the denial of (6.3.3) would state,

> for every day there exists a man for whom that day is not a day of judgment,

while (6.3.4) is false if

> there exists a man for whom every day fails to be judgment day.

The point is that an assertion fails to be true "for every" object if "there exists" an object for which the assertion is false. This is what is really meant by the remark, "the exception proves the rule." The exception (a single exception) proves that the rule is false. (The unfortunate custom of misinterpreting this excellent proverb, which uses the word "prove" in an archaic sense as equivalent to "test," is definitely to be deplored.) Equivalently, if there does not exist an object for which an assertion is true, then there are no exceptions to the denial of the assertion; and one has the rule that for every object the negation of the assertion is true. Though these points are quite simple, some time has been spent on them, since forming the negation of statements is a process which is required very frequently in mathematics, particularly in connection with "indirect proofs," a subject which will be discussed shortly.

For statements of existence there is a special understanding in mathematical language which differs from the customs of ordinary language. This has to do with the question of unambiguousness or *uniqueness*. In common parlance, it is usually assumed that the use of the singular ("there is · · ·") implies that there is just one object satisfying the requirements. Thus, "There is a fountain · · ·" indicates that there is only one fountain appropriately filled. If more than one object qualifies under the remark, then the plural is customarily used; thus, "Great fleas have little fleas · · ·." In mathematical language, however, the singular is almost always used, and it is understood that no implication concerning uniqueness or multiplicity is intended. For example, in the statement (6.3.1) the words "there exists an element of A · · ·" do not indicate in any way that there may not be many such elements. There may or may not be a multiplicity of elements. All that is guaranteed by the statement is that there is (at least) one. It may help the reader to consider that a parenthetical "at least" or "or more" is always understood in statements of existence. The reason for this convention is simply that, in most cases, when a statement of existence is given, it is not known whether there is just one, or more than one, qualifying element. If this point is of interest, it must be settled separately; very frequently it is of no particular importance. In the less usual case, in which it is known that there is only one element, and in which it is desired to indicate this fact, explicit statement is made; thus, "there is (exists) one *and only one* element · · ·," or "there is a *unique* element · · ·."

6.4. Symbols. The need for great precision, which is a characteristic of mathematical language, forces certain other customs that will not be familiar from common language. In particular, it is usual to introduce a name for the element under discussion to facilitate reference later in the sentence. This device avoids the use of reference words such as "which," "that," and so on, which may have dubious antecedents in a complicated sentence. The device is particularly valuable when a number of elements are under discussion, and in such cases replaces the legal fraternity's "party of the first part," and the like. In such simple cases as the statements (6.3.1) and (6.3.2) the device is not needed, but if it were used, the statements would appear as follows:

(6.4.1) there exists $a \in A$ such that $a \in B$,

and

(6.4.2) for every $b \in B$, it is true that $b \in A$.

From this it is seen that the use of names for reference provides a convenient shorthand even for sentences so simple that the device is not required for clarity.

In more complicated statements the virtue of employing reference labels is clearer. Suppose that a set G and an operation $\circ$ on $G \times G$ to G are in the domain of discourse. Then consider the following statement:

(6.4.3) for every a, $b \in G$, there exists $x \in G$, such that $a \circ x = b$.

An attempt to say this without the use of reference labels would lead to something like the following:

(6.4.4) for every pair of elements of the set under consideration, there exists a third element of the set, such that the second element of the given pair is the correspondent, under the given operation, of the ordered pair consisting of, first, the first of the given elements, and secondly, the element whose existence is claimed.

It would be easy, though pointless, to give much more extreme examples. However, it is important to realize that the use of reference labels (symbols) is only a practical necessity, rather than an inherent conceptual necessity. Thus one can *imagine* all mathematics written without any use of symbols, although it would certainly be unreadable. This point is emphasized since many people seem to feel that mathematics is in essence the manipulation of symbols. Such a view is a particularly unfortunate instance of failure to see the woods for the trees.

The constant use of symbols to facilitate reference requires a convention to prevent one's rapidly exhausting all known alphabets. Obviously it would be ideal if one never repeated the use of a particular symbol or letter, except to mean precisely the element or object so labeled initially. Equally obviously, such an ideal arrangement would bring most mathematics books to a close in about five pages, simply through a shortage of printers' marks. Fortunately for the existence of mathematics books and the sanity of printers, a simple convention solves this difficulty. It is necessary to distinguish three apparently different ways in which symbols are introduced, corresponding to three different purposes for their introduction.

First of all, there are symbols, like the a, b, x of statement (6.4.3), that are introduced in the first part of a statement simply for reference in the last part of the statement. The statement may be two or three sentences instead of just one, but it quite clearly expresses a complete thought and is "self-contained." In such cases it is understood that the letter or symbol introduced has done its duty, when the statement is completed and proper reference to the symbol has been made. Having done its duty, the symbol is released from all obligation to the statement which introduced it, and is ready to go to work in any other statement to mean anything whatsoever. Thus the a of statement (6.4.1) is under no obligation to refer to the same thing as the a of statement (6.4.3).

One consequence of the convention described in the preceding paragraph should be noticed particularly, since it is troublesome for many students. The use of the symbol a in a statement such as (6.4.3) is completely self-contained. The symbol is introduced in the first part of the sentence, referred to in the second part and then forgotten. In particular, it would not make the slightest difference to the meaning of this statement if the symbol a were changed to anything else in the world; that is, almost anything, since A, B already have meaning, and are therefore ruled out. Thus

$$\text{there exists } q \in A \text{ such that } q \in B$$

and

$$\text{there exists } \xi \in A \text{ such that } \xi \in B$$

mean exactly the same as (6.4.1). Similarly, (6.4.3) could be written,

(6.4.5) $\quad$ for every ♀, $+ \in G$, there exists $? \in G$ such that ♀ $\circ\, ? = +$, without changing the sense in any way. Of course, it is considered very bad taste to introduce gratuitous confusion by the use of such symbols as in (6.4.5), and this will not be done if it can be avoided; but on occasion it is impossible to avoid the use of a notation that requires very careful thought to be understood.

The situation described above, in which a symbol is released from all obligation as soon as reference has been made to it, is often expressed by saying that the symbol is "bound out" of the statement. In the remainder of the book, it will always be understood that symbols *introduced* in the statements of theorems (or corollaries or lemmas) are bound out and may be used in any other connection immediately.

A second use of symbols for later reference requires the preservation of the identity of the symbol for a somewhat longer period. In the proofs of theorems it is frequently necessary to introduce a name for an element in order to refer to that element repeatedly throughout the proof. This is really no different from the preceding situation, if we conceive of the entire proof as constituting a single, rather elaborate statement which is not completed until the end of the proof.

It would be desirable to insist that any symbol introduced in a proof should have a unique meaning within that particular proof. Actually, this rule will be followed whenever possible; however, as proofs become more and more elaborate, demanding the use of large numbers of symbols, the rule becomes impractical. Hence we adopt the following convention: If a symbol, for example, x, has been introduced in a proof, any subsequent assertion involving x will refer to the *same* x (with the original meaning) except if the assertion has one of these forms or their variants:

there exists $x \cdots$ such that $\cdots$;
for every $x \cdots$, it is true that $\cdots$;
define x to be $\cdots$.

The phrases "there exists x," "for every x" and "define x to be" then signify that use of the symbol x with the old meaning has come to an end, and that until "further notice" (end of the proof, or another occurrence of "there exists x," "for every x" or "define x to be"), x will carry the new meaning being introduced. In any case, once the proof is complete, all symbols introduced in the proof are released from bondage and are available for new duties.

Finally, it is usually necessary to introduce a certain number of "durable" symbols which retain a particular significance throughout an entire theory. In particular, the objects (sets, relations, functions, and the like) which constitute the basis must have names which are invariable, and which are not applied to anything else, throughout the discussion of the theory concerning that basis. In addition, other objects (new relations, special elements or subsets of the basic sets, and so on) may become objects of discourse, not just in an individual theorem, but in many theorems. The convention here is twofold; first, names of objects in the basis are permanent and may not be used in any other sense, and, secondly, a new name may be introduced by an explicit, displayed definition, after which it also is permanent. The definition may state something like this:

let e denote the unique element of G such that $\cdots$.

After such an explicit introduction by definition, not occurring in the proof of a theorem but inserted "between theorems," the symbol introduced may not be used in any sense other than that specified in the definition, for the remainder of the theory.

The "durable" symbols, that is, symbols representing objects in the basis, or symbols introduced by explicit definitions, may occur in the statement of theorems without being "bound out." The distinction is that the "bound out" symbols are introduced in the statement for purposes of reference within the statement, while the "durable" symbols were previously introduced and are used in the statement of the theorem to refer back to their earlier use. Thus, in the statement (6.4.1), the symbols A and B are durable. Similarly, in the statement (6.4.3), the symbols G and $\circ$ are durable.

Again, this use of symbols is similar to the other, if an entire theory is regarded as a single thought. The durable symbols are really bound out at the end of the theory; they may even be regarded as bound out at the end of a theorem, if the foundation of the theory is explicitly placed in the hypothesis of the theorem. Differences in the three uses of symbols are thus due solely to our form of presentation.

To summarize, it is not permitted to use a symbol for more than one meaning in the following circumstances:

symbols introduced in statements of theorems, lemmas, corollaries or axioms: within the statements;

symbols introduced in proofs: within the proofs (unless released by our convention);

symbols denoting objects in the basis: within the theory;

symbols introduced by displayed definition: within the theory subsequent to the definition.

On the other hand, it is always permitted to use different symbols for the same object. Here again, mathematical custom differs somewhat from ordinary usage. In common language, when two different names are used, as in "Jack and Jill went up the hill," it is quite properly assumed that two separate and distinct people were involved in the subsequent misadventures. In mathematical language, when two labels are introduced, as in "let a, b be elements of the set S," the situation must be understood somewhat as follows: "We are introducing two names for elements of the set S, since, as far as we know now, there may be two *distinct* elements involved; but if it subsequently turns out that both names actually refer to the same element ($a = b$), don't sue us." The rule is that two names must be used as long as two distinct elements *might* be involved. The use of two names is not a guarantee of distinctness.

In a statement of generality involving a pair of elements, such as (6.4.3), "for every $a, b \in G, \cdots$," it is always understood that the statement made is true for *every* pair of elements, *distinct or not*, in the set G. Hence a special case of (6.4.3) is

$$\text{for every } a \in G, \text{ there exists } x \in G, \text{ such that } a \circ x = a.$$

This is merely the special case of (6.4.3) which arises when $a = b$, and which is understood to be included by the words "every $a, b \in G$." Special choices may always be made for any symbol occurring in a statement immediately after the words "for every." Clearly, however, one may not assign any special choices of a symbol appearing after the words "there exists." A statement of existence merely guarantees that there is *some* element which performs the desired tricks. With this element one must be satisfied, and glad to get it; one certainly cannot expect or require it to perform any further tricks simultaneously. Thus, a statement like

$$\text{(6.4.6)} \qquad \text{for every } a, b \in G \text{ (there exists } b \in G \text{ such that) } a \circ b = b$$

is certainly *not* a special case of (6.4.3). Without the nonsensical assertion of existence of a previously introduced element (which assertion we have enclosed in parentheses), the statement (6.4.6) is perfectly reasonable and might be true of some sets G and operations $\circ$ on $G \times G$ to G; but it certainly does not follow from (6.4.3). It is easy to find examples of G and $\circ$ where (6.4.3) is true and (6.4.6) is false. Notice, however, that if (6.4.6) is true, then (6.4.3) is also true, and in fact $x = b$ satisfies the requirement of (6.4.3). This emphasizes the point, mentioned above, that the use of a new symbol x in (6.4.3) does not prevent the possibility that $x = a$ or $x = b$, but rather simply keeps an open mind on the subject.

6.5. Proofs. It has already been mentioned that the theorems of a mathematical theory consist of assertions whose truth is usually not obvious. For this reason it is necessary to give a proof, that is, a series of statements which makes the truth of the theorem obvious.

Now the word "obvious" is a rather dangerous one. There is an incident, which has become something of a legend in mathematical circles, that illustrates this danger. A certain famous mathematician was lecturing to a group of students and had occasion to use a formula which he wrote down with the remark, "This statement is obvious." Then he paused and looked rather hesitantly at the formula. "Wait a moment," he said. "Is it obvious? I think it's obvious." More hesitation, and then, "Pardon me, gentlemen, I shall return." Then he left the room. Thirty-five minutes later he returned; in his hands was a sheaf of papers covered with calculations, on his face a look of quiet satisfaction. "I was right, gentlemen. It is obvious," he said, and proceeded with his lecture.

While this incident is a little extreme, the word "obvious" is used, or misused, all too often, to refer to something that would be a lot of trouble to prove. When properly used, the word refers to a statement of implication whose validity will be immediately accepted as apparent by the audience. Clearly, the meaning of the term depends on the training and experience of the audience, so that in addressing a group of professional chemists, one could use the word to refer to something that an eminent physician might find not only not obvious but completely incomprehensible.

As the word "obvious," so also the word "proof" has a meaning which is dependent on the audience for whom the proof is intended. All that is required of a proof is that it convince the audience of the truth of the implication at hand. In this book, the proofs of the early theorems will be rather detailed, since we wish to convince as large an audience as possible, consistent with keeping the bulk of the book within reasonable limits. Subsequently, as the reader is presumed to become more at ease with the symbolism and the ideas, the proofs are given in somewhat less detail.

Now it must be said that there is no simple test that can be applied to determine the validity of a proof, that is, to determine that an alleged proof really is a proof. Mathematical history contains rare instances of arguments that were generally accepted as proofs for hundreds of years, before being successfully challenged by a very ingenious mathematician, who pointed out a possibility that had been overlooked in the alleged proof. And more recently, every year there appear, in the mathematical journals of the world, a certain number of papers which point out that some statement, allegedly proved in a preceding paper, was not only erroneously proved (that is, not proved) but was, in fact, incorrect. These facts are mentioned for the benefit of those who feel that there is some magic formula for a proof which makes it immutable and unarguable henceforth and forevermore.

Not only is there no magic formula for determining the validity of a proof; there is also no formula for constructing a proof. In fact, the first proof given for a new theorem is seldom either as simple or as ingenious as possible, and the proofs of famous and important theorems presented in textbooks usually represent the fruits of the labors of many mathematicians, who have refined and simplified the method of demonstration, subsequent to the first enunciation of the results. For this reason many of the famous proofs of mathematics resemble a championship chess game; the tyro can recognize that all the moves are legal and that a checkmate is achieved in the end, but only experience and practice can provide a background for an appreciation of the import of the moves.

Although it is not possible to give complete rules for the construction of proofs, it is possible to compare and contrast certain types of proofs that most commonly occur. Clearly, one can distinguish between proofs of statements of existence and proofs of statements of generality. In addition, there is a useful distinction between so-called direct and indirect proofs. Finally, among proofs of existence statements, one can distinguish between what might be called constructive and deductive proofs.

The terms *direct* and *indirect* can be applied both to existence proofs and to proofs of generality. Briefly, a *direct proof* starts with the assumptions of the theorem, and of course, the axioms, which are always understood to be part of the assumptions of every theorem, and demonstrates directly that the conclusion of the theorem must be true. The form for such a proof is the one previously outlined. It is desired to prove that

$$A \text{ implies } B;$$

this may be accomplished perhaps by showing successively

$$\begin{aligned} &A \text{ implies } C,\\ &C \text{ implies } D,\\ &D \text{ implies } E,\\ &E \text{ implies } B. \end{aligned}$$

The desired result is then demonstrated.

An *indirect proof* proceeds in quite a different manner. Briefly, it consists of showing that the theorem asserted must be true, since the assumption of its falsity would contradict some known fact or assumption. An indirect proof might also be called a double negative proof. Instead of proving that the theorem is true, one proves that it is not false. An indirect proof always starts with the equivalent of the remark: "Assume that the statement to be proved is false." Then from this assumption, and the axioms, one attempts to derive an assertion that contradicts a previously demonstrated assertion or that is self-contradictory (C and not C are true). Such a contradiction shows that the assertion, "Assume the statement is false," is an inadmissible one, that is, cannot be valid. Thus the statement must be true. The form for an indirect proof may be indicated as follows: It is desired to prove that

A implies B.

Assume that the statement is false, so that

A and not B are both true.

Then one shows that, as a consequence of this assumption,

C and not C are both true.

But this is absurd, so that some fallacy must have been introduced. The only possible fallacy is the assumption that the statement is false. Thus, it is false that the statement is false; hence the statement is true.

The rather famous game of the black and white hats affords a good illustration of the use of indirect proof, divorced from mathematical nomenclature. The game requires three players, seated in a circle facing one another, and a referee who places on the head of each player a hat which may be either black or white. No player sees his own hat. The rule is that a player who observes a black hat on the head of either opponent must raise his hand. The first player to *deduce* (not guess) the color of his own hat announces the color and wins the game. Actually, the only time that the game is any fun, is when all three hats are black. Suppose, for example, only two hats are black and one is white. Then, one of the black hat wearers, say Joe, will see his black-hatted opponent raise his hand, indicating that he sees a black hat. Joe knows it must be his own hat, since he can see that the third player has a white hat. So Joe immediately announces that his own hat must be black. But, if all three hats are black, then the story is different. All three hands go up at once, of course, but no one can be sure immediately that his own hat is black. However, after a reasonable time, an ingenious player is able to deduce that he has a black hat. The method used to demonstrate this fact is a typical indirect proof. "*Assume*," he says to himself, "that my hat is white. Then this would be a game with two black hats, and one white hat. But then (according to the analysis given above) the game would be trivial, and my two black-hatted opponents would know that they had black hats. They would immediately announce that they have black hats. This *contradicts* the fact that they are sitting there looking foolish. Thus, the assumption that I have a white hat leads to a contradiction of known fact. So my hat is black."

The reader must be prepared to meet indirect proofs very frequently in the remainder of the book. The warning that an indirect proof is being given always consists of the words, "*assume* that so and so," where so and so represents the negation of the statement to be proved. (It is in this connection that the process of negating statements is of such common occurrence in mathematics.) Then the proof proceeds on normal lines until a contradiction is reached. At this point it is understood that the proof has been completed; the remaining argument, to the effect that the contradiction establishes the proof of the desired assertion, is omitted, since it is the same in all indirect proofs. Frequently the proof closes with a phrase such as "this contradiction completes the proof."

One point in connection with indirect proofs might well be emphasized. This is the fact that, unless and until one has arrived at a contradiction of known fact, one has proved precisely nothing. In particular, one might arrive at a fact which is known to be true. This would not imply anything whatsoever with respect to the truth or falsity of the original assertion. Since a "true" fact is one which is a consequence of the axioms alone, it is not surprising that, from the axioms, together with an additional assumption, one can arrive at true facts, whether the additional assumption is true or false. This would seem to be a simple point but it has been misstated in mathematical literature; every so often one runs across a remark that implies that true results can follow only from true assumptions.

The following simple example illustrates strikingly that truth may follow from falsity. Let us admit that

(6.5.1) Rhode Island is in the United States.

Assume that

(6.5.2) Salt Lake City is in Rhode Island.

Then from (6.5.2), in view of (6.5.1), it follows that

Salt Lake City is in the United States,

which is incontrovertibly true. Must one accept the premise since the conclusion is correct?

Now we wish to say a word concerning the *direct* proof of a statement of *generality*. Such a statement might assert,

for every $a \in A$, it is true that such and such.

The *direct* proof of such a statement always starts with an equivalent of

let $a \in A$ (that is, let a be an element of A).

This a is thought of as being a particular specific element, fixed throughout the proof. However, care is taken not to use any property of a which is not true of *every* element of A. In other words, while a is thought of as a specific element, it is considered that it might be any specific element whatever of A. Hence, if the proof demonstrates that "such and such" is true of a, the proof of the generality statement is understood to be complete.

The indirect proof of a statement of generality proceeds, of course, on quite different lines. Again the statement is,

for every $a \in A$, it is true that such and such.

The *indirect* proof of this type of statement starts with the phrase,

assume the assertion is false,

or equivalently,

suppose that there exists $a \in A$, for which such and such is false.

Then the proof proceeds,

let $a \in A$ for which such and such is false.

Here a is not any element whatsoever of A, but a specific one whose existence is guaranteed by the supposition of the indirect proof. Again, for the remainder of the proof the element a is fixed. And, of course, the proof is complete when a contradiction is reached.

For proofs of statements of *existence*, there is no standard method even for beginning the proof. The most common type of existence proof is direct, and what one might call *constructive*. In such a proof one starts with previously isolated specific elements and from them, and the relations, functions, and so on, which are given, one defines an element, which can be shown to have the desired property. On the other hand, it is (surprisingly) sometimes possible to demonstrate that elements with specific properties must exist without actually "determining" any such element. Such an existence proof might be called *deductive*. Suppose that one wishes to prove that

there exists $a \in A$ such that so and so is true.

The constructive method would be to *define* an element of the desired nature with the help of previously known elements, functions, relations, and so on. The deductive method would be as follows:

let B be the set of all elements of A for which so and so is not true.

Then, in order to prove the assertion, it is sufficient to show that B does not encompass the whole of A, that is, to show that B is a proper subset of A ($B \subsetneqq A$). In fact, since B is a subset of A, all that is required is to show that $B \neq A$. This may sometimes be done by demonstrating that B has some property that A fails to have. Examples of such deductive existence proofs will be given later in the book. Like generality proofs, existence proofs may be either direct or indirect.

Now a word must be said about the proof of a statement such as:

(6.5.3) there exists a unique element of A, such that so and so is true.

In order to fit this statement into our pattern of existence statements and generality statements, we break it into two separate statements, namely,

(6.5.4) there exists (at least) an element of A, such that so and so is true;

and

there do not exist two distinct elements of A, such that so and so is true.

The second of these statements, being the negation of an existence statement, can be written also as a generality statement, namely,

(6.5.5) for every $a, b \in A$ for which so and so is true, it follows that $a = b$.

From this it is seen that (6.5.3) is really a compound statement, involving the conjunction of an existence statement (6.5.4) and a generality statement (6.5.5). Correspondingly, the proof of a statement like (6.5.3) always consists of two parts, an existence proof for (6.5.4) and a generality proof for (6.5.5).

It must be recognized that proofs may be very elaborate in construction. For example, instead of proving a generality assertion for "every element in A" in one effort, it may be convenient to break the set A into a number of distinct sets, say A_1, A_2, A_3 (where $A = (A_1 + A_2) + A_3$), and treat the "cases" $a \in A_1$, $a \in A_2$, $a \in A_3$ separately and by different methods. Again, a proof may be direct but contain certain steps that are proved by subsidiary indirect proofs. In short, the preceding discussion of proofs must be considered not as an analysis of all possible proofs but only as an indication of certain simple types that are commonly met, alone or in combination. In the next chapter, most of the types of proofs described above will be illustrated.

(6.5.6) Project: Analyze the game of black and white hats with four players.

Chapter 7

GROUPS

7.1. Introduction. [No Basis.] This chapter will be devoted to the beginnings of a mathematical theory known as *group theory*. Group theory is the study of the consequences of one of the simplest foundations (basis and axioms) that have proved to be significant in the development of mathematics. The investigation will serve to illustrate concretely most of the remarks made in Chapter 6. In addition, the study will serve later to further our program, since group theory has several *instances* which are of mathematical importance. Thus the results obtained will be applied later to lead to useful facts concerning other branches of mathematics.

The foundation of group theory is as follows:

Basis: $(G, \circ)$, where G is a set and $\circ$ an operation on $G \times G$ to G.

Axioms:

I. For every $a, b, c \in G$,

$$(a \circ b) \circ c = a \circ (b \circ c).$$

II. For every $a, b \in G$, there exists $x \in G$ such that

$$a \circ x = b.$$

III. For every $a, b \in G$, there exists $y \in G$ such that

$$y \circ a = b.$$

Any system $(G, \circ)$ which satisfies these axioms is called a *group*.

Remark 1: For an explanation of the use of parentheses in Axiom I see the examples in (5.6), where, it should be noted, the equality demanded by Axiom I was not true.

Remark 2: It should be noticed that II and III do not assert the uniqueness of the x and y involved in their statements.

Remark 3: A third statement, parallel to II and III, would be

for every $a, b \in G$, there exists $z \in G$ such that $a \circ b = z$.

It should be observed that this statement, and the uniqueness of this z, follow at once from the statement that $\circ$ is an operation on $G \times G$ to G, that is, a function whose domain is $G \times G$, and whose range is a subset of G.

7.2. Examples. [No Basis.] It has been indicated that there are many instances of groups occurring in various branches of mathematics. Some part of the importance of group theory will be appreciated when it is learned that these examples include the following:

the positive, negative and zero integers with the operation *plus* (Chapter 19);

the positive rational numbers with the operation *times* (Chapter 16);

the real numbers with the operation *plus* (Chapter 19);

the real numbers, excluding zero, with the operation *times* (Chapter 19).

However, it may surprise the reader to learn that the greatest usefulness of group theory comes from its application to instances different from the above.

Of course, if the reader has faithfully obeyed our admonition of (2.5), conscientiously to forget the meanings of all mathematical terms until they are properly introduced, the last paragraph is completely meaningless to him. For this reason we give two quite trivial examples of groups, merely to show that such things can exist, without drawing on any previous mathematical knowledge.

(7.2.1) Example: *Let G be a two-element set, that is, let*

$$G = [m, n], \text{ where } m \neq n.$$

Let $\circ$ be the operation on $G \times G$ to G indicated by the following table:

	m	n
m	m	n
n	n	m

Then $(G, \circ)$ is a group.

In order to show that $(G, \circ)$ is a group, we shall prove that Axioms I, II, III are satisfied for this particular instance of $(G, \circ)$.

Consider first Axiom I. This requires that, for every choice of three elements of G (distinct or not), a certain equality holds. Now it is easy to see that there are the following choices for three elements of G:

$$(m, m, m),\ (m, m, n),\ (m, n, m),\ (m, n, n),$$
$$(n, m, m),\ (n, m, n),\ (n, n, m),\ (n, n, n).$$

For each of these choices, Axiom I requires an appropriate equality to hold. Thus Axiom I requires that all the following statements be true:

$$\begin{aligned}
(m \circ m) \circ m &= m \circ (m \circ m),\\
(m \circ m) \circ n &= m \circ (m \circ n),\\
(m \circ n) \circ m &= m \circ (n \circ m),\\
(m \circ n) \circ n &= m \circ (n \circ n),\\
(n \circ m) \circ m &= n \circ (m \circ m),\\
(n \circ m) \circ n &= n \circ (m \circ n),\\
(n \circ n) \circ m &= n \circ (n \circ m),\\
(n \circ n) \circ n &= n \circ (n \circ n).
\end{aligned}$$

Referring to the table defining $\circ$, we find that

$$(m \circ m) = m, \quad (m \circ n) = n, \quad (n \circ m) = n, \quad (n \circ n) = m.$$

Hence the statements to be proved become

$$\begin{aligned}
m \circ m &= m \circ m,\\
m \circ n &= m \circ n,\\
n \circ m &= m \circ n,\\
n \circ n &= m \circ m,\\
n \circ m &= n \circ m,\\
n \circ n &= n \circ n,\\
m \circ m &= n \circ n,\\
m \circ n &= n \circ m.
\end{aligned}$$

All these statements can be immediately verified as true from the definition of $\circ$. This shows that Axiom I is true. (Incidentally, the foregoing should give some idea of how much territory is covered by a generality statement like Axiom I. In this instance G has only two elements. The number of individual assertions covered by the general statement of Axiom I, when G has a large number of elements, is quite fearsome.)

For Axiom II there are, fortunately, fewer cases to consider than for Axiom I, since Axiom II considers only two elements of G rather than three. In fact, Axiom II requires only the existence of elements x_1, x_2, x_3, x_4, such that

$$\begin{aligned}
m \circ x_1 &= m, & n \circ x_2 &= m,\\
m \circ x_3 &= n, & n \circ x_4 &= n.
\end{aligned}$$

From the table defining $\circ$, it is seen that these statements are satisfied with $x_1 = m$, $x_2 = n$, $x_3 = n$, $x_4 = m$.

The truth of Axiom III is shown in precisely the same way as the validity of Axiom II. Hence $(G, \circ)$ constitutes a group.

We give a second example of a group to provide the reader with an opportunity to test his understanding of the proof given for (7.2.1).

(7.2.2) EXAMPLE: *Let* $G = [p, q, r]$, *where* $p \neq q$, $q \neq r$, $r \neq p$. *Let* $\circ$ *be the operation on* $G \times G$ *to* G *indicated by the following table:*

	p	q	r
p	p	q	r
q	q	r	p
r	r	p	q

Then $(G, \circ)$ *constitutes a group.*

We leave the verification of this fact to the reader.

It may be noticed that the operations $\circ$ in the instances (7.2.1) and (7.2.2) satisfy one further condition not required in the axioms for a group, namely,

$$\text{for every } a, b \in G, a \circ b = b \circ a.$$

Hence the reader might feel that the generality $a \circ b = b \circ a$ is a necessary truth for groups. For this reason we hasten to mention that this is definitely not so. Groups in which $a \circ b = b \circ a$ (for every $a, b \in G$) are of great importance and common occurrence; so much so that special theories of this type of group have been developed. Such groups are known as *commutative* groups. However, the theory of noncommutative groups has also proved to be useful, for example, in modern physics.

To show that commutativity ($a \circ b = b \circ a$) is not a requisite of groups, we give one more example (instance) of a group.

(7.2.3) EXAMPLE: *Let* $G = [p, q, r, s, t, u]$, *where every two elements are distinct. Let* $\circ$ *be the operation on* $G \times G$ *to* G *indicated by the following table:*

	p	q	r	s	t	u
p	p	q	r	s	t	u
q	q	p	u	t	s	r
r	r	s	p	q	u	t
s	s	r	t	u	q	p
t	t	u	s	r	p	q
u	u	t	q	p	r	s

Then $(G, \circ)$ *is a group.*

We leave to the reader the straightforward but quite arduous task of demonstrating the truth of this assertion, if he is so inclined (it is not particularly recommended). We merely mention that the verification of Axiom I requires the demonstration of 216 equalities!

Notice that the group defined above is definitely not commutative. In fact, $q \circ r = s$ while $r \circ q = u$, so that $q \circ r \neq r \circ q$. Similarly, $t \circ u \neq u \circ t$, and so on. (However, certain pairs of elements, like (s, u), do *commute*: $s \circ u = u \circ s = p$.)

The reader may have noticed that, in the table defining the operations in each of (7.2.1), (7.2.2), (7.2.3), every row, as well as every column, of the table contains each element of the group (in fact, just once). It is quite easy to see that this is required by Axioms II and III; in fact, whenever the operation can be defined by a table, Axioms II and III will be true precisely when the table has this property. Now it might be wondered if this property also insures Axiom I, that is, if Axiom I must be true whenever Axioms II and III are true (at least for cases when the operation is defined by a table). The answer to this is unfortunately in the negative, as is shown by the following example:

(7.2.4) EXAMPLE: *Let* $G = [e, f, g, h, i]$, *where every two elements are distinct. Let* $\circ$ *be defined by the following table:*

	e	f	g	h	i
e	e	f	g	h	i
f	f	e	h	i	g
g	g	i	e	f	h
h	h	g	i	e	f
i	i	h	f	g	e

Then Axioms II *and* III *are satisfied by* $(G, \circ)$ *but Axiom* I *is not.*

The fact that II and III are satisfied follows, since each row, as well as each column, of the table contains every element of G. To show that I is not satisfied, we note that

$$(f \circ f) \circ g = e \circ g = g,$$

while

$$f \circ (f \circ g) = f \circ i = h;$$

hence

$$(f \circ f) \circ g \neq f \circ (f \circ g).$$

Thus $(G, \circ)$, as defined in (7.2.4), is *not a group*.

The preceding example illustrates that Axioms II and III may be true while Axiom I is false. It is easy to give examples where Axioms I and II are true and Axiom III is false, such as:

(7.2.5) EXAMPLE: *Let* $G = [j, k]$, *where* $j \neq k$. *Let* $\circ$ *be defined by the following table:*

	j	k
j	j	j
k	k	k

The reader should verify that Axiom I is valid. Similarly, Axiom II is easily seen to be true. However, Axiom III is *not* satisfied. In fact, there is no element $y \in G$ for which $y \circ j = k$, because both $j \circ j = j$ and $k \circ j = j$. Hence $(G, \circ)$ as defined in (7.2.5) is *not a group*.

In a similar way it is possible to give examples where Axioms I and III are valid but Axiom II is not, such as:

(7.2.6) EXAMPLE: *Let* $G = [v, w]$, *where* $v \neq w$. *Let* $\circ$ *be defined by the following table:*

	v	w
v	v	w
w	v	w

The reader should show that Axioms I and III are satisfied and Axiom II is not. Hence, again, this is *not a group*.

(7.2.7) PROJECT: Prove that $(G, \circ)$ in (7.2.2) is a group.

(7.2.8) PROJECT: Prove that $(G, \circ)$ in (7.2.5) satisfies Axioms I and II.

(7.2.9) PROJECT: Prove that $(G, \circ)$ in (7.2.6) satisfies Axioms I and III but not II.

7.3. Theory of Groups. [BASIS: $(G, \circ)$; AXIOMS: I, II, III.] By this time the reader should have a somewhat better understanding of what is involved in the concept of a group. We proceed to develop some of the consequences of Axioms I, II, III, that is, some of the properties of groups. First, for convenience, we restate the foundation.

BASIS: $(G, \circ)$, where G is a set, and $\circ$ is an operation on $G \times G$ to G.

AXIOMS:

I. For every $a, b, c \in G$,

$$(a \circ b) \circ c = a \circ (b \circ c).$$

II. For every $a, b \in G$ there exists $x \in G$ such that

$$a \circ x = b.$$

III. For every $a, b \in G$ there exists $y \in G$ such that

$$y \circ a = b.$$

(7.3.1) Theorem: *There exists* $e^* \in G$ *such that, for every* $a \in G$, $a \circ e^* = a$.

Remark: Recall the distinction between this assertion and the following:

$$\text{for every } a \in G, \text{ there exists } e^* \in G, \text{ such that } a \circ e^* = a.$$

This assertion is an immediate consequence (a special case) of Axiom II alone. The former is nonobvious, inasmuch as it requires that one e^* be effective for every a.

Proof of (7.3.1): The set G is a fundamental set, and so is not empty [see (4.6)]. Hence there exists $b \in G$. Then there exists $e^* \in G$ such that

(1) $$b \circ e^* = b \qquad \text{[by II, with } a = b\text{].}$$

Also, for every $a \in G$, there exists $y \in G$ such that

(2) $$y \circ b = a \qquad \text{[by III].}$$

Thus

(3) $$(y \circ b) \circ e^* = a \circ e^* \qquad \text{[by (2)].}$$

On the other hand,

(4) $$(y \circ b) \circ e^* = y \circ (b \circ e^*) \qquad \text{[by I],}$$

and

(5) $$y \circ (b \circ e^*) = y \circ b \qquad \text{[by (1)].}$$

Then

(6) $$a \circ e^* = a \qquad \text{[by (3), (4), (5), (2)].}$$

But a is any element of G (introduced after e^* and with no reference to e^*, or to the element b on which e^* might depend). Hence the statement of the theorem is demonstrated.

Remark: The preceding proof is a fairly typical example of a constructive existence proof. Here the existence of e^* is demonstrated by defining a specific e^* that jumps through the requisite hoop. In particular, e^* was chosen as an element, guaranteed to exist by Axiom II, for which $b \circ e^* = b$, for a previously chosen b. The surprising point in the proof is that the element b, on which e^* presumably depends, can be chosen quite at random.

The proof of the next theorem is quite parallel to that of (7.3.1) and will be given somewhat more briefly.

(7.3.2) THEOREM: *There exists* $e_* \in G$ *such that, for every* $a \in G$, $e_* \circ a = a$.

PROOF: There exists $b \in G$. Then there exists $e_* \in G$ such that

(1) $$e_* \circ b = b \qquad \text{[by III, with } a = b\text{]}.$$

Also, for every $a \in G$, there exists $y \in G$, such that

(2) $$b \circ y = a \qquad \text{[by II]}.$$

Thus

$$\begin{aligned} e_* \circ a &= e_* \circ (b \circ y) && \text{[by (2)]} \\ &= (e_* \circ b) \circ y && \text{[by I]} \\ &= b \circ y && \text{[by (1)]} \\ &= a && \text{[by (2)]}. \end{aligned}$$

This completes the proof.

The next theorem states that there is a single element that performs the duties of both the e^* of (7.3.1) and the e_* of (7.3.2) simultaneously. Furthermore, it states that there is only one such element.

(7.3.3) THEOREM: *There exists a unique element* $e \in G$ *such that, for every* $a \in G$,

$$a \circ e = a \quad \text{and} \quad e \circ a = a.$$

REMARK: Recall that this statement, asserting the existence and uniqueness of a certain element, must be treated as a compound statement. Thus the proof will have two parts, an existence proof and a uniqueness proof.

PROOF OF EXISTENCE: By (7.3.1), there exists $e^* \in G$ such that,

(1) $$\text{for every } a \in G,\ a \circ e^* = a.$$

Also, by (7.3.2), there exists $e_* \in G$ such that,

(2) $$\text{for every } a \in G,\ e_* \circ a = a.$$

Now we employ (1), with $a = e_*$, obtaining

(3) $$e_* \circ e^* = e_*.$$

Similarly, by (2), with $a = e^*$,

(4) $$e_* \circ e^* = e^*.$$

Hence

$$e_* = e^* \qquad \text{[by (3), (4)]}.$$

Let e denote this element, that is, $e \equiv e_* = e^*$. Then

$$a \circ e = a \qquad \text{[by (1)]}.$$

But also, by (2),

$$e \circ a = a.$$

This completes the existence proof.

Proof of Uniqueness: Suppose that e_1 and e_2 are elements of G satisfying the requirements of the theorem, so that, for every $a \in G$,

$$a \circ e_1 = a,$$

and

$$e_1 \circ a = a; \tag{5}$$

for every $b \in G$,

$$b \circ e_2 = b, \tag{6}$$

and

$$e_2 \circ b = b.$$

Then, by (5) with $a = e_2$,

$$e_1 \circ e_2 = e_2. \tag{7}$$

Also, by (6) with $b = e_1$,

$$e_1 \circ e_2 = e_1. \tag{8}$$

Hence

$$e_1 = e_2 \qquad \text{[by (7), (8)]}.$$

This shows that any two elements e_1, e_2 that satisfy the requirements of (7.3.3) are actually identical, that is, there is only one such element. This completes the uniqueness proof.

Remark: This is a quite typical direct uniqueness proof. As was mentioned earlier, a uniqueness statement can be written as a generality assertion, namely,

> for every $a, b \in G$ for which so and so is true, it follows that $a = b$.

Hence, like any direct generality proof, a direct uniqueness proof starts with an equivalent of the phrase,

> let $a, b \in G$ for which so and so is true.

The proof is of course complete when it is shown that $a = b$. It should be observed that this pattern was carried out in the proof just given.

(7.3.4) Definition: Let e denote the unique element of G such that, for every $a \in G$, $a \circ e = e \circ a = a$. This element e is called the *identity* element of $(G, \circ)$.

Remark: The identity element is so designated because it preserves the identity of any element when used in the operation $\circ$. Thus it behaves as the "zero" in ordinary addition and the "one" in ordinary multiplication will be expected to behave. In (7.3.4) we have an illustration of the introduction of the "durable" symbol e to denote an element whose unique existence has been demonstrated.

It should be verified that the identity elements in (7.2.1), (7.2.2), (7.2.3) are the elements denoted respectively by m, p, p.

(7.3.5) THEOREM: *For every* $a \in G$, *there exists a unique* $a' \in G$ *such that*

(a) $$a \circ a' = e,$$

and

(b) $$a' \circ a = e.$$

PROOF OF EXISTENCE: Let $a \in G$. Then there exists [by II] an element $a' \in G$ such that

(1) $$a \circ a' = e,$$

so that (a) is established. Moreover, by III, there exists $y \in G$ such that

(2) $$y \circ a = e.$$

Now

(3) $$\begin{aligned} y \circ (a \circ a') &= y \circ e && \text{[by (1)]} \\ &= y && \text{[by (7.3.4)].} \end{aligned}$$

On the other hand,

(4) $$\begin{aligned} y \circ (a \circ a') &= (y \circ a) \circ a' && \text{[by I]} \\ &= e \circ a' && \text{[by (2)]} \\ &= a' && \text{[by (7.3.4)].} \end{aligned}$$

Comparing (3) and (4), we find

(5) $$y = a'.$$

Hence

$$a' \circ a = e \qquad \text{[by (2), (5)],}$$

and (b) is proved.

PROOF OF UNIQUENESS: To prove that a', satisfying (a) and (b), is unique, suppose that a_1' and a_2' both satisfy (a) and (b), that is, that

(6) $$\begin{aligned} a \circ a_1' &= e, \\ a_1' \circ a &= e, \end{aligned}$$

and

(7) $$\begin{aligned} a \circ a_2' &= e, \\ a_2' \circ a &= e. \end{aligned}$$

Then

$$\begin{aligned} a_1' \circ (a \circ a_2') &= a_1' \circ e && \text{[by (7)]} \\ &= a_1' && \text{[by (7.3.4)].} \end{aligned}$$

Moreover,

$$\begin{aligned} a_1' \circ (a \circ a_2') &= (a_1' \circ a) \circ a_2' && \text{[by I]} \\ &= e \circ a_2' && \text{[by (6)]} \\ &= a_2' && \text{[by (7.3.4)].} \end{aligned}$$

Thus $a_1' = a_2'$. This completes the proof of (7.3.5).

(7.3.6) DEFINITION: For every $a \in G$, define a' to be the unique element of G such that

$$a \circ a' = a' \circ a = e.$$

This element exists uniquely, for every a, by (7.3.5). The element a' is called the *inverse* of a.

REMARK: The inverse of an element is called the *negative* of that element when the operation is called "plus" (denoted by $+$) and is called the *reciprocal* when the operation is called "times" (denoted by $\times$ or $\cdot$).

The reader should verify that, in (7.2.2), $q = r'$, $r = q'$, while $p = p'$. This last is inevitable, since $p = e$, and since $e = e'$ is true in any group [see (7.3.12)]. It would be instructive also to find the inverses of all elements in the groups (7.2.1), (7.2.3).

(7.3.7) THEOREM: *For every* $a \in G$, $(a')' = a$.
REMARK: The symbol $(a')'$ means, of course, the inverse of a'.
PROOF: Let $a \in G$. By the definition of $(a')'$,

(1) $$(a')' \circ a' = e,$$
(2) $$(a') \circ (a')' = e,$$

and $(a')'$ is the *only* element satisfying (1) and (2). But, by (7.3.6),

$$\begin{aligned} a \circ a' &= e, \\ a' \circ a &= e, \end{aligned}$$

so that a also satisfies the same requirements. Thus, by the uniqueness part of (7.3.5), a must be the same as $(a')'$, that is, $(a')' = a$.

(7.3.8) THEOREM: *If* $a, b \in G$ *are such that* $a \neq b$, *then* $a' \neq b'$.
REMARK: This theorem could be succinctly stated as follows: Distinct elements have distinct inverses. Theorem (7.3.8) provides the first opportunity to illustrate an indirect proof.
PROOF OF (7.3.8): *Suppose* the theorem is false. Then there exist $a, b \in G$ such that

(1) $$a \neq b \quad \text{and} \quad a' = b'.$$

But, since $a' = b'$,

(2) $$(a')' = (b')'.$$

By (7.3.7),

(3) $$(a')' = a \quad \text{and} \quad (b')' = b.$$

Hence, from (2) and (3),

$$a = b.$$

But this *contradicts* the first part of (1). This completes the proof.

(7.3.9) THEOREM:

(a) *If* $a, b \in G$, *there exists a unique element* $x \in G$ *such that* $a \circ x = b$; *and it is true that* $x = a' \circ b$.

(b) *If* $a, b \in G$, *there exists a unique element* $y \in G$ *such that* $y \circ a = b$; *and it is true that* $y = b \circ a'$.

REMARK: This is a strengthening of Axioms II and III; these axioms stated the existence but not the uniqueness of x and y. This theorem may be thought of as giving the rules for "solving equations." Thus, suppose one is given a, b and wishes to "determine" x so that

$$a \circ x = b.$$

This may be done by "operating on the left of both sides of the equation" with the element a', as follows:

$$a' \circ (a \circ x) = a' \circ b.$$

But the left side may be written

$$(a' \circ a) \circ x \qquad \text{[by I]},$$

and, since $a' \circ a = e$, $e \circ x = x$, one has

$$x = a' \circ b.$$

It will be seen that this procedure includes the usual high school algebraic rules for "solving equations," since both plus and times will turn out to be group operations (in appropriate number systems).

PROOF OF (7.3.9.a): Let $a, b \in G$. The existence of x follows from II. Now let x be an element such that

(1) $$a \circ x = b.$$

Then

(2) $$\begin{aligned} x &= e \circ x && \text{[by (7.3.4)]} \\ &= (a' \circ a) \circ x && \text{[by (7.3.6)]} \\ &= a' \circ (a \circ x) && \text{[by I]} \\ &= a' \circ b && \text{[by (1)]}. \end{aligned}$$

Hence, for every element x such that $a \circ x = b$, we have $x = a' \circ b$, and the last part of (a) is established. To prove uniqueness, let $x_1, x_2 \in G$ such that $a \circ x_1 = a \circ x_2 = b$. Then $x_1 = a' \circ b$ and $x_2 = a' \circ b$ by (2). Hence $x_1 = x_2$.

PROOF OF (7.3.9.b): The proof here is parallel to that of (a) and we leave it as an exercise for the reader to carry out the steps in detail.

(7.3.10) COROLLARY:

(a) *If $a \in G$, there exists a unique element $x \in G$ such that $a \circ x = a$; and it is true that $x = e$.*

(b) *If $a \in G$, there exists a unique element $y \in G$ such that $y \circ a = a$; and it is true that $y = e$.*

(7.3.11) COROLLARY:

(a) *If $a \in G$, there exists a unique element $x \in G$ such that $a \circ x = e$; and it is true that $x = a'$.*

(b) *If $a \in G$, there exists a unique element $y \in G$ such that $y \circ a = e$; and it is true that $y = a'$.*

(7.3.12) COROLLARY: $e' = e$.

The proofs of these immediate consequences of (7.3.9) are left for the reader.

(7.3.13) THEOREM: *If $a, b \in G$, then $(a \circ b)' = b' \circ a'$.*

PROOF: Suppose $a, b \in G$. Clearly

$$\begin{aligned} (b' \circ a') \circ (a \circ b) &= b' \circ (a' \circ (a \circ b)) && \text{[by I]} \\ &= b' \circ ((a' \circ a) \circ b) && \text{[by I]} \\ &= b' \circ (e \circ b) && \text{[by (7.3.6)]} \\ &= b' \circ b && \text{[by (7.3.4)]} \\ &= e && \text{[by (7.3.6)].} \end{aligned}$$

But, by (7.3.11.b), there is a unique element $(a \circ b)'$ such that

$$(a \circ b)' \circ (a \circ b) = e.$$

Thus

$$b' \circ a' = (a \circ b)'.$$

The results that we have given comprise the most elementary properties of a group. Groups have been studied extensively, particularly in recent years; many applications, both to other branches of mathematics and to modern physics, have been found. However, the main purpose of our presentation of the beginnings of group theory is to illustrate, in as simple a case as possible, the nature of a mathematical theory.

(7.3.14) PROJECT: Prove (7.3.9.b).

(7.3.15) PROJECT: Prove (7.3.10), (7.3.11), (7.3.12).

(7.3.16) PROJECT: It was noted that $e' = e$ [by (7.3.12)]. Thus e is an element $x \in G$ such that $x' = x$. Is it true conversely that, if $x \in G$, $x' = x$, then $x = e$? Why?

(7.3.17) PROJECT: By the definition of e, we have $e \circ e = e$. Is it true conversely that if $x \in G$, $x \circ x = x$, then $x = e$? Why?

(7.3.18) PROJECT: Let $a \in G$. Define functions F, H, K, L on G to G thus:

$$\begin{aligned} F &\equiv (a \circ x;\, x \in G); \\ H &\equiv (y \circ a;\, y \in G); \\ K &\equiv ((a' \circ x) \circ a;\, x \in G); \\ L &\equiv (x';\, x \in G). \end{aligned}$$

Prove that each is a one-to-one correspondence between G and G.

(7.3.19) PROJECT: Find the identity and all inverses in (7.2.3).

7.4. The Postulational Method. [NO BASIS.] The reader should now have a clearer picture of the nature of a mathematical system as it was described in the preceding chapter. It is not very farfetched to consider any mathematical system as a rather elaborate game of solitaire: The selected basis (consisting of one or more basic sets, operations, functions, or relations) makes up the "men" or "cards" with which the game is played; the list of axioms describes the initial configuration—the position with which you start; the object of the game is to arrive at other configurations. Finally, the rules of the game are logic.

Theoretically, one could amuse himself by inventing bases and writing down axioms at will, and then drawing as many inferences from them as possible. This sort of amusement may be quite impractical, however. To see why, let us consider the following example:

BASIS: $(A, \circ)$, where A is a set, and $\circ$ is an operation on $A \times A$ to A.

AXIOMS:

I. For every $a, b \in A$, $a \circ b = b \circ a$.

II. For every $a, b \in A$, $a \circ b = b$.

III. For every $a \in A$, there exists $b \in A$ such that $b \neq a$.

These are rather harmless-looking axioms, but let us find a few of their consequences.

(7.4.1) THEOREM: *For every $a, b \in A$, $a \circ b = a$.*

PROOF: Let $a, b \in A$. Then $b \circ a = a$ [by II]. But $b \circ a = a \circ b$ [by I]. Thus $a \circ b = a$.

(7.4.2) THEOREM: *For every $a, b \in A$, $a = b$.*

PROOF: Let $a, b \in A$. Then $a \circ b = a$ [by (7.4.1)]. But $a \circ b = b$ [by II]. Thus $a = b$.

(7.4.3) THEOREM: *For every* $a \in A$, $a \neq a$.

PROOF: Let $a \in A$. By III, there exists $b \in A$ such that $a \neq b$. But $a = b$ by (7.4.2). Thus $a \neq a$.

Now this last theorem (7.4.3) is somewhat disturbing. The assertion $a \neq a$ is a complete contradiction. Have we deduced falsity from truth?

Actually, if what has been done is examined with care, it will be found that we have not deduced falsity from truth. Recall our earlier remarks [(6.1)] that the foundation is really understood to appear in the *hypothesis* of every theorem. Thus (7.4.3), written out in full, would be:

> for every basis $(A, \circ)$ satisfying Axioms I, II, III, it is true that, for every $a \in A$, $a \neq a$.

This implies that *if* there is a basis $(A, \circ)$ satisfying I, II, III, and *if* there is an element in the set A, then this element does something completely ridiculous and impossible (specifically, it is not the same element as itself). Or the last statement can be rewritten still more informatively as follows:

> if there were a basis $(A, \circ)$ satisfying I, II, III, then impossible things would be true.

From this one concludes, not that false can proceed from true, but simply that *there cannot be* a basis $(A, \circ)$ satisfying I, II, III. Briefly and inelegantly, there ain't no such animal.

We emphasize this phenomenon, because it is rather disturbing to find that contradictions can arise from perfectly respectable-looking axioms. When such a contradiction arises, it shows that *no basis can satisfy the axioms.* Therefore the theory could not have any instances. This situation is expressed by saying that the axioms are *inconsistent.*

The clearest example of an inconsistent system of axioms is simply a pair of axioms in which the second is exactly the negation of the first. However, the example above indicates that the inconsistency may be hidden a little deeper, so that one might develop the theory considerably before running across a contradiction.

The reader will probably not question the desirability of avoiding inconsistent axioms. Actually, as will be discussed shortly, a theory developed on the basis of inconsistent axioms must be considered as true (the technical phrase is "vacuously true"). That is, a theory saying that, for every basis for which certain things are true, other things must also be true, tells no lie, even if there is no such basis. But the development of a series of theorems explaining what fascinating things would be true of a basis if only there were one, which there isn't, cannot be considered as a very elevating pursuit.

Now the question arises, "how can one be sure of avoiding inconsistent axioms?" It has already been mentioned that the contradiction may be hidden quite deep, and one might not happen to stumble on any indication of inconsistency for some time. The clue to the answer is contained in the remark that an inconsistent theory cannot have any instances. The only way known at present to be sure that a system of axioms is consistent is to produce an instance in which all the axioms are satisfied. It is considered shockingly bad taste to investigate any system of axioms unless it is shown that there is an instance satisfying them. This is one reason that, in the preceding section, before investigating the properties of groups, we paused to present several specific examples of groups (7.2.1), (7.2.2), (7.2.3). Partly, of course, these examples were intended to familiarize the reader with the notion of a group. But, in addition, they served to answer the relevant, indeed essential, question, "can such things be?" For this purpose, of course, one example would have sufficed.

We return to the matter of a "vacuously true" statement, already mentioned. Consider the following statement:

(7.4.4) every American who was married on the moon has four heads.

Let us accept it as a fact that no American has ever been married on the moon (for lack of evidence to the contrary). In spite of this fact (or, better, because of it) the statement (7.4.4) must be considered as true. One sometimes apologizes for considering it true by saying that it is *vacuous* or *vacuously true*, but it still has to be considered as true. The reason for this necessity is simply that it can be proved. The method of proof is indirect. Thus,

assume the statement is false.

Then, recalling how to form negations, we have,

there exists an American who was married on the moon and who does not have four heads.

In particular,

there exists an American who was married on the moon.

But this *contradicts* known fact. Hence (7.4.4) has been proved.

The prototype of a vacuously true remark is as follows:

let $A = \Theta$ (A be empty, A have no elements).

Then,

for every $a \in A$, it is true that so and so.

This statement is true regardless of what is required of a by "so and so." In brief, anything said about every (nonexistent) element of the empty set is perfectly correct.

Of course, one tries to avoid making vacuous statements. It is small consolation to be right when you aren't talking about anything. But, because of the great generality of mathematics, and because of the large number of cases that may be covered by a single statement, it is impossible to avoid making statements that *may* be vacuous in certain circumstances or for certain instances. For example, any statement made about groups that involves three distinct elements would be vacuous in case one were dealing with (7.2.1), in which example there were only two elements in the group. For this reason, the fact that a vacuous statement is true is actually a great convenience in mathematics. It eliminates the necessity of continually ruling out specifically any instance or circumstance in which the general statement being made would become vacuous.

It was stated in (5.4) that absurd relations are functions. That this is reasonable is now clear in view of our remarks about vacuous truth. Let A, B be sets and Θ the absurd relation on $A \times B$ (the empty subset of $A \times B$). The requirement (5.4.2) for a function may be phrased

> for every b_1, $b_2 \in B$ such that there exists $a \in A$ for which $(a, b_1) \in \Theta$ and $(a, b_2) \in \Theta$, it is true that $b_1 = b_2$.

Now *no* elements b_1, $b_2 \in B$ exist such that $a \in A$ exists with $(a, b_1) \in \Theta$, $(a, b_2) \in \Theta$; hence it follows that the requirement is vacuously true.

We now return to the consideration of axiomatic systems to discuss a point of some interest, though of much less importance than consistency, namely, the matter of *independence*. Clearly it would have been possible to enlarge the axioms for a group by adding as extra axioms any of the theorems which we proved. This could not change the theory in any way. Anything formerly provable would still be provable (use the same proof and disregard the extra axioms). On the other hand, nothing new could be added. Anything that could be proved from the enlarged system of axioms could be proved from the former system by first demonstrating the theorems, since after a theorem is demonstrated it can be used in subsequent proofs just as an axiom is used. The issue here is really a matter of taste. It is simply inelegant to include an axiom that need not be assumed, but could be demonstrated as a theorem from the remaining axioms.

Systems of axioms in which one is actually a consequence of the remaining are called *dependent*. The method of demonstrating that a system of axioms is *independent* (not dependent) is to show that no axiom can possibly be a consequence of the remaining ones. This is done by exhibiting, for each axiom, an instance in which this axiom is not satisfied, while the remaining ones are. The reader should recall that this was done, for the case of group theory, in (7.2.4), (7.2.5), (7.2.6). Hence these examples serve to show that the axioms for group theory are independent.

A third property of systems of axioms that is sometimes considered is that of being *categorical.* We are not now in a position to describe this property precisely, and so we simply remark that a system of axioms is categorical if there is "essentially" only one instance for it. The three quite different instances of groups [(7.2.1), (7.2.2), (7.2.3)] given earlier show that the axioms of group theory are not categorical (or would show this if we were able to define the property at this stage). The noncategorical nature of the group axioms is responsible for a great part of the importance and usefulness of groups; there are many quite different instances, and hence many applications. The concept of categorical systems of axioms is treated in (14.3).

Of the three properties of a system of axioms discussed above, it is well to remember that *consistency* is almost a requisite, *independence* is rather nice, and *categoricalness* is not even particularly desirable, except for certain purposes.

7.5. Conclusion. [No Basis.] The description of a mathematical system given in this chapter was not made exhaustive in the hope that it would avoid being exhausting. However, enough has been said to provide a rather solid basis for acquiring an understanding of the nature of modern mathematics. Our anatomy course has progressed through a reasonably careful examination of the skeleton of mathematics. In the succeeding chapters we shall see how to put a little meat on the bones.

Chapter 8

THE POSITIVE INTEGERS

8.1. Introduction. [No Basis.] In the somewhat fanciful discussion of the development of mathematics given in an earlier chapter, it was pointed out that mathematics originated with the study of the counting numbers. The counting numbers, it will be recalled, are a series of grunts or noises used to answer the question, "how many?"

The usefulness of counting, and preserving tallies, led gradually to the development of the bookkeeper's art, reckoning or arithmetic. Note that reckoning is an art, rather than a science, and has only a rather strained relationship to mathematics. In fact, the usual mathematician is a miserably poor calculator; this never ceases to astonish the usual mathematician's usual neighbor, who feels that living next door to a real live mathematician should be of some help when March 15 approaches. The popular misunderstanding of the nature of mathematics is nowhere better illustrated than by the custom of referring to the freak lightning calculators of the stage as "mathematical wizards."

The connection between reckoning and mathematics is as follows. Reckoning consists of the processes of "adding," "multiplying," and so on, in terms of some specific symbolism for the counting numbers. The processes of addition and multiplication are suggestive of *operations*, in the mathematical sense; that is, each associates, with every pair of counting numbers, a third counting number (their sum or product). Hence it is to be hoped, in the light of the preceding chapters, that the intuitive counting numbers, together with "plus" and "times," might constitute an *instance* (in some sense) of an abstract mathematical system which is worth studying. Such an abstract system exists and is called the system of positive integers.

The study of the system of positive integers, including an investigation of the basic properties of the operations *plus* and *times*, is not only a branch of mathematics, but in many respects is the most fundamental branch of mathematics. Almost all other mathematical theories utilize the results obtained in this study. However, the study is *not* the study of reckoning. In fact, all the basic results can be, and in this book will be, obtained without the introduction of any systematic universal symbolism for positive integers.

The procedure to be adopted in developing a theory of positive integers is as follows. We shall abstract (state in abstract form) a few properties of the counting numbers that are fundamental. The abstract statements will constitute axioms for positive integers. From the axioms we shall develop a few of their consequences—indeed, enough to introduce all the familiar concepts and prove their elementary properties. In this way, the counting numbers will be eliminated; their role in mathematics will be played by the abstract system which we now develop.

8.2. Axioms for the Positive Integers. [No Basis.] Clearly the counting numbers themselves will be represented, in our mathematical system, by some abstract set I (the positive integers). But in order that I will correspond suitably to the intuitive counting numbers, it is necessary to assume something about the "structure" of the set I. This is most conveniently done by demanding the existence of some special relation, operation or function.

There are many intuitive operations, relations, functions, and the like, that are commonly considered in connection with counting numbers. In addition to the two operations "plus" and "times" already mentioned, there are relations "less than," "greater than," "divisible by," "divides" and others. Correspondingly, there is considerable freedom in the choice of how many and which of these relations shall be represented in the basis. For example, it is possible to include both "plus" and "times" as fundamental undefined operations (in the basis) and assume a sufficient number of their properties to enable one to prove all their remaining properties. Or, alternatively, one may use only "plus" as basic and *define* the operation "times" in terms of it.

The foundation we shall use has the virtue of assuming about as little as possible and providing for the introduction of almost all the important operations and relations by definition. This foundation is due essentially to Peano, who first formulated a postulational basis for the counting numbers. In addition to assuming an apparent minimum, the Peano axioms are psychologically satisfying, in that they make the theory follow what was probably the historical course of the development of counting numbers; thus the relation chosen as basic by Peano is really historically fundamental.

There is only one basic relation in the Peano foundation for positive integers, that based on the extremely primitive notion "is next after." This relation is closely associated with a characteristic feature of the counting numbers; these "numbers" are not simply a collection of noises, but a "succession" of noises, noises that come in a definite "order." This "order" is an essential feature of counting; a child who recognizes the names of all numbers up to twenty, but cannot remember in what order they come, has not learned to count.

It is easy to see that the intuitive relation (pairing) that associates adjacent pairs of counting numbers has the defining property of a function. Not only is there a number "next after" any other number, but there is a unique such. Hence, the concept that the counting numbers come "in order" may be abstracted by including in the basis a *function* σ on I to I.

Now the intuitive function "is next after" has many special properties, and it would be impossible to decide without experimentation, how many of them, or which of them, should be converted into axioms concerning σ. Fortunately for us, Peano has performed the necessary experimentation, and we need only follow in his footsteps.

The first property of the "next after" or "successor" function, which we wish to note, is that distinct counting numbers have distinct successors; that is, no number is the successor of two different numbers. The corresponding requirement for σ would be the following:

(8.2.1) for every $m, n \in I$, if $m \neq n$, then $\sigma(m) \neq \sigma(n)$.

We shall see later that this fact could also be expressed by stating that σ is a one-to-one correspondence, or that σ^* is a function [see (10.2.2)].

Next we note that, among the counting numbers, there is a special number "one" which is *not* "next after" any other number. This fact can be paralleled in our abstract system by including a special element of I in the basis, which element may be denoted by 1, and then assuming

(8.2.2) for every $m \in I$, $\sigma(n) \neq 1$.

The third and final property of the "successor" function which it is desired to convert into an axiom concerning $(I, 1, \sigma)$ is somewhat more difficult to formulate. The intuitive fact we have in mind is that continued counting, that is, continued passing to the "successor," starting with "one," eventually gives any desired number. This means that the counting numbers constitute a single chain, without side branches, gaps or detours (to mix metaphors thoroughly).

In order to put this intuitive fact in a form suitable for abstraction, we note that continued taking of successors will generate a set of counting numbers, with the property that the set contains the successor of any number in it. "Starting with 'one'" can be assured by demanding that "one" be in the set. Intuitively, then, any set of counting numbers which (a) contains "one," and (b) contains the successor of any number in it, must be the entire set of all counting numbers. Accordingly, for the abstract basis $(I, 1, \sigma)$, we require the following:

(8.2.3) Let H be a subset of I such that
(a) $1 \in H$;
(b) for every $q \in H$, $\sigma(q) \in H$.
Then $H = I$.

We have been led to the following *foundation* for the theory of positive integers:

BASIS: $(I, 1, \sigma)$, where I is a set, 1 is an element of I, and σ is a function on I to I.

AXIOMS:

I. For every $m, n \in I$, if $m \neq n$, then $\sigma(m) \neq \sigma(n)$.

II. For every $m \in I$, $\sigma(m) \neq 1$.

III. Let H be a subset of I such that

(a) $1 \in H$;

(b) for every $q \in H$, $\sigma(q) \in H$.

Then $H = I$.

Any system $(I, 1, \sigma)$ satisfying Axioms I, II, III is called a *basic system of positive integers*. Elements of I are called *positive integers*.

REMARK: The third of these axioms is called the axiom of *induction* and is the powerful member of the trio. The method of using III is almost always the same and should be observed in the proofs that follow. It is desired to prove that some statement is true for *every element of* I. One defines a subset H of I as the subset consisting of all these elements of I for which the given statement is true. Then one proves that this subset H satisfies the requirements (a), (b) of III. From this, one is guaranteed by III that $H = I$. Hence the set of elements for which the statement is true is all of I; in other words, the statement holds for every element of I.

In the last chapter, the concept of consistency of a system of axioms was introduced; it should be recalled that the only known assurance of the consistency of a system of axioms is the exemplification of the basis by an instance which does satisfy the axioms. The best instance for a basis $(I, 1, \sigma)$ satisfying I, II, III is (counting numbers, "one," "is next after"). Such an instance as this is not as satisfactory an exemplification of the basis as those given in the case of groups, inasmuch as our knowledge of counting numbers is intuitive and insufficiently precise for us to *prove* that the axioms are true. Nevertheless, it is the best instance available. It is not too unreasonable, then, that some have doubted that the abstract statements I, II, III do accurately picture the intuitive facts which suggested them; in fact, the consistency of I, II, III has not been universally accepted. Nevertheless, the vast majority of mathematicians have a strong belief in the consistency of the axioms for positive integers. And in any case, the system $(I, 1, \sigma)$ has been used to great advantage in mathematics without any contradictory consequences having been found as yet. Since almost all mathematics uses positive integers in some way, it is rather unfortunate that their existence must remain a conviction rather than a certainty.

We shall now proceed to an investigation of the mathematical system $(I, 1, \sigma)$ satisfying I, II, III. As has been suggested, the entire direction taken by this investigation is determined by mathematical history and in particular by the development of the intuitive instance of the counting numbers. However, it cannot be overemphasized that no specific reference to this instance shall occur in the body of the theory, and that all our theorems are proved, and thus are valid, for *any* basis $(I, 1, \sigma)$ satisfying I, II, III. To focus attention on this fact, we have used the rather unusual terminology "counting numbers" for the elements in the intuitive instance, and shall consistently use the phrase "positive integers" for the elements of any set I which, together with some element $1 \in I$ and some function σ on I to I, satisfies Axioms I, II, III.

8.3. Fundamentals of Positive Integers. [Basis: $(I, 1, \sigma)$; Axioms: I, II, III.] For convenience of reference, we restate the foundation for positive integers.

Basis: $(I, 1, \sigma)$, where I is a set, $1 \in I$, and σ is a function on I to I.
Axioms:
I. For every $m, n \in I$, with $m \neq n$, then $\sigma(m) \neq \sigma(n)$.
II. For every $m \in I$, $\sigma(m) \neq 1$.
III. Let $H \subset I$ such that
(a) $1 \in H$;
(b) for every $q \in H$, $\sigma(q) \in H$.
Then $H = I$.

In this section, we shall prove two facts concerning the positive integers which are so fundamental that it is quite surprising that it is not necessary to include them among the axioms. The first of these facts states, for the intuitive instance, that no counting number is "next after" itself.

(8.3.1) Theorem: *For every $n \in I$, $\sigma(n) \neq n$.*

Remark: The proof of this theorem affords a typical example of the use of III. It is essential for the reader to follow the proof very carefully, so that he thoroughly understands the procedure, since a great many of the proofs in the remainder of the chapter follow the same pattern.

Proof of (8.3.1): Let H be the set consisting of every element $n \in I$ for which $\sigma(n) \neq n$; that is, define

$$H \equiv [n \in I; \sigma(n) \neq n] \subset I. \tag{1}$$

We shall prove, with the help of III, that $H = I$. To do this, we must show that the requirements III(a), III(b) are satisfied for the particular set H defined by (1).

First,

(2) $$1 \in H,$$

since $\sigma(1) \neq 1$, by II. Hence H satisfies III(a).

To show that H satisfies III(b), let $q \in H$. Then, by (1),

(3) $$\sigma(q) \neq q.$$

But, from (3) and I,

(4) $$\sigma(\sigma(q)) \neq \sigma(q).$$

Now (4) shows, in view of (1), that $\sigma(q) \in H$. In short,

$$q \in H \text{ implies } \sigma(q) \in H,$$

and III(b) is verified.

We have shown that the set H, defined by (1), satisfies the hypotheses (a), (b) of III, so that the conclusion $H = I$ follows. Thus

$$I = [n; \sigma(n) \neq n].$$

But this implies

$$I \subset [n; \sigma(n) \neq n],$$

whence

$$n \in I \text{ implies } n \in [n; \sigma(n) \neq n],$$

that is,

$$\text{for every } n \in I, \ \sigma(n) \neq n.$$

This completes the proof.

The second fact to be proved in this section states, for the intuitive instance, that "one" is the only counting number which is not "next after" some other number.

(8.3.2) THEOREM: *Let* $m \in I$ *and* $m \neq 1$. *Then there exists* $p \in I$ *such that* $\sigma(p) = m$.

REMARK: We wish to prove that every positive integer is either a "successor" or is 1. Thus the set which is to be proved equal to I is the set consisting of all successors *and* the element 1.

PROOF OF (8.3.2): Define

(1) $$H \equiv [1] + [n \in I; \text{there exists } p \in I \text{ for which } \sigma(p) = n] \subset I.$$

Clearly

$$1 \in H,$$

since $[1] \subset H$ by (1).

Now let $q \in H$. We wish to show that $\sigma(q) \in H$. But this is obvious from (1), since there exists p (namely, $p = q$) for which $\sigma(p) = \sigma(q)$.

We have shown that the set H satisfies (a), (b) of III, so that III gives $H = I$. Thus

$$(2) \qquad I = [1] + [n;\text{ there exists } p \in I \text{ for which } \sigma(p) = n].$$

Now let $m \in I$ and $m \neq 1$, so that

$$m \in' [1].$$

Then, from (2),

$$m \in [n;\text{ there exists } p \in I \text{ for which } \sigma(p) = n].$$

This completes the proof.

The further investigation of the positive integers does not readily suggest itself and entails the introduction of new relations, functions and operations. Specifically, there are two operations that can be defined in terms of σ, which have proved to be of immeasurable importance, both for the further development of mathematics and (in the instance of the counting numbers) in everyday life. These are the operations to which the names *plus* and *times* have been given. The remainder of this chapter will be devoted to the definition of these operations and the investigation of their nature.

(8.3.3) PROJECT: Let $(I, 1, \sigma)$ satisfy I, II, III. Define $J \equiv I - [1]$ and the function φ thus: $\varphi \equiv (\sigma(n); n \in J)$. Prove that φ is on J to J and that $(J, \sigma(1), \varphi)$ satisfies I, II, III.

8.4. Operations and Sequences. [BASIS: $(I, 1, \sigma)$; AXIOMS: I, II, III.] The major task now confronting us is the introduction of two binary operations $+$, $\times$, corresponding to the intuitive concepts of "adding" and "multiplying." Now $+$ (or $\times$) is to provide a mechanism for associating with every $m, n \in I$ a unique corresponding element of I; so it is clear that $+$ will be an operation on $I \times I$ to I. In view of the apparent meagerness of our tools (Axioms I, II, III), it may be far from clear how our task can be accomplished. In order to bring the problem closer to the axioms, it is desirable to obtain a more complete understanding of operations generally than was achieved in Chapter 5. What we have to say in the next paragraphs may be formulated quite generally, but we prefer to keep the discussion as special as possible for the present purposes, in the interest of clarity and definiteness.

To accomplish our purpose we shall require the concept *sequence*. The word "sequence" (or "series") is used popularly to indicate a continued succession. Thus in a "sequence" there are a "first," a "second," "and so on." This loose description is clearly not sufficiently precise to define the term for mathematical purposes. Not only does it depend on the intuitive counting numbers, but it contains the words "and so on," a vague concept which we do not wish to include in the logical basis.

In order to obtain a precise mathematical concept which will serve the purpose of an intuitive "sequence," it is sufficient to replace the counting numbers by I. Then we consider a relation which "pairs" every element of I with a particular "term" of the "sequence." But for each element of I there is a unique "corresponding item" of the "sequence." Thus the relation described is actually a function on I.

We are led to the following:

(8.4.1) DEFINITION: Let A be a set. Then a function on I to A is called a *sequence in* A, or a *sequence of elements of* A. In particular, a function on I to I is called a *sequence of positive integers*, or simply a *sequence*.

(8.4.2) DEFINITION: The set of all sequences (of positive integers) is denoted by $\mathcal{S}$.

REMARK: Note that $\mathcal{S}$ is a very august set; each element of $\mathcal{S}$ is a sequence (function on I to I). It should be observed that we already know two elements of $\mathcal{S}$, namely σ and E (E being the identity relation on $I \times I$).

We now show that any *operation* on $I \times I$ to I can be associated with a particular *sequence of sequences*, or *sequence in* $\mathcal{S}$. Let $\circ$ be any given binary operation on $I \times I$ to I, and let $m \in I$ be any element, which is to be regarded for the moment as fixed. Then

(8.4.3) $$(m \circ n;\, n \in I)$$

is clearly a function on I to I, in accordance with the notation for functions introduced in (5.4.9). Thus (8.4.3) is a sequence. Remembering now that m is any element of I, we may conclude that, for every $m \in I$, there has been specified, with the help of the operation $\circ$, a unique element of $\mathcal{S}$, that is, a unique sequence, given by (8.4.3). But the specification, for each $m \in I$, of a unique element (sequence) of $\mathcal{S}$ defines a function *on* I *to* $\mathcal{S}$. For the domain I has been specified, and, for each $m \in I$, the correspondent in $\mathcal{S}$ under the function has been set forth in (8.4.3). In the notation of (5.4.9), this function on I to $\mathcal{S}$ may be denoted by

(8.4.4) $$((m \circ n;\, n \in I);\, m \in I).$$

To sum up, we have shown that a binary operation on $I \times I$ to I leads us to a certain function (8.4.4) on I to the set $\mathcal{S}$ of all sequences. Thus we are led to a sequence of sequences. This is a difficult idea and must be thought about quite carefully. It must be remembered that the correspondent, under the function (8.4.4), of every element of I is itself a function.

It is important to show now that the entire process can be reversed. In other words, not only does every operation on $I \times I$ to I lead to a sequence in $\mathcal{S}$, but every sequence in $\mathcal{S}$ defines an operation on $I \times I$ to I. To see this, let

$$(\varphi_m;\, m \in I) \tag{8.4.5}$$

be any function on I to $\mathcal{S}$. Thus the correspondent of $m \in I$ under the function (8.4.5) is the sequence denoted by φ_m. Since, for every $m \in I$, φ_m is a sequence, it should be noted that, for every $m, n \in I$, $\varphi_m(n)$ is an element of I. Let us define an operation $\circ$ by first specifying the domain to be $I \times I$, and secondly specifying that, for every $(m, n) \in I \times I$,

$$m \circ n = \varphi_m(n). \tag{8.4.6}$$

Since $m \circ n = \varphi_m(n) \in I$, the operation $\circ$ is on $I \times I$ *to* I. Thus the function (8.4.5) on I to $\mathcal{S}$ leads to an operation $\circ$. We shall refer to $\circ$ as *the associated operation to the sequence* (8.4.5).

It is now considerably easier to attack the problem of introducing operations. Instead of dealing with them directly, we work with sequences in $\mathcal{S}$, passing over to the associated operations later. It should be recalled that a function is defined when the domain is set forth, and all correspondents under the function are specified. Hence, to define a function on I to $\mathcal{S}$, we specify the domain to be I, and then show, for every $m \in I$, what element of $\mathcal{S}$ (sequence) is to be the correspondent of m. Since something is to be done for every $m \in I$, the technique using Axiom III suggests itself: A set H, of all $m \in I$ for which the job can be done, is defined; it is shown by III that $H = I$. The next two sections put this program into action in the execution of our task.

8.5. The Operation + (Plus). [BASIS: $(I, 1, \sigma)$; AXIOMS: I, II, III.] Let us review briefly the intuitive background of the operation "plus." Suppose one has two counting numbers m and n in mind. Each of these can be thought of as representing the "manyness" of some collection of objects. Thus one may imagine two (disjoint) sets of objects such that, on applying the counting process to the elements of these sets, one arrives at the noises "m" and "n," respectively. Then a natural question is, "at what noise would one arrive if one counted the collection obtained by 'lumping together' the two original sets?" The answer to this question is a counting number, which is commonly called the "sum of m and n."

The intuitive meaning of "plus" shows that it is closely connected with the set-theoretic sum. This connection explains the somewhat unfortunate use of the same symbol + to denote both set-theoretic sum and the operation plus on $I \times I$ to I.

The process of introducing, by definition, an operation on $I \times I$ to I which will parallel, abstractly, the intuitive operation just described, is quite similar to finding an axiomatic foundation for an intuitive concept. The procedure is to select a few of the properties of the intuitive idea and use them as defining properties. All remaining properties are then proved from the chosen few.

There are two properties of the intuitive "plus" which are evident, and which we shall employ. The first is that, for any counting number m, the number "m plus one" is the same as the "next after m." The second is that, for any counting numbers m and n, the "next after m plus n" is the same as "m plus the next after n." In terms of the operation + on $I \times I$ which we wish to define, these requirements are as follows:

$$m + 1 = \sigma(m);$$
$$m + \sigma(n) = \sigma(m + n).$$

Since we plan to deal first with a sequence in $\mathcal{S}$, and introduce + later as the associated operation, we must translate the above requirements into corresponding demands for a sequence in $\mathcal{S}$. Let a sequence of elements of $\mathcal{S}$ be denoted by $(\alpha_m;\, m \in I)$. Since + is to be the associated operation, we shall have $\alpha_m(n) = m + n$, for every $m, n \in I$. Accordingly, the requirements given for + correspond to the following demands for $(\alpha_m;\, m \in I)$:

(a) $$\alpha_m(1) = \sigma(m);$$
(b) $$\alpha_m(\sigma(n)) = \sigma(\alpha_m(n)).$$

Our first step will be to prove the existence of a sequence in $\mathcal{S}$ satisfying (a) and (b). The second task is to prove the uniqueness of such a sequence in $\mathcal{S}$. The existence is shown by producing, for each $m \in I$, a unique sequence (element of $\mathcal{S}$), which will be the correspondent of m.

(8.5.1) THEOREM: *For every $m \in I$, there exists a sequence (of positive integers) $\alpha \in \mathcal{S}$, such that*

(a) $$\alpha(1) = \sigma(m);$$
(b) $$\textit{for every } n \in I,\ \alpha(\sigma(n)) = \sigma(\alpha(n)).$$

PROOF: Define

(1) $H \equiv [m;$ there exists $\alpha \in \mathcal{S}$ satisfying (a), (b)$] \subset I$.

First we show $1 \in H$. To do this, we prove the existence of $\alpha \in \mathcal{S}$ which satisfies (a), (b), with $m = 1$. To this end define $\alpha \equiv \sigma$. Then

$$\alpha(1) = \sigma(1),$$

so that (a) is satisfied. Also, for every $n \in I$,

$$\alpha(\sigma(n)) = \sigma(\sigma(n)) = \sigma(\alpha(n)),$$

so that (b) is satisfied. This shows that, for $m = 1$, there exists an appropriate α, namely $\alpha = \sigma$. Hence, by (1), $1 \in H$.

Next, suppose $q \in H$. This means, according to (1), that there is a sequence $\beta \in \mathcal{S}$ such that

(2) $\beta(1) = \sigma(q)$;
(3) for every $n \in I$, $\beta(\sigma(n)) = \sigma(\beta(n))$.

We wish to show that $\sigma(q) \in H$. To this end, define $\alpha \in \mathcal{S}$ by the requirement that, for every $n \in I$,

(4) $$\alpha(n) = \sigma(\beta(n)).$$

Then

(5) $$\begin{aligned} \alpha(1) &= \sigma(\beta(1)) && \text{[by (4)]} \\ &= \sigma(\sigma(q)) && \text{[by (2)]}. \end{aligned}$$

Moreover, for every $n \in I$,

(6) $$\begin{aligned} \alpha(\sigma(n)) &= \sigma(\beta(\sigma(n))) && \text{[by (4)]} \\ &= \sigma(\sigma(\beta(n))) && \text{[by (3)]} \\ &= \sigma(\alpha(n)) && \text{[by (4)]}. \end{aligned}$$

But (5) and (6) are (a) and (b) with $m = \sigma(q)$. Hence it has been shown that, for $m = \sigma(q)$, there exists a sequence α satisfying (a) and (b). Thus $\sigma(q) \in H$. We have proved that if $q \in H$ then $\sigma(q) \in H$.

From the preceding, III(a) and III(b) are true of H. Hence, by III, $H = I$, that is,

for every $m \in I$, there exists α satisfying (a) and (b).

This completes the proof.

(8.5.2) Theorem: *Let $m \in I$. If $\alpha, \beta \in \mathcal{S}$ are such that both satisfy* (a), (b) *of* (8.5.1), *then $\alpha = \beta$.*

Proof: Let $m \in I$. Suppose α and β both satisfy (a) and (b) of (8.5.1), so that

(1) $\alpha(1) = \sigma(m) = \beta(1)$;
(2) for every $n \in I$, $\alpha(\sigma(n)) = \sigma(\alpha(n))$;
(3) for every $n \in I$, $\beta(\sigma(n)) = \sigma(\beta(n))$.

Define

$$H \equiv [n; \alpha(n) = \beta(n)] \subset I.$$

Then $1 \in H$, by (1).

Suppose $q \in H$, so that

$$\alpha(q) = \beta(q). \tag{4}$$

Then

$$\alpha(\sigma(q)) = \sigma(\alpha(q)) \quad \text{[by (2)]}, \tag{5}$$
$$\beta(\sigma(q)) = \sigma(\beta(q)) \quad \text{[by (3)]}, \tag{6}$$

so that

$$\alpha(\sigma(q)) = \beta(\sigma(q)) \quad \text{[by (4), (5), (6)]}. \tag{7}$$

Hence $\sigma(q) \in H$.

By III, $H = I$. This shows that, for every $n \in I$,

$$\alpha(n) = \beta(n).$$

The proof is complete. [See (5.4.7).]

(8.5.3) Definition: We define a function on I to $\mathcal{S}$ as follows: For each $m \in I$, the correspondent of m under the function is required to be the unique sequence satisfying (a) and (b) of (8.5.1). The correspondent of m is denoted by α_m, and the function by $(\alpha_m; m \in I)$.

Remark: The function $(\alpha_m; m \in I)$ has by definition these properties: Its domain is I. Also,

for every $m \in I$, $\alpha_m(1) = \sigma(m)$;
for every $m \in I$, and for every $n \in I$, $\alpha_m(\sigma(n)) = \sigma(\alpha_m(n))$.

It has not yet been asserted that such a function on I to $\mathcal{S}$ is unique. That this is true is now easily seen. If $(\beta_m; m \in I)$ is another such function, then for each $m \in I$, the sequences α_m, β_m satisfy the hypotheses of (8.5.2) (in place of α, β), and so must be equal. But $\alpha_m = \beta_m$ for every $m \in I$ yields equality of the functions $(\alpha_m; m \in I)$, $(\beta_m; m \in I)$ by (5.4.7).

(8.5.4) Definition: We define the operation $+$ on $I \times I$ to I as the associated operation to the function $(\alpha_m; m \in I)$ on I to $\mathcal{S}$. Thus for every m, $n \in I$,

$$m + n = +(m, n) = \alpha_m(n).$$

The basic properties of the operation $+$ are now to be developed. For a reason to be given later, we prefer to use, for a while, the notation $+(m, n)$ rather than the more familiar $m + n$.

(8.5.5) Theorem: *For every* $m \in I$,

(a) $$+(m, 1) = \sigma(m);$$
(b) $$+(1, m) = \sigma(m).$$

Proof: Part (a) is simply a restatement of (8.5.1.a) in the new terminology.

To prove (b), we must show that, for every $m \in I$, $\alpha_1(m) = \sigma(m)$. But this will be proved when it is shown that $\alpha_1 = \sigma$. It is known that α_1 has the properties (a), (b) of (8.5.1) with $m = 1$, that is,

(1) $\alpha_1(1) = \sigma(1)$;

(2) for every $n \in I$, $\alpha_1(\sigma(n)) = \sigma(\alpha_1(n))$.

But clearly σ also has these properties:

$\sigma(1) = \sigma(1)$;

for every $n \in I$, $\sigma(\sigma(n)) = \sigma(\sigma(n))$.

Hence the equality of α_1 and σ follows from (8.5.2). This completes the proof.

(8.5.6) Theorem: *For every $m, n \in I$,*

(a) $$+(m, \sigma(n)) = \sigma(+(m, n));$$

(b) $$+(\sigma(m), n) = \sigma(+(m, n)).$$

Proof: Part (a) is a restatement of (8.5.1.b).

To prove (b), let $m \in I$. We recall that, by (8.5.4),

(1) for every $n \in I$, $+(\sigma(m), n) = \alpha_{\sigma(m)}(n)$.

Let us define a sequence β as follows:

$$\beta \equiv (\sigma(\alpha_m(n)); n \in I),$$

so that,

(2) for every $n \in I$, $\beta(n) = \sigma(\alpha_m(n)) = \sigma(+(m, n))$.

We wish to show that $\beta = \alpha_{\sigma(m)}$. Now, by (8.5.3),

(3) $\alpha_{\sigma(m)}(1) = \sigma(\sigma(m))$;

(4) for every $n \in I$, $\alpha_{\sigma(m)}(\sigma(n)) = \sigma(\alpha_{\sigma(m)}(n))$.

But we shall show that β also satisfies these conditions. First,

(5) $\beta(1) = \sigma(\alpha_m(1))$ [by (2), with $n = 1$]

$= \sigma(\sigma(m))$ [by (8.5.3)].

Moreover,

(6) for every $n \in I$, $\beta(\sigma(n)) = \sigma(\alpha_m(\sigma(n)))$ [by (2)]

$= \sigma(\sigma(\alpha_m(n)))$ [by (8.5.3)]

$= \sigma(\beta(n))$ [by (2)].

Thus, by (5), (6),

(7) $\beta(1) = \sigma(\sigma(m))$;

(8) for every $n \in I$, $\beta(\sigma(n)) = \sigma(\beta(n))$.

Comparison of (7), (8) with (3), (4) shows that β and $\alpha_{\sigma(m)}$ satisfy the hypotheses of (8.5.2); thus

(9) $\beta = \alpha_{\sigma(m)}$ [by (8.5.2)].

Now

$$\begin{aligned} +(\sigma(m), n) &= \alpha_{\sigma(m)}(n) && \text{[by (8.5.4)]} \\ &= \beta(n) && \text{[by (9)]} \\ &= \sigma(+(m, n)) && \text{[by (2)].} \end{aligned}$$

This completes the proof.

(8.5.7) THEOREM: *For every* $m, n \in I$,

$$+(n, m) = +(m, n).$$

PROOF: Let $m \in I$. Define

$$H \equiv [n; +(n, m) = +(m, n)] \subset I.$$

First, $1 \in H$, by (8.5.5).

Now let $q \in H$, so that

$$(1) \qquad +(q, m) = +(m, q).$$

Then

$$\begin{aligned} +(\sigma(q), m) &= \sigma(+(q, m)) && \text{[by (8.5.6.b)]} \\ &= \sigma(+(m, q)) && \text{[by (1)]} \\ &= +(m, \sigma(q)) && \text{[by (8.5.6.a)],} \end{aligned}$$

so that $\sigma(q) \in H$. Thus $q \in H$ implies $\sigma(q) \in H$.

It follows from III that $H = I$, whence, for every m, $+(n, m) = +(m, n)$, for every n. This completes the proof.

(8.5.8) THEOREM: *For every* $m, n, p \in I$,

$$+(+(m, n), p) = +(m, +(n, p)).$$

PROOF: Let $m, n \in I$. Define

$$H \equiv [p; +(+(m, n), p) = +(m, +(n, p))] \subset I.$$

First, $1 \in H$, since

$$\begin{aligned} +(+(m, n), 1) &= \sigma(+(m, n)) && \text{[by (8.5.5.a)]} \\ &= +(m, \sigma(n)) && \text{[by (8.5.6.a)]} \\ &= +(m, +(n, 1)) && \text{[by (8.5.5.a)].} \end{aligned}$$

Now let $q \in H$, that is, let

$$(1) \qquad +(+(m, n), q) = +(m, +(n, q)).$$

Then

$$\begin{aligned} +(+(m, n), \sigma(q)) &= \sigma(+(+(m, n), q)) && \text{[by (8.5.6.a)]} \\ &= \sigma(+(m, +(n, q))) && \text{[by (1)]} \\ &= +(m, \sigma(+(n, q))) && \text{[by (8.5.6.a)]} \\ &= +(m, +(n, \sigma(q))) && \text{[by (8.5.6.a)],} \end{aligned}$$

so that $\sigma(q) \in H$. Thus $q \in H$ implies $\sigma(q) \in H$.

By III, $H = I$, and the proof is complete.

REMARK: In the two preceding theorems we have chosen to use $+(m, n)$ rather than $m + n$ in order to avoid the contempt for these theorems that the reader's familiarity with them, in the latter notation, might breed. Henceforth we shall use $m + n$ instead of $+(m, n)$. Expressed in this more usual notation, (8.5.7) and (8.5.8) state:

(8.5.9) THEOREM: *For every* $m, n \in I$, $n + m = m + n$.

(8.5.10) THEOREM: *For every* $m, n, p \in I$, $(m + n) + p = m + (n + p)$.

The two theorems (8.5.9) and (8.5.10) are expressed verbally by saying that the operation $+$ is *commutative* and *associative*. As an illustration of the use of these theorems, we prove here a result which will be needed later.

(8.5.11) LEMMA: *For every* $m, n, p, q \in I$,

$$(m + n) + (p + q) = (m + p) + (n + q).$$

PROOF: We have

$$\begin{aligned}(m + n) + (p + q) &= m + (n + (p + q)) && \text{[by (8.5.10)]}\\ &= m + ((n + p) + q) && \text{[by (8.5.10)]}\\ &= m + ((p + n) + q) && \text{[by (8.5.9)]}\\ &= m + (p + (n + q)) && \text{[by (8.5.10)]}\\ &= (m + p) + (n + q) && \text{[by (8.5.10)].}\end{aligned}$$

REMARK: The statement (8.5.5), translated into the familiar notation, is

(8.5.12) $$\text{for every } n \in I,\ \sigma(n) = n + 1.$$

The fact expressed by (8.5.12) is particularly significant, since it provides a description of the basic function σ in terms of the operation $+$. This description makes possible a useful reformulation of the axioms:

I′: For every $m, n \in I$, if $m \neq n$, then $m + 1 \neq n + 1$.
II′: For every $m \in I$, $m + 1 \neq 1$.
III′: Let $H \subset I$ such that
(a) $1 \in H$;
(b) for every $q \in H$, $q + 1 \in H$.
Then $H = I$.

We conclude this section with the proof of an exceedingly important theorem about the operation $+$. The proof will use the reformulation of the axioms.

(8.5.13) THEOREM: *Let* $m, n \in I$. *If* $m \neq n$, *then, for every* $p \in I$, $m + p \neq n + p$.

PROOF: Let $m, n \in I$ such that $m \neq n$. Define

$$H \equiv [p; m + p \neq n + p].$$

Now, since $m \neq n$, $m + 1 \neq n + 1$, by I′; hence $1 \in H$.

Suppose $q \in H$, that is, $m + q \neq n + q$. Then, by I′, $(m + q) + 1 \neq (n + q) + 1$. Hence, by (8.5.10), $m + (q + 1) \neq n + (q + 1)$. Thus $q + 1 \in H$.

We have shown that H satisfies the hypotheses of III′, whence $H = I$ by III′. This completes the proof.

(8.5.14) COROLLARY: *Let $m, n \in I$. If there exists $p \in I$ such that $m + p = n + p$, then $m = n$.*

REMARK: This corollary is a precise statement of one of the "rules of cancellation" which elementary students sin against so often.

PROOF: This corollary is really a contrapositive of (8.5.13) and so needs no proof. However, it might be instructive to see how a contrapositive statement of a theorem may be proved from the theorem.

The proof is indirect. Let $m, n \in I$. We show that if the conclusion, $m = n$, is false, the hypothesis cannot be true. Thus *suppose* $m \neq n$. Then, by (8.5.13), for every $p \in I$, $m + p \neq n + p$. Hence there does not exist $p \in I$ for which $m + p = n + p$, contrary to the hypothesis. This completes the proof.

(8.5.15) COROLLARY: *For every $m, p \in I$, $m \neq m + p$.*

PROOF: *Suppose* there exist $m, p \in I$ such that $m = m + p$.

Then

$$\begin{aligned} m + 1 &= (m + p) + 1 \\ &= m + (p + 1) \qquad [\text{by } (8.5.10)]. \end{aligned}$$

But then

$$1 = p + 1 \qquad [\text{by } (8.5.14)].$$

This contradicts II′. The proof is complete.

8.6. The Operation × (Times). [BASIS: $(I, 1, \sigma)$; AXIOMS: I, II, III.] We now proceed to the introduction of the other fundamental operation on $I \times I$ to I, the operation $\times$ (times).

Intuitively, the operation $\times$ bears the same relation to the (set-theoretic) cartesian product as $+$ bears to the set-theoretic sum. Hence, if m and n are counting numbers which denote the "manyness" of two sets M and N, then $m \times n$ is the "manyness" of the set $M \times N$. The reader might try this out on two simple sets, for example, those in (4.8.8).

The method used to introduce $\times$ is similar to the method of introducing $+$. Again we seek defining properties, that is, properties of $\times$ from which all others may be deduced. And again these properties are formulated for the appropriate function on I to $\mathcal{S}$. After proving the existence and uniqueness of this function, we shall define $\times$ as the associated operation. The only difference between the procedures of this section and those of the preceding lies in the defining properties.

(8.6.1) Theorem: *For every* $m \in I$, *there exists a sequence* $\mu \in \mathcal{S}$, *such that*

(a) $\mu(1) = m;$

(b) *for every* $n \in I$, $\mu(n + 1) = \mu(n) + m.$

Proof: Define

(1) $H \equiv [m;$ there exists $\mu \in \mathcal{S}$ satisfying (a), (b)$]$.

First we show that $1 \in H$. To this end, define μ as the identity function on I to I (that is, the identity relation on $I \times I$), so that, for every $p \in I$, $\mu(p) = p$. Of course, $\mu \in \mathcal{S}$, and $\mu(1) = 1$, so that (a) holds. Moreover, for every $n \in I$,

$$\mu(n + 1) = n + 1 = \mu(n) + 1,$$

and (b) is established. Therefore $1 \in H$.

Next, suppose $q \in H$. This means that there is a function $\lambda \in \mathcal{S}$ such that

(2) $\lambda(1) = q;$

(3) for every $n \in I$, $\lambda(n + 1) = \lambda(n) + q.$

Now define $\mu \in \mathcal{S}$ by the requirement that

(4) for every $n \in I$, $\mu(n) = \lambda(n) + n.$

Then

(5)
$$\begin{aligned} \mu(1) &= \lambda(1) + 1 && \text{[by (4)]} \\ &= q + 1 && \text{[by (2)].} \end{aligned}$$

Moreover, for every $n \in I$,

(6)
$$\begin{aligned} \mu(n + 1) &= \lambda(n + 1) + (n + 1) && \text{[by (4)]} \\ &= (\lambda(n) + q) + (n + 1) && \text{[by (3)]} \\ &= (\lambda(n) + n) + (q + 1) && \text{[by (8.5.11)]} \\ &= \mu(n) + (q + 1) && \text{[by (4)].} \end{aligned}$$

But (5) and (6) are (a) and (b) with $m = q + 1$. Hence, for $m = q + 1$, there exists a function $\mu \in \mathcal{S}$ satisfying (a) and (b), so that $q + 1 \in H$.

Thus $q \in H$ implies $q + 1 \in H$. By III′, $H = I$. This completes the proof.

(8.6.2) THEOREM: *Let* $m \in I$. *If* $\mu, \lambda \in \mathcal{S}$ *both satisfy* (a), (b) *of* (8.6.1), *then* $\mu = \lambda$.

PROOF: Let $m \in I$. Suppose μ and λ both satisfy (a), (b) of (8.6.1), so that

(1) $\mu(1) = m = \lambda(1)$;
(2) for every $n \in I$, $\mu(n + 1) = \mu(n) + m$;
(3) for every $n \in I$, $\lambda(n + 1) = \lambda(n) + m$.

Define

$$H \equiv [n \in I; \mu(n) = \lambda(n)].$$

Then $1 \in H$ by (1).
Suppose $q \in H$, so that

(4) $$\mu(q) = \lambda(q).$$

Then

(5) $$\mu(q + 1) = \mu(q) + m \quad \text{[by (2)]}$$
(6) $$\lambda(q + 1) = \lambda(q) + m \quad \text{[by (3)]},$$

so that

(7) $$\mu(q + 1) = \lambda(q + 1) \quad \text{[by (4), (5), (6)]}.$$

Hence $q + 1 \in H$.
By III′, $H = I$. This completes the proof.

(8.6.3) DEFINITION: We define a function on I to $\mathcal{S}$ as follows: For each $m \in I$, the correspondent of m under the function is the unique sequence satisfying (a) and (b) of (8.6.1). The correspondent of m is denoted by μ_m, and the function by $(\mu_m; m \in I)$.

REMARK: As in the case of $(\alpha_m; m \in I)$ [see (8.5.3)], the function $(\mu_m; m \in I)$ is the unique function with certain properties, namely,

for every $m \in I$, $\mu_m(1) = m$;
for every $m \in I$, and for every $n \in I$, $\mu_m(n + 1) = \mu_m(n) + m$.

(8.6.4) DEFINITION: We define the operation $\times$ on $I \times I$ to I as the associated operation to the function $(\mu_m; m \in I)$ on I to $\mathcal{S}$; thus, for every $m, n \in I$,

$$m \times n = \times(m, n) = \mu_m(n).$$

(8.6.5) THEOREM: *For every* $m \in I$,

(a) $$\times(m, 1) = m;$$
(b) $$\times(1, m) = m.$$

PROOF: This is left for the reader.

(8.6.6) THEOREM: *For every* $m, n \in I$,

$$\times(m + 1, n) = \times(m, n) + n.$$

PROOF: This is parallel to the proof of (8.5.6.b) and is left for the reader.

(8.6.7) THEOREM: *For every* $m, n \in I$,

$$\times(m, n + 1) = \times(m, n) + m.$$

PROOF: This is a restatement of (8.6.1.b) in the new terminology.

We show next that the operation $\times$ is commutative.

(8.6.8) THEOREM: *For every* $m, n \in I$, $\times(n, m) = \times(m, n)$.
PROOF: Let $m \in I$. Define

$$H \equiv [n; \times(n, m) = \times(m, n)].$$

First, $1 \in H$ by (8.6.5).
Now let $q \in H$, that is, let

(1) $$\times(q, m) = \times(m, q).$$

Then

$$\begin{aligned} \times(q + 1, m) &= \times(q, m) + m && \text{[by (8.6.6)]} \\ &= \times(m, q) + m && \text{[by (1)]} \\ &= \times(m, q + 1) && \text{[by (8.6.7)]}, \end{aligned}$$

so that $q + 1 \in H$. Thus $q \in H$ implies $q + 1 \in H$.
It follows from III′ that $H = I$, so that, for every $m \in I$, and for every $n \in I$, $\times(n, m) = \times(m, n)$. This completes the proof.

The next theorem expresses a fundamental joint property of $+$ and $\times$.

(8.6.9) THEOREM: *For every* $m, n, p \in I$,

$$\times(m, n + p) = \times(m, n) + \times(m, p).$$

PROOF: Let $m, n \in I$. Define

(1) $$H \equiv [p; \times(m, n + p) = \times(m, n) + \times(m, p)].$$

First, $1 \in H$, since

$$\begin{aligned} \times(m, n + 1) &= \times(m, n) + m && \text{[by (8.6.7)]} \\ &= \times(m, n) + \times(m, 1) && \text{[by (8.6.5.a)]}. \end{aligned}$$

Now let $q \in H$, that is, let

(2) $$\times(m, n + q) = \times(m, n) + \times(m, q).$$

Then

$$\begin{aligned}\times(m, n + (q + 1)) &= \times(m, (n + q) + 1) && \text{[by (8.5.10)]}\\ &= \times(m, n + q) + m && \text{[by (8.6.7)]}\\ &= (\times(m, n) + \times(m, q)) + m && \text{[by (2)]}\\ &= \times(m, n) + (\times(m, q) + m) && \text{[by (8.5.10)]}\\ &= \times(m, n) + \times(m, q + 1) && \text{[by (8.6.7)]},\end{aligned}$$

so that $q + 1 \epsilon H$. Thus $q \epsilon H$ implies $q + 1 \epsilon H$.
Thus $H = I$ by III′. This completes the proof.

Finally we prove that $\times$ is associative.

(8.6.10) THEOREM: *For every* $m, n, p \epsilon I$,

$$\times(\times(m, n), p) = \times(m, \times(n, p)).$$

PROOF: Let $m, n \epsilon I$. Define

$$H \equiv [p; \times(\times(m, n), p) = \times(m, \times(n, p))].$$

First, $1 \epsilon H$, since

$$\begin{aligned}\times(\times(m, n), 1) &= \times(m, n) && \text{[by (8.6.5.a)]}\\ &= \times(m, \times(n, 1)) && \text{[by (8.6.5.a)]}.\end{aligned}$$

Now let $q \epsilon H$, that is, let

(1) $$\times(\times(m, n), q) = \times(m, \times(n, q)).$$

Then

$$\begin{aligned}\times(\times(m, n), q + 1) &= \times(\times(m, n), q) + \times(m, n) && \text{[by (8.6.7)]}\\ &= \times(m, \times(n, q)) + \times(m, n) && \text{[by (1)]}\\ &= \times(m, \times(n, q) + n) && \text{[by (8.6.9)]}\\ &= \times(m, \times(n, q + 1)) && \text{[by (8.6.7)]},\end{aligned}$$

so that $q + 1 \epsilon H$. Thus $q \epsilon H$ implies $q + 1 \epsilon H$.
Hence $H = I$ by III′. This completes the proof.

The reader has probably realized, particularly in view of the preceding section, that the results (8.6.5), (8.6.8), (8.6.9), (8.6.10) are facts which he has repeatedly heard or seen asserted in the notation wherein $\times(m, n)$ appears as $m \times n$. Actually, $m \times n$ is usually written $m \cdot n$ or even mn. This last notation, although somewhat unfortunate, does not actually lead to any ambiguity, since no significance has been attached to the juxtaposition of two symbols for elements of I. However, we prefer to avoid the notation mn and generally shall use the dot notation $m \cdot n$.

(8.6.11) DEFINITION: $\cdot \equiv \times$.

Thus, for every $m, n \in I$, $m \cdot n = m \times n = \times(m, n)$. Translating the results (8.6.5), (8.6.8), (8.6.9), (8.6.10) into this notation gives the familiar looking statements that follow.

(8.6.12) THEOREM: *For every* $m \in I$, $m \cdot 1 = 1 \cdot m = m$.

(8.6.13) THEOREM: *For every* $m, n \in I$, $m \cdot n = n \cdot m$.

(8.6.14) THEOREM: *For every* $m, n, p \in I$, $m \cdot (n + p) = (m \cdot n) + (m \cdot p)$.

(8.6.15) THEOREM: *For every* $m, n, p \in I$, $(m \cdot n) \cdot p = m \cdot (n \cdot p)$.

The theorems (8.6.13) and (8.6.15) state that $\cdot$ is commutative and associative. The more complicated (8.6.14) is usually expressed by saying that $\cdot$ is *distributive* with respect to $+$.

It should be mentioned that the analogue, for the operation $\cdot$, of (8.5.13) is valid, but it is more conveniently proved with the help of some of the results of the next chapter. Accordingly, we postpone it until (9.2.16).

(8.6.16) PROJECT: Prove (8.6.5).

(8.6.17) PROJECT: Prove (8.6.6).

8.7. Notation. [BASIS: $(I, 1, \sigma)$; AXIOMS: I, II, III.] We conclude this chapter with remarks concerning certain notational usages and the introduction of special symbols for certain particular positive integers.

Let $m, n, p \in I$. Then the symbol

(8.7.1) $$m + n + p$$

has no meaning at the moment. There are, however, two ways of inserting parentheses into (8.7.1) to make it a meaningful symbol, the results being

$$(m + n) + p \quad \text{and} \quad m + (n + p).$$

Now, by (8.5.10), these two elements are actually the same, whence it is reasonable to use (8.7.1) to represent the common meaning of $(m + n) + p$ and $m + (n + p)$. Thus

$$m + n + p \equiv (m + n) + p = m + (n + p).$$

Similar considerations for the operation $\cdot$ lead to the definition

$$m \cdot n \cdot p \equiv (m \cdot n) \cdot p = m \cdot (n \cdot p).$$

Let us consider now the symbol

(8.7.2) $$m + n \cdot p.$$

This also has no meaning as it stands; however, there are, as before, two ways of introducing parentheses into (8.7.2), yielding

$$(m + n) \cdot p \tag{8.7.3}$$

and

$$m + (n \cdot p). \tag{8.7.4}$$

It should be observed that (8.7.3) and (8.7.4) are not always equal. For if $m = 1, n = 1, p = \sigma(1) = 1 + 1$, then

$$\begin{aligned} m + (n \cdot p) &= 1 + (1 \cdot (1 + 1)) \\ &= 1 + (1 + 1) && \text{[by (8.6.12)]} \\ &= 1 + 1 + 1. \end{aligned}$$

On the other hand,

$$\begin{aligned} (m + n) \cdot p = (1 + 1) \cdot p &= p \cdot (1 + 1) && \text{[by (8.6.13)]} \\ &= (p \cdot 1) + (p \cdot 1) && \text{[by (8.6.14)]} \\ &= p + p && \text{[by (8.6.12)]} \\ &= (1 + 1) + (1 + 1) && \text{[since } p = 1 + 1\text{]} \\ &= (1 + 1 + 1) + 1 && \text{[by (8.5.10)]} \\ &= \sigma(1 + 1 + 1) && \text{[by (8.5.12)].} \end{aligned}$$

Since $\sigma(1 + 1 + 1) \neq (1 + 1 + 1)$, by (8.3.1), it is seen that, at least in the particular case considered, $(m + n) \cdot p \neq m + (n \cdot p)$. Despite the fact that (8.7.3) and (8.7.4) are not necessarily equal, it is convenient to use the notation (8.7.2) to mean one of these two things. General mathematical custom dictates that $m + n \cdot p$ be used to denote $m + (n \cdot p)$. A similar agreement is made with respect to $m \cdot n + p$ or $m \cdot n + p \cdot q$; in all cases the operation $\cdot$ is "performed" first. Thus the conclusion of (8.6.14) could be written

$$m \cdot (n + p) = m \cdot n + m \cdot p.$$

There are a few positive integers whose occurrence in what follows is so frequent that it is convenient to introduce special symbols for them.

(8.7.5) Definition:

(a) $2 \equiv 1 + 1 (= \sigma(1))$;
(b) $3 \equiv 2 + 1$;
(c) $4 \equiv 3 + 1$;
(d) $5 \equiv 4 + 1$;
(e) $6 \equiv 5 + 1$;
(f) $7 \equiv 6 + 1$;
(g) $8 \equiv 7 + 1$;
(h) $9 \equiv 8 + 1$.

Remark: While in (8.7.5) no definition except (a) is meaningful *by itself*, each acquires meaning with the help of the preceding definition(s). Thus $4 \equiv 3 + 1 = 2 + 1 + 1 = 1 + 1 + 1 + 1$.

It is possible now to *prove* the familiar rules which the positive integers 2, 3, 4, 5, 6, 7, 8, 9 obey. The next theorem is an example.

(8.7.6) THEOREM: $2 \cdot 2 = 4$.

PROOF:

$$\begin{aligned} 2 \cdot 2 &= 2 \cdot (1 + 1) && \text{[by (8.7.5.a)]} \\ &= 2 \cdot 1 + 2 \cdot 1 && \text{[by (8.6.14)]} \\ &= 2 + 2 && \text{[by (8.6.12)]} \\ &= 2 + (1 + 1) && \text{[by (8.7.5.a)]} \\ &= (2 + 1) + 1 && \text{[by (8.5.10)]} \\ &= 3 + 1 && \text{[by (8.7.5.b)]} \\ &= 4 && \text{[by (8.7.5.c)].} \end{aligned}$$

REMARK: The proof just given shows also that $2 + 2 = 4$.

(8.7.7) PROJECT: Prove that, if $m, n, p, q \epsilon I$, then
(a) $(m + n + p) \cdot q = m \cdot q + n \cdot q + p \cdot q$;
(b) $(m + n) \cdot (p + q) = m \cdot p + n \cdot p + m \cdot q + n \cdot q$;
(c) $(m + n) \cdot (m + n) = m \cdot m + 2 \cdot m \cdot n + n \cdot n$;
(d) $(m + n) \cdot (m + n) \cdot (m + n)$
$$= m \cdot m \cdot m + 3 \cdot m \cdot m \cdot n + 3 \cdot m \cdot n \cdot n + n \cdot n \cdot n.$$

(8.7.8) PROJECT: Prove each of the following:
(a) $3 \cdot 2 = 6$; (b) $4 \cdot 2 = 8$; (c) $3 \cdot 3 = 9$;
(d) $3 + 2 = 5$; (e) $5 + 2 = 7$; (f) $6 + 3 = 9$.

8.8. Conclusion. [BASIS: $(I, 1, \sigma)$; AXIOMS: I, II, III.] It has been seen that each of the operations $+$, $\cdot$ is associative. Let us recall that associativity is one of the requirements for group operations (Axiom I for groups). It is natural to inquire whether the set I, together with either of the operations $+$, $\cdot$, is a group. The answer is unfortunately in the negative, since Axioms II and III (for groups) are not satisfied for either operation. For example, there is no element $x \epsilon I$ such that

$$x + 1 = 1,$$

as II′ states. Similarly, it is easy to show that there is no positive integer y such that

$$y \cdot 2 = 1.$$

The proof of this fact is left for the reader.

That neither $(I, +)$ nor $(I, \cdot)$ is a group is a serious drawback and limits the usefulness of the positive integers; because of this handicap, there are many purposes for which the positive integers are unsuited. Accordingly, other "number systems" have been developed which largely eliminate this failing. Some of these systems will be describea in subsequent chapters.

(8.8.1) PROJECT: Prove that there exists no element $y \epsilon I$ such that $y \cdot 2 = 1$.

Chapter 9

FUNDAMENTAL RELATIONS ON THE POSITIVE INTEGERS

9.1. Introduction. [BASIS: $(I, 1, \sigma)$; AXIOMS: I, II, III.] It was proved in (8.8) that it is not true that, for *every* $m, n \in I$,

(9.1.1) there exists $x \in I$ such that $m + x = n$;

it was also proved that it is not true that, for *every* $m, n \in I$,

(9.1.2) there exists $y \in I$ such that $m \cdot y = n$.

However, it may well happen that there exist pairs (m, n) of positive integers for which (9.1.1) or (9.1.2) holds. For example, if $m = 1$, $n = 2$, then (9.1.1) is true, since $x = 1$ is effective. Similarly, if $m = 1$, $n = 1$, then (9.1.2) is true, since $y = 1$ is effective. It appears that the set of pairs $(m, n) \in I \times I$ for which (9.1.1) holds is a non-empty proper subset of $I \times I$. This subset is, of course, a relation on $I \times I$; as such it is given the name *is less than*. Similarly, the proper non-empty subset of $I \times I$ consisting of those pairs (m, n) for which (9.1.2) holds is a relation called *divides*. These relations derive their importance from the fact that they distinguish those pairs to which the group processes embodied in the group axioms II, III are applicable. That these relations occupy a central position in the theory of positive integers will be seen from the exposition of them to be given in the remainder of the present chapter. In particular, the significance of regarding σ as a mathematical description of the intuitive "succession" in which the counting numbers occur will be investigated through our study of the relation *is less than*.

9.2. The Relation $<$ (Is Less Than). [BASIS: $(I, 1, \sigma)$; AXIOMS: I, II, III.]

(9.2.1) DEFINITION:

$$< \equiv [(m, n);\text{ there exists } p \in I \text{ such that } m + p = n].$$

Hence one writes $m < n$ (read "m is less than n") if and only if there exists $p \in I$ such that $m + p = n$.

REMARK: It is clear that, for every $m, p \in I$, $(m, m + p) \in <$, whence

$$m < m + p.$$

In particular, for every $m \in I$, $m < m + 1$.

(9.2.2) Definition: We define relations $>$, $\leqq$, $\geqq$ on $I \times I$ by the requirement that, for every $m, n \in I$,

(a) $m > n$ if and only if $n < m$;
(b) $m \leqq n$ if and only if $m < n$ or $m = n$;
(c) $m \geqq n$ if and only if $m > n$ or $m = n$.

Remark: These definitions could be expressed more compactly with the help of the notations introduced in (5.3) as follows (E is the identity relation on $I \times I$):

(a) $> \equiv <^*$;
(b) $\leqq \equiv < + E$;
(c) $\geqq \equiv > + E = (\leqq)^*$.

(9.2.3) Notation: The negatives of the relations $<$, $>$, $\leqq$ are written respectively $\nless$, $\ngtr$, $\nleqq$.

Remark: Note that the statement $m \nleqq n$ means $m \nless n$ *and* $m \neq n$. The notations $<'$ and $-<$, which, in accordance with (5.3), might be used to indicate the negative of $<$, will never appear, in deference to mathematical custom.

Remark: We suggest that at this point the reader remind himself of the important theorem (8.5.13) and the corollaries (8.5.14) and (8.5.15) because of their significance for the relation $<$. For example, (8.5.14) implies that, for every $m, n \in I$, there is at most one $p \in I$ such that $m + p = n$. In fact, if $m + p = n$ and $m + q = n$, then $m + p = m + q$, and so $p = q$ by (8.5.14). This unique p, if it exists, is called the *difference between n and m*. [A few properties of this difference will be studied in (9.5).] It has been pointed out that there need not exist such a p. Our next theorem implies that p cannot exist if $m = n$.

(9.2.4) Theorem: *For every $m \in I$, $m \nless m$.*

Proof: *Suppose* there exists $m \in I$ such that $m < m$. Then there exists $p \in I$ such that $m + p = m$. But this contradicts (8.5.15). The proof is complete.

(9.2.5) Theorem: *If $m, n \in I$ such that there exists $q \in I$ for which $m < q$ and $q < n$, then $m < n$.*

Proof: Let $m, n, q \in I$ such that $m < q$ and $q < n$. Since $m < q$, there exists $p \in I$ such that

(1) $$m + p = q.$$

Since $q < n$, there exists $r \in I$ such that

(2) $$q + r = n.$$

From (1) and (2) we have

$$(m + p) + r = n,$$

or, since $+$ is associative,

$$m + (p + r) = n,$$

whence $m < n$ by (9.2.1).

Theorem (9.2.5) expresses that the relation $<$ is *transitive*.

(9.2.6) COROLLARY: *Let $m, n \in I$. Then,*
(a) *if there exists $q \in I$ for which $m < q$ and $q \leqq n$, then $m < n$;*
(b) *if there exists $q \in I$ for which $m \leqq q$ and $q < n$, then $m < n$;*
(c) *if there exists $q \in I$ for which $m \leqq q$ and $q \leqq n$, then $m \leqq n$.*

PROOF OF (a): The proof is very simple but is given in detail because it is our first example of a proof by "considering cases." Let $m, n, q \in I$ such that

$$m < q \quad \text{and} \quad q \leqq n.$$

Since $q \leqq n$, we have *either* $q < n$ or $q = n$. These possibilities are treated separately.

Case 1: $q < n$. Since $m < q$, we have $m < n$ by (9.2.5).
Case 2: $q = n$. Since $m < q$, we have $m < n$.

PROOFS OF (b) AND (c): These are left for the reader.

(9.2.7) THEOREM: *If $m, n \in I$ such that $m < n$, then $n \nless m$.*

PROOF: *Suppose* there exist $m, n \in I$ such that $m < n$ and $n < m$. Then $m < m$ by (9.2.5). But this contradicts (9.2.4).

(9.2.8) THEOREM: *If $m, n \in I$ such that $m \leqq n$ and $n \leqq m$, then $m = n$.*

PROOF: This is an immediate consequence of (9.2.6) and (9.2.4), as the reader may show.

(9.2.9) THEOREM: *For every $m \in I$, either $1 = m$ or $1 < m$.*

PROOF: Let $m \in I$. Then, either $1 = m$ or $1 \neq m$. In the latter case, by (8.3.2), there exists $p \in I$ such that

$$m = \sigma(p) = p + 1 = 1 + p;$$

thus $1 < m$.

REMARK: A more compact form for (9.2.9) is this:

for every $m \in I$, $1 \leqq m$ (or, equivalently, $m \geqq 1$).

(9.2.10) THEOREM: *Let* $m, n \in I$. *Then,*

(a) *if* $m < n + 1$, *then* $m \leqq n$;
(b) *if* $m < n$, *then* $m + 1 \leqq n$.

PROOF OF (a): Let $m < n + 1$. Then there exists $r \in I$ such that

(1) $$m + r = n + 1.$$

By (9.2.9), $1 = r$ or $1 < r$. If $1 = r$, then $m = n$ by (1), (8.5.14), so that $m \leqq n$ is true in this case. If $1 < r$, there exists $s \in I$ such that $1 + s = r$. From (1) we have

(2) $$m + s + 1 = n + 1,$$

whence, by (8.5.14), $m + s = n$, and $m < n$. Thus, in this case also, $m \leqq n$.

PROOF OF (b): This is left for the reader.

(9.2.11) THEOREM: *If* $m, n \in I$ *such that* $m < n$, *then, for every* $r \in I$, $m + r < n + r$.

PROOF: Let $m, n \in I$ such that $m < n$. Then there exists $p \in I$ such that

$$m + p = n.$$

Therefore, for every $r \in I$,

$$(m + p) + r = n + r,$$

whence

$$(m + r) + p = n + r,$$

so that

$$m + r < n + r.$$

(9.2.12) COROLLARY: *If* $m, n, p, q \in I$ *such that* $m < n$ *and* $p \leqq q$, *then* $m + p < n + q$.

PROOF: If $p = q$, this is (9.2.11). Suppose $p < q$. Now, since $m < n$,

(1) $$m + p < n + p \qquad \text{[by (9.2.11)]}.$$

But, since $p < q$,

(2) $$n + p = p + n < q + n = n + q \qquad \text{[by (9.2.11)]}.$$

But (1) and (2) yield $m + p < n + q$ by (9.2.5).

(9.2.13) THEOREM: *Let* $m, n \in I$. *If there exists* $r \in I$ *such that* $m + r < n + r$, *then* $m < n$.

PROOF: Let $m, n \in I$ such that there exists $r \in I$ with $m + r < n + r$. Hence there exists $p \in I$ such that

$$(m + r) + p = n + r,$$

or, equivalently,

$$(m + p) + r = n + r.$$

Then, by (8.5.14), $m + p = n$, whence $m < n$.

(9.2.14) THEOREM: *If $m, n \in I$, then $m = n$ or $m < n$ or $n < m$.*

PROOF: Let $m \in I$. Define

$$H \equiv [n; m = n \text{ or } m < n \text{ or } n < m].$$

Now $1 \in H$, since $1 = m$ or $1 < m$ by (9.2.9).

Suppose that $q \in H$. Then there are three cases to consider, namely, $m = q$, $m < q$, $q < m$. We shall show that, in all cases, $q + 1 \in H$.

First, if $q = m$, then, by (9.2.1), $m < m + 1 = q + 1$; hence $q + 1 \in H$.

Secondly, if $m < q$, then, since $q < q + 1$, we have $m < q + 1$ by (9.2.5). Hence again $q + 1 \in H$.

Finally, if $q < m$, then, by (9.2.10.b), $q + 1 \leqq m$. But then $q + 1 < m$ or $q + 1 = m$, whence $q + 1 \in H$.

Thus we have shown that $q \in H$ implies $q + 1 \in H$.

Now III′ yields $H = I$, that is, for every $m, n \in I$, either $m = n$ or $m < n$ or $n < m$.

REMARK: Theorems (9.2.5), (9.2.7), and (9.2.14) state the most important properties of $<$. In (15.4) it will be seen that (9.2.5) and (9.2.7) show that I is *partially ordered* by the relation $<$, and that (9.2.14) expresses the fact that I is *linearly ordered* by $<$. In view of (9.2.4) and (9.2.7), it is seen that, for every $m, n \in I$, no more than one of the three statements $m = n$, $m < n$, $n < m$ is true. Thus (9.2.14) implies that *exactly* one of these three statements must be true.

Since, for every pair (m, n), exactly one of the statements $m < n$, $m > n$, $m = n$ is true, the three relations $<$, $>$, E constitute a "subdivision" of the set $I \times I$ of all pairs (m, n). That is, every pair $(m, n) \in I \times I$ is in either the set $<$, the set $>$ or the set E, and the set-theoretic product of any two of these sets is Θ. Such a subdivision of $I \times I$ is very useful in proofs. Often, when it is desired to prove some assertion "for every $m, n \in I$, it is true that $\cdots$" ("for every element $(m, n) \in I \times I$, it is true that $\cdots$"), it is convenient to consider the three "cases" $m < n$, $m > n$, $m = n$ separately, applying a (possibly) different method in each case. The proofs of (9.2.16), (9.2.21) will illustrate this technique.

(9.2.15) THEOREM: *If $m, n \in I$ such that $m < n$, then, for every $p \in I$,*

$$m \cdot p < n \cdot p.$$

Proof: Let $m < n$, so that there exists $r \in I$ such that $m + r = n$. Then $n \cdot p = (m + r) \cdot p = m \cdot p + r \cdot p$, whence $m \cdot p < n \cdot p$.

(9.2.16) Corollary: *If $m, n \in I$ such that $m \neq n$, then, for every $p \in I$,*

$$m \cdot p \neq n \cdot p.$$

Proof: Let $m \neq n$. Then, by (9.2.14), either $m < n$ or $n < m$. If $m < n$, then, for every $p \in I$, $m \cdot p < n \cdot p$, and so $m \cdot p \neq n \cdot p$ by (9.2.4). If $n < m$, then, for every $p \in I$, $n \cdot p < m \cdot p$, and again $n \cdot p \neq m \cdot p$.

Remark: These last two results, (9.2.15) and (9.2.16), are the analogues for $\cdot$ of (9.2.11) and (8.5.13), respectively.

(9.2.17) Corollary: *Let $m, n \in I$. If there exists $p \in I$ such that $m \cdot p = n \cdot p$, then $m = n$.*

Proof: This is a contrapositive of (9.2.16) and so needs no proof.

(9.2.18) Corollary: *Let $m, p \in I$ such that $m = m \cdot p$. Then $p = 1$.*

Proof: If $m = m \cdot p$, then $1 \cdot m = p \cdot m$, and $1 = p$ by (9.2.17).

(9.2.19) Corollary: *If $m, p \in I$, then $m \leqq m \cdot p$.*

Proof: If $p = 1$ then $m \cdot p = m$. If $p \neq 1$ then $1 < p$ by (9.2.9), whence $1 \cdot m < p \cdot m$, by (9.2.15), or $m < m \cdot p$.

(9.2.20) Corollary: *If $m, p \in I$ such that $m \cdot p = 1$, then $m = 1$ and $p = 1$.*

Proof: Let $m \cdot p = 1$. Suppose $m \neq 1$. Then $1 < m$ by (9.2.9), and so $p < m \cdot p$ by (9.2.15), or $p < 1$. This contradicts (9.2.9), so that $m = 1$. Then $1 = m \cdot p = p$.

(9.2.21) Theorem: *Let $m, n \in I$. If there exists $p \in I$ such that $m \cdot p < n \cdot p$, then $m < n$.*

Proof: Let $m, n \in I$ such that there exists p such that $m \cdot p < n \cdot p$. Then, by (9.2.14), either $m = n$ or $m < n$ or $n < m$. If $m = n$, then, for every $p \in I$, $m \cdot p = n \cdot p$, contradicting the assumption that there exists $p \in I$ such that $m \cdot p < n \cdot p$. If $n < m$, then, for every $p \in I$, $n \cdot p < m \cdot p$ by (9.2.15), again contradicting the assumption in view of (9.2.7). Thus $m < n$.

(9.2.22) Theorem: *If $m, n, p, q \in I$ such that $m < n$ and $p \leqq q$, then $m \cdot p < n \cdot q$.*

Proof: If $p = q$, this is the same as (9.2.15). If $p < q$, then

$$m \cdot p < n \cdot p \qquad \text{[by (9.2.15)]},$$

and

$$n \cdot p < n \cdot q \qquad \text{[by (9.2.15)]}.$$

Hence

$$m \cdot p < n \cdot q \qquad \text{[by (9.2.5)]}.$$

(9.2.23) PROJECT: Determine the domain and range of the relations $<$, $\leqq$. Which, if any, of the relations $<$, $>$, $\leqq$, $\geqq$ are functions? Why?

(9.2.24) PROJECT: Let m, n, p, $q \in I$ such that $m + n = p + q$. Prove that, if $m < p$, then $q < n$. Also prove that, if $m \leqq p$, then $q \leqq n$.

(9.2.25) PROJECT: Prove (9.2.6.b), (9.2.6.c).

(9.2.26) PROJECT: Prove (9.2.8).

(9.2.27) PROJECT: Prove (9.2.10.b).

9.3. Least and Greatest Elements. [BASIS: $(I, 1, \sigma)$; AXIOMS: I, II, III.] In this section we continue the study of the relation $<$, with particular reference to its behavior on subsets of I. The system $(I, 1, \sigma)$ is one of many "number systems" which are fundamental in mathematics. For each of these systems there is a relation which satisfies most of the properties which were shown to hold for the relation $<$ on $I \times I$. In fact, the similarities are so numerous that it is customary to use the same symbol $<$ for all these relations. However, most of the results of the present section have no valid analogues for the other "number systems" to be discussed. Thus this section will present some of the important distinguishing features of the relation $<$ on $I \times I$.

(9.3.1) DEFINITION: Let $S \subset I$. An element $m \in I$ is a *least (element) in* S in case

(a) $m \in S$;
(b) for every $q \in S$, $m \leqq q$.

(9.3.2) COROLLARY: *Let $S \subset I$. If m and n are leasts in S, then $m = n$.*

PROOF: Suppose m, n are leasts in S. Then, since m is a least in S and since $n \in S$, we have, by (9.3.1.b), $m \leqq n$. Similarly, since n is a least, $n \leqq m$. But then $m = n$ by (9.2.8).

(9.3.3) DEFINITION: Let $S \subset I$. An element $m \in I$ is called a *greatest (element) in* S in case

(a) $m \in S$;
(b) for every $q \in S$, $m \geqq q$.

(9.3.4) COROLLARY: *Let $S \subset I$. If m and n are greatests in S, then $m = n$.*

PROOF: Similar to the proof of (9.3.2).

REMARK: Notice that it has not been asserted that every set S has a least and a greatest. It might be observed that, according to (9.2.9), the set I does have a least, namely, 1. On the other hand, it can easily be seen that I does not have a greatest. In fact, if m is a greatest in I, then, for every $p \in I$, $p \leqq m$ and, in particular, $m + 1 \leqq m$. But $m < m + 1$ by (9.2.1), so that $m < m$ by (9.2.6.a). This contradicts (9.2.4).

(9.3.5) Definition: Let $m \in I$. Then define

$$I_m \equiv [k; k \leqq m].$$

(9.3.6) Lemma: *For every* $q \in I$,

(a) $$I_{q+1} = I_q + [q + 1].$$

Moreover, $I_1 = [1]$.

Proof: We recall that two sets are equal in case each is a subset of the other [(4.6.4)]. Let us prove first that

(1) $$I_q + [q + 1] \subset I_{q+1}.$$

If $k \in [q + 1]$, then obviously $k = q + 1$, and $k \in I_{q+1}$. If $k \in I_q$, then $k \leqq q$. But $q < q + 1$ by (9.2.1). Hence, by (9.2.6.b), $k < q + 1$, so that $k \in I_{q+1}$. This proves the inclusion (1).

The reverse inclusion,

(2) $$I_{q+1} \subset I_q + [q + 1],$$

is verified next. If $k \in I_{q+1}$, then $k = q + 1$ or $k < q + 1$. In the first case, $k \in [q + 1]$. In the other case, $k < q + 1$, so that $k \leqq q$ by (9.2.10.a), whence $k \in I_q$. In both cases,

$$k \in I_q + [q + 1],$$

and (2) is proved. The two inclusions (1) and (2) yield (a).

Evidently $[1] \subset I_1$. To prove the reverse inclusion, let $k \in I_1$, whence $k \leqq 1$. But $k \geqq 1$ by (9.2.9). Hence $k = 1$ by (9.2.8), whence $k \in [1]$. This proves $I_1 \subset [1]$. Therefore $I_1 = [1]$.

Remark: It has already been mentioned that a subset of I need not have a greatest; in particular, I itself has no greatest. The next two theorems show that a non-empty subset of I does have a greatest precisely when it is a subset of I_m, for some $m \in I$.

(9.3.7) Theorem: *Let* $m \in I$. *For every* $S \subset I_m$ *such that* $S \neq \Theta$, *there exists a greatest in* S.

Proof: The proof uses the induction axiom III′. Define

(1) $H \equiv [m;$ if $S \subset I_m$ and $S \neq \Theta$, then there exists a greatest in $S]$.

First we show that $1 \in H$. To see this, note that, by (9.3.6),

(2) $$I_1 = [1].$$

Now, by (2), I_1 has only two subsets, Θ and $[1]$. Thus if $S \subset I_1$ and $S \neq \Theta$, then $S = [1]$, and S does have a greatest, namely, 1. This shows that $1 \in H$.

Now, suppose $q \in H$. We shall show that $q + 1 \in H$. To this end, let

(3) $$S \subset I_{q+1} \quad \text{and} \quad S \neq \Theta.$$

We consider two cases, according as $q + 1 \in S$ or $q + 1 \in' S$. (Recall that $q + 1 \in' S$ means $q + 1$ is *not* an element of S.)

Suppose first that $q + 1 \in S$. Now, since $S \subset I_{q+1}$ by (3), for every $k \in S$ it is true that $k \in I_{q+1}$. Thus $k \leqq q + 1$ by (9.3.5). Then $q + 1$ is a greatest in S by (9.3.3). Accordingly, in this case there is a greatest in S.

Now consider the alternate case, $q + 1 \in' S$. From (3) and (9.3.6), we have

$$S \subset I_q + [q + 1].$$

Hence, for every $k \in S$, $k \in I_q$ or $k = q + 1$. But $k = q + 1$ is impossible since $q + 1 \in' S$; hence $k \in I_q$. Thus

(4) $$S \subset I_q.$$

But $q \in H$. Then, since $S \subset I_q$ by (4), and $S \neq \Theta$ by (3), there is a greatest in S by (1).

We have shown that, if $q \in H$, then (3) implies that there is a greatest in S. But this shows that $q + 1 \in H$. Hence $q \in H$ implies $q + 1 \in H$.

Now III′ gives $H = I$; that is, for every $m \in I$, if $S \subset I_m$ and $S \neq \Theta$, then there is a greatest in S. This completes the proof.

(9.3.8) Theorem: *Let $S \subset I$ such that there is a greatest in S. Then there exists $m \in I$ such that $S \subset I_m$.*

Proof: Let $S \subset I$ and suppose S has a greatest element m. Then, by (9.3.3), for every $k \in S$, $k \leqq m$. Thus

$$S \subset [k; k \leqq m] = I_m.$$

Remark: The last two theorems have shown the conditions under which a subset of I has a greatest. The next theorem states that *every* non-empty subset of I has a least. This fact expresses that I is *well-ordered* by the relation $<$, as will be seen in (15.4).

(9.3.9) Theorem: *Let $S \subset I$ and $S \neq \Theta$. Then there is a least in S.*

Proof: Let $S \subset I$ and $S \neq \Theta$. Define

(1) $$T \equiv [m \in I; \text{for every } k \in S,\ m \leqq k].$$

We show first that T has a greatest. First, $T \neq \Theta$; in fact, $1 \in T$, since $1 \leqq k$ for every $k \in I$, by (9.2.9). Now, since $S \neq \Theta$, there exists $n \in S$. Then, for every $m \in T$, $m \leqq n$ by (1). Hence

$$T \subset I_n = [m;\, m \leqq n].$$

Thus T satisfies the hypotheses of (9.3.7), and so there is a greatest element q in T.

It will now be shown that q is a least in S. Since $q \in T$, it follows from (1) that

(2) $$\text{for every } k \in S,\ q \leqq k.$$

In view of (9.3.1), it remains only to show that

(3) $$q \in S.$$

This is proved indirectly. Suppose that $q \in' S$. Then, for every $k \in S$, $q \neq k$; thus, by (2), $q < k$, whence $q + 1 \leqq k$ by (9.2.10.b). Thus, for every $k \in S$, $q + 1 \leqq k$, so that $q + 1 \in T$ by (1). But, since $q < q + 1$, this contradicts the definition of q as a greatest in T. Thus (3) is true.

From (2) and (3) it is seen that q is a least in S. This completes the proof.

REMARK: Theorem (9.3.9) is a very "powerful" result. In fact, it is "equivalent to" the induction axiom III, in the following sense: From Axioms I and II, the basic properties of $<$, and (9.3.9), the induction axiom can be proved. Correspondingly, an argument based on (9.3.9) can be used, in future proofs, to replace the usual "induction" argument.

(9.3.10) PROJECT: Prove (9.3.4).

(9.3.11) PROJECT: For each of the following sets $S \subset I$, determine whether a least exists and whether a greatest exists. Find all leasts and greatests that do exist. In (b), (c), (e) treat all cases.
(a) $S = [1, 2, 4]$;
(b) $S = I - [n]$ (n being any element of I);
(c) $S = I_m - I_n$ (m, n being any elements of I);
(d) $S = [2 \cdot k;\, k \in I]$;
(e) $S = I - I_n$ (n being any element of I).

(9.3.12) PROJECT: Let $S \subset I$, $S \neq \Theta$ and let φ be a function on S to I such that

$$m, n \in S,\ m < n \text{ implies } \varphi(m) \leqq \varphi(n).$$

Define $T \equiv$ range of φ. Prove:
(a) if m_0 is a least in S, then $\varphi(m_0)$ is a least in T;
(b) if n_0 is a greatest in S, then $\varphi(n_0)$ is a greatest in T.

(9.3.13) PROJECT: Let $S \subset I$, and let m be a greatest in S. Define

$$T \equiv [\, k \in I;\, p \in S \text{ implies } k > p].$$

Prove that $m + 1$ is a least in T.

9.4. The Relation | (Divides). [BASIS: $(I, 1, \sigma)$; AXIOMS: I, II, III.] In this section, we introduce and study briefly another relation on $I \times I$; it is defined in terms of the operation $\cdot$ in the same way that $<$ is defined in terms of the operation $+$. It will be seen that, in spite of the parallelism of the definitions, many of their properties are quite different.

(9.4.1) DEFINITION: Define a relation $|$ on $I \times I$ thus:

$$| \equiv [(m, n);\text{ there exists } p \in I \text{ such that } m \cdot p = n].$$

COROLLARY: *If $m, n \in I$, then $m \mid n$* (read "m is a divisor of n" or "m divides n") *if and only if there exists $p \in I$ such that $m \cdot p = n$.*

PROOF: This is obvious, since $m \mid n$ means $(m, n) \in |$.

(9.4.2) NOTATION: The negative of $|$ is written $|'$.

(9.4.3) THEOREM: *For every $m \in I$, $m \mid m$.*

PROOF: This is clear since $m \cdot 1 = m$.

(9.4.4) THEOREM: *If $m, n \in I$ such that there exists $q \in I$ for which $m \mid q$ and $q \mid n$, then $m \mid n$.*

PROOF: Since $m \mid q$, there exists $p \in I$ such that

(1) $$m \cdot p = q.$$

Since $q \mid n$, there exists $r \in I$ such that

(2) $$q \cdot r = n.$$

From (1) and (2) we have

$$(m \cdot p) \cdot r = n,$$

or

$$m \cdot (p \cdot r) = n,$$

whence $m \mid n$.

(9.4.5) THEOREM: *If $m, n \in I$ such that $m \mid n$, then $m \leqq n$.*

PROOF: If $m \mid n$, then there exists $p \in I$ such that $m \cdot p = n$. But $m \leqq m \cdot p = n$, by (9.2.19).

(9.4.6) THEOREM: *If $m, n \in I$ such that $m \mid n$ and $n \mid m$, then $m = n$.*

PROOF: Let $m \mid n$ and $n \mid m$. Then $m \leqq n$ and $n \leqq m$ by (9.4.5), whence $m = n$ by (9.2.8).

(9.4.7) THEOREM: *If $m, n, q \in I$ such that $m \mid (n + q)$ and $m \mid n$, then $m \mid q$.*

PROOF: Since $m \mid (n + q)$, there exists $r \in I$ such that

$$(1) \qquad m \cdot r = n + q;$$

since $m \mid n$, there exists $s \in I$ such that

$$(2) \qquad m \cdot s = n.$$

Now $n + q > n$, so that $m \cdot r > m \cdot s$. Hence, by (9.2.21), $r > s$. Thus there exists $t \in I$ such that

$$(3) \qquad r = s + t.$$

Then

$$\begin{aligned} n + q &= m \cdot r && \text{[by (1)]} \\ &= m \cdot (s + t) && \text{[by (3)]} \\ &= m \cdot s + m \cdot t \\ &= n + m \cdot t && \text{[by (2)].} \end{aligned}$$

Thus, by the cancellation rule (8.5.14),

$$q = m \cdot t,$$

so that $m \mid q$. This completes the proof.

The reader should have observed one striking difference between the relation $\mid$ and the relation $<$, namely, that $m \mid m$ while $m \not< m$. Actually $\mid$ behaves more like $\leqq$ than it does like $<$. Notice that, in view of (9.4.4), $\mid$ does have, in common with both $<$ and $\leqq$, the property of being transitive [see (9.2.5) and (9.2.6.c)]. However, the analogy between $\mid$ and $\leqq$ breaks down very quickly. In fact, according to (9.2.14), for every $m, n \in I$, either $m = n$ or $m < n$ or $n < m$; thus either $m \leqq n$ or $n \leqq m$. However, it is not true of every m, n that either $m \mid n$ or $n \mid m$. This can be seen by a simple example. Let $m = 2$, $n = 3$. Since $n = m + 1$, $m < n$. But if $n \mid m$, $n \leqq m$ by (9.4.5). Thus $n \mid' m$. If $m \mid n$, then there exists $q \in I$ such that $m \cdot q = n$. Hence $2 \cdot q = n$. If $q = 1$, we have $2 = 2 \cdot 1 = n = 3$, which is a contradiction. If $q \neq 1$, then $q = s + 1$, for some s; and we have

$$n = 2 \cdot (s + 1) = 2 \cdot s + 2 \cdot 1,$$

or

$$2 + 1 = 2 + 2 \cdot s,$$

whence

$$1 = 2 \cdot s \qquad \text{[by (8.5.14)],}$$

so that $2 = 1$ by (9.2.20), contrary to $1 < 2$. Thus $m \mid' n$.

If we call $m \in I$ a *divisor* of $n \in I$ if $m \mid n$, then every $n \in I$ such that $n \neq 1$ has (at least) two divisors, namely, n and 1, since $n \mid n$ and $1 \mid n$. Those positive integers ($\neq 1$) which have no more than two divisors are distinguished from those which have additional divisors by the following definition, which we now state for reference.

(9.4.8) DEFINITION: Let $n \in I$. Then n is called a *prime* (number) if $n \neq 1$, and if, for every m such that $m \mid n$, it is true that $m = 1$ or $m = n$.

Although a considerable part of the study of the set I is devoted to the investigation of the properties of prime numbers, we shall not consider them here; in (12.5) a fundamental theorem concerning primes is treated.

We now prove an exceedingly important theorem with many uses both in practical computation and for the further theory of positive integers.

(9.4.9) THEOREM: *If $m, n \in I$ such that $m < n$ and $m \mid' n$, then there exist unique elements $q, r \in I$ such that*

(a) $$n = m \cdot q + r \quad \textit{and} \quad r < m.$$

PROOF OF EXISTENCE: Define

(1) $$S \equiv [s; m \cdot s < n].$$

It will be shown that S has a greatest. First, $S \neq \Theta$; in fact, $1 \in S$, since $m \cdot 1 = m < n$. Next, for every $s \in S$,

$$s \leqq m \cdot s \qquad \text{[by (9.2.19)]},$$

and

$$m \cdot s < n \qquad \text{[by (1)]},$$

so that

(2) $$s < n \qquad \text{[by (9.2.6.b)]}.$$

But, since (2) holds for every $s \in S$, we have

$$S \subset I_n = [s; s \leqq n].$$

It has been shown that S satisfies the hypotheses of (9.3.7), whence there is a greatest element q in S.

Since $q \in S$,

$$m \cdot q < n \qquad \text{[by (1)]},$$

whence, by the definition of $<$, there exists $r \in I$ such that

(3) $$n = m \cdot q + r.$$

It must now be shown that $r < m$.

Since, by (9.2.14), either $r = m$ or $r > m$ or $r < m$, it is sufficient to show that $r = m$ and $r > m$ are false. If $r = m$, then, by (3),

$$n = m \cdot q + m = m \cdot q + m \cdot 1 = m \cdot (q + 1),$$

whence $m \mid n$, contrary to the hypothesis $m \nmid n$. If $r > m$, there exists $t \in I$ such that $r = m + t$. Then

$$\begin{aligned} n &= m \cdot q + m + t \\ &= m \cdot (q + 1) + t, \end{aligned}$$

whence $m \cdot (q + 1) < n$ and $q + 1 \in S$ by (1). But $q + 1 > q$. Thus $q + 1 \in S$ contradicts the fact that q is a greatest in S. Consequently $r > m$ leads to a contradiction and is false. Then $r < m$, as the only remaining possibility, has been demonstrated. This completes the proof.

PROOF OF UNIQUENESS: Suppose $q, r, u, v \in I$ such that

$$n = m \cdot q + r, \quad \text{and} \quad r < m; \tag{4}$$

$$n = m \cdot u + v, \quad \text{and} \quad v < m. \tag{5}$$

It will be proved that $q = u$ and $r = v$.

We prove $q = u$ again by considering the alternatives $q = u$, $q < u$, $q > u$. If $q < u$, then there exists p such that $u = q + p$. From (5),

$$n = m \cdot (q + p) + v,$$

or

$$n = m \cdot q + m \cdot p + v. \tag{6}$$

But, from (4) and (6),

$$m \cdot q + r = m \cdot q + m \cdot p + v.$$

Then, by (8.5.14),

$$r = m \cdot p + v,$$

whence

$$r > m \cdot p. \tag{7}$$

But

$$m \cdot p \geqq m \qquad \text{[by (9.2.19)]}. \tag{8}$$

From (7) and (8),

$$r > m \qquad \text{[by (9.2.6.b)]}.$$

This contradicts part of (4), and so $q < u$ is impossible. The case $q > u$ leads to a contradiction in a similar way (in fact, simply interchange q, r with u, v in the above argument). It follows that $q = u$. But then, by (4) and (5),

$$n = m \cdot q + r = m \cdot q + v,$$

whence $r = v$ by (8.5.14). This completes the proof of the theorem.

REMARK: Let $m, n \in I$ and $m < n$. Then either $m \mid n$ or $m \mid' n$. If $m \mid' n$, then, by (9.4.9), there exist unique elements q and r such that

$$n = m \cdot q + r \quad \text{and} \quad r < m.$$

The unique element q is called the *quotient* (or, better, *incomplete quotient*) of n by m, and r is called the *remainder*. In the other case, $m \mid n$, there exists q such that

$$n = m \cdot q.$$

It is easy to see from (9.2.17) that this q is also unique. In this case, q is called the *quotient* of n by m, and it is said that there is *no* remainder. Much time is spent in elementary school learning manipulative rules for determining q and r for special m, n, in terms of the particular symbolism for elements of I which goes under the name "Arabic notation." But the fact that they exist and are unique for every m, n is, of course, never proved.

We close this section by proving a converse of (9.4.9).

(9.4.10) THEOREM: *If $m, n \in I$ such that there exist $q, r \in I$ for which*

$$n = m \cdot q + r \quad \textit{and} \quad r < m,$$

then $m \mid' n$.

PROOF: The proof is indirect. Suppose $m \mid n$. Then $m \mid (m \cdot q + r)$. But clearly $m \mid (m \cdot q)$. Hence, by (9.4.7), $m \mid r$. But then, by (9.4.5), $m \leqq r$. This contradicts $r < m$. The proof is complete.

(9.4.11) PROJECT: Of the positive integers 1, 2, 3, 4, 5, 6, 7, 8, 9, which pairs are in the relation $\mid$?

(9.4.12) PROJECT: Prove that, if $m, n, q \in I$ such that $m \mid n$ and $m \mid q$, then $m \mid (n + q)$. How is this result related to (9.4.7)?

(9.4.13) PROJECT: Prove that, if $m, n, q \in I$, then $m \mid n$ or $m \mid q$ implies $m \mid (n \cdot q)$. Is the converse valid?

(9.4.14) PROJECT: Prove that, if $m \mid 1$, then $m = 1$.

(9.4.15) PROJECT: Determine which of the positive integers 1, 2, 3, 4, 5, 6, 7, 8, 9 are primes.

(9.4.16) PROJECT: Show that (9.4.9) applies if $m = 3$, $n = 5$. Determine q, r.

9.5. Even and Odd. [BASIS: $(I, 1, \sigma)$; AXIOMS: I, II, III.] In this section we discuss briefly the definition and properties of *even* and *odd* positive integers. Since the positive integer 2 is essentially involved, we recall its definition.

(9.5.1) DEFINITION: Define $2 \equiv 1 + 1$.

It is important to note that 1 is the only positive integer less than 2, as we show next.

(9.5.2) LEMMA: *Let $m \in I$ and $m < 2$. Then $m = 1$.*

PROOF: Let $m < 2 = 1 + 1$. By (9.2.10.a), $m \leqq 1$. But $m < 1$ contradicts (9.2.9). Hence $m = 1$.

(9.5.3) DEFINITION: An element $m \in I$ is called

(a) *even*, if $2 \mid m$;

(b) *odd*, if $2 \mid' m$.

REMARK: Clearly, every element of I is either even or odd, and not both.

(9.5.4) THEOREM: *Let $m \in I$. Then*

(a) *m is even if and only if there exists $q \in I$ such that*

$$m = 2 \cdot q;$$

(b) *m is odd if and only if either $m = 1$ or there exists $q \in I$ such that*

$$m = 2 \cdot q + 1.$$

PROOF: Part (a) is obvious from (9.5.3.a) and (9.4.1).

To prove (b), notice first that 1 is odd. In fact, $2 \mid' 1$ since $2 \nleqq 1$ [see (9.4.5)]. So we consider only the case $m \neq 1$. Let m be odd and $m \neq 1$. Then, by (9.5.2), $m \nless 2$. Also $m \neq 2$ since $2 \mid' m$. Hence $2 < m$. Since $2 \mid' m$, we may apply (9.4.9), and find that there exist $q, r \in I$ such that

$$m = 2 \cdot q + r \quad \text{and} \quad r < 2.$$

But $r < 2$ implies $r = 1$ by (9.5.2). Thus

$$m = 2 \cdot q + 1.$$

This proves the "only if" part of (b).

To prove the "if" part of (b), suppose

$$m = 2 \cdot q + 1.$$

Since $1 < 2$, it follows that $2 \mid' m$ by (9.4.10). Thus m is odd. This completes the proof.

(9.5.5) THEOREM: *Let $m, n \in I$. Then,*

(a) *if m is even and n is even, then $m + n$ is even;*

(b) *if m is even and n is odd, then $m + n$ is odd;*

(c) *if m is odd and n is odd, then $m + n$ is even.*

PROOF: We prove only the most difficult part, (c). Let $m, n \in I$ be odd. There are the following cases to consider:

$$\begin{array}{ll} (1) & m = 1, \quad n = 1; \\ (2) & m = 1, \quad n \neq 1; \\ (3) & m \neq 1, \quad n = 1; \\ (4) & m \neq 1, \quad n \neq 1. \end{array}$$

In case (1), $m + n = 1 + 1 = 2$, and $m + n$ is even.

In case (2), by (9.5.4.b), there exists $q \in I$ such that $n = 2 \cdot q + 1$. Then

$$\begin{aligned} m + n &= 1 + (2 \cdot q + 1) \\ &= 2 \cdot q + 1 + 1 \\ &= 2 \cdot q + 2 \\ &= 2 \cdot (q + 1). \end{aligned}$$

Hence $m + n$ is even.

Case (3) is the same as case (2) with m and n interchanged.

In case (4), by (9.5.4.b), there exist $p, q \in I$ such that

$$m = 2 \cdot p + 1, \quad n = 2 \cdot q + 1.$$

Then

$$\begin{aligned} m + n &= (2 \cdot p + 1) + (2 \cdot q + 1) \\ &= 2 \cdot p + 2 \cdot q + 2 \\ &= 2 \cdot (p + q + 1). \end{aligned}$$

Again, $m + n$ is even.

The proofs of (a) and (b) are left for the reader.

(9.5.6) THEOREM: *Let $m, n \in I$. Then,*

(a) *if m is even and n is even, then $m \cdot n$ is even;*

(b) *if m is even and n is odd, then $m \cdot n$ is even;*

(c) *if m is odd and n is odd, then $m \cdot n$ is odd.*

PROOF: Again we prove only part (c). For this case, if either $m = 1$ or $n = 1$, the result is obvious. Hence suppose $m \neq 1$, $n \neq 1$. Then, by (9.5.4.b), there exist $p, q \in I$ such that

$$m = 2 \cdot p + 1, \quad n = 2 \cdot q + 1.$$

Then

$$\begin{aligned} m \cdot n &= (2 \cdot p + 1) \cdot (2 \cdot q + 1) \\ &= (2 \cdot p + 1) \cdot (2 \cdot q) + (2 \cdot p + 1) \\ &= (2 \cdot p) \cdot (2 \cdot q) + 2 \cdot q + 2 \cdot p + 1 \\ &= 2 \cdot (2 \cdot p \cdot q + q + p) + 1. \end{aligned}$$

Hence $m \cdot n$ is odd by (9.5.4.b).

Parts (a) and (b) are obvious from (9.5.4.a).

(9.5.7) PROJECT: Prove that $I_3 = [1, 2, 3]$, $I_4 = [1, 2, 3, 4]$.

(9.5.8) PROJECT: Name the even positive integers among 1, 2, 3, 4, 5, 6, 7, 8, 9. Prove your answer correct.

(9.5.9) PROJECT: Prove (9.5.5.a), (9.5.5.b).

(9.5.10) PROJECT: Prove (9.5.6.a), (9.5.6.b).

9.6. The Operation – (Minus). [BASIS: $(I, 1, \sigma)$; AXIOMS: I, II, III.] In Chapter 8 we defined and studied in some detail the fundamental operations *plus*, *times*, both on $I \times I$ to I. We now discuss briefly a secondary operation, that called *minus*. It is usual to define $m - n$ as that element $p \in I$ such that $n + p = m$. Since the existence of such an element p means, by definition, that $m > n$, it will be necessary to limit ourselves to pairs $(m, n) \in >$. The uniqueness of p, when it exists, has already been proved, but we shall restate the results that we need.

(9.6.1) LEMMA: *If $m, n \in I$, and $m > n$, there exists a unique element $p \in I$ such that $n + p = m$.*

PROOF: The existence of p follows from (9.2.2) and (9.2.1). If $n + p = m$, $n + q = m$, then $n + p = n + q$, whence $p = q$ by (8.5.14), and the uniqueness is proved.

(9.6.2) DEFINITION: If $m, n \in I$, $m > n$, we define $m - n$ as the unique $p \in I$ given in (9.6.1). Thus $m - n = p$, where $n + p = m$.

REMARK: It is clear that $-$ is defined as an operation on $>$ to I by the following:

$$- \equiv (m - n;\ (m, n) \in I \times I,\ m > n).$$

(9.6.3) COROLLARY: *If $m, n, p \in I$ such that $m + n = p$, then $p > n$ and $p - n = m$.*

PROOF: Let $m + n = p$. Then, by (9.2.2) and (9.2.1), $p > n$. Moreover, by (9.6.2),

$$\begin{aligned} n + (p - n) &= p \\ &= m + n \\ &= n + m. \end{aligned}$$

But then $p - n = m$ by (8.5.14).

(9.6.4) REMARK: The definition (9.6.2) and corollary (9.6.3) may be summarized as follows:
(a) if $m, n \in I$, then $(m + n) - n = m$;
(b) if $m > n$, then $(m - n) + n = m$.

(9.6.5) THEOREM: *Let $m, n, p \in I$. Then,*
(a) *if $n > p$, then $(m + n) - p = m + (n - p)$;*
(b) *if $m > n + p$ (or equivalently, if $m > n$ and $m - n > p$), then $(m - n) - p = m - (n + p)$;*
(c) *if $m > n$ and $n > p$, then $(m - n) + p = m - (n - p)$.*

REMARK: These are "mixed" associative laws. Note that each equality is true only under appropriate hypotheses, namely, hypotheses which insure that the symbols involved are defined. A more complete list of such laws is found in (9.6.6).

PROOF OF (a): Clearly, by (9.6.4.b),

$$m + (n - p) + p = m + n.$$

Hence, by (9.6.3),

$$m + (n - p) = (m + n) - p.$$

PROOF OF (b): We have

$$\begin{aligned} ((m - n) - p) + (n + p) &= (n + p) + ((m - n) - p) \\ &= ((n + p) + (m - n)) - p \quad \text{[by (a)]} \\ &= (p + (n + (m - n))) - p \\ &= (p + m) - p \\ &= m. \end{aligned}$$

Then, by (9.6.3),

$$(m - n) - p = m - (n + p).$$

PROOF OF (c): Evidently

$$\begin{aligned} (m - n) + p + (n - p) &= (m - n) + n \\ &= m. \end{aligned}$$

Then, by (9.6.3),

$$(m - n) + p = m - (n - p).$$

(9.6.6) COROLLARY: *Let m, n, $p \in I$. Then*

(a) $$(m + n) - p = \begin{cases} m + (n - p) & \text{if } n > p \\ m - (p - n) & \text{if } p > n \text{ and } m > p - n; \end{cases}$$

(b) $$(m - n) - p = \begin{cases} m - (n + p) & \text{if } m > n + p \\ (m - p) - n & \text{if } m > p \text{ and } m - p > n; \end{cases}$$

(c) $$(m - n) + p = \begin{cases} (m + p) - n & \text{if } m > n \\ m - (n - p) & \text{if } m > n \text{ and } n > p \\ m + (p - n) & \text{if } m > n \text{ and } p > n. \end{cases}$$

PROOF: These are either restatements of (9.6.5) or immediate consequences. Details of proof are left to the reader.

REMARK: Recall that, if $m, n, p \in I$, it is customary to assign a meaning to $m + n + p$, namely,

$$m + n + p \equiv (m + n) + p = m + (n + p).$$

In a similar way, it is customary to assign meanings to expressions such as $m - n + p$. However, as is seen from (9.6.6), it is necessary to be more cautious in the insertion of parentheses in this case. For it is easy to see that

$$(m - n) + p \neq m - (n + p).$$

The rule, roughly speaking, is that one should avoid inserting parentheses in such a way that the symbol $-$ (minus) appears immediately in front of the first parenthesis. Specifically, we have the following:

(9.6.7) NOTATION: Let $m, n, p \in I$. Then

(a) $$m + n - p \equiv (m + n) - p \quad \text{if } m + n > p$$
$$= m + (n - p) \quad \text{if } n > p;$$

(b) $$m - n + p \equiv (m + p) - n \quad \text{if } m + p > n$$
$$= (m - n) + p \quad \text{if } m > n;$$

(c) $$m - n - p \equiv (m - n) - p \quad \text{if } m > n + p.$$

We have presented only a very few results concerning the operation $-$. To carry the theory further, however, would serve no useful purpose, since the results can be obtained more conveniently as special cases of results concerning the real numbers [see Chapters 19 and 20].

(9.6.8) PROJECT: Prove (9.6.6).

(9.6.9) PROJECT: Prove that, if $m, n, p \in I$, then,
(a) if $m > p$ and $n > p$, then $m < n$ if and only if $m - p < n - p$;
(b) if $p > m$ and $p > n$, then $m < n$ if and only if $p - m > p - n$;
(c) if $m > n$, then $(m - n) \cdot p = m \cdot p - n \cdot p$.

9.7. Conclusion. [NO BASIS.] In the last two chapters, we have presented the beginnings of the theory of positive integers. This theory has been very considerably developed, and many rather large books have been devoted to its exposition. What we have given are only the first steps. However, we have presented enough of the basic results to form a background for the use of the positive integers in subsequent investigations.

In (8.2), a system $(I, 1, \sigma)$ satisfying Axioms I, II, III was called a *basic system* of positive integers. As we have seen in the last two chapters however, most of the important results in the theory of $(I, 1, \sigma)$ concern the operations $+, \cdot$ on $I \times I$ to I and the relation $<$. The notation σ can be replaced by $(m + 1; m \in I)$ after $+$ is defined [see (8.5.12)]. Accordingly, it is more usual to consider the mathematical system $(I, 1, <, +, \cdot)$ as a system of positive integers. Since our basis for positive integers is $(I, 1, \sigma)$, we distinguish this system by calling it a *basic* system of positive integers; the system $(I, 1, <, +, \cdot)$ will be referred to as an *algebraic system of positive integers.*

Since the positive integers are of great importance in almost all of mathematics, we shall adopt the following:

(9.7.1) CONVENTION: *In the remainder of the book, whenever a basis for a mathematical theory is presented, a system* $(I, 1, \sigma)$ *satisfying Axioms* I, II, III *of Chapter* 8 *is tacitly assumed to be appended to that basis. Free use of the entire theory of* $(I, 1, \sigma)$, *and hence of* $(I, 1, <, +, \cdot)$, *will always be made.*

9.8. Project. [BASIS: $(I, 1, \sigma)$; AXIOMS: I, II, III.] Develop a theory parallel to that in (9.6), in which $\cdot$ replaces $+$ and $|^*$ replaces $>$. First prove

(9.8.1) LEMMA: *If* $m, n \in I$, *and* $m \,|^*\, n$ *(that is,* $n \mid m$*), there exists a unique element* $p \in I$ *such that* $n \cdot p = m$.

Next, introduce an operation on $|^*$ to I:

(9.8.2) DEFINITION: If $m, n \in I$, $m \,|^*\, n$, define $m \div n$ as the unique $p \in I$ given in (9.8.1). Thus $m \div n = p$, where $n \cdot p = m$.

From this point, using (9.6) as a guide, state and prove appropriate theorems about $\div$.

Chapter 10

FINITE SETS

10.1. Introduction. [No Basis (except $(I, 1, \sigma)$).] In the last two chapters we saw that it is possible to develop an abstract mathematical system of which the intuitive counting numbers constitute an intuitive instance. In this section it will be shown that the abstract system $(I, 1, \sigma)$ can replace the counting numbers for enumeration purposes. *Intuitive* counting aims at ascribing, in accordance with certain (intuitive) principles, a counting number to a set; the counting number answers the question "how many elements?" To replace this process by a *mathematical* counting process it will suffice to ascribe an *element of I* to an abstract set in accordance with mathematical rules reflecting the intuitive ones. Thus the intuitive concepts

"three stones," "three objects"

are to be replaced by a mathematical concept

"3 elements,"

where $3 = 1 + 1 + 1 \in I$.

In order to see how this may be accomplished, recall that the intuitive counting process consists of pairing or associating a particular counting number with each member of the set to be counted, making sure that all counting numbers up to and including a specific one are used. To obtain a mathematical notion parallel to this intuitive process, we shall, of course, replace the counting numbers by elements of I. The requirement that all counting numbers to a certain one be used can be paralleled by employing those elements of I which constitute one of the sets $I_n \subset I$, where, for $n \in I$,

$$I_n = [m \in I; m \leqq n].$$

Finally, it will be necessary to find a precise formulation of the "pairing" or "association" that occurs in the intuitive process. Clearly, if S is the set to be enumerated, the intuitive "pairing" of elements of S with counting numbers can be paralleled by a *relation* on $S \times I$. But the type of relation to be used is restricted. For, in the intuitive instance, an element of S is associated with only one counting number. This means that in the mathematical analogue we should use a relation of the kind called functions [see (5.4)]. Moreover, in the intuitive process, distinct elements of S are always associated with distinct counting numbers. This may be paralleled by requiring that the transpose relation [see (5.3)] also be a function. But relations which are functions and whose transposes are also functions are precisely those relations which are called one-to-one correspondences [see (5.5)]. Accordingly, it is indicated that the intuitive process of counting the elements of a set S can be paralleled by the mathematical requirement of determining an $n \in I$ for which there exists a one-to-one correspondence between S and the set I_n.

The preceding discussion suggests three definitions.

(10.1.1) Definition: If S, T are sets, we say that S *is equivalent to* T, and write $S \sim T$, if there exists a one-to-one correspondence between S and T. The negation of the statement $S \sim T$ is written $S \sim' T$.

Remark: If S, T are subsets of a set W, it is natural to ask whether $S \sim T$ is meaningful if S or T is empty. Reference to (5.4.1) and (7.4) shows that the empty subset of $W \times W$ is a function with empty domain and range, since (5.4.1) is vacuously satisfied. Because $\Theta^* = \Theta$, this function is a one-to-one correspondence, so that $\Theta \sim \Theta$. Moreover, if $S \neq \Theta$, the existence of a function on S to Θ is impossible, whence $S \sim \Theta$ implies $S = \Theta$. The reader should verify that if $S = [x]$, $T = [y]$, then $S \sim T$.

(10.1.2) Definition: Let S be a set. Then S is *finite* if there exists $n \in I$ such that $I_n \sim S$. On the other hand, S is *infinite* if S is neither empty nor finite, that is, if $S \neq \Theta$ and if, for every $n \in I$, $I_n \sim' S$.

Remark: The remark after (10.1.1), together with the fact that, for every $n \in I$, $I_n \neq \Theta$, shows that a finite set cannot be empty. It is perhaps more usual to define *finite* in such a way as to include the empty set, but our definition which excludes this seems convenient. It is seen that a set must fall in only one of the three classes, empty, finite or infinite. Intuitive experience with sets might lead one to expect that every non-empty set is finite. However it will later be shown that this is not the case; specifically it will be shown that the set I is infinite.

(10.1.3) Definition: Let S be a set and let $n \in I$. Then S *has* (*exactly*) n elements in case $I_n \sim S$.

Remark: Comparison of (10.1.2) and (10.1.3) shows that a set with n elements is finite, and, on the other hand, that, for every finite set S, there exists $n \in I$ such that S has n elements.

It might be instructive to indicate in a simple case that the definition

(10.1.3) does indeed adequately parallel our intuitive requirements for a counting process. Our intuition dictates that

$$
\begin{aligned}
&[\text{you, I, the lamp-post}],\\
&[\text{Tom, Dick, Harry}],\\
&[a, b, c] \quad (\text{where } a \neq b,\ b \neq c,\ c \neq a)
\end{aligned}
\tag{10.1.4}
$$

are sets with "three" elements, while

$$
\begin{aligned}
&[\text{Tom, Harry}],\\
&[x],\\
&[1, 2, 3, 4],\\
&[(a, b), c]
\end{aligned}
$$

are not such. It will now be shown that (10.1.4) is a set with 3 elements in accordance with the definition (10.1.3).

(10.1.5) Theorem: *If* $S = [a,\ b,\ c]$, *where* $a \neq b,\ b \neq c,\ c \neq a$, *then* $I_3 \sim S$.

Proof: Since $3 = 1 + 1 + 1$, it is easily seen that $m \in I$, $m < 3$ implies $m = 1$ or $m = 2$. [See Project (9.5.7).] Thus

$$I_3 = [1, 2, 3].$$

Now define a relation R on $I_3 \sim S$ by $R \equiv [(1, a), (2, b), (3, c)]$. This relation can be represented by the following table:

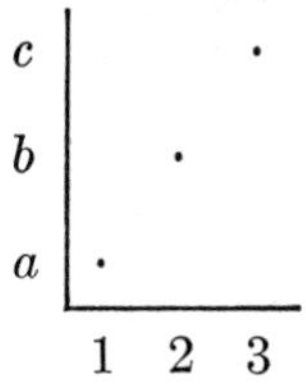

It is easy to verify that R is a function with domain I_3 and range S, and that R^* is a function on S to I_3. Thus R is a one-to-one correspondence between I_3 and S, so that $I_3 \sim S$.

The converse of (10.1.5), that a set with 3 elements is of the form (10.1.4), is quite evident and is left for the reader. It is hoped that this discussion has made (10.1.3) acceptable to the intuition of the reader.

(10.1.6) Project: Prove that if $S = [x]$, $T = [y]$, then $S \sim T$; and, conversely, if $S = [x]$ and $S \sim T$, then T is of the form $[y]$.

(10.1.7) Project: Prove that if $S \sim I_3$, then S is of the form $[a, b, c]$, that is, prove that there exist $a, b, c \in S$ such that $a \neq b$, $b \neq c$, $c \neq a$, and such that $S = [a, b, c]$. (This is the converse of (10.1.5).)

(10.1.8) Project: Prove that if $S = [a, b]$, with $a \neq b$, then S has 2 elements, and conversely.

10.2. Equivalent Sets. [NO BASIS.] From the definitions (10.1.2) and (10.1.3), it is apparent that any discussion of finite sets will require some examination of the content of the assertion of equivalence of two sets. Also, a further study of the sets I_n is necessary. The next sections will be devoted to these investigations. In this section there will be given several results concerning one-to-one correspondences, which results are frequently convenient in establishing the existence of one-to-one correspondences between sets, that is, in establishing the equivalence of sets.

(10.2.1) THEOREM: *Let S, T be sets, and let F be a one-to-one correspondence between S and T. (Thus domain of $F = S$, range of $F = T$, and F, F^* are functions.) Then,*

(a) *for every $x \in S$, $F^*(F(x)) = x$;*
(b) *for every $y \in T$, $F(F^*(y)) = y$.*

REMARK: In (a), $F^*(F(x))$ denotes the F^*-correspondent of $F(x)$; this is meaningful, since F^* is a function on T to S, and since $F(x) \in T$. A similar comment applies to (b).

PROOF OF (a): Suppose $x \in S$. The statement $F^*(F(x)) = x$ means

$$F(x)\ F^*\ x,$$

or, equivalently,

$$x\ F\ F(x);$$

this last is evident since $F(x)$ is the (unique) element $y \in T$ such that $x\ F\ y$ [see (5.4)].

PROOF OF (b): This is similar to the proof of (a).

(10.2.2) THEOREM: *Let S, T be sets and F a function with domain S and range T. Then the following statements are equivalent:*
(a) *F is a one-to-one correspondence;*
(b) *$x_1, x_2 \in S$, $x_1 \neq x_2$ implies $F(x_1) \neq F(x_2)$;*
(c) *there exists a function G on T to S such that, for every $x \in S$, $G(F(x)) = x$, and, for every $y \in T$, $F(G(y)) = y$.*

PROOF: There are six implications to be established, namely,

(a) implies (b); (b) implies (a);
(b) implies (c); (c) implies (b);
(c) implies (a); (a) implies (c).

Only three of these will be proved, namely,

(a) implies (c); (c) implies (b); (b) implies (a).

The remaining three can then be inferred; for example, since (a) implies (c) and (c) implies (b), it follows that (a) implies (b).

First, suppose (a) is true. Define $G \equiv F^*$. Then (c) is true by (10.2.1). Hence (a) implies (c).

Next, assume (c) holds. To prove (b) indirectly, assume that there exist $x_1, x_2 \in S$ such that $x_1 \neq x_2$ and such that $F(x_1) = F(x_2)$. By (c),

$$x_1 = G(F(x_1)) = G(F(x_2)) = x_2,$$

contradicting $x_1 \neq x_2$. Thus (b) is true, and we have shown that (c) implies (b).

Finally, let (b) hold. It will be shown that F^* is a function. Suppose $y \in T$, $x_1, x_2 \in S$ and

$$y \, F^* \, x_1, \quad y \, F^* \, x_2;$$

we prove $x_1 = x_2$. Now

$$x_1 \, F \, y, \quad x_2 \, F \, y,$$

or

$$y = F(x_1), \quad y = F(x_2),$$

whence

$$F(x_1) = F(x_2).$$

If $x_1 \neq x_2$, then, by (b), $F(x_1) \neq F(x_2)$, which is false. Hence $x_1 = x_2$. This shows F^* is a function, so that (a) holds. Thus (b) implies (a). The proof is complete.

(10.2.3) Corollary: *Let S, T be sets and F a function with domain S and range T. If* (10.2.2.c) *holds, then G as in* (10.2.2.c) *is unique and equal to F^*.*

Proof: Since (10.2.2.c) implies (10.2.2.a), F^* is a function. Let G be any function as in (10.2.2.c). Now G, F^* have T as domain. Let $y \in T$ and define

$$x_1 \equiv F^*(y), \quad x_2 \equiv G(y).$$

Then $y \, F^* \, x_1$, whence $x_1 \, F \, y$, and $y = F(x_1)$. Therefore

$$x_2 = G(y) = G(F(x_1)) = x_1.$$

It has been shown that

$$y \in T \text{ implies } G(y) = F^*(y),$$

whence $F^* = G$ by (5.4.7). This completes the proof, since if G_1, G_2 are any functions as in (10.2.2.c), then $G_1 = F^* = G_2$ by our argument.

The statements (10.2.2.b) and (10.2.2.c) will serve as useful criteria by which it may be ascertained whether or not a function F is a one-to-one correspondence.

(10.2.4) Theorem: *Let S, T, U be sets, then*

(a) $S \sim S$;
(b) $S \sim T$ *implies* $T \sim S$;
(c) *if* $S \sim T$ *and* $T \sim U$, *then* $S \sim U$.

PROOF OF (a): The identity E on S to S is a one-to-one correspondence (since $E^* = E$), whence $S \sim S$.

PROOF OF (b): If $S \sim T$, there exists a one-to-one correspondence F between S and T. Then F^* is a function with domain T and range S. Since $(F^*)^* = F$, $(F^*)^*$ is a function, whence F^* is a one-to-one correspondence between T and S. Therefore $T \sim S$.

PROOF OF (c): If $S \sim T$ and $T \sim U$, there exist functions F, G such that

F is a one-to-one correspondence between S and T;
G is a one-to-one correspondence between T and U.

Define a function H on S to U so that,

$$\text{for every } x \in S,\ H(x) = G(F(x)).$$

First, we prove that U is the range of H. Let $z \in U$. Then $G^*(z) \in T$, and

$$x \equiv F^*(G^*(z)) \in S.$$

Then

$$\begin{aligned} H(x) &= G(F(F^*(G^*(z)))) \\ &= G(G^*(z)) && \text{[by (10.2.1.b)]} \\ &= z && \text{[by (10.2.1.b)].} \end{aligned}$$

The existence of $x \in S$ such that $H(x) = z$ yields that U is the range of H.

It will now be shown that H is a one-to-one correspondence by application of (10.2.2.c). To this end, define K on U to S so that,

$$\text{for every } z \in U,\ K(z) \equiv F^*(G^*(z)).$$

Then, for every $z \in U$,

$$\begin{aligned} H(K(z)) &= G(F(F^*(G^*(z)))) \\ &= G(G^*(z)) && \text{[by (10.2.1.b)]} \\ &= z && \text{[by (10.2.1.b)];} \end{aligned}$$

and, for every $x \in S$,

$$\begin{aligned} K(H(x)) &= F^*(G^*(G(F(x)))) \\ &= F^*(F(x)) && \text{[by (10.2.1.a)]} \\ &= x && \text{[by (10.2.1.a)].} \end{aligned}$$

Thus, by (10.2.2.c), H is a one-to-one correspondence between S and U. This establishes $S \sim U$ and completes the proof.

REMARK: If, in a given mathematical theory, all sets under discussion are subsets of one set A, then (10.2.4) is of particular significance. Let us define $\mathfrak{M}$ as the set of *all* subsets of A; that is, let the elements of $\mathfrak{M}$ be subsets of A, and let every subset of A appear as an element of $\mathfrak{M}$. The relation

$$R \equiv [(S, T) \in \mathfrak{M} \times \mathfrak{M}; S \sim T]$$

on $\mathfrak{M} \times \mathfrak{M}$ has the property

$$S\ R\ T \text{ if and only if } S \sim T;$$

so far as the theory in question is concerned, statements about general equivalence of sets become statements about R. In particular, (10.2.4.a) yields that R is *reflexive*, (10.2.4.b) that R is *symmetric*, and (10.2.4.c) that R is *transitive* [see (15.2.3)]. The importance of these properties of R will be discussed in (15.2).

(10.2.5) THEOREM: *If S, T, U, V are sets such that*

$$S \cdot T = U \cdot V = \Theta, \quad S \sim U, \quad T \sim V,$$

then $S + T \sim U + V$.

PROOF: If $S \sim U$ and $T \sim V$, there exist functions F, G such that

F is a one-to-one correspondence between S and U;
G is a one-to-one correspondence between T and V.

Define a function H on $S + T$ to $U + V$ so that, for every $x \in S + T$,

$$(1) \qquad H(x) = \begin{cases} F(x) & \text{if } x \in S \\ G(x) & \text{if } x \in T. \end{cases}$$

(Note this application of "piecewise definition" of a function as described at the end of (5.4).)

First we prove that $U + V$ is the range of H. Let $z \in U + V$. Then either $z \in U$ or $z \in V$. If $z \in U$, then

$$x \equiv F^*(z) \in S,$$

and

$$\begin{aligned} H(x) &= F(x) \\ &= F(F^*(z)) \\ &= z \qquad \text{[by (10.2.1.b)].} \end{aligned}$$

If $z \in V$, then

$$x \equiv G^*(z) \in T,$$

and

$$\begin{aligned} H(x) &= G(x) \\ &= G(G^*(z)) \\ &= z \qquad \text{[by (10.2.1.b)].} \end{aligned}$$

In either case it follows that, for $z \in U + V$, there exists $x \in S + T$ such that $H(x) = z$. Hence $U + V$ is the range of H.

It will now be shown that H is a one-to-one correspondence by application of (10.2.2.b). To this end, let $x_1, x_2 \in S + T$ with $x_1 \neq x_2$. There are four cases to consider:

(a) $x_1, x_2 \in S;$
(b) $x_1, x_2 \in T;$
(c) $x_1 \in S, \quad x_2 \in T;$
(d) $x_1 \in T, \quad x_2 \in S.$

In case (a), $H(x_1) = F(x_1)$ and $H(x_2) = F(x_2)$ by (1). But $F(x_1) \neq F(x_2)$ by (10.2.2). Hence $H(x_1) \neq H(x_2)$. In case (b), $H(x_1) = G(x_1)$ and $H(x_1) = G(x_2)$ by (1). But $G(x_1) \neq G(x_2)$ by (10.2.2). Hence $H(x_1) \neq H(x_2)$. In case (c), $H(x_1) = F(x_1) \in U$ and $H(x_2) = G(x_2) \in T$ by (1). Hence $H(x_1) \neq H(x_2)$ follows from $T \cdot U = \Theta$. Case (d) is treated exactly as is case (c) with x_1 and x_2 interchanged. It has been shown that, if $x_1, x_2 \in S + T$ with $x_1 \neq x_2$, then $H(x_1) \neq H(x_2)$. Thus H is a one-to-one correspondence between $S + T$ and $U + V$ by (10.2.2). This completes the proof.

(10.2.6) THEOREM: *If φ is a one-to-one correspondence between sets S and T, and if $U \subset S$, then*

$$\psi \equiv (\varphi(x); x \in U)$$

is a one-to-one correspondence between U and $\varphi(U)$, and $U \sim \varphi(U)$.

REMARK: The notation $\varphi(U)$ was introduced in (5.4.8) to mean $[\varphi(x); x \in U]$.

PROOF: Clearly ψ has domain U and range $\varphi(U)$ and satisfies the criterion (10.2.2.b) because φ satisfies the same criterion. Hence ψ is a one-to-one correspondence between U and $\varphi(U)$, whence $U \sim \varphi(U)$.

(10.2.7) THEOREM: *If φ is a one-to-one correspondence between sets S and T, and if $U \subset S$, then $\varphi(S - U) = T - \varphi(U)$.*

PROOF: Let $y \in \varphi(S - U)$. Then there exists $x \in S - U$ with $y = \varphi(x)$. Thus $y \in T$. If $y \in \varphi(U)$, there exists $x' \in U$ with $y = \varphi(x')$. But since $x \in' U$, $x' \in U$, we have $x \neq x'$; but this contradicts

$$x = \varphi^*(y) = x'.$$

Hence $y \in T - \varphi(U)$, and we have proved

$$\varphi(S - U) \subset T - \varphi(U).$$

Conversely, suppose $y \in T - \varphi(U)$. Define $x \equiv \varphi^*(y)$, whence $x \in S$, $y = \varphi(x)$. Suppose $x \in U$. Then $y = \varphi(x) \in \varphi(U)$, contrary to $y \in' \varphi(U)$. Thus $x \in S - U$, and $y \in \varphi(S - U)$. This establishes

$$T - \varphi(U) \subset \varphi(S - U)$$

and completes the proof.

(10.2.8) Corollary: *If φ is a one-to-one correspondence between sets S and T, and if $U \subsetneqq S$, then $\varphi(U) \subsetneqq T$.*

Proof: Evidently $\varphi(U) \subset T$. If $\varphi(U) = T$, then $T - \varphi(U) = \Theta$, so that, by (10.2.7), $\varphi(S - U) = \Theta$. But $S - U \sim \varphi(S - U)$ by (10.2.6), whence $S - U = \Theta$. Thus $U = S$, contrary to the hypothesis.

(10.2.9) Project: Let S, T be sets, F a function with domain S and range T, and G a function on T to S. Assume that, for every $x \in S$, $G(F(x)) = x$. Prove:
(a) F is a one-to-one correspondence between S and T;
(b) for every $y \in T$, $F(G(y)) = y$;
(c) $G = F^*$.
How does this result differ from those in (10.2.2) and (10.2.3)?

(10.2.10) Project: Let S, T be sets, and F, G be functions on S to T and on T to S, respectively. Suppose that, for every $x \in S$, $G(F(x)) = x$, and that, for every $y \in T$, $F(G(y)) = y$. Prove that the range of F is T, that $G = F^*$, and that F is a one-to-one correspondence between S and T. How does this result differ from those in (10.2.2) and (10.2.3)?

(10.2.11) Project: Prove the following false: If S, T are sets, if F and G are functions on S to T and on T to S, respectively, and if for every $x \in S$, $G(F(x)) = x$, then F is a one-to-one correspondence between S and T.

(10.2.12) Project: Let S and T be sets, and let φ be a function on S to T. Let $U, V \subset S$. Prove:
(a) $\varphi(U + V) = \varphi(U) + \varphi(V)$;
(b) if $U \subset V$, then $\varphi(U) \subset \varphi(V)$;
(c) $\varphi(U) - \varphi(V) \subset \varphi(U - V)$;
(d) $\varphi(U \cdot V) \subset \varphi(U) \cdot \varphi(V)$.
If φ is a one-to-one correspondence between S and $\varphi(S)$, how may these results be strengthened?

(10.2.13) Project: Extend (10.2.5) to six sets.

10.3. Equivalence and the Sets I_n. [No Basis.] This section will be devoted to preliminary results concerning the sets I_n which will pave the way for the proof of the fundamental theorems on finite sets to be presented in the next section.

(10.3.1) Lemma: *Let $n \in I$, $p \in I_{n+1}$. Then $I_n \sim I_{n+1} - [p]$.*
Proof: Define

$$H \equiv [n \in I; p \in I_{n+1} \text{ implies } I_n \sim I_{n+1} - [p]].$$

To prove $1 \in H$, let $p \in I_2$. Then $p = 1$ or $p = 2$. If $p = 1$, then $I_2 - [p] = [2]$, $I_1 = [1]$, so that $I_1 \sim I_2 - [p]$. If $p = 2$, then

$I_1 = I_2 - [p]$, whence again $I_1 \sim I_2 - [p]$. Suppose now that $q \in H$, so that

(1) $$k \in I_{q+1} \text{ implies } I_q \sim I_{q+1} - [k].$$

To prove that $q + 1 \in H$, let $p \in I_{q+2}$. If $p \in I_{q+1}$, then, by (1),

(2) $$I_q \sim I_{q+1} - [p].$$

Now obviously

(3) $$[q + 1] \sim [q + 2],$$

and

(4) $$I_q \cdot [q + 1] = (I_{q+1} - [p]) \cdot [q + 2] = \Theta;$$

by (2), (3), (4) and (10.2.5),

$$I_{q+1} = I_q + [q + 1] \sim (I_{q+1} - [p]) + [q + 2] = I_{q+2} - [p].$$

Finally, let $p \epsilon' I_{q+1}$. Then $p = q + 2$, and

$$I_{q+1} \sim I_{q+1} = I_{q+2} - [q + 2] = I_{q+2} - [p].$$

Hence $q + 1 \in H$. By III′, $H = I$, and the proof is complete.

(10.3.2) Lemma: *Let* $n \in I$, $n > 1$. *Then* $I_1 \sim' I_n$.

Proof: If $I_1 \sim I_n$, there exists a one-to-one correspondence φ between I_n and I_1. Clearly $\varphi(1), \varphi(n) \in I_1$, so that $\varphi(1) = \varphi(n) = 1$. But by (10.2.2.b), $\varphi(1) \neq \varphi(n)$. This contradiction completes the proof.

(10.3.3) Lemma: *If* $m, n \in I$, $m > 1$ *and* $n > 1$, *then* $I_m \sim I_n$ *implies* $I_{m-1} \sim I_{n-1}$.

Proof: Since $I_m \sim I_n$, there exists a one-to-one correspondence φ between I_m and I_n. Then, by (10.2.6), (10.2.7),

$$I_{m-1} \sim \varphi(I_{m-1}) = I_n - [\varphi(m)].$$

But, by (10.3.1),

$$I_n - [\varphi(m)] \sim I_{n-1}.$$

Thus $I_{m-1} \sim I_{n-1}$ by (10.2.4.c).

(10.3.4) Lemma: *If* $m, n, k \in I$, $m > k$, $n > k$, *then* $I_m \sim I_n$ *implies* $I_{m-k} \sim I_{n-k}$.

Proof: Define

$$H \equiv [k \in I;\ m, n \in I,\ m, n > k,\ I_m \sim I_n \text{ implies } I_{m-k} \sim I_{n-k}].$$

Clearly $1 \in H$ by (10.3.3). Suppose $q \in H$, and let $m, n \in I$, $m > q + 1$, $n > q + 1$, $I_m \sim I_n$. Then $m, n > q$, so that $I_{m-q} \sim I_{n-q}$. Now $m > q + 1$ yields the existence of $r \in I$ with $m = q + 1 + r$, whence

$m - q = 1 + r > 1$. Similarly $n - q > 1$. By (10.3.3), $I_{(m-q)-1} \sim I_{(n-q)-1}$. This means, by (9.6.5.b), that $I_{m-(q+1)} \sim I_{n-(q+1)}$; therefore $q + 1 \in H$. Thus, by III′, $H = I$, and the proof is complete.

(10.3.5) Theorem: *If $m, n \in I$ and $I_m \sim I_n$, then $m = n$.*

Proof: By (9.2.14), $m = n$ or $m < n$ or $m > n$. Suppose that $m < n$. If $m = 1$, we have $I_m \sim' I_n$ by (10.3.2), contrary to the hypothesis. Hence $m \neq 1$, and $m > 1$. Define $k \equiv m - 1$. Then $m > k$, $n > k$, whence, by (10.3.4),

$$I_{m-k} \sim I_{n-k}.$$

But $m = k + 1$, whence $m - k = 1$, and we have

(1) $$I_1 \sim I_{n-k}.$$

If $n - k \neq 1$, then (1) contradicts (10.3.2), so that $n - k = 1$. Thus

$$n = k + 1 = m,$$

contrary to our assumption that $m < n$. This contradiction proves that $m \nless n$. Similarly $m \ngtr n$. Hence $m = n$, and the proof is complete.

(10.3.6) Project: In (10.3.1) determine explicitly a one-to-one correspondence between I_n and $I_{n+1} - [p]$. Treat all cases.

10.4. The Counting Process. [No Basis.] Enough information concerning the properties of sets, and in particular the sets I_n, with respect to equivalence has now been presented to enable us to proceed with the fundamental results on the counting process as defined by (10.1.3). Intuitive counting suggests that, for every finite set, the number of its elements should be unique. With the results of the previous sections it is now trivial to show that this is the case.

(10.4.1) Theorem: *Let S be a set having m elements and having n elements. Then $m = n$.*

Proof: By the definition (10.1.3), we have $S \sim I_m$ and $S \sim I_n$. Hence, by (10.2.4), $I_m \sim I_n$. But then $m = n$ by (10.3.5).

(10.4.2) Corollary: *If S is finite, then there exists a unique $n \in I$ such that S has (exactly) n elements.*

Proof: Existence of n follows from (10.1.2) and uniqueness from (10.4.1).

(10.4.3) Definition: Let S be a finite set. Then $n(S)$ is defined to be the unique $n \in I$ given by (10.4.2), and is called the *order of S*.

(10.4.4) Theorem: *Let S, T be sets. Then,*

(a) *if S is finite and $S \sim T$, then T is finite;*

(b) *if S, T are finite, then $S \sim T$ if and only if* $$n(S) = n(T).$$

PROOF OF (a): Since S is finite, there exists $n \in I$ with $S \sim I_n$. By (10.2.4), $T \sim I_n$, whence T is finite.

PROOF OF (b): Suppose S, T finite and $S \sim T$. By (10.4.3), $S \sim I_{n(S)}$, $T \sim I_{n(T)}$, whence $I_{n(S)} \sim I_{n(T)}$ by (10.2.4). Thus $n(S) = n(T)$ by (10.3.5). This proves the forward implication. Now suppose $n(S) = n(T)$. Then since

$$S \sim I_{n(S)} = I_{n(T)} \sim T,$$

it follows from (10.2.4.c) that $S \sim T$.

(10.4.5) LEMMA: *Let $m \in I$. If $S \subset I_m$, then either $S = \Theta$, or S is finite and $n(S) \leqq m$.*

PROOF: Define

$$H \equiv [m \in I;\, S \subset I_m,\, S \neq \Theta \text{ implies } S \text{ is finite and } n(S) \leqq m].$$

Let $S \subset I_1$, $S \neq \Theta$. Then $S = I_1$, whence $S \sim I_1$, and $n(S) = 1$. Therefore $1 \in H$. Suppose $q \in H$, and let $S \subset I_{q+1}$, $S \neq \Theta$. If $S \subset I_q$, then S is finite (since $q \in H$), and $n(S) \leqq q < q + 1$. Suppose $S \not\subset I_q$. Then $q + 1 \in S$ and

$$S - [q + 1] \subset I_q.$$

Then (again since $q \in H$) $S - [q + 1] = \Theta$ or $S - [q + 1]$ is finite and

$$n(S - [q + 1]) \leqq q. \tag{1}$$

In the former case, $S = [q + 1]$ and $n(S) = 1 < q + 1$. In the latter case,

$$S - [q + 1] \sim I_{n(S - [q+1])}.$$

But

$$[q + 1] \sim [n(S - [q + 1]) + 1],$$

and

$$(S - [q + 1]) \cdot [q + 1] = I_{n(S-[q+1])} \cdot [n(S - [q + 1]) + 1] = \Theta,$$

so that (10.2.5) applies, yielding

$$S \sim I_{n(S-[q+1])+1}.$$

Hence, by (10.1.3), (1), (9.2.11),

$$n(S) = n(S - [q + 1]) + 1 \leqq q + 1.$$

In all cases, $n(S) \leqq q + 1$, so that $q + 1 \in H$. By III′, $H = I$, and the proof is complete.

(10.4.6) LEMMA: *Let $m \in I$. If $S \subset I_m$, $S \sim I_m$, then $S = I_m$.*

PROOF: Define

$$H \equiv [m \in I;\, S \subset I_m,\, S \sim I_m \text{ implies } S = I_m].$$

Then $1 \epsilon H$, since $S \subset I_1$ yields $S = I_1$ or $S = \Theta$, and $S \sim I_1$ yields $S \neq \Theta$. Suppose $q \epsilon H$, and let $S \subset I_{q+1}$, $S \sim I_{q+1}$. Now it is impossible that $S \subset I_q$, since otherwise, by (10.4.5), $S = \Theta$ (contrary to $S \sim I_{q+1}$) or $n(S) \leqq q$, contrary to $n(S) = q + 1$ in view of $S \sim I_{q+1}$. Hence $q + 1 \epsilon S$. Now there exists a one-to-one correspondence φ between S and I_{q+1}. By (10.2.6),

$$S - [q + 1] \sim \varphi(S - [q + 1]).$$

But, by (10.2.7),

$$\varphi(S - [q + 1]) = I_{q+1} - \varphi([q + 1]) = I_{q+1} - [\varphi(q + 1)].$$

Thus

$$S - [q + 1] \sim I_{q+1} - [\varphi(q + 1)].$$

By (10.3.1),

$$I_q \sim I_{q+1} - [\varphi(q + 1)],$$

whence

$$S - [q + 1] \sim I_q.$$

Since $S - [q + 1] \subset I_q$, we have (since $q \epsilon H$)

$$S - [q + 1] = I_q.$$

Thus $S = I_{q+1}$, and $q + 1 \epsilon H$. By III′, $H = I$, and the proof is complete.

(10.4.7) THEOREM: *Let S be a finite set, and let $T \subset S$. Then $T = \Theta$, or T is finite and $n(T) \leqq n(S)$. Moreover, $n(T) = n(S)$ if and only if $T = S$.*

PROOF: Let S be finite, and let $T \subset S$, $T \neq \Theta$. Since S is finite, there exists a one-to-one correspondence φ between S and $I_{n(S)}$. Hence, by (10.2.6),

(1) $$T \sim \varphi(T).$$

But $\varphi(T) \subset I_{n(S)}$ and $\varphi(T) \neq \Theta$ by (1). Hence, by (10.4.5), $\varphi(T)$ is finite and

$$n(\varphi(T)) \leqq n(S).$$

But, by (1), (10.4.4), T is finite, and

(2) $$n(\varphi(T)) = n(T),$$

so that

$$n(T) \leqq n(S).$$

If $n(T) = n(S)$, then $n(\varphi(T)) = n(S)$ by (2), whence, by (10.4.4.b),

$$\varphi(T) \sim S \sim I_{n(S)}.$$

By (10.4.6), $\varphi(T) = I_{n(S)}$. If $T \neq S$, then, by (10.2.8), $\varphi(T) \neq I_{n(S)}$. This contradiction proves $T = S$. Finally, the converse,

$$T = S \text{ implies } n(T) = n(S),$$

is obvious.

(10.4.8) THEOREM: *If S, T are finite sets, and if $S \cdot T = \Theta$, then $S + T$ is finite, and*

$$n(S + T) = n(S) + n(T).$$

PROOF: The proof will only be sketched; details may be supplied by the reader. We have

$$S \sim I_{n(S)}, \quad T \sim I_{n(T)}.$$

But it is easily proved that

$$I_{n(T)} \sim J \equiv [n(S) + p;\, p \in I_{n(T)}],$$

since the function

$$(n(S) + p;\, p \in I_{n(T)})$$

has appropriate domain and range and satisfies (10.2.2.b). Hence, by (10.2.5),

$$S + T \sim I_{n(S)} + J = I_{n(S)+n(T)},$$

so that the desired conclusion follows.

(10.4.9) THEOREM: *If S, T are finite sets, and if $S \subset T$, then either $T - S = \Theta$, or $T - S$ is finite and*

$$n(T - S) = n(T) - n(S).$$

PROOF: The proof is left for the reader.

(10.4.10) THEOREM: *If S, T are finite, and if $S \cdot T \neq \Theta$, then $S \cdot T$ and $S + T$ are finite and*

$$n(S + T) + n(S \cdot T) = n(S) + n(T).$$

PROOF: Again the proof will only be outlined. Define $A \equiv S - S \cdot T$. If $A = \Theta$, then $S \subset T$, whence the result follows readily. Otherwise, (10.4.9) applies, yielding

(1) $$n(A) = n(S) - n(S \cdot T).$$

Now it is easily shown that $A \cdot T = \Theta$, whence, by (10.4.8),

(2) $$n(A + T) = n(A) + n(T).$$

Since $A + T = S + T$, (1) and (2) yield

$$n(S + T) = n(S) + n(T) - n(S \cdot T),$$

whence the desired result follows.

Two further results are stated without complete proof.

(10.4.11) Theorem: *If S, T, U, V are sets, then $S \sim T$, $U \sim V$ implies $S \times U \sim T \times V$.*

Proof: If φ, ψ are one-to-one correspondences with $T = \varphi(S)$, $V = \psi(U)$, then

$$\sigma \equiv ((\varphi(x), \psi(y)); (x, y) \in S \times U)$$

may be proved to be a one-to-one correspondence between $S \times U$ and $T \times V$.

(10.4.12) Theorem: *If S, T are finite sets, then $S \times T$ is finite and*

$$n(S \times T) = n(S) \cdot n(T).$$

Proof: It is established first by induction that

$$I_{n(S)} \times I_{n(T)} \sim I_{n(S) \cdot n(T)},$$

whence the result follows by (10.4.11).

Remark: The theorems (10.4.8), (10.4.9), (10.4.12) show how the operations *plus, minus, times* relate to the counting process. The intuitive remarks in (8.1), (8.5) and (8.6) have now been completely expressed in mathematical terms.

(10.4.13) Project: Prove (10.4.8).

(10.4.14) Project: Prove (10.4.9).

(10.4.15) Project: Prove (10.4.10).

(10.4.16) Project: Prove (10.4.11).

(10.4.17) Project: Prove (10.4.12).

Chapter 11

INDUCTIVE DEFINITION AND THE PRINCIPLE OF CHOICE

[No Basis]

11.1. Tuples and Sequences. In the last three chapters we have seen that it is possible to develop an abstract mathematical system which can replace the intuitive counting numbers. In particular, in the last chapter it was shown that the use of the counting numbers for enumeration can be replaced by a precise mathematical enumeration process.

Now there is one other intuitive use for the counting numbers in addition to answering the question "how many?" namely, to provide an "order of precedence." This use is so important that special words "first," "second," "third" are used to replace "one," "two," "three" when it is desired to indicate that the counting numbers are being used to establish an "ordering." The intuitive nature of the "ordering" process is that the labels "first," "second," and so on, are associated with or assigned to the objects to be "ordered." The mathematical analogue of this process would first of all replace the designations "first," "second" by elements 1, 2 of I. Then the "association" of elements of I with elements of the set A under consideration would be accomplished by defining a function on $I \times A$. If the set A is finite, then the domain of the function could be the set $I_{n(A)}$. If the domain of the function is I, then this function becomes what we have already called in (8.4.1) a *sequence* and replaces the intuitive notion of a "continued succession." If the domain of the function is a set I_n, for $n \in I$, the function might be called a *finite* sequence, but we shall prefer to call a function on I_n to A an *ordered n-tuple* or, simply, an *n-tuple in A*.

(11.1.1) Definition: Let A be any set and let $n \in I$. An *n-tuple in A*, or an *n-tuple of elements of A*, is a function $(a_m; m \in I_n)$ on I_n to A. The set of all n-tuples is denoted by A^n. A *tuple in A* is an n-tuple for some $n \in I$; that is, a tuple in A is a function on $I \times A$ for which there exists $n \in I$ such that I_n is the domain of the function.

When convenient, a more picturesque notation for n-tuples is sometimes used; for example, the 3-tuple $(a_m; m \in I_3)$ is also denoted by (a_1, a_2, a_3). This suggests that the concept of n-tuple is a generalization of the basic concept of ordered pair. It is of interest to note in what sense this is true. Consider the meaning of 2-*tuple* as a function on I_2 to A. To specify such a 2-tuple, one must give the element a_1 of A which is the correspondent of 1, and the element a_2 which is the correspondent of 2. Then, clearly, (a_1, a_2) is an ordered pair. Conversely, every ordered pair in $A \times A$ determines, in an obvious way, a unique 2-tuple. In short, the set A^2 of all 2-tuples and the set $A \times A$ of ordered pairs in A admit a one-to-one correspondence between them. While our point of view necessitates regarding 2-tuples and ordered pairs as distinct concepts, no harm will be done in subsequent work if these concepts are treated as though they were the same. Even simpler is the concept 1-*tuple*. In fact, the set A^1 of all 1-tuples in A admits in an obvious way a one-to-one correspondence between itself and A.

In this chapter we shall consider in some detail the concepts of tuples and sequences in A. In particular, we shall be concerned with an important method of defining tuples and sequences in A; the method is known as *inductive definition*.

(11.1.2) PROJECT: Prove that, if A is a set, then

$$A^1 = [[(1, a)]; a \in A];$$
$$A^2 = [[(1, a), (2, b)]; (a, b) \in A \times A].$$

(11.1.3) PROJECT: Prove that, if A is a set, then $A \sim A^1$.

(11.1.4) PROJECT: Prove that, if A is a set, then $A \times A \sim A^2$.

11.2. " . . . and so on." In order to clarify the procedure to be developed, let us consider first a special problem of defining a sequence in I. Suppose that k is any given element of I. By means of the operation $\cdot$ on $I \times I$ to I, it is possible to speak of the element $k \cdot k \in I$. Moreover, as we have seen, the fact that $\cdot$ is associative makes it possible to define $k \cdot k \cdot k$ as the common value of $k \cdot (k \cdot k)$ and $(k \cdot k) \cdot k$. Let us call $k \cdot k$ a "product with 'two' factors k," and $k \cdot k \cdot k$ a "product with 'three' factors k," where, of course, "two" and "three" are counting numbers. Going backwards for a moment, let us call k itself a "product with 'one' factor k." Thus, starting with the element k of I, we have defined a particular element of I corresponding to each of the first "three" counting numbers. The following table shows this "correspondence":

Counting number	Name of concept	Concept in symbols
one	product with one factor k	k
two	product with two factors k	$k \cdot k$
three	product with three factors k	$k \cdot k \cdot k$

(11.2.1) TABLE

Intuitively, it seems reasonable that the "correspondence" indicated above can be "extended," and that the concepts which appear are only the beginning of a "chain of concepts." Indeed, it is quite natural to introduce, as the next step in the "chain," the concept "product with 'four' factors k," or $k \cdot k \cdot k \cdot k$ as the common value of $(k \cdot k \cdot k) \cdot k$ and $k \cdot (k \cdot k \cdot k)$. Hence, intuitively, one is tempted to put "and so on" under the table (11.2.1) and claim that an entire "chain of concepts" has been defined.

But we have resolved to eliminate the counting numbers from mathematics and replace them by elements of I. Thus we should replace the table (11.2.1) by the following:

Element of I	"Corresponding" element of I
1	k
2	$k \cdot k$
3	$k \cdot k \cdot k$

(11.2.2) TABLE

This table specifies, for each of the elements 1, 2, 3 of I, a unique corresponding element; that is, (11.2.2) defines a 3-tuple. But the table (11.2.2) is admittedly only part of what is wanted; if one can imagine the table completed, it would specify, for *every* element of I, a unique corresponding element of I. But such a specification would define a sequence α on I to I. This sequence α should be such that

$$\begin{aligned} \alpha(1) &= k, \\ \alpha(2) &= k \cdot k, \\ \alpha(3) &= k \cdot k \cdot k, \\ &\text{"and so on."} \end{aligned} \tag{11.2.3}$$

However, we cannot accept (11.2.3) as a definition of a sequence α. For the concept "and so on" is quite vague, and we do not wish to include it in the logical language basis. Although it is unlikely that anyone would go seriously astray concerning what is intended by "and so on" in such a simple case as (11.2.3), in more complicated cases the intent may be by no means clear. And, perhaps even more to the point, whenever the content of the use of "and so on" is really clear, there is a way of stating the process which avoids the objectionable phrase.

Now the phrase "and so on" in a situation like (11.2.3) is intuitively clear exactly when one can discern some "rule" for proceeding from any step to the next. For example, in (11.2.3) it is clear that each $\alpha(n)$ is obtained from the preceding by "multiplying" the preceding by k; symbolically,

$$\text{for every } n \in I,\ \alpha(n+1) = k \cdot \alpha(n). \tag{11.2.4}$$

This requirement, together with

$$\alpha(1) = k, \tag{11.2.5}$$

says everything that is contained in (11.2.3) without the use of the ambiguous "and so on."

Now we come to the central question. Do (11.2.5) and (11.2.4) define a sequence α? According to our principles, we may define a sequence α as the unique sequence satisfying (11.2.5) and (11.2.4), provided we first *prove* that there *is* a *unique* sequence satisfying (11.2.5) and (11.2.4). It happens that we *can* prove the unique existence of a sequence satisfying (11.2.5) and (11.2.4), using the *induction* axiom for positive integers. Accordingly, we can use (11.2.5) and (11.2.4) to define a sequence; this and similar definitions are called inductive definitions because of the use of the induction axiom in the preliminary proof of justification.

Actually we can prove the unique existence of a sequence in a very general case which includes the case just discussed. Since instances similar to the specific one discussed occur repeatedly in mathematics, it is uneconomical to justify each individually. Instead, we shall give a general treatment in the next sections that will include all the cases that will arise. When the general theory is finished, we shall return to the specific case discussed, that of "repeated multiplication." It might interest the reader to note that, when the unique existence of α satisfying (11.2.5), (11.2.4) has been proved, we shall be led to what appears in the algebra books as the "theory of exponents." In fact, the usual notation for $\alpha(n)$ is k^n.

It has been seen that, in order to make possible the definition of certain sequences, we must develop some precise mathematical principle to replace the phrase "and so on" in (11.2.3). Conceptually such a principle might be unnecessary for the definition of an n-tuple rather than a sequence, provided n has been specified. In this case, (11.2.3) is thought of as extending, not indefinitely, but to a definite "termination point." Thus a 3-tuple is completely defined by (11.2.2); a 4-tuple would be defined by adding one line to the table (11.2.2). But when n is not specified, our point of view is such that a principle is required. In this case, the definition is accomplished by what is sometimes called "incomplete induction," to distinguish it from the "complete induction" applicable to the definition of sequences.

11.3. Inductive Definition. We consider first the problem of "complete" induction, that is, we assume that it is desired to define a sequence in A. In generalizing the situation of the last section, we mention first that α may be allowed to be a sequence in an arbitrary set A, and not necessarily a sequence in I. Then the significant features of (11.2.5) and (11.2.4), stated heuristically, are the following:

(11.3.1) $\alpha(1)$ is a specified element of A;
(11.3.2) for every $n \in I$, $\alpha(n + 1) \in A$ is "determined" when $\alpha(n) \in A$ is known.

Another formulation of (11.3.2) is this:

(11.3.3) for every $n \in I$, and for every $\alpha(n) \in A$, there is a unique "corresponding" $\alpha(n + 1) \in A$.

But the existence of a unique $\alpha(n + 1) \in A$ "corresponding" to $\alpha(n) \in A$ will be assured if we can refer to some initially given function F on A to A and then demand the following:

(11.3.4) for every $n \in I$, $\alpha(n + 1) = F(\alpha(n))$.

Finally, a generalization of (11.3.4) is possible which preserves the essential feature of (11.3.3). This is obtained by referring not to a single function F, but rather to various functions, one "corresponding" to each $n \in I$. Thus we should assume there to be given a sequence $(F_n; n \in I)$ of functions on A to A and replace (11.3.4) by the requirement that

$$\text{for every } n \in I, \ \alpha(n + 1) = F_n(\alpha(n)).$$

If it happens that $n \neq m$ implies $F_n = F_m$, then our requirement reduces to (11.3.4), in which F is the single function equal to all F_n for $n \in I$. In the case of the preceding section, for example, $F = (k \cdot m; m \in I)$ is effective.

We have now arrived at the precise statement of our problem. We wish to prove the following:

(11.3.5) THEOREM: *Let A be a set, and let $(F_n; n \in I)$ be a sequence of functions on A to A. Finally, let $x \in A$. Then there exists a unique sequence α in A such that*

(a) $\alpha(1) = x$;
(b) *for every* $n \in I$, $\alpha(n + 1) = F_n(\alpha(n))$.

We have taken special pains to arrive at the statement of (11.3.5) gradually, because the result possesses considerable generality. Theorem (11.3.5) justifies definition by complete induction. If it is desired to define an n-tuple rather than a sequence, then the appropriate theorem of justification is the following:

(11.3.6) THEOREM: *Let A be a set, let $n \in I$, and let $(F_m; m \in I)$ be a sequence of functions on A to A. Finally, let $x \in A$. Then there exists a unique n-tuple α in A such that*

(a) $\alpha(1) = x;$
(b) *for every* $m < n, \alpha(m + 1) = F_m(\alpha(m)).$

The next section will be devoted to the proofs of (11.3.6) and (11.3.5).

11.4. Justification of Inductive Definition. It might be thought that (11.3.6) is simply a special case of (11.3.5); actually it is convenient to prove (11.3.6) first and then extend this result to the "complete" theorem (11.3.5). Both the original proof of (11.3.6) and the extension to (11.3.5) require the use of the induction axiom.

First, the existence part of (11.3.6) will be demonstrated. For convenience, we state this as a lemma.

(11.4.1) LEMMA: *Let A be a set, and let $(F_m; m \in I)$ be a sequence of functions on A to A. Finally, let $x \in A$. Then, for every $n \in I$, there exists a function β on I_n to A such that*

(a) $\beta(1) = x;$
(b) *for every* $m < n, \beta(m + 1) = F_m(\beta(m)).$

PROOF: Define

(1) $H \equiv [n \in I;$ there exists a function β on I_n to A such that (a) and (b) are true$]$.

It will be proved, with the help of III′, that $H = I$.

First, to show $1 \in H$, we must prove the existence of a function β on I_1 to A such that

(2) $\beta(1) = x;$
(3) for every $m < 1, \beta(m + 1) = F_m(\beta(m)).$

But, by (9.3.6), $I_1 = [1]$, so that the domain of β contains only the element 1. Hence β is defined by the specification of $\beta(1)$. We define $\beta(1) \equiv x$. Then (2) is satisfied. But (3) is vacuously true, since $m < 1$ is not true for any $m \in I$, by (9.2.9). Thus (3) requires that a certain equality hold for every element of the set $[m \in I; m < 1]$, which is empty. (This situation illustrates strikingly the importance of recognizing the truth of vacuous statements.)

Now suppose $q \in H$, that is, suppose there exists a function γ on I_q to A such that

(4) $\gamma(1) = x;$
(5) for every $m < q, \gamma(m + 1) = F_m(\gamma(m)).$

It is to be shown that $q + 1 \epsilon H$. To this end, define β on I_{q+1} to A so that, for every $m \epsilon I_{q+1} = I_q + [q + 1]$,

$$(6) \qquad \beta(m) = \begin{cases} \gamma(m) & \text{for } m \epsilon I_q \\ F_q(\gamma(q)) & \text{for } m = q + 1. \end{cases}$$

It is now to be shown that

(7) $\beta(1) = x$;

(8) for every $m < q + 1$, $\beta(m + 1) = F_m(\beta(m))$.

But, since $1 \epsilon I_q$,

$$\begin{aligned} \beta(1) &= \gamma(1) && [\text{by } (6)] \\ &= x && [\text{by } (4)], \end{aligned}$$

and (7) is verified. To prove (8), note first that, if $m < q + 1$, then $m \leqq q$ by (9.2.10.a), so that either $m < q$ or $m = q$. If $m < q$, then $m + 1 \epsilon I_q$ by (9.2.10.b), and

$$\begin{aligned} \beta(m + 1) &= \gamma(m + 1) && [\text{by } (6)] \\ &= F_m(\gamma(m)) && [\text{by } (5)] \\ &= F_m(\beta(m)) && [\text{by } (6)]. \end{aligned}$$

If $m = q$, then

$$\begin{aligned} \beta(m + 1) &= \beta(q + 1) \\ &= F_q(\gamma(q)) && [\text{by } (6)] \\ &= F_q(\beta(q)) && [\text{by } (6)] \\ &= F_m(\beta(m)). \end{aligned}$$

Thus (8) is satisfied. The existence of β on I_{q+1} to A satisfying (7) and (8) shows that $q + 1 \epsilon H$, in view of (1).

It has been shown that $1 \epsilon H$ and that, if $q \epsilon H$, then $q + 1 \epsilon H$. Hence, by III′, $H = I$. This completes the proof.

Next it will be shown that, for every $n \epsilon I$, the function proved to exist in (11.4.1) is unique; this will establish the uniqueness part of (11.3.6).

(11.4.2) LEMMA: *Let A be a set, and let $(F_m; m \epsilon I)$ be a sequence of functions on A to A. Further, let $x \epsilon A$ and $n \epsilon I$. Finally, let β, γ be functions on I_n to A such that*

(a) $\beta(1) = x$, $\gamma(1) = x$;

(b) *for every* $m < n$, $\beta(m + 1) = F_m(\beta(m))$,
$\gamma(m + 1) = F_m(\gamma(m))$.

Then $\beta = \gamma$.

PROOF: Define

(1) $H \equiv [n \epsilon I;$ for every β, γ, which are functions on I_n to A satisfying (a), (b), it is true that $\beta = \gamma]$.

It is to be shown that $H = I$.

To show that $1 \in H$, let β, γ be functions on I_1 to A satisfying (a) and (b) with $n = 1$. Since $I_1 = [1]$, to prove $\beta = \gamma$ it is sufficient to show that $\beta(1) = \gamma(1)$. But this is obvious from (a).

Suppose now that $q \in H$, so that,

(2) if β', γ' are functions on I_q to A such that

(2a) $\beta'(1) = x, \gamma'(1) = x,$

(2b) for every $m < q$, $\beta'(m + 1) = F_m(\beta'(m))$, and $\gamma'(m + 1) = F_m(\gamma'(m))$,

then $\beta' = \gamma'$.

Now let β, γ be functions on I_{q+1} to A such that

(3) $\beta(1) = x, \gamma(1) = x;$

(4) for every $m < q + 1$, $\beta(m + 1) = F_m(\beta(m))$, and $\gamma(m + 1) = F_m(\gamma(m))$.

To prove that $q + 1 \in H$, we show that $\beta = \gamma$. Define β', γ' as functions on I_q to A so that,

(5) for every $m \in I_q$, $\beta'(m) = \beta(m)$; $\gamma'(m) = \gamma(m)$.

Thus $\beta' = (\beta(m);\ m \in I_q)$ and $\gamma' = (\gamma(m);\ m \in I_q)$. Now it will be shown that β', γ' satisfy (2a) and (2b). First, since $1 \in I_q$,

$$\begin{aligned} \beta'(1) &= \beta(1) && \text{[by (5)]} \\ &= x && \text{[by (3)]}, \end{aligned}$$

and similarly for γ'. Also, for every $m < q$, $m + 1 \in I_q$, by (9.2.10.b), and so

$$\begin{aligned} \beta'(m + 1) &= \beta(m + 1) && \text{[by (5)]} \\ &= F_m(\beta(m)) && \text{[by (4)]} \\ &= F_m(\beta'(m)) && \text{[by (5)]}, \end{aligned}$$

and similarly for γ'. Thus β' and γ' satisfy (2a) and (2b); accordingly, by (2), $\beta' = \gamma'$. In view of (5), this shows that

(6) for every $m \in I_q$, $\beta(m) = \gamma(m)$.

Since $I_{q+1} = I_q + [q + 1]$ by (9.3.6), in order to prove $\beta = \gamma$ it is sufficient to show, in addition to (6), that

(7) $\beta(q + 1) = \gamma(q + 1)$.

But (7) is clear from (4) and (6) with $m = q$. This completes the proof that $\beta = \gamma$ and shows that $q + 1 \in H$.

It has been shown that $1 \in H$ and that, if $q \in H$, then $q + 1 \in H$. Hence, by III′, $H = I$. This completes the proof.

The preceding two lemmas establish the existence and uniqueness parts of (11.3.6) and so constitute its proof. For convenience of reference, we restate (11.3.6).

(11.4.3) THEOREM: *Let A be a set, let $n \in I$, and let $(F_m; m \in I)$ be a sequence of functions on A to A. Finally, let $x \in A$. Then there exists a unique n-tuple α in A such that*

(a) $\alpha(1) = x$;
(b) *for every* $m < n$, $\alpha(m + 1) = F_m(\alpha(m))$.

(11.4.4) DEFINITION: Let A be a set, $x \in A$, $n \in I$, and let $(F_m; m \in I)$ be a sequence of functions on A to A. Then the unique n-tuple α in A such that

$$\alpha(1) = x,$$
$$\text{for every } m < n,\ \alpha(m + 1) = F_m(\alpha(m)),$$

is called the n-tuple in A *defined inductively by x and $(F_m; m \in I)$*. If (as is often the case) all functions F_m are the same function F, the n-tuple is said to be *defined inductively by x and F*.

It is now rather easy to prove the main theorem (11.3.5) on complete induction. First we restate the theorem.

(11.4.5) THEOREM: *Let A be a set, and let $(F_n; n \in I)$ be a sequence of functions on A to A. Finally, let $x \in A$. Then there exists a unique sequence α in A such that*

(a) $\alpha(1) = x$;
(b) *for every* $n \in I$, $\alpha(n + 1) = F_n(\alpha(n))$.

PROOF OF EXISTENCE: Define, for every $m \in I$,

(1) $\alpha_m \equiv$ the unique function of I_m to A such that
  (1a) $\alpha_m(1) = x$;
  (1b) for every $n < m$, $\alpha_m(n + 1) = F_n(\alpha_m(n))$.

(The unique existence, for every $m \in I$, of such an m-tuple α_m was established in (11.4.3).) Now define α as a sequence in A (function on I to A) by

(2) $$\alpha \equiv (\alpha_m(m); m \in I).$$

Thus, for every $m \in I$, $\alpha(m) = \alpha_m(m)$. It is to be shown that (a) and (b) are true.

Clearly

$$\alpha(1) = \alpha_1(1) \quad \text{[by (2)]}$$
$$= x \quad \text{[by (1a)]},$$

so that (a) is true.

To prove (b), it is first shown that

$$n \in I \text{ implies } \alpha_{n+1}(n) = \alpha_n(n).$$

To show this, let $n \in I$ and define γ on I_n to A thus:

$$\gamma \equiv (\alpha_{n+1}(m);\, m \in I_n), \tag{3}$$

so that $\gamma(m) = \alpha_{n+1}(m)$ for every $m \in I_n$. Since $1 \in I_n$,

$$\begin{aligned} \gamma(1) &= \alpha_{n+1}(1) && \text{[by (3)]} \\ &= x && \text{[by (1a)].} \end{aligned}$$

Also, for every $p < n$, $p + 1 \in I_n$, and so

$$\begin{aligned} \gamma(p+1) &= \alpha_{n+1}(p+1) && \text{[by (3)]} \\ &= F_p(\alpha_{n+1}(p)) && \text{[by (1b)]} \\ &= F_p(\gamma(p)) && \text{[by (3)].} \end{aligned}$$

Thus γ is a function on I_n to A such that

$$\begin{aligned} &\gamma(1) = x; \\ &\text{for every } p < n,\ \gamma(p+1) = F_p(\gamma(p)). \end{aligned}$$

But, by (1), α_n is also a function on I_n to A such that

$$\begin{aligned} &\alpha_n(1) = x; \\ &\text{for every } p < n,\ \alpha_n(p+1) = F_p(\alpha_n(p)). \end{aligned}$$

Thus, by (11.4.2), $\gamma = \alpha_n$. Therefore, for every $p \in I_n$, $\gamma(p) = \alpha_n(p)$. In particular, for $p = n$,

$$\begin{aligned} \alpha_n(n) &= \gamma(n) \\ &= \alpha_{n+1}(n) && \text{[by (3)].} \end{aligned} \tag{4}$$

Now, from (4), it is easy to prove (b). In fact, for every $n \in I$,

$$\begin{aligned} \alpha(n+1) &= \alpha_{n+1}(n+1) && \text{[by (2)]} \\ &= F_n(\alpha_{n+1}(n)) && \text{[by (1b)]} \\ &= F_n(\alpha_n(n)) && \text{[by (4)]} \\ &= F_n(\alpha(n)) && \text{[by (2)].} \end{aligned}$$

This completes the proof of existence.

Proof of Uniqueness: Let α, β be sequences in A, both satisfying (a) and (b). Define

$$H \equiv [n \in I;\, \alpha(n) = \beta(n)].$$

Now $1 \in H$ by (a). Suppose that $q \in H$, so that

$$\alpha(q) = \beta(q). \tag{5}$$

Then, by (b),

$$\alpha(q+1) = F_q(\alpha(q)),$$
$$\beta(q+1) = F_q(\beta(q)),$$

whence, by (5),

$$\alpha(q+1) = \beta(q+1).$$

Hence $q + 1 \in H$. By III′, $H = I$. This completes the proof of uniqueness.

On the basis of (11.4.5), we may make the following definition:

(11.4.6) DEFINITION: Let A be a set, $x \in A$, and let $(F_n;\ n \in I)$ be a sequence of functions on A to A. Then the unique sequence α in A such that

$$\alpha(1) = x,$$
$$\text{for every } n \in I,\ \alpha(n+1) = F_n(\alpha(n)),$$

is called *the sequence in A defined inductively by x and $(F_n;\ n \in I)$*. If all functions F_n are the same function F, the sequence is said to be *defined inductively by x and F*.

Before concluding this section, let us examine (11.4.3) critically. If, for example, $n = 3$, then the unique 3-tuple α has the properties

$$\alpha(1) = x,\ \alpha(2) = F_1(\alpha(1)) = F_1(x),$$
$$\alpha(3) = F_2(\alpha(2)) = F_2(F_1(x)).$$

While the hypothesis gives a sequence $(F_m;\ m \in I)$ of functions on A to A, only F_1 and F_2 are employed in the full determination of α. Nowhere do the functions F_m with $m > 2$ appear. It is natural to suspect that the hypothesis is too strong, that perhaps in it the sequence $(F_m;\ m \in I)$ may be replaced by the 2-tuple $(F_m;\ m \in I_2)$. The next theorem shows that this weakening of the hypothesis is possible.

(11.4.7) THEOREM: *Let A be a set, let $n \in I$, $n > 1$, and let $(F_m;\ m \in I_{n-1})$ be an $(n-1)$-tuple of functions on A to A. Finally, let $x \in A$. Then there exists a unique n-tuple α in A such that*

(a) $\alpha(1) = x;$

(b) *for every* $m < n$, $\alpha(m+1) = F_m(\alpha(m)).$

PROOF: Define a sequence $(F'_m;\ m \in I)$ of functions on A to A so that

$$(1) \qquad F'_m = \begin{cases} F_m & \text{if } m < n \\ F_{n-1} & \text{if } m \geqq n. \end{cases}$$

In accordance with (11.4.4), let α be the n-tuple defined inductively by x and $(F'_m;\ m \in I)$. Evidently (a) holds, and (b) follows since $m < n$ implies $F_m = F'_m$. This proves the existence. To prove the uniqueness, let β, γ be n-tuples satisfying (a), (b). Again, define $(F'_m; m \in I)$ as in (1). Then

$$\begin{aligned} &\beta(1) = x,\ \gamma(1) = x; \\ &\text{for every } m < n,\ \beta(m+1) = F'_m(\beta(m)), \\ &\qquad\qquad\qquad\quad \gamma(m+1) = F'_m(\gamma(m)); \end{aligned}$$

hence, by the uniqueness in (11.4.3), $\beta = \gamma$.

REMARK: In (1), the definition of F'_m for $m \geqq n$ might seem artificial; this is indeed the case. In fact, *any* definition here would have been equally effective. (One may prove that in (11.4.3) two sequences $(F_m; m \in I)$, $(F'_m; m \in I)$ give rise to the same n-tuple α whenever $m \leqq n$ implies $F_m = F'_m$.) The hypothesis $n > 1$ in (11.4.7) is needed, since the symbol I_{n-1} is involved.

(11.4.8) DEFINITION: Let A be a set, $x \in A$, $n \in I$, $n > 1$, and let $(F_m; m \in I_{n-1})$ be an $(n-1)$-tuple of functions on A to A. Then the unique n-tuple α in A satisfying (a), (b) of (11.4.7) is called the n-tuple in A *defined inductively by x and $(F_m; m \in I_{n-1})$*. If all the functions F_m are the same function F, the n-tuple is said to be *defined inductively by x and F*.

(11.4.9) PROJECT: Let A be a set, $x \in A$, and let $(F_n; n \in I)$ be a sequence of functions on A to A. Construct a table like (11.2.2) showing in the right column the correspondents of 1, 2, 3, 4, 5, 6 under the sequence α in A defined inductively by x and $(F_n; n \in I)$.

(11.4.10) PROJECT: Let A be a set, $x \in A$, and E the identity function on A to A. Determine the sequence α in A which is defined inductively by x and E.

(11.4.11) PROJECT: What sequence α in I is inductively defined by 1 and σ? By 1 and $F \equiv (n + k; k \in I)$ (n being any element of I)?

11.5. The Principle of Choice. In spite of the extreme generality of the result (11.4.5), this theorem is not sufficient for all purposes. Specifically, it is sometimes necessary to find a sequence α in A in terms of an element x of A and a sequence of *relations* $(R_n; n \in I)$ on $A \times A$, which relations are not necessarily functions. In order to treat this still more general case, we are forced to discuss first a rather subtle question of logic.

It has been our avowed intention to accept all logical concepts as primitive, and thus to avoid the need of setting forth an explicit language basis for them or of formally stating any logical principles. As long as our intuitions with respect to these matters agree reasonably well with the intuitions of others, particularly those who are trying to comprehend our reasoning, serious misunderstandings or battles will not occur. For the most part, this is actually the case. There is, however, one respect in which different people have been found to possess different attitudes toward the logical concept of existence. Moreover, these differences in attitude may be great enough to cause difficulty in the communication of mathematical ideas. We shall therefore analyze in some detail the way in which we think of assertions of existence.

In order to lead up to the problem we wish to discuss, let us first give a particular existence theorem belonging to the theory of positive integers.

(11.5.1) THEOREM: *Let R be a non-absurd relation on $I \times I$ (that is, let $R \subset I \times I$, $R \neq \Theta$). Then there exists a function F on the domain of R to I such that $F \subset R$.*

PROOF: The proof is made, as we have made many before, by showing how F may be defined, that is, by producing a particular F which will fill the bill. Let D be the domain of R, so that $D \neq \Theta$. For every $n \in D$, the set

$$S \equiv [m \in I; n \, R \, m]$$

is not empty, by the definition of the domain of a relation [see (5.3.7)]. Now, by (9.3.9), (9.3.2), the set S has a unique least element k. Let us define a function F on D to I so that the correspondent under it of every $n \in D$ is this unique k. It follows that, for every $n \in D$, $F(n) \in S$, whence $n \, R \, F(n)$. This last statement means that $F \subset R$. This completes the proof.

The really striking thing about the proof is that (9.3.9), (9.3.2) were used only to secure for every $n \in D$ some unique element k of S. The fact that this k was the *least* m such that $n \, R \, m$ was nowhere needed; indeed, this fact might seem completely extraneous. All that is required of k is that it be an element of the non-empty set S. This suggests an alternate proof of (11.5.1) as follows:

ALTERNATE PROOF OF (11.5.1): Let D be the domain of R, so that $D \neq \Theta$. For every $n \in D$, the set

$$S \equiv [m \in I; n \, R \, m]$$

is not empty, by the definition of the domain. For each $n \in D$, let k be any element of S. Now define a function F on D to I so that the correspondent under it of every $n \in D$ is this k. Then, as before, $F \subset R$.

The logical point to be discussed is the question of the validity of this alternate proof. There are many mathematicians and logicians who do not accept it as a valid demonstration. The particular step objected to is the "selection" of an arbitrary $k \in S$ and the use of this k in the definition of F; the attitude being that one must, in some way, display a *unique* $k \in S$ (as was done in the first proof) before having the right to use k for further work. Some say that, if only one set $S \neq \Theta$ were involved, the selection of an arbitrary $k \in S$ would be permissible; but, since, for each $n \in D$, there is a corresponding set S, and hence (as, for example, when $D = I$) there may be needed a vast number of "simultaneous selections," the selection process is not valid. Others feel that in no case does the assertion $S \neq \Theta$ give one the right to select an element of S for subsequent use, even if only one set is involved. Those who accept the validity of the alternate proof claim that the assertion $S \neq \Theta$ of itself justifies the selection of $k \in S$, and that the non-uniqueness of k merely means that the F eventually defined is also non-unique.

It may be observed that until now we have avoided raising this issue even implicitly, by carefully proving the uniqueness of any elements we wished to use in a subsequent definition. Thus, for example, before defining α_m in the proof of (11.4.5), we proved [in (11.4.3)] the unique existence of the functions required.

Of course the entire argument is avoidable in the specific case of (11.5.1), since a completely unassailable proof has been given, and the validity of (11.5.1) is not in question. However, if, in (11.5.1), we replace the relation R on $I \times I$ by a relation on $A \times B$, where A and B are arbitrary sets, then the first, unassailable proof can no longer be given. For in arbitrary sets there is no analogue for the theorems (9.3.9), (9.3.2) by means of which a unique $k \in S$ is determined. The alternate proof, however, would apply equally well to any sets; it employs no special properties of the set I. Hence, when it is desired to generalize the theorem (11.5.1) to relations on arbitrary sets, the very validity of the result is in question if the alternate proof is not acceptable.

We do not take sides on the question of the acceptability of the alternate proof. Such proofs will be avoided because they are not universally accepted. But as to the validity of the generalization of (11.5.1) we do take sides. This result seems vital for some important mathematical theorems, since no proofs have been devised avoiding its use. Hence we incorporate it into our attitude toward existence by asserting it (without proof, of course) in the following form.

(11.5.2) Principle of Choice: *If A and B are (non-empty) sets and R is any relation on $A \times B$ whose domain is A, then there exists a function F on A to B such that $F \subset R$.*

The principle of choice is ascribed to Zermelo and is generally called the "axiom of choice." Whether we "believe" (11.5.2) or not is beside the point. If we do, then we believe propositions whose proofs seem to require it; if not, then (11.5.2) is regarded as constituting part of the hypotheses of these propositions. At any rate, whenever (11.5.2) is used in a proof, that fact will be clearly stated.

There are many equivalent ways of formulating the principle of choice; some dozens of formulations exist in the literature. We give an indication of the variety of statements possible by stating another formulation which will be proved equivalent to (11.5.2).

(11.5.3) ALTERNATE PRINCIPLE OF CHOICE: *If A and B are (non-empty) sets and $(R_n; n \in I)$ is a sequence of relations on $A \times B$, each having domain A, then there exists a sequence $(F_n; n \in I)$ of functions on A to B such that, for every $n \in I$, $F_n \subset R_n$.*

PROOF OF EQUIVALENCE: Clearly (11.5.3) implies (11.5.2) as a special case. It will be shown that (11.5.2) implies (11.5.3). Define $\mathbf{S}$ and $\mathcal{R}$ by

$$\mathbf{S} \equiv [\text{all functions on } A \text{ to } B];$$
$$\mathcal{R} \equiv [(n, F) \in I \times \mathbf{S}; F \subset R_n].$$

Then $\mathcal{R}$ is a relation on $I \times \mathbf{S}$. First, it is shown that $\mathcal{R}$ has domain I. To do this, we prove that, for every $n \in I$, there exists $F \in \mathbf{S}$ such that $F \subset R_n$. But this follows from (11.5.2) with $R = R_n$. It is now evident that $\mathbf{S} \neq \Theta$.

Now apply (11.5.2) with A, B, R replaced by I, $\mathbf{S}$, $\mathcal{R}$, respectively. Then (11.5.2) yields that there exists a function $\mathfrak{F}$ on I to $\mathbf{S}$ such that $\mathfrak{F} \subset \mathcal{R}$. For every $n \in I$, define

$$F_n \equiv \mathfrak{F}(n) \in \mathbf{S}.$$

Since $\mathfrak{F} \subset \mathcal{R}$, $(n, \mathfrak{F}(n)) \in \mathcal{R}$. Thus $F_n = \mathfrak{F}(n) \subset R_n$. This completes the proof.

A further indication of how it is possible to rephrase the principle of choice can be obtained by noticing that no special properties of I were used in the proof of (11.5.3) from (11.5.2). Hence it is possible to replace I by an arbitrary set. The particular statement of (11.5.3) is chosen because it is best adapted to the first application of the principle of choice to be given.

(11.5.4) PROJECT: The principle of choice is often stated thus: *Let $\mathfrak{M}$ be a (non-empty) set whose elements are non-empty subsets of a set T. Suppose that $S_1, S_2 \in \mathfrak{M}$, $S_1 \neq S_2$ implies $S_1 \cdot S_2 = \Theta$. Then there exists a subset U of T such that, for every $S \in \mathfrak{M}$, $U \cdot S$ is finite and has exactly* 1 *element.* Show that this statement is implied by (11.5.2).

11.6. General Inductive Definition. At the beginning of Section 4, it was mentioned that a more general theorem on inductive definition would be needed. It was necessary first to discuss the principle of choice because the proof of the more general result uses this principle. The general theorem on inductive definition may now be stated and proved.

(11.6.1) THEOREM: *Let A be a (non-empty) set, and let $(R_n; n \in I)$ be a sequence of relations on $A \times A$, each having domain A. Finally, let $x \in A$. Then there exists a sequence α in A, such that*

(a) $\alpha(1) = x$;

(b) *for every* $n \in I$, $\alpha(n) \, R_n \, \alpha(n + 1)$.

PROOF: By (11.5.3) with $B = A$, there exists a sequence $(F_n; n \in I)$ of functions on A to A such that, for every $n \in I$, $F_n \subset R_n$. Then, by (11.4.5), there exists a sequence α in A, such that

(1) $\alpha(1) = x$;

(2) for every $n \in I$, $\alpha(n + 1) = F_n(\alpha(n))$.

But (2) may also be written

$$\alpha(n) \, F_n \, \alpha(n + 1),$$

or, equivalently,

$$(\alpha(n), \alpha(n + 1)) \in F_n.$$

Then, since $F_n \subset R_n$, $(\alpha(n), \alpha(n + 1)) \in R_n$, or

(3) $$\alpha(n) \, R_n \, \alpha(n + 1).$$

Thus (a) and (b) are true by (1) and (3). This completes the proof.

The two theorems (11.4.5) and (11.6.1) should be carefully compared. Notice, in particular, that (11.4.5) is *not* a special case of (11.6.1), since (11.6.1) says nothing about the uniqueness of the sequence which is proved to exist. Moreover, the proof of (11.4.5) does not require the use of the principle of choice, while the proof of (11.6.1) apparently does.

(11.6.2) DEFINITION: Let A be a set, $x \in A$, and let $(R_n; n \in I)$ be a sequence of relations on $A \times A$ with domain A. Let α be any sequence in A such that

$\alpha(1) = x$;

for every $n \in I$, $\alpha(n) \, R_n \, \alpha(n + 1)$.

Then α is said to be *a sequence in A defined inductively by x and* $(R_n; n \in I)$. If all relations R_n are the same relation R, α is said to be a sequence in A *defined inductively by x and R*.

The next chapter will be devoted to some applications of (incomplete) inductive definition.

(11.6.3) PROJECT: Let $m \in I$. Prove, without using (11.6.1), the existence of a sequence α in I which is inductively defined by m and $<$. By establishing the existence of another sequence β with $\beta \neq \alpha$, show that in (11.6.1) uniqueness is impossible.

Chapter 12

EXTENDED OPERATIONS AND APPLICATIONS

[No Basis]

12.1. Introduction. It has been seen that binary operations on $A \times A$ to A, where A is a set, play a considerable role in mathematics; for example, group theory centers about such an operation, and most of the theory of positive integers involves essentially the operations $+$, $\cdot$ on $I \times I$ to I. Associated with a given operation $\circ$ on $A \times A$ to A are certain "extensions," which may be introduced with the help of the machinery of inductive definition.

If $a_1, a_2 \in A$, then $a_1 \circ a_2 \in A$, so that, if also $a_3 \in A$, then $(a_1 \circ a_2) \circ a_3 \in A$. We have thus associated with the elements $a_1, a_2, a_3 \in A$ the unique element $(a_1 \circ a_2) \circ a_3$ of A. This association clearly has the character of a function whose domain is the set A^3 of all 3-tuples in A, and whose range is a subset of A. Now if $a_1, a_2, a_3, a_4 \in A$, then $((a_1 \circ a_2) \circ a_3) \circ a_4 \in A$, so that we have a function on A^4 to A. We shall be concerned with the precise definition and the study of the properties of the entire chain of functions suggested by the initial steps indicated. The functions on A^n to A for $n \in I$ so obtained will be the desired extensions of $\circ$.

It should be noted that, after the beginning stage $a_1 \circ a_2$ in the construction of the extensions, a certain latitude is possible in selecting the mode of continuation. Thus one might elect to associate $a_1 \circ (a_2 \circ a_3)$ rather than $(a_1 \circ a_2) \circ a_3$ with (a_1, a_2, a_3); and corresponding to (a_1, a_2, a_3, a_4) one might specify, for example, $a_1 \circ ((a_2 \circ a_3) \circ a_4)$. However, under certain circumstances, these various choices lead to the same extensions. Operations having but one extension may be shown to be those called *associative*, in accordance with the following:

(12.1.1) Definition: If A is a set, and if $\circ$ is an operation on $A \times A$ to A, then $\circ$ is *associative* if

$$a, b, c \in A \text{ implies } (a \circ b) \circ c = a \circ (b \circ c).$$

The extensions of associative operations are more significant for the applications to be made than those for non-associative operations, and so most of our attention is devoted to these operations. (It will be recalled that group operations and $+$, $\cdot$ on $I \times I$ to I are associative.)

There is another source of latitude in the construction of extensions of an operation $\circ$. Indeed, at the outset, where a function on A^2 to A is introduced, it would be possible to select $a_2 \circ a_1$, rather than $a_1 \circ a_2$, as the element to be associated with $(a_1, a_2) \in A^2$. Increasing latitude exists at the subsequent stages; for example, associated with $(a_1, a_2, a_3) \in A^3$ might be $(a_2 \circ a_1) \circ a_3$ or $a_3 \circ (a_1 \circ a_2)$, or any of several other possibilities. Again, for certain operations, the multiplicity of extensions is considerably reduced; this is true, in particular, for those operations called *commutative*, in accordance with the following:

(12.1.2) DEFINITION: If A is a set, and if $\circ$ is an operation on $A \times A$ to A, then $\circ$ is *commutative* if

$$a, b \in A \text{ implies } a \circ b = b \circ a.$$

Particularly significant results are obtained for operations which are both associative and commutative, as are $+, \cdot$ on $I \times I$ to I. (Of course, such results will apply to group operations only in the case of commutative groups.)

Although the aim of the present chapter is to obtain properties of certain particular operations, it is more economical to make the treatment general, so that application may easily be made to each desired special case; thus the need for proving similar theorems for the special operations separately is obviated.

12.2. Extensions of Operations.

(12.2.1) LEMMA: *Suppose A is a set and $\circ$ is an operation on $A \times A$ to A. Let $n \in I$ and $(a_k; k \in I_n)$ be an n-tuple in A. Then there exists a unique n-tuple $(b_m; m \in I_n)$ such that*

(a) $b_1 = a_1$;

(b) *for every* $m < n$, $b_{m+1} = b_m \circ a_{m+1}$.

PROOF OF EXISTENCE: If $n = 1$, define $(b_m; m \in I_1)$ so that $b_1 = a_1$. Then (a) holds, and (b) is vacuously true. Let $n > 1$, and define an $(n - 1)$-tuple $(F_m; m \in I_{n-1})$ of functions on A to A as follows:

$$\text{for } a \in A,\ m \in I_{n-1},\ F_m(a) = a \circ a_{m+1}.$$

Then, by (11.4.7) with $x = a_1$, there exists a unique function α on I_n to A such that

(1) $\alpha(1) = a_1$;

(2) for every $m < n$, $\alpha(m + 1) = F_m(\alpha(m)) = \alpha(m) \circ a_{m+1}$.

Define, for every $m \in I_n$, $b_m \equiv \alpha(m)$. Then (1), (2) yield (a), (b).

PROOF OF UNIQUENESS: If $n = 1$, uniqueness is evident in view of (a). If $n > 1$, n-tuples $(b_m; m \in I_n)$, $(c_m; m \in I_n)$ satisfying (a), (b) are functions β, γ on I_n to A satisfying (1), (2). Hence they are equal by (11.4.7).

(12.2.2) DEFINITION: Suppose A is a set and $\circ$ is an operation on $A \times A$ to A. Let $n \in I$ and $(a_k;\ k \in I_n)$ be an n-tuple in A. Then the unique n-tuple $(b_m;\ m \in I_n)$ whose unique existence was proved in (12.2.1) is called the $\circ$-*associate* of $(a_k;\ k \in I_n)$. For every $m \in I_n$, the element b_m is given the notation

$$\bigcirc_m(a_k;\ k \in I_n).$$

(12.2.3) COROLLARY: *If A is a set, if $\circ$ is an operation on $A \times A$ to A, if $n \in I$ and if $(a_k;\ k \in I_n)$ is an n-tuple in A, then, for every $m \in I_n$,*

$$\bigcirc_m(a_k;\ k \in I_n) = \bigcirc_m(a_k;\ k \in I_m).$$

PROOF: Lemma (12.2.1), applied to the n-tuple $(a_k;\ k \in I_n)$, yields that there exists a unique n-tuple $(b_k;\ k \in I_n)$ such that

(1) $b_1 = a_1$;
(2) for every $k < n$, $b_{k+1} = b_k \circ a_{k+1}$.

But, if $m < n$, (12.2.1) applied to the m-tuple $(a_k;\ k \in I_m)$ yields that there exists a unique m-tuple $(c_k;\ k \in I_m)$ such that

(3) $c_1 = a_1$;
(4) for every $k < m$, $c_{k+1} = c_k \circ a_{k+1}$.

Since $m \leqq n$, from (1) and (2) it is seen that the m-tuple $(b_k;\ k \in I_m)$ satisfies the requirements uniquely determining $(c_k;\ k \in I_m)$; thus

(5) for every $j \in I_m$, $b_j = c_j$.

But, by the definition (12.2.2),

$$b_j = \bigcirc_j(a_k;\ k \in I_n), \quad c_j = \bigcirc_j(a_k;\ k \in I_m).$$

Hence, from (5) with $j = m$,

$$\bigcirc_m(a_k;\ k \in I_n) = \bigcirc_m(a_k;\ k \in I_m).$$

This completes the proof.

The notation introduced in (12.2.2), while convenient, is not customary. The usual notation is introduced in the next definition.

(12.2.4) DEFINITION: If A is a set, if $\circ$ is an operation on $A \times A$ to A, if $n \in I$, and if $(a_k;\ k \in I_n)$ is an n-tuple in A, then

$$\bigcirc_{k=1}^{n} a_k \equiv \bigcirc_n(a_k;\ k \in I_n).$$

(12.2.5) Corollary: *If A is a set, if $\circ$ is an operation on $A \times A$ to A, if $m, n \in I$, $m \leqq n$, and if $(a_k; k \in I_n)$ is an n-tuple in A, then*

(a) $$\bigcirc_{k=1}^{m} a_k = \bigcirc_m (a_k; k \in I_n).$$

In particular,

(b) $$\bigcirc_{k=1}^{1} a_k = a_1.$$

Proof: By the definition (12.2.4),

$$\bigcirc_{k=1}^{m} a_k = \bigcirc_m (a_k; k \in I_m).$$

Hence (a) is an immediate consequence of (12.2.3). Then (b) follows from the definition of $\bigcirc_1(a_k; k \in I_n)$.

(12.2.6) Corollary: *If A is a set, if $\circ$ is an operation on $A \times A$ to A, if $n \in I$, $n > 1$, and if $(a_k; k \in I_n)$ is an n-tuple in A, then*

$$\bigcirc_{k=1}^{n} a_k = \left(\bigcirc_{k=1}^{n-1} a_k\right) \circ a_n.$$

Proof: This follows immediately from (12.2.5) and the fact that

$$\bigcirc_n (a_k; k \in I_n) = \bigcirc_{n-1} (a_k; k \in I_n) \circ a_n.$$

Remark: When the operation $\circ$ is denoted by $+$, it is customary to use $\sum$ (for "sum") in place of $\bigcirc$. Hence $\sum_{m=1}^{n} a_m$ means the element b_n in the unique n-tuple $(b_m; m \in I_n)$ such that

$$b_1 = a_1;$$
$$\text{for every } m < n,\ b_{m+1} = b_m + a_{m+1};$$

$\sum_{m=1}^{n} a_m$ is called the *sum* of $(a_m; m \in I_n)$. Similarly, if $\circ$ is denoted by $\cdot$ or $\times$, then $\prod$ (for "product") replaces the symbol $\bigcirc$. Hence $\prod_{m=1}^{n} a_m$ means the element c_n in the unique n-tuple $(c_m; m \in I_n)$ such that

$$c_1 = a_1;$$
$$\text{for every } m < n,\ c_{m+1} = c_m \cdot a_{m+1};$$

$\prod_{m=1}^{n} a_m$ is called the *product* of $(a_m; m \in I_n)$.

We illustrate the use of (12.2.6) by proving an important result on sums of positive integers.

(12.2.7) Theorem: *Let $n, j \in I$. Then*

$$\sum_{m=1}^{n} j = n \cdot j.$$

REMARK: The notation $\sum_{m=1}^{n} j$ means, of course, the sum of the n-tuple $(j; m \in I_n)$ or, more explicitly, the sum of the n-tuple $(a_m; m \in I_n)$ which is defined by the requirement that, for every $m \in I_n$, $a_m = j$. Such an n-tuple is called a *constant n-tuple.*

PROOF: The proof is by induction. Let $j \in I$, and define

$$H \equiv \left[n \in I; \sum_{m=1}^{n} j = n \cdot j \right].$$

Now $1 \in H$, since, by (12.2.5.b),

$$\sum_{m=1}^{1} j = j = 1 \cdot j.$$

Suppose $q \in H$, so that

(1) $$\sum_{m=1}^{q} j = q \cdot j.$$

Then

$$\begin{aligned} \sum_{m=1}^{q+1} j &= \left(\sum_{m=1}^{q} j \right) + j && \text{[by (12.2.6)]} \\ &= q \cdot j + 1 \cdot j && \text{[by (1)]} \\ &= (q + 1) \cdot j && \text{[by (8.6.14]}, \end{aligned}$$

whence $q + 1 \in H$. It follows from III′ that $H = I$, and the proof is complete.

REMARK: The theorem (12.2.7) is a statement of the connection between "multiplication" and "repeated addition" which is generally used as the "definition" of "multiplication" in elementary school.

We close this section by proving one more result concerning the extension of the operation + on $I \times I$ to I, a generalization of the distributive law.

(12.2.8) THEOREM: *Let $n \in I$ and $(a_m; m \in I_n)$ be an n-tuple in I. Finally, let $k \in I$. Then*

(a) $$\sum_{m=1}^{n} (k \cdot a_m) = k \cdot \sum_{m=1}^{n} a_m.$$

PROOF: Let

$$H \equiv [n \in I; \text{ for every } k \in I \text{ and every } (a_m; m \in I_n), \text{ (a) is true}].$$

It will be shown that $H = I$. First $1 \in H$, since

$$\sum_{m=1}^{1} (k \cdot a_m) = k \cdot a_1 = k \cdot \sum_{m=1}^{1} a_m.$$

Now suppose $q \in H$, so that, for every $k \in I$ and every $(a_m; m \in I_q)$,

$$(1) \qquad \sum_{m=1}^{q}(k \cdot a_m) = k \cdot \sum_{m=1}^{q} a_m.$$

Then

$$\begin{aligned}
\sum_{m=1}^{q+1}(k \cdot a_m) &= \left(\sum_{m=1}^{q}(k \cdot a_m)\right) + k \cdot a_{q+1} && \text{[by (12.2.6)]} \\
&= \left(k \cdot \sum_{m=1}^{q} a_m\right) + k \cdot a_{q+1} && \text{[by (1)]} \\
&= k \cdot \left(\sum_{m=1}^{q} a_m + a_{q+1}\right) && \text{[by (8.6.14)]} \\
&= k \cdot \sum_{m=1}^{q+1} a_m && \text{[by (12.2.6)].}
\end{aligned}$$

Thus $q \in H$ implies $q + 1 \in H$. By III′, $H = I$, and the proof is complete.

(12.2.9) Project: Prove that, if $n \in I$, then $\prod_{m=1}^{n} 1 = 1$.

(12.2.10) Project: Prove that, if $n \in I$, then

$$2 \cdot \sum_{m=1}^{n} m = n \cdot (n + 1).$$

12.3. General Associative and Commutative Laws. In (12.1) it was indicated that the particular extension considered in the preceding section is only one of many that might have been considered. It was further indicated that many of these possible extensions coincide for associative operations and still more of them coincide for operations that are both associative and commutative. In this section, we shall consider some of the implications of assuming associativity or both associativity and commutativity of the given operation.

In order to formulate these results, it will be necessary to introduce a slight extension of the notation of (12.2.4).

(12.3.1) Definition: Let A be a set and $\circ$ an operation on $A \times A$ to A. Let $n \in I$, $n > 1$, and let $(a_k; k \in I_n)$ be an n-tuple in A. Let $m \in I_{n-1}$. Then

$$\bigcirc_{k=m+1}^{n} a_k \equiv \bigcirc_{n-m}(a_{m+k}; k \in I_{n-m}) = \bigcirc_{k=1}^{n-m} a_{m+k}.$$

(12.3.2) Corollary: *If $(a_k; k \in I_n)$ is an n-tuple in A, and if $q \in I_n$, then*

$$\bigcirc_{k=q}^{q} a_k = a_q.$$

Proof: If $q = 1$, this is (12.2.5.b). If $q > 1$, then $q = (q - 1) + 1$, and, from (12.3.1), (12.2.5.b), it follows that

$$\bigcirc_{k=q}^{q} a_k = \bigcirc_{k=(q-1)+1}^{q} a_k = \bigcirc_{k=1}^{q-(q-1)} a_{(q-1)+k}$$
$$= \bigcirc_{k=1}^{1} a_{(q-1)+k} = a_{(q-1)+1} = a_q.$$

With the notation of (12.3.1), it is now possible to state a general associative law.

(12.3.3) Theorem: *Let A be a set and $\circ$ an associative operation on $A \times A$ to A. Let $n \in I$, $n > 1$; let $(a_k;\, k \in I_n)$ be an n-tuple in A, and let $m \in I_{n-1}$. Then*

(a) $$\bigcirc_{k=1}^{n} a_k = \left(\bigcirc_{k=1}^{m} a_k\right) \circ \left(\bigcirc_{k=m+1}^{n} a_k\right).$$

Remark: It is easy to see that this result "includes" the associative law if one applies it first with $n = 3$, $m = 1$ and then with $n = 3$, $m = 2$ and equates the two right-hand elements obtained.

Proof: The proof is by induction. Define

$H' \equiv [n \in I;\, n > 1$, and for every $(a_k;\, k \in I_n)$, $m \in I_{n-1}$, (a) is true];
$H \equiv [1] + H'$.

It will be proved that $H = I$. Obviously $1 \in H$ by definition.

Let $q \in H$, with the aim of proving that $q + 1 \in H$. If $q = 1$, it is to be shown that $2 \in H'$, that is, for every $(a_k;\, k \in I_2)$ and every $m \in I_1$,

$$\bigcirc_{k=1}^{2} a_k = \left(\bigcirc_{k=1}^{m} a_k\right) \circ \left(\bigcirc_{k=m+1}^{2} a_k\right).$$

But $m \in I_1$ means $m = 1$, so that it suffices to show that

$$\bigcirc_{k=1}^{2} a_k = \left(\bigcirc_{k=1}^{1} a_k\right) \circ \left(\bigcirc_{k=2}^{2} a_k\right),$$

which is trivial in view of (12.3.2).

Suppose now that $q > 1$, whence $q \in H'$, and let us show that $q + 1 \in H'$. A $(q + 1)$-tuple $(a_k;\, k \in I_{q+1})$ and $m \in I_q$ are supposed given. If $m = q$, we have, by (12.2.6) and (12.3.2),

$$\bigcirc_{k=1}^{q+1} a_k = \left(\bigcirc_{k=1}^{q} a_k\right) \circ a_{q+1}$$
$$= \left(\bigcirc_{k=1}^{q} a_k\right) \circ \left(\bigcirc_{k=q+1}^{q+1} a_k\right)$$
$$= \left(\bigcirc_{k=1}^{m} a_k\right) \circ \left(\bigcirc_{k=m+1}^{q+1} a_k\right),$$

and (a) holds with $n = q + 1$. On the other hand, if $m < q$, then

$$\begin{aligned}
\bigcirc_{k=1}^{q+1} a_k &= \left(\bigcirc_{k=1}^{q} a_k\right) \circ a_{q+1} && \text{[by (12.2.6)]} \\
&= \left(\left(\bigcirc_{k=1}^{m} a_k\right) \circ \left(\bigcirc_{k=m+1}^{q} a_k\right)\right) \circ a_{q+1} && \text{[since } q \in H'\text{]} \\
&= \left(\bigcirc_{k=1}^{m} a_k\right) \circ \left(\left(\bigcirc_{k=m+1}^{q} a_k\right) \circ a_{q+1}\right) && \text{[since } \circ \text{ is associative]} \\
&= \left(\bigcirc_{k=1}^{m} a_k\right) \circ \left(\left(\bigcirc_{k=1}^{q-m} a_{m+k}\right) \circ a_{m+(q-m+1)}\right) && \text{[by (12.3.1)]} \\
&= \left(\bigcirc_{k=1}^{m} a_k\right) \circ \left(\bigcirc_{k=1}^{q-m+1} a_{m+k}\right) && \text{[by (12.2.6)]} \\
&= \left(\bigcirc_{k=1}^{m} a_k\right) \circ \left(\bigcirc_{k=m+1}^{q+1} a_k\right) && \text{[by (12.3.1)].}
\end{aligned}$$

Again (a) holds with $n = q + 1$. Thus $q + 1 \in H'$ and hence $q + 1 \in H$. By III′, $H = I$. Therefore, for $n \in I$, either $n = 1$, or $n > 1$ and $n \in H'$. This completes the proof.

We close this section with the proof of two general commutativity results that hold for the extensions of a commutative (and associative) operation.

(12.3.4) DEFINITION: Let A be a set and $\circ$ an associative operation on $A \times A$ to A. If $n \in I$, $n > 1$, if $(a_k; k \in I_n)$ is an n-tuple in A, and if $m \in I_n$, define

$$\bigcirc_{\substack{k=1 \\ k \neq m}}^{n} a_k$$

to be

$$\begin{aligned}
&\bigcirc_{k=2}^{n} a_k && \text{if } m = 1; \\
&\bigcirc_{k=1}^{n-1} a_k && \text{if } m = n; \\
\left(\bigcirc_{k=1}^{m-1} a_k\right) \circ &\left(\bigcirc_{k=m+1}^{n} a_k\right) && \text{if } m \neq 1, n.
\end{aligned}$$

(12.3.5) THEOREM: *Let A be a set and $\circ$ an associative and commutative operation on $A \times A$ to A. If $n \in I$, $n > 1$, if $(a_k; k \in I_n)$ is an n-tuple in A, and if $m \in I_n$, then*

$$\bigcirc_{k=1}^{n} a_k = a_m \circ \left(\bigcirc_{\substack{k=1 \\ k \neq m}}^{n} a_k\right) = \left(\bigcirc_{\substack{k=1 \\ k \neq m}}^{n} a_k\right) \circ a_m.$$

PROOF: The second equality is evident since $\circ$ is commutative. If $m = 1$ or $m = n$, the result follows immediately from (12.3.3), (12.2.6); we leave the details to the reader. Let $m \neq 1, n$, whence $1 < m$, $m < n$. Then

$$\bigcirc_{k=1}^{n} a_k = \left(\bigcirc_{k=1}^{m} a_k\right) \circ \left(\bigcirc_{k=m+1}^{n} a_k\right) \qquad \text{[by (12.3.3)]}$$

$$= \left(\left(\bigcirc_{k=1}^{m-1} a_k\right) \circ a_m\right) \circ \left(\bigcirc_{k=m+1}^{n} a_k\right) \qquad \text{[by (12.2.6)]}$$

$$= a_m \circ \left(\left(\bigcirc_{k=1}^{m-1} a_k\right) \circ \left(\bigcirc_{k=m+1}^{n} a_k\right)\right)$$

$$= a_m \circ \left(\bigcirc_{\substack{k=1\\k\neq m}}^{n} a_k\right) \qquad \text{[by (12.3.4)],}$$

and the proof is complete.

A simple consequence of (12.3.5) for the case $A = I$, $\circ = \cdot$, that will be useful later, is given next.

(12.3.6) COROLLARY: *Let $(a_j;\, j \in I_n)$ be an n-tuple in I and let $k \in I_n$. Then $a_k \mid \left(\prod_{j=1}^{n} a_j\right)$, that is, there exists $u \in I$ such that*

$$\prod_{j=1}^{n} a_j = a_k \cdot u.$$

PROOF: If $n > 1$ this is an immediate consequence of (12.3.5) with $u = \prod_{\substack{j=1\\j\neq k}}^{n} a_j$. If $n = 1$ (whence $k = 1$), the corollary is true with $u = 1$ by (12.2.5.b).

Theorem (12.3.5) is clearly a generalization of the commutative law as can be seen by considering the case $n = m = 2$. In intuitive terms, (12.3.5) states that any particular element can be "pulled out in front" without affecting the value of $\bigcirc_{k=1}^{n} a_k$. From (12.3.5) it is possible to prove a still more general commutative law as will be shown next. First a definition is required:

(12.3.7) DEFINITION: Let $m, n \in I$, and let $(a_k;\, k \in I_m)$ and $(b_l;\, l \in I_n)$ be m- and n-tuples in a set A. Then $(b_l;\, l \in I_n)$ is a *rearrangement* of $(a_k;\, k \in I_m)$ if there exists a one-to-one correspondence φ between I_n and I_m such that,

(a) for every $l \in I_n$, $b_l = a_{\varphi(l)}$.

(12.3.8) Corollary: *Let* $(b_l; l \in I_n)$ *be a rearrangement of* $(a_k; k \in I_m)$. *Then* $m = n$, *and* $(a_k; k \in I_m)$ *is a rearrangement of* $(b_l; l \in I_n)$. *Moreover,*

$$[a_k; k \in I_m] = [b_l; l \in I_n].$$

Proof: The fact that $m = n$ follows from (10.3.5). Now φ^* is a one-to-one correspondence between I_m and I_n; moreover, by (10.2.1.b), for every $k \in I_m$, $\varphi(\varphi^*(k)) = k$, whence (12.3.7.a) with $l = \varphi^*(k)$ yields

$$(1) \qquad a_k = a_{\varphi(\varphi^*(k))} = b_{\varphi^*(k)},$$

so that $(a_k; k \in I_m)$ is a rearrangement of $(b_l; l \in I_n)$. By (12.3.7.a), $l \in I_n$ implies $b_l \in [a_k; k \in I_m]$, since there exists $k \in I_m$, namely, $k = \varphi(l)$, with $b = a_k$. Hence

$$[b_l; l \in I_n] \subset [a_k; k \in I_m].$$

The reverse inclusion similarly follows from (1) and the proof is complete.

Remark: It should be noted that, although it is true that, if $(b_l; l \in I_n)$ is a rearrangement of $(a_k; k \in I_m)$, then $[a_k; k \in I_m] = [b_l; l \in I_n]$, the converse of this implication is not true due to the possibility that $a_k = a_j$ with $k \neq j$. The reader should construct simple examples to verify this fact.

We now state the general commutative law with which this section will be concluded.

(12.3.9) Theorem: *Let A be a set and $\circ$ an associative and commutative operation on $A \times A$ to A. Let $n \in I$, let $(a_m; m \in I_n)$ be an n-tuple in A, and let $(b_m; m \in I_n)$ be a rearrangement of $(a_m; m \in I_n)$. Then*

$$\text{(a)} \qquad \bigcirc_{m=1}^{n} a_m = \bigcirc_{m=1}^{n} b_m.$$

Proof: The proof is by induction. Define

$$H \equiv [n \in I;\ \text{if } (b_m; m \in I_n) \text{ is a rearrangement of } (a_m; m \in I_n), \text{ then (a) is true}].$$

Clearly $1 \in H$, since the only one-to-one correspondence between $I_1 = [1]$ and itself is the identity. Thus

$$\bigcirc_{m=1}^{1} a_m = a_1 = b_1 = \bigcirc_{m=1}^{1} b_m.$$

Now suppose $q \in H$, with the aim of proving $q + 1 \in H$. Let $(a_m; m \in I_{q+1})$ by a $(q + 1)$-tuple in A, and let $(b_m; m \in I_{q+1})$ be a rearrangement of $(a_m; m \in I_{q+1})$. The fact that $(b_m; m \in I_{q+1})$ is a rearrangement of $(a_m; m \in I_{q+1})$ means, according to the definition (12.3.7), that there is a one-to-one correspondence φ between I_{q+1} and I_{q+1} such that, for every $m \in I_{q+1}$,

$$b_m = a_{\varphi(m)}.$$

In particular,

$$b_{q+1} = a_{\varphi(q+1)}.$$

Now define $k \equiv \varphi(q+1)$, so that $k \in I_{q+1}$, and

(1) $$b_{q+1} = a_k.$$

We have

(2) $$\bigcirc_{m=1}^{q+1} b_m = \left(\bigcirc_{m=1}^{q} b_m\right) \circ b_{q+1} \qquad \text{[by (12.2.6)]};$$

and, on the other hand,

(3) $$\bigcirc_{m=1}^{q+1} a_m = \left(\bigcirc_{\substack{m=1\\ m\neq k}}^{q+1} a_m\right) \circ a_k \qquad \text{[by (12.3.5)]}.$$

Define a q-tuple $(c_m;\ m \in I_q)$ in A so that, for every $m \in I_q$,

(4) $$c_m = \begin{cases} a_m & \text{if } m < k \\ a_{m+1} & \text{if } m \geqq k. \end{cases}$$

Then it is easily seen from (4) and (12.3.4) that

(5) $$\bigcirc_{\substack{m=1\\ m\neq k}}^{q+1} a_m = \bigcirc_{m=1}^{q} c_m.$$

It will now be shown that the q-tuple $(b_m;\ m \in I_q)$ is a rearrangement of $(c_m;\ m \in I_q)$. To this end, define a function ψ on I_q to I_q so that, for every $m \in I_q$,

(6) $$\psi(m) = \begin{cases} \varphi(m) & \text{if } \varphi(m) < k \\ \varphi(m) - 1 & \text{if } \varphi(m) > k. \end{cases}$$

It should be noticed that (6) defines $\psi(m)$ for every $m \in I_q$, since $\varphi(m) = k$ occurs only for $m = q + 1$ and therefore for no $m \in I_q$. Then, for every $m \in I_q$,

$$b_m = a_{\varphi(m)} = c_{\psi(m)} \qquad \text{[by (4), (6)]}.$$

Moreover, it is easily verified that ψ is a one-to-one correspondence between I_q and I_q. Thus $(b_m;\ m \in I_q)$ is a rearrangement of $(c_m;\ m \in I_q)$. Then the fact that $q \in H$ implies that

(7) $$\bigcirc_{m=1}^{q} c_m = \bigcirc_{m=1}^{q} b_m.$$

From (7) and (5) it follows that

$$\bigcirc_{m=1}^{q} b_m = \bigcirc_{\substack{m=1\\ m\neq k}}^{q+1} a_m,$$

whence, by (1),

(8) $$\left(\bigcirc_{m=1}^{q} b_m\right) \circ b_{q+1} = \left(\bigcirc_{\substack{m=1\\ m\neq k}}^{q+1} a_m\right) \circ a_k.$$

Comparison of (8), (2), (3) shows

$$\bigcirc_{m=1}^{q+1} a_m = \bigcirc_{m=1}^{q+1} b_m,$$

whence $q + 1 \epsilon H$. It has been shown that $1 \epsilon H$, and that $q \epsilon H$ implies $q + 1 \epsilon H$. Thus, by III′, $H = I$, and the proof is complete.

(12.3.10) PROJECT: In (12.3.3), let $n = 5$ and write the conclusion (a) for $m = 1, 2, 3, 4$ without using the symbol $\bigcirc$.

(12.3.11) PROJECT: Treat the cases $m = 1$, $m = n$ in the proof of (12.3.5).

(12.3.12) PROJECT: Let (a_1, a_2, a_3) be a 3-tuple in a set A. Determine all its rearrangements.

(12.3.13) PROJECT: Prove the statement in the remark following (12.3.8) by constructing an appropriate example.

(12.3.14) PROJECT: In (12.3.5), and also in (12.3.9), let (a_1, a_2, a_3) be a 3-tuple and write the conclusions without using the symbol $\bigcirc$, displaying a separate equality for every rearrangement.

(12.3.15) PROJECT: In the proof of (12.3.9), the function ψ defined by (6) is stated to be a one-to-one correspondence between I_q and I_q. Prove this fact.

12.4. Powers. A particularly important special case of $\bigcirc_{m=1}^{n} a_m$ arises when the n-tuple $(a_m;\, m \epsilon I_n)$ in A is a constant, that is, when there exists an element $a \epsilon A$ such that $a_m = a$ for every $m \epsilon I_n$.

(12.4.1) DEFINITION: If A is a set and $\circ$ an associative operation on $A \times A$ to A, and if $(a_m;\, m \epsilon I_n)$ is an n-tuple in A such that, for $m \epsilon I_n$, $a_m = a \epsilon A$, then

$$\bigcirc_{m=1}^{n} a_m = \bigcirc_{m=1}^{n} a$$

is called the n-th $\circ$-*power* of a. If $\circ$ is written $\cdot$ or $\times$, so that $\bigcirc$ is written $\prod$, the notation a^n is used for the n-th $\circ$-power, that is,

$$a^n = \prod_{m=1}^{n} a.$$

REMARK: One result concerning $\circ$-powers with $\circ = +$ and $A = I$ has already been obtained in (12.2.7). It should be noted that the discussion of (11.2) is an intuitive introduction to $\circ$-powers with $A = I$ and $\circ = \cdot$.

Two results which are simple consequences of the results of the last sections will be given here.

(12.4.2) THEOREM: *Let A be a set and $\circ$ an associative operation on $A \times A$ to A. Let $a \in A$ and $m, n \in I$. Then*

$$\left(\bigcirc_{q=1}^{m} a\right) \circ \left(\bigcirc_{q=1}^{n} a\right) = \bigcirc_{q=1}^{m+n} a.$$

PROOF: Consider the $(m + n)$-tuple $(a;\ q \in I_{m+n})$. Then

$$\bigcirc_{q=1}^{m+n} a = \left(\bigcirc_{q=1}^{m} a\right) \circ \left(\bigcirc_{q=m+1}^{m+n} a\right) \qquad \text{[by (12.3.3)]}$$

$$= \left(\bigcirc_{q=1}^{m} a\right) \circ \left(\bigcirc_{q=1}^{n} a\right) \qquad \text{[by (12.3.1)].}$$

(12.4.3) COROLLARY: *Let A be a set and $\cdot$ an associative operation on $A \times A$ to A. Let $a \in A$ and $m, n \in I$. Then*

$$a^m \cdot a^n = a^{m+n}.$$

PROOF: This is simply a restatement of (12.4.2) using the notation $a^n \equiv \prod_{q=1}^{n} a.$

(12.4.4) THEOREM: *Let A be a set and $\circ$ an associative operation on $A \times A$ to A. Let $a \in A$ and $m, n \in I$. Then*

(a) $$\bigcirc_{s=1}^{m}\left(\bigcirc_{r=1}^{n} a\right) = \bigcirc_{r=1}^{m \cdot n} a.$$

PROOF: Let $n \in I$, and define

$$H \equiv [m \in I;\ \text{(a) is true}].$$

Now $1 \in H$, since

$$\bigcirc_{s=1}^{1}\left(\bigcirc_{r=1}^{n} a\right) = \bigcirc_{r=1}^{n} a = \bigcirc_{r=1}^{1 \cdot n} a \qquad \text{[by (12.3.2)].}$$

Suppose $q \in H$. Then

$$\bigcirc_{s=1}^{q+1}\left(\bigcirc_{r=1}^{n} a\right) = \left(\bigcirc_{s=1}^{q}\left(\bigcirc_{r=1}^{n} a\right)\right) \circ \left(\bigcirc_{r=1}^{n} a\right) \qquad \text{[by (12.2.6)]}$$

$$= \left(\bigcirc_{r=1}^{q \cdot n} a\right) \circ \left(\bigcirc_{r=1}^{n} a\right) \qquad \text{[since } q \in H\text{]}$$

$$= \bigcirc_{r=1}^{q \cdot n+n} a \qquad \text{[by (12.4.2)]}$$

$$= \bigcirc_{r=1}^{(q+1) \cdot n} a,$$

so that $q + 1 \in H$. Thus $H = I$ by III′, and the proof is complete.

(12.4.5) Corollary: *Let A be a set and $\cdot$ an associative operation on $A \times A$ to A. Let $a \in A$ and $m, n \in I$. Then*

$$(a^m)^n = a^{m \cdot n}.$$

Proof: This is a restatement of (12.4.4).

Remark: The two results (12.4.3) and (12.4.5) may be recognized as the familiar "laws of exponents."

(12.4.6) Project: Let $a, m, n \in I$, $m < n$. Prove that $a^n \mid^* a^m$, and that $a^n \div a^m = a^{n-m}$. This is another familiar "law of exponents."

12.5. The Fundamental Theorem of Arithmetic. This section will be devoted to a result in the theory of the positive integers which is so important that it has been called the fundamental theorem of arithmetic. Its proof will require many of the results obtained earlier in this chapter applied to the operation $\cdot$ on $I \times I$ to I. The result to be obtained concerns the "representation" of positive integers as "finite products" of prime numbers.

Recall that a positive integer is called a prime if it is not 1, and if the only positive integers which divide it are itself and 1 [see (9.4.8)]. From this definition it follows that, if $m \in I$ is not a prime, then either $m = 1$ or there exists $t \in I$ such that $t \mid m$ and $1 < t$, $t < m$. Since $t \mid m$ means $m = t \cdot u$ for some $u \in I$, every positive integer other than 1 and not a prime can be written as a "product." Intuitively, one might feel, since, if t and u are not primes, they in turn can be written as products, that this "process" can be "continued" until prime factors are arrived at. Thus it is suggested that any positive integer (>1) is an (extended) product of primes. The next theorem will establish this fact.

(12.5.1) Theorem: *Let $m \in I$, $m > 1$. Then there exist $n \in I$ and an n-tuple $(p_j; j \in I_n)$ of primes such that*

(a) $$m = \prod_{j=1}^{n} p_j.$$

Proof: Suppose the theorem is false. Then, by (9.3.9), there is a least positive integer $s > 1$ for which there does not exist a tuple of primes satisfying (a) with $m = s$. Now s is not a prime, for if it were, then, by (12.3.2),

$$s = \prod_{j=1}^{1} p$$

would be true with $p = s$ (a prime). Since $s > 1$ is not prime, there exist $t, u \in I$ such that $1 < t$, $1 < u$ and

(1) $$s = t \cdot u.$$

By (9.2.18) and (9.2.19), $t < s$ and $u < s$. Then, by the definition of s (as a least), it follows that t and u are "products of primes," that is, that there exists an n_1-tuple $(q_j;\ j \in I_{n_1})$ of primes and an n_2-tuple $(r_j;\ j \in I_{n_2})$ of primes such that

$$(2) \qquad t = \prod_{j=1}^{n_1} q_j$$

and

$$(3) \qquad u = \prod_{j=1}^{n_2} r_j.$$

Thus, from (1), (2), (3),

$$(4) \qquad s = \left(\prod_{j=1}^{n_1} q_j\right) \cdot \left(\prod_{j=1}^{n_2} r_j\right).$$

Now define an $(n_1 + n_2)$-tuple $(p_j;\ j \in I_{n_1+n_2})$ as follows:

$$(5) \qquad p_j \equiv \begin{cases} q_j & \text{if } j \leqq n_1 \\ r_{j-n_1} & \text{if } n_1 < j \leqq n_1 + n_2. \end{cases}$$

Then, from (5) and (4), it follows, in view of (12.3.1), that

$$s = \left(\prod_{j=1}^{n_1} p_j\right) \cdot \left(\prod_{j=n_1+1}^{n_1+n_2} p_j\right).$$

Thus, by (12.3.3),

$$(6) \qquad s = \prod_{j=1}^{n_1+n_2} p_j,$$

where, by (5), p_j is a prime for every $j \in I_{n_1+n_2}$. But this contradicts the definition of s as a positive integer for which (6) is impossible. This completes the proof.

It is clear that, for any $m \in I$, an n-tuple of primes $(p_j;\ j \in I_n)$ such that $m = \prod_{j=1}^{n} p_j$ is not unique; in fact, from the general commutativity theorem (12.3.9), if $m = \prod_{j=1}^{n} p_j$ and if $(q_j;\ j \in I_n)$ is a rearrangement of $(p_j;\ j \in I_n)$, then $m = \prod_{j=1}^{n} q_j$. The main result to be demonstrated in this section is that the n-tuple of primes such that $m = \prod_{j=1}^{n} p_j$ is "unique except for rearrangements." This is conveniently demonstrated with the help of several lemmas.

(12.5.2) Lemma: *Let a, b, $p \in I$ such that p is a prime and $p \mid a \cdot b$. Then $p \mid a$ or $p \mid b$.*

Proof: Suppose the theorem is false, so that the set

(1) $[p \in I;\ p$ is a prime, and there exist $a, b \in I$ such that $p \mid a \cdot b$, $p \nmid a,\ p \nmid b]$

is not empty. Then, by (9.3.9), the set (1) has a least. Let p_1 denote this least. Since p_1 is in the set (1), the set

(2) $[a \in I;$ there exists $b \in I$ such that $p_1 \mid a \cdot b,\ p_1 \mid' a,\ p_1 \mid' b]$

is not empty and so has a least a_1. Then, since a_1 is in the set (2), $p_1 \mid' a_1$, and the set

(3) $$[b \in I;\ p_1 \mid a_1 \cdot b,\ p_1 \mid' b]$$

is not empty. Let b_1 denote the least in (3). Then we have

(4) $$p_1 \mid a_1 \cdot b_1, \quad p_1 \mid' a_1, \quad p_1 \mid' b_1.$$

It is easy to see (since $\cdot$ is commutative) that the set (3) is a subset of (2). Hence, from the definition of a_1 as a least,

(5) $$a_1 \leqq b_1.$$

It is also easy to see that $a_1 > 1$, $b_1 > 1$. For example, if $a_1 = 1$, then $p_1 \mid a_1 \cdot b_1$ implies $p_1 \mid b_1$, contrary to $p_1 \mid' b_1$.

Now it will be shown that $b_1 < p_1$. This is proved indirectly. Suppose

(6) $$p_1 \leqq b_1.$$

Then, since $p_1 \mid' b_1$, $p_1 \neq b_1$, whence $p_1 < b_1$. The "quotient and remainder" theorem (9.4.9) yields that there exist $s, r \in I$ such that

(7) $$b_1 = p_1 \cdot s + r \quad \text{and} \quad r < p_1.$$

Then

$$a_1 \cdot b_1 = a_1 \cdot (p_1 \cdot s + r) = a_1 \cdot p_1 \cdot s + a_1 \cdot r.$$

Clearly $p_1 \mid (a_1 \cdot p_1 \cdot s)$ and $p_1 \mid (a_1 \cdot p_1 \cdot s + a_1 \cdot r)$. Thus, by (9.4.7), (4),

(8) $$p_1 \mid a_1 \cdot r, \quad p_1 \mid' a_1.$$

But, by (7), (6), $r < b_1$. By the definition of b_1 as a least in (3), $r < b_1$ shows that r is not in the set (3). Hence (8) implies $p_1 \mid r$, so that $p_1 \leqq r$, contrary to (7). This contradiction shows that the assumption (6) is false and that

(9) $$b_1 < p_1.$$

Hence, by (5),

(10) $$a_1 < p_1.$$

From (4), it follows that there exists $c \in I$ such that

(11) $$p_1 \cdot c = a_1 \cdot b_1.$$

Clearly $c > 1$, for otherwise $p_1 = a_1 \cdot b_1$, with $a_1 > 1$, $b_1 > 1$, contrary to the fact that p_1 is prime. Then, by (12.5.1), there exist $n \in I$ and an n-tuple $(q_j; j \in I_n)$ of primes, such that

$$c = \prod_{j=1}^{n} q_j.$$

From (12.3.6), it follows that there exists $u \in I$ such that

$$(12) \qquad c = q_1 \cdot u.$$

Then, by (11), (12),

$$(13) \qquad p_1 \cdot q_1 \cdot u = a_1 \cdot b_1.$$

Now it will be shown that

$$(14) \qquad q_1 < p_1.$$

If $p_1 \leqq q_1$, then, by (9), (10), $a_1 \cdot b_1 < p_1 \cdot p_1 \leqq p_1 \cdot q_1 \leqq p_1 \cdot q_1 \cdot u$, contrary to (13). This establishes (14). Then (14) and the definition of p_1 as least in the set (1) show that q_1 is not in the set (1). But q_1 is prime and, by (13), $q_1 \mid a_1 \cdot b_1$. Hence either $q_1 \mid a_1$ or $q_1 \mid b_1$. It will now be shown that both of these possibilities lead to a contradiction.

Suppose $q_1 \mid a_1$, so that there exists $d \in I$ such that

$$(15) \qquad a_1 = q_1 \cdot d.$$

Then by (13), (15),

$$p_1 \cdot q_1 \cdot u = q_1 \cdot d \cdot b_1,$$

whence

$$p_1 \cdot u = d \cdot b_1,$$

and $p_1 \mid d \cdot b_1$. But $d < a_1$ by (15), since $q_1 \neq 1$ (q_1 is a prime), so that d is not an element of (2). Hence $p_1 \mid d$ or $p_1 \mid b_1$. The second possibility contradicts (4). But, if $p_1 \mid d$, then $p_1 \mid q_1 \cdot d$, and, by (15), $p_1 \mid a_1$, contrary to (4).

The possibility $q_1 \mid b_1$ may be shown to lead to a contradiction in a similar manner; this is left for the reader.

This completes the proof, since the assumption that (1) is non-empty has been proved false.

The next lemma may be phrased verbally as follows: "If a prime divides a product of primes, it is one of the primes in the product."

(12.5.3) Lemma: *Let p be a prime, $n \in I$, and $(q_j; j \in I_n)$ an n-tuple of primes such that*

$$p \,\Big|\, \prod_{j=1}^{n} q_j.$$

Then there exists $k \in I_n$ such that $p = q_k$.

PROOF: The proof is by induction. Define

$$H \equiv [n \in I; \text{ if } p \text{ is prime, } (q_j;\, j \in I_n) \text{ is an } n\text{-tuple of primes with } p \,\Big|\, \prod_{j=1}^{n} q_j, \text{ then there exists } k \in I_n \text{ such that } p = q_k].$$

First, $1 \in H$. For, if $p \,\Big|\, \prod_{j=1}^{1} q_j$, then $p \mid q_1$, whence, since q_1 is prime, $p = 1$ or $p = q_1$. But $p \neq 1$ since p is a prime, whence $p = q_1$.

Now suppose $m \in H$, with the aim of showing $m + 1 \in H$. Let p be a prime, and let $(q_j;\, j \in I_{m+1})$ be an $(m + 1)$-tuple of primes such that

$$p \,\Big|\, \prod_{j=1}^{m+1} q_j.$$

Then, by (12.2.6),

$$p \,\Big|\, \left(\prod_{j=1}^{m} q_j\right) \cdot q_{m+1}.$$

Hence, by (12.5.2),

$$p \,\Big|\, \prod_{j=1}^{m} q_j \quad \text{or} \quad p \mid q_{m+1}.$$

If $p \,\Big|\, \prod_{j=1}^{m} q_j$, then the fact that $m \in H$ shows that

(1) there exists $k \in I_m$ such that $p = q_k$.

Otherwise, if $p \mid q_{m+1}$, the fact that p and q_{m+1} are prime shows that

(2) $p = q_{m+1}$.

Since either (1) or (2) is true, it is seen that there exists $k \in I_{m+1}$ such that $p = q_k$. Thus $m + 1 \in H$. Hence, by III′, $H = I$, and the proof is complete.

Now the main result of this section can be stated as follows:

(12.5.4) THEOREM: *Let $m, n \in I$, and let $(p_j;\, j \in I_m)$ and $(q_j;\, j \in I_n)$ be, respectively, an m-tuple and an n-tuple of primes such that*

$$\prod_{j=1}^{m} p_j = \prod_{j=1}^{n} q_j.$$

Then $m = n$, and $(q_j;\, j \in I_n)$ is a rearrangement of $(p_j;\, j \in I_m)$.

PROOF: A separate proof that $m = n$ is unnecessary by (12.3.8). The proof of the second statement is by induction. Define

$$H \equiv [m \in I; \text{ if } (p_j;\, j \in I_m) \text{ is an } m\text{-tuple of primes, if } n \in I, \text{ if } (q_j;\, j \in I_n) \text{ is an } n\text{-tuple of primes, and if } \prod_{j=1}^{m} p_j = \prod_{j=1}^{n} q_j, \text{ then } (q_j;\, j \in I_n) \text{ is a rearrangement of } (p_j;\, j \in I_m)].$$

First, it is easily shown that $1 \in H$. For if

$$(1) \qquad \prod_{j=1}^{1} p_j = p_1 = \prod_{j=1}^{n} q_j,$$

then, by (9.4.3), $p_1 \Big| \prod_{j=1}^{n} q_j$. Thus, by (12.5.3), there exists $k \in I_n$ such that $p_1 = q_k$. It will be shown indirectly that $n = 1$. Suppose $n > 1$. Then, from (1), (12.3.5),

$$p_1 = q_k \cdot \prod_{\substack{j=1 \\ j \neq k}}^{n} q_j > q_k = p_1,$$

which is a contradiction. Thus $n = 1$, and

$$p_1 = \prod_{j=1}^{1} q_j = q_1,$$

whence $1 \in H$.

Now suppose $g \in H$. It will be shown that $g + 1 \in H$. To this end, let $(p_j; j \in I_{g+1})$ be a $(g+1)$-tuple of primes and $(q_j; j \in I_n)$ an n-tuple of primes such that

$$(2) \qquad \prod_{j=1}^{g+1} p_j = \prod_{j=1}^{n} q_j.$$

By (2) and the general associative law (12.3.3),

$$(3) \qquad \left(\prod_{j=1}^{g} p_j\right) \cdot p_{g+1} = \prod_{j=1}^{n} q_j,$$

so that $p_{g+1} \Big| \prod_{j=1}^{n} q_j$. Then, from (12.5.3), there exists $h \in I_n$ such that

$$(4) \qquad p_{g+1} = q_h.$$

Now clearly $n > 1$, since otherwise $q_h = q_1 = p_{g+1}$, and $p_{g+1} \cdot \prod_{j=1}^{g} p_j = p_{g+1}$, which is impossible. Hence, by (3), (12.3.5),

$$p_{g+1} \cdot \prod_{j=1}^{g} p_j = q_h \cdot \prod_{\substack{j=1 \\ j \neq h}}^{n} q_j,$$

whence, by (4),

$$(5) \qquad \prod_{j=1}^{g} p_j = \prod_{\substack{j=1 \\ j \neq h}}^{n} q_j.$$

Since $g \in H$, (5) shows that the $(n-1)$-tuple $(r_j; j \in I_{n-1})$ defined so that

$$(6) \qquad r_j = \begin{cases} q_j & \text{if } j < h \\ q_{j+1} & \text{if } h \leqq j \leqq n-1 \end{cases}$$

is a rearrangement of the g-tuple $(p_j;\ j \in I_g)$. Hence $n - 1 = g$, and there is a one-to-one correspondence φ between I_g and I_{n-1} such that,

$$\text{(7)} \qquad \text{for every } j \in I_g,\ r_j = p_{\varphi(j)}.$$

Now define a function ψ on I_n so that, for every $j \in I_n$,

$$\psi(j) = \begin{cases} \varphi(j) & \text{if } j < h \\ g + 1 & \text{if } j = h \\ \varphi(j - 1) & \text{if } h < j \leqq n. \end{cases}$$

It is easily seen that ψ is a one-to-one correspondence between $I_n = I_{g+1}$ and I_n, and that, for every $j \in I_n$, $q_j = p_{\psi(j)}$; details are left for the reader. This shows that $(q_j;\ j \in I_n)$ is a rearrangement of $(p_j;\ j \in I_{g+1})$; hence $g + 1 \in H$.

It has been shown that $1 \in H$ and that, if $g \in H$, then $g + 1 \in H$. Hence $H = I$, and the proof is complete.

(12.5.5) PROJECT: At the end of the proof of (12.5.2), show that $q_1 \mid b_1$ leads to a contradiction.

(12.5.6) PROJECT: Prove that the function ψ, defined after (7) in the proof of (12.5.4), is a one-to-one correspondence between I_n and I_n.

(12.5.7) PROJECT: Apply (12.5.4) to the non-primes among 2, 3, 4, 5, 6, 7, 8, 9.

Chapter 13

INFINITE SETS

[No Basis]

13.1. Introduction. In Chapter 10, a broad classification of sets was made employing three categories, namely, empty sets, finite sets and infinite sets; finite sets were studied there in some detail. In the remark following (10.1.2) it was indicated that not every non-empty set is finite. Hence there is some point to an investigation of the properties of infinite sets. It will be found natural to subdivide infinite sets into two categories, which are referred to by the terms *countable* and *uncountable*. In order to study infinite sets effectively, we shall need a deeper knowledge of set theory than has been required for the development of the theories presented thus far. Moreover, certain results pertaining to equivalence of sets are required. Accordingly, we shall first devote our attention to the general set-theoretic considerations, and then we shall turn to the study of infinite sets.

13.2. Set-Theoretic Sums and Products. It will be recalled that two sets A, B always give rise to another set, $A + B$, which is called their set-theoretic sum and consists of all elements of A together with all elements of B [(4.7)]. A natural question is whether application of this idea is limited to two sets. For example, one may ask whether three sets have a set-theoretic sum. The answer is immediate, for if A, B, C are sets, then $(A + B) + C$ must be admitted as a set (since $A + B$ is a set and C is a set), and, moreover, $(A + B) + C$ consists of the elements of A, B, C all "lumped together." (Of course, $A + (B + C)$ might have been used as well; that $(A + B) + C = A + (B + C)$ follows immediately.)

A little reflection shows now that four sets may be similarly treated; indeed the array

$$\begin{array}{c} A + B, \\ (A + B) + C, \\ ((A + B) + C) + D \end{array} \tag{13.2.1}$$

suggests strongly that we apply inductive definition to obtain a sequence of set-theoretic sums. Without carrying out the details, we merely mention that we should meet certain difficulties; in fact, it is not clear what the set A of (11.4.5) should be. Moreover, even if the difficulties could be overcome, the final result would be far too special for later purposes. For it is conceivable that in some theory so many sets are under consideration that no inductively defined set-theoretic sum would "lump together" *all* the elements of all the sets; and it will appear that such an all-inclusive set-theoretic sum is desirable and useful.

Hence we are led to broaden the principle of "lumping together." Instead of insisting merely that if two sets are before us, their set-theoretic sum is also before us, let us demand that if *any sets whatever* are under consideration, their set-theoretic sum may be formed. More specifically, let us accept from logic the following principle.

(13.2.2) PRINCIPLE: *Let $\mathfrak{M}$ be a set whose elements are themselves sets. Then there exists a set S such that,*

(a) *for every $A \in \mathfrak{M}$, $A \subset S$;*
(b) *for every $x \in S$, there exists $A \in \mathfrak{M}$ with $x \in A$.*

It follows immediately that S is unique. For let S_1, S_2 both have properties (a), (b). Then, if $x \in S_1$, there exists [by (b)] $A \in \mathfrak{M}$ with $x \in A$. But, by (a), $A \subset S_2$. Hence $x \in S_2$. This shows that $S_1 \subset S_2$. Similarly, $S_2 \subset S_1$, whence $S_1 = S_2$.

The unique set S of (13.2.2) is called the *set-theoretic sum of the sets in* $\mathfrak{M}$, and is denoted by

$$\sum \mathfrak{M} \quad \text{or by} \quad \sum [A; A \in \mathfrak{M}].$$

Thus $\sum \mathfrak{M}$ consists of all the elements of the sets in $\mathfrak{M}$ "lumped together." In particular, if $\mathfrak{M} = [A, B]$, then

$$\sum \mathfrak{M} = A + B,$$

so that our earlier set-theoretic sum of two sets appears as a special case of the newly introduced extended set-theoretic sum.

A similar extension of the concept of set-theoretic product is possible. Again let $\mathfrak{M}$ be a set whose elements are themselves sets. The set of all elements which are members of every set in $\mathfrak{M}$ is called the *set-theoretic product of the sets in* $\mathfrak{M}$; it is denoted by

$$\prod \mathfrak{M} \quad \text{or} \quad \prod [A; A \in \mathfrak{M}].$$

Thus

$$\prod \mathfrak{M} \equiv [x \in \sum \mathfrak{M}; A \in \mathfrak{M} \text{ implies } x \in A].$$

In particular, if $\mathfrak{M} = [A, B]$, then

$$\prod \mathfrak{M} = A \cdot B,$$

so that the extended set-theoretic product includes the set-theoretic product of two sets as a special case.

It is worth noting that no further principle like (13.2.2) is necessary for the introduction of $\prod \mathfrak{M}$. In fact, (13.2.2) makes possible the definition of both $\sum \mathfrak{M}$ and $\prod \mathfrak{M}$. Another remark is this. A theory concerning a set $\mathfrak{M}$ of sets can be regarded as a theory concerning certain subsets of a single set, namely, $\sum \mathfrak{M}$, since by (13.2.2.a) every element of $\mathfrak{M}$ is a subset of $S = \sum \mathfrak{M}$.

Many general theorems pertaining to set-theoretic sums and products could now be proved. Such theorems constitute a good portion of set theory and may be found in treatises on the subject. A few examples will serve to indicate the nature of the results.

(13.2.3) Theorem: *If $\mathfrak{M}$, $\mathfrak{N}$ are sets whose elements are sets, then*

$$\sum \mathfrak{M} + \sum \mathfrak{N} = \sum (\mathfrak{M} + \mathfrak{N}).$$

Proof: Define $S \equiv \sum \mathfrak{M} + \sum \mathfrak{N}$. If $x \in S$, then $x \in \sum \mathfrak{M}$ or $x \in \sum \mathfrak{N}$. Hence either

(1) there exists $A \in \mathfrak{M}$ such that $x \in A$,

or

(2) there exists $B \in \mathfrak{N}$ such that $x \in B$.

If (1) is true, $A \in (\mathfrak{M} + \mathfrak{N})$; if (2) is true, $B \in (\mathfrak{M} + \mathfrak{N})$, so that in either case $x \in \sum (\mathfrak{M} + \mathfrak{N})$. This proves

(3) $$S \subset \sum (\mathfrak{M} + \mathfrak{N}).$$

On the other hand, let $x \in \sum (\mathfrak{M} + \mathfrak{N})$. Then there exists $C \in (\mathfrak{M} + \mathfrak{N})$ such that $x \in C$. But either $C \in \mathfrak{M}$ or $C \in \mathfrak{N}$; in the former case $x \in \sum \mathfrak{M}$, and in the latter $x \in \sum \mathfrak{N}$. In either case $x \in \left(\sum \mathfrak{M} + \sum \mathfrak{N}\right) = S$. Thus

(4) $$\sum (\mathfrak{M} + \mathfrak{N}) \subset S.$$

By (3), (4), we have the desired result.

(13.2.4) Theorem: *If M is a set whose elements are sets each of which has sets for its elements, then*

$$\sum [\sum \mathfrak{M}; \mathfrak{M} \in M] = \sum (\sum M).$$

Remark: This generalizes (13.2.3), for if $M = [\mathfrak{M}, \mathfrak{N}]$, then (13.2.4) yields (13.2.3). The reader should study (13.2.4) carefully and carry through a proof.

(13.2.5) THEOREM: *Let S be a set, and let $\mathfrak{M}$ be a set whose elements are subsets of S. Then*

(a) $$\prod[S - A; A \in \mathfrak{M}] = S - \sum\mathfrak{M};$$

(b) $$\sum[S - A; A \in \mathfrak{M}] = S - \prod\mathfrak{M}.$$

PROOF OF (a): Let $x \in \prod[S - A; A \in \mathfrak{M}]$, that is, suppose

$$A \in \mathfrak{M} \text{ implies } x \in (S - A).$$

Then $x \in S$ and $x \in' \sum\mathfrak{M}$, and hence

$$x \in (S - \sum\mathfrak{M}).$$

We have then

$$\prod[S - A; A \in \mathfrak{M}] \subset S - \sum\mathfrak{M}.$$

Proof of the reverse inclusion is left for the reader.

PROOF OF (b): This is similar to the proof of (a) and is left to the reader.

REMARK: A special case of (13.2.5) was stated in (4.7):

$$A \supset B \text{ implies } B + (A - B) = A.$$

This follows from (13.2.5) by putting $S = A$, $\mathfrak{M} = [B, A - B]$, as is easily seen.

(13.2.6) THEOREM: *Let $\mathfrak{M}$, $\mathfrak{N}$ be sets of sets such that $\mathfrak{M} \subset \mathfrak{N}$. Then*

(a) $$\sum\mathfrak{M} \subset \sum\mathfrak{N};$$

(b) $$\prod\mathfrak{M} \supset \prod\mathfrak{N}.$$

The proof is left to the reader.

We close this section with a few remarks about sequences of sets. It will be recalled [see (8.4.1)] that a sequence of elements of a set $\mathfrak{M}$ is a function on I to $\mathfrak{M}$. In particular, if $\mathfrak{M}$ has sets as its elements, a sequence of elements of $\mathfrak{M}$ is a sequence of sets. Such a sequence of sets is also called a sequence of subsets of $\sum\mathfrak{M}$ (since every member of $\mathfrak{M}$ is a subset of $\sum\mathfrak{M}$). Let $(A_n; n \in I)$ be a sequence of sets (of $\mathfrak{M}$). Then $\mathfrak{N} \equiv [A_n; n \in I]$ is itself a set whose elements are sets; in fact, $\mathfrak{N} \subset \mathfrak{M}$, $\mathfrak{N}$ being the range of the function $(A_n; n \in I)$. It is customary to denote $\sum\mathfrak{N}$ and $\prod\mathfrak{N}$ respectively by

$$\sum_{n \in I} A_n, \quad \prod_{n \in I} A_n,$$

or simply

$$\sum A_n, \quad \prod A_n,$$

instead of the more cumbersome

$$\sum[A_n; n \in I], \quad \prod[A_n; n \in I].$$

Similarly, if $H \subset I$, we define

$$\sum_{n \in H} A_n \equiv \sum[A_n;\, n \in H],$$

$$\prod_{n \in H} A_n \equiv \prod[A_n;\, n \in H].$$

An important result which is needed later is the following.

(13.2.7) THEOREM: *Let $\mathfrak{M}$ be a set of sets, and let*

$$(A_n;\, n \in I), \quad (B_n;\, n \in I)$$

be sequences in $\mathfrak{M}$. Suppose that, for every $n \in I$, $A_n \subset B_n$. Then

(a) $$\sum_{n \in I} A_n \subset \sum_{n \in I} B_n;$$

(b) $$\prod_{n \in I} A_n \subset \prod_{n \in I} B_n.$$

PROOF OF (a): Let $x \in \sum A_n$. Then there exists $n \in I$ such that $x \in A_n$. Hence $x \in B_n$, and $x \in \sum B_n$.

PROOF OF (b): This is left to the reader.

(13.2.8) PROJECT: Prove (13.2.4).

(13.2.9) PROJECT: Complete the proof of (13.2.5.a) and prove (13.2.5.b).

(13.2.10) PROJECT: Prove (13.2.6).

(13.2.11) PROJECT: Prove (13.2.7.b).

13.3. Two Theorems on Equivalence. It was proved [see (10.4.7), (10.4.4.b)] that, if S, T are sets such that $S \subset T$, $T \sim S$ *and T is finite*, then $S = T$. The question arises as to what conclusion, if any, can be drawn if the hypothesis that T be finite is deleted. Preliminary to a detailed study of this situation, a general theorem pertaining to sets S, T with $S \subset T$, $T \sim S$ is needed. Before proving this theorem [(13.3.3)], we prove an extension of (10.2.5) to a case in which more sets are involved.

(13.3.1) THEOREM: *Let $\mathfrak{M}$ be a set of sets (that is, let $\mathfrak{M}$ have sets as its elements). Further, let $(S_n;\, n \in I)$, $(T_n;\, n \in I)$ be sequences in $\mathfrak{M}$ such that*

$$m, n \in I,\ m \neq n \text{ implies } S_m \cdot S_n = \Theta;$$
$$m, n \in I,\ m \neq n \text{ implies } T_m \cdot T_n = \Theta.$$

If, for every $n \in I$, $S_n \sim T_n$, then $\sum S_n \sim \sum T_n$.

PROOF: Define $S \equiv \sum S_n$, $T \equiv \sum T_n$. The procedure of the proof that $S \sim T$ is to construct a one-to-one correspondence between S and T

combining individual correspondences between the S_n and T_n for $n \in I$. If there were a unique correspondence between S_n and T_n, the task would be simplified, since a sequence of functions (correspondences) would be available, and the set-theoretic sum of these functions might serve as a correspondence between S and T. But there are possibly many correspondences between S_n and T_n, so that the principle of choice suggests itself as a device to obtain just one.

Note first that, if S or T is empty, the other is empty also, so that $S \sim T$. Assume $S, T \neq \Theta$. Let us apply (11.5.2), with

$$A \equiv I, \quad B \equiv [\text{all relations on } S \times T] \neq \Theta,$$
$$R \equiv [(n, \varphi) \in A \times B;\ \varphi \text{ is a one-to-one correspondence between } S_n \text{ and } T_n].$$

First, it is shown that A is the domain of R. Since by our hypothesis, $n \in I$ $(=A)$ implies $S_n \sim T_n$, we have

(1) for every $n \in A$, there exists a one-to-one correspondence φ between S_n and T_n.

But such a φ as in (1) is a subset of $S_n \times T_n$, hence of $S \times T$, whence $\varphi \in B$. Thus

(2) for every $n \in A$, there exists $\varphi \in B$ such that $n\ R\ \varphi$.

By (2), A is the domain of R. The hypothesis of (11.5.2) is verified, so that the conclusion follows, namely,

(3) there exists a function F on A to B with $F \subset R$.

But (3) states that there exists a sequence $(\varphi_n; n \in I)$ such that

$$(4) \qquad (\varphi_n; n \in I) \subset R.$$

An alternate way of stating (4) is

$$[(n, \varphi_n); n \in I] \subset R,$$

or

$$(5) \qquad n \in I \text{ implies } n\ R\ \varphi_n.$$

Finally, (5) says that

$n \in I$ implies that φ_n is a one-to-one correspondence between S_n and T_n.

Since, for every $n \in I$, $\varphi_n \subset S_n \times T_n$, we have $\varphi_n \subset S \times T$.

Having "selected" a sequence of one-to-one correspondences, we define

$$\varphi \equiv \sum_{n \in I} \varphi_n \subset S \times T.$$

It will be shown that φ is a one-to-one correspondence between S and T. This task is divided into four steps:

(6) $S =$ domain of φ;
(7) $T =$ range of φ;
(8) φ is a function; that is, $x \varphi y_1$, $x \varphi y_2$ implies $y_1 = y_2$;
(9) φ^* is a function; that is, $x_1 \varphi y$, $x_2 \varphi y$ implies $x_1 = x_2$.

To prove (6), let $x \in S$. There exists $n \in I$ with $x \in S_n$. (That n is moreover unique follows from the fact that $n_1 \neq n_2$ implies $S_{n_1} \cdot S_{n_2} = \Theta$.) Define $y \equiv \varphi_n(x) \in T_n$, whence

$$(x, y) \in \varphi_n \subset \varphi,$$

and $x \varphi y$. This proves that S is the domain of φ.

To prove (7), let $y \in T$, so that there exists (a unique) $n \in I$ with $y \in T_n$. Define $x \equiv \varphi_n^*(y)$, whence $x \varphi_n y$, and $x \varphi y$. Thus T is the range of φ.

Now suppose that $x \varphi y_1$, $x \varphi y_2$, whence

$$(x, y_1),\ (x, y_2) \in \varphi,$$

and there exist (by the definition of φ) $n_1, n_2 \in I$ such that

$$(x, y_1) \in \varphi_{n_1},\ (x, y_2) \in \varphi_{n_2}.$$

Now the domain of φ_{n_1} is S_{n_1}, and that of φ_{n_2} is S_{n_2}, whence $x \in S_{n_1}, S_{n_2}$. If $n_1 \neq n_2$, then $S_{n_1} \cdot S_{n_2} = \Theta$, contrary to $x \in S_{n_1} \cdot S_{n_2}$; hence $n_1 = n_2$. We have, therefore,

$$x \varphi_{n_1} y_1,\ x \varphi_{n_1} y_2,$$

and it follows that $y_1 = y_2$, since φ_{n_1} is a function. This completes the proof of (8).

Finally, the proof of (9) is similar, being obtained by merely interchanging the symbols φ, φ^*, the symbols x, y and the symbols S, T in the argument just given.

This completes the proof.

(13.3.2) Corollary: *If $\mathfrak{M}$ is a set of sets, if $m \in I$, and if $(S_n; n \in I_m)$, $(T_n; n \in I_m)$ are m-tuples in $\mathfrak{M}$ such that*

$$n_1, n_2 \in I_m,\ n_1 \neq n_2 \text{ implies } S_{n_1} \cdot S_{n_2} = T_{n_1} \cdot T_{n_2} = \Theta,$$

and

$$\text{for every } n \in I_m,\ S_n \sim T_n,$$

then

$$\sum[S_n; n \in I_m] \sim \sum[T_n; n \in I_m].$$

Proof: The idea of the proof is as follows. Define a sequence $(S_n'; n \in I)$ so that $S_n' = S_n$ for every $n \in I_m$, and $S_n' = \Theta$ otherwise. (This Θ is, of course, the empty subset of $\sum\mathfrak{M}$, and may be regarded as appended to the elements of $\mathfrak{M}$ if not one of them originally.) A similar sequence $(T'_n; n \in I)$ is defined. The hypotheses of (13.3.1) are then true for $(S'_n; n \in I)$ and $(T'_n; n \in I)$, whence $\sum S'_n \sim \sum T'_n$, and the result follows. Details are left for the reader.

REMARK: An alternate proof of (10.2.5) consists in specializing (13.3.2) with $m = 2$, as the reader may verify. Thus (13.3.2) clearly generalizes (10.2.5). While the proof given for (13.3.2) depends on the principle of choice, since (13.3.1) is used, an inductive proof employing (10.2.5) exists which does not rest on the principle of choice.

(13.3.3) THEOREM: *If S, T, U are sets such that*

$$S \subset U \subset T, \quad T \sim S,$$

then $U \sim T$.

REMARK: This is one of the most fundamental results in set theory. It guarantees that, whenever a set is equivalent to a (proper) subset of itself (a possibility that may at first seem startling, but which will subsequently be seen to be of the utmost significance), then all subsets "lying between them" are equivalent to both.

PROOF: While the proof is technically somewhat intricate, the underlying plan is simple. It is to construct two sequences of sets (indeed, subsets of T) satisfying the hypotheses of (13.3.1) and having set-theoretic sums equal to U and T respectively. The conclusion of (13.3.1) will then yield the desired result. Certain auxiliary sequences are introduced first, and the final sequences are defined with their help. Use of (13.3.1) entails use of the principle of choice.

The program is begun by defining $\mathfrak{M} \equiv [\text{all subsets of } T]$. Let us now investigate how the equivalence of T and S yields a function on $\mathfrak{M}$ to $\mathfrak{M}$. Since $T \sim S$, there exists a one-to-one correspondence φ between T and S. Recalling the notation $\varphi(V)$ defined in (5.4.8) for $V \in \mathfrak{M}$,

$$(1) \qquad \varphi(V) = [\varphi(x); x \in V],$$

we see that $\varphi(V) \subset T$, whence $\varphi(V) \in \mathfrak{M}$. Thus each $V \in \mathfrak{M}$ determines a unique corresponding element of $\mathfrak{M}$, namely, $\varphi(V)$. In other words,

$$\Phi \equiv (\varphi(V); V \in \mathfrak{M})$$

is a function on $\mathfrak{M}$ to $\mathfrak{M}$. An important property of Φ is that

(2) $\quad W \subset V$ implies $\Phi(W) \subset \Phi(V)$ (that is, $\varphi(W) \subset \varphi(V)$);

the proof is immediate from (1).

There are now two sequences in $\mathfrak{M}$ defined inductively, the first by T and Φ and the second by U and Φ [see (11.4.5), (11.4.6)]. If we denote these sequences by $(T'_n; n \in I)$ and $(U'_n; n \in I)$, then we have

(3a) $T'_1 = T$;
(3b) for every $n \in I$, $T'_{n+1} = \Phi(T'_n) = \varphi(T'_n)$;
(4a) $U'_1 = U$;
(4b) for every $n \in I$, $U'_{n+1} = \Phi(U'_n) = \varphi(U'_n)$.

These are the auxiliary sequences mentioned above; some of their properties will be proved before the final sequences are defined.

First we shall prove

(5) for every $n \in I$, $T'_{n+1} \subset U'_n \subset T'_n$.

Define

$$H \equiv [n \in I;\ T'_{n+1} \subset U'_n \subset T'_n].$$

Clearly $1 \in H$, since

$$T'_2 = \varphi(T'_1) = \varphi(T) = \text{range of } \varphi = S \subset U = U'_1,$$

and

$$U'_1 = U \subset T = T'_1.$$

Suppose $q \in H$. Then

$$T'_{q+1} \subset U'_q \subset T'_q,$$

whence, by (3b), (2), (4b),

$$T'_{q+2} = \varphi(T'_{q+1}) \subset \varphi(U'_q) = U'_{q+1}.$$

Moreover, by (4b), (2), (3b),

$$U'_{q+1} = \varphi(U'_q) \subset \varphi(T'_q) = T'_{q+1},$$

so that

$$T'_{q+2} \subset U'_{q+1} \subset T'_{q+1}.$$

Thus $q + 1 \in H$. Hence, by III′, $H = I$, and (5) is proved.

Immediate corollaries of (5) are

(6) for every $n \in I$, $U'_{n+1} \subset T'_{n+1} \subset U'_n$;

(7) for every $n \in I$, $T'_{n+1} \subset T'_n$ and $U'_{n+1} \subset U'_n$.

To prove (6), we note that (5) yields, with n replaced by $n + 1$, $U'_{n+1} \subset T'_{n+1}$; also, $T'_{n+1} \subset U'_n$ is the first inclusion in (5). Then (7) is obvious from (5) and (6).

Another useful property is that

(8) $$\prod T'_n = \prod U'_n.$$

To prove (8), we note first that, since by (5) $n \in I$ implies $U'_n \subset T'_n$, we have $\prod T'_n \supset \prod U'_n$ by (13.2.7.b). Moreover, (5) and (13.2.7.b) yield

$$\prod [T'_{n+1};\ n \in I] \subset \prod U'_n.$$

But

$$\prod T'_n = T'_1 \cdot \left(\prod T'_{n+1}\right) \subset \prod T'_{n+1},$$

so that $\prod T'_n \subset \prod U'_n$. Hence (8) holds.

Finally, two consequences of (7) are needed, namely,

(9) $m, n \in I, m > n$ implies $T'_m \subset T'_{n+1}$;

(10) $m, n \in I, m > n$ implies $U'_m \subset U'_{n+1}$.

To prove (9), let $m, n \in I, m > n$ and define

$$H \equiv [k \in I; T'_{n+k} \subset T'_{n+1}].$$

Evidently $1 \in H$. Suppose $q \in H$, that is, $T'_{n+q} \subset T'_{n+1}$. Then, by (7), $T'_{n+q+1} \subset T'_{n+q}$, and

$$T'_{n+(q+1)} \subset T'_{n+1}.$$

Hence $q + 1 \in H$. Thus $H = I$ by III′, whence $m - n \in H$, and

$$T'_m = T'_{n+(m-n)} \subset T'_{n+1}.$$

This proves (9); the proof of (10) is similar.

We are now ready to introduce the final sequences. Define $(T_n; n \in I)$, $(U_n; n \in I)$ so that

(11) $T_1 = \prod T'_k; \quad T_n = T'_{n-1} - T'_n$ if $n > 1$;

(12) $U_1 = \prod U'_k; \quad U_n = U'_{n-1} - U'_n$ if $n > 1$.

It is to be established that

(13) $m, n \in I, m \neq n$ implies $T_m \cdot T_n = \Theta$;

(14) $m, n \in I, m \neq n$ implies $U_m \cdot U_n = \Theta$;

(15) $n \in I$ implies $T_n \sim U_n$;

(16) $\sum T_n = T$;

(17) $\sum U_n = U$.

To prove (13), let $m, n \in I, m \neq n$. Then either $m > n$ or $m < n$. Suppose first $m > n$. If $n = 1$, then $m > 1$, and

$$T_n = T_1 = \prod T'_k, \quad T_m = T'_{m-1} - T'_m.$$

Let $x \in T'_{m-1} - T'_m$, whence $x \,\epsilon'\, T'_m$ and $x \,\epsilon'\, \prod T'_k$. Hence $T_m \cdot T_n = \Theta$. If $n \neq 1$, then $m, n > 1$, and

$$T_m = T'_{m-1} - T'_m, \quad T_n = T'_{n-1} - T'_n.$$

Since $m > n$, $m - 1 > n - 1$ by (9.2.13), so that, by (9) (with m, n replaced by $m - 1, n - 1$),

$$T'_{m-1} \subset T'_n.$$

Hence $x \epsilon T_m$ implies $x \epsilon T'_{m-1}$, so that $x \epsilon T'_n$. Consequently, $x \epsilon T_m$ implies $x \epsilon' T_n$, and $T_m \cdot T_n = \Theta$. The case $m < n$ is similarly treated. This proves (13). The proof of (14) is similar.

To establish (15), let $n \epsilon I$. If $n = 1$, then by (8), (11), (12),

$$T_n = T_1 = \prod T'_k = \prod U'_k = U_1 = U_n,$$

whence $T_n \sim U_n$ by (10.2.4.a). Suppose $n \neq 1$, so that $n > 1$. It will now be shown that the function

$$(\varphi(x);\, x \epsilon (T'_{n-1} - U'_{n-1})) \tag{18}$$

is a one-to-one correspondence between $T'_{n-1} - U'_{n-1}$ and $T'_n - U'_n$. To this end, we see first that the domain of (18) is $T'_{n-1} - U'_{n-1}$. Moreover,

$$\begin{aligned} T'_n - U'_n &= \Phi(T'_{n-1}) - \Phi(U'_{n-1}) && \text{[by (3b), (4b)]} \\ &= [\varphi(x);\, x \epsilon T'_{n-1}] - [\varphi(x);\, x \epsilon U'_{n-1}] && \text{[by (1)]} \\ &= [\varphi(x);\, x \epsilon (T'_{n-1} - U'_{n-1})] && \text{[by (10.2.6), (10.2.7)],} \end{aligned}$$

so that $T'_n - U'_n$ is the range of (18). Now by (10.2.6), (18) is a one-to-one correspondence between $T'_{n-1} - U'_{n-1}$ and $T'_n - U'_n$. This proves

$$T'_n - U'_n \sim T'_{n-1} - U'_{n-1}. \tag{19}$$

By (10.2.4.a),

$$U'_{n-1} - T'_n \sim U'_{n-1} - T'_n. \tag{20}$$

Moreover,

$$(T'_n - U'_n) \cdot (U'_{n-1} - T'_n) = \Theta, \tag{21}$$

$$(T'_{n-1} - U'_{n-1}) \cdot (U'_{n-1} - T'_n) = \Theta; \tag{22}$$

for if (21) is false, there exists $x \epsilon T'_n$ with $x \epsilon' T'_n$, which is impossible, and if (22) is false, a similar contradiction arises. Now (19), (20), (21), (22) state the hypotheses of (10.2.5) with S, T, U, V there replaced by

$$T'_n - U'_n, \quad U'_{n-1} - T'_n, \quad T'_{n-1} - U'_{n-1}, \quad U'_{n-1} - T'_n,$$

respectively. The conclusion of (10.2.5) then follows, namely,

$$\begin{aligned} U'_{n-1} - U'_n &= (T'_n - U'_n) + (U'_{n-1} - T'_n) \quad \text{[by an easy verification]} \\ &\sim (T'_{n-1} - U'_{n-1}) + (U'_{n-1} - T'_n) = T'_{n-1} - T'_n. \end{aligned}$$

Hence $U_n \sim T_n$ by (11), (12); thus (15) is proved.

It remains to prove (16), (17). Since the proofs are similar, we shall give but one, that of (17). Suppose first that $x \epsilon \sum U_n$. Then there exists $n \epsilon I$ with $x \epsilon U_n$. If $n = 1$, $x \epsilon \prod U'_k$, so that $x \epsilon U'_1$, whence $x \epsilon U$ by (4a). If $n \neq 1$, then $n > 1$, and $x \epsilon U'_{n-1} - U'_n$. If $n - 1 = 1$, then again $x \in U$; otherwise we apply (10) with m, n replaced by $n - 1$, 1 to obtain $x \in U_2' \subset U_1' = U$. This proves

$$\sum U_n \subset U. \tag{23}$$

Conversely, let $x \in U$. If, for every $k \in I$, $x \in U_k'$, then $x \in \prod U_k' = U_1$, so that $x \in \sum U_n$. Otherwise, there exists $k \in I$ such that $x \epsilon' U_k'$. In other words,

$$H \equiv [k \in I; x \epsilon' U_k'] \neq \Theta.$$

Moreover, $1 \epsilon' H$, since $x \in U = U_1'$. By (9.3.9), there exists a least in H; define n to be this least. Then $n \neq 1$, since $1 \epsilon' H$. Moreover, $n - 1 \epsilon' H$. Hence $x \epsilon' U_n'$, and $x \in U_{n-1}'$, whence

$$x \in U_{n-1}' - U_n' = U_n.$$

It follows that $x \in \sum U_n$. This proves

$$U \subset \sum U_n, \tag{24}$$

which, together with (23), establishes (17).

By virtue of (13), (14), (15), the hypotheses of (13.3.1) are satisfied by the sequences $(T_n; n \in I)$, $(U_n; n \in I)$. The conclusion, $\sum T_n \sim \sum U_n$, thus follows, yielding $T \sim U$ in view of (16), (17). The proof is complete.

(13.3.4) PROJECT: Prove (13.3.2).

(13.3.5) PROJECT: Prove, with the help of (13.3.3), the following theorem: *Let A, B be sets such that there exist $C \subset A$, $D \subset B$ such that $A \sim D$, $B \sim C$; then $A \sim B$.*

13.4. Characterization of Infinite Sets. Our first theorem establishes the existence of infinite sets.

(13.4.1) THEOREM: *I is infinite.*

PROOF: Suppose I is not infinite. Since I is not empty, I is finite, and $I \sim I_{n(I)}$. But

$$I_{n(I)} \subset I_{n(I)+1} \subset I,$$

so that, by (13.3.3),

$$I_{n(I)+1} \sim I,$$

whence

$$I_{n(I)+1} \sim I_{n(I)}.$$

But, by (10.4.4.b),

$$n(I) + 1 = n(I),$$

which is false. Hence I is infinite. (Use of the principle of choice is implicit in the use of (13.3.3).)

REMARK: Of course, the existence of an infinite set still depends on the consistency of the axioms for $(I, 1, \sigma)$. In view of our firm belief in the consistency of these axioms [see (8.2)], we are not greatly concerned by this situation. Should inconsistency ever be established, our entire discussion of finite sets and the counting process would become vacuous; indeed, almost all mathematical theories would be seriously affected if not completely destroyed.

It is desirable now to characterize infinite sets without employing explicitly the system $(I, 1, \sigma)$. First it is shown that any set which contains a proper subset equivalent to the whole set must be infinite.

(13.4.2) THEOREM: *Let S be a set such that there exists $T \subsetneqq S$ such that $T \sim S$. Then S is infinite.*

PROOF: Suppose that S is not infinite. Then $T \subsetneqq S$ implies $S \neq \Theta$, so that also $T \neq \Theta$, whence S, T are finite; moreover, $T \sim S$ implies $n(T) = n(S)$ by (10.4.4.b). Hence, by (10.4.7), $T = S$. This contradiction completes the proof.

The next result shows that I is a "smallest" infinite set in the sense that every infinite set contains a subset equivalent to I.

(13.4.3) THEOREM: *Let S be an infinite set. Then there exists $T \subset S$ with $T \sim I$.*

PROOF: The major step in the proof is the construction of a sequence $(x_n;\, n \in I)$ in S such that

(1) $$m \neq n \text{ implies } x_m \neq x_n.$$

Then $T \equiv [x_n;\, n \in I]$ will be proved equivalent to I. The principle of choice is used.

Define

$$\mathfrak{M} \equiv [\text{all (non-empty) finite subsets of } S].$$

Clearly $\mathfrak{M} \neq \Theta$, since, for every $x \in S$, $[x] \in \mathfrak{M}$. Define a relation R on $\mathfrak{M} \times \mathfrak{M}$ thus:

$$R \equiv [(U, V) \in \mathfrak{M} \times \mathfrak{M};\ U \subsetneqq V \text{ and } n(V - U) = 1].$$

It is easy to see that $\mathfrak{M}$ is the domain of R. For, if $U \in \mathfrak{M}$, there exists $x \in S$ with $x \in' U$, since otherwise $x \in S$ implies $x \in U$, whence $U = S$, and S is finite, contrary to the hypothesis. If $V \equiv U + [x]$, then $U \subsetneqq V$, and $n(V - U) = n([x]) = 1$, whence $U\, R\, V$. Let x_0 be any element of S, and let $(U_n;\, n \in I)$ be any sequence in $\mathfrak{M}$ inductively defined by $[x_0]$ and R [see (11.6.2)]. Then

$$U_1 = [x_0];$$

(2) $$n \in I \text{ implies } U_n \subsetneqq U_{n+1},\ n(U_{n+1} - U_n) = 1.$$

Since, in view of (2), (10.4.4.b), for every $n \in I$,

$$U_{n+1} - U_n \sim [1],$$

it follows that, for every $n \in I$, there exists a unique element $x \in S$ with $x \in U_{n+1} - U_n$. Hence we may define a sequence $(x_n; n \in I)$ so that, for every $n \in I$, x_n is the unique element of $U_{n+1} - U_n$. Thus $[x_n] = U_{n+1} - U_n$.

Before proving (1), we establish that, for every $n \in I$,

(3) $$k \in I \text{ implies } U_n \subsetneqq U_{n+k}.$$

Let $n \in I$, and define

$$H \equiv [k \in I; U_n \subsetneqq U_{n+k}].$$

By (2), $1 \in H$. If $q \in H$, then $U_n \subsetneqq U_{n+q}$; by (2), $U_{n+q} \subsetneqq U_{n+q+1}$, whence

$$U_n \subsetneqq U_{n+q+1},$$

and $q + 1 \in H$. Hence $H = I$, and (3) is proved. A corollary of (3) is

(4) $$n < m \text{ implies } U_n \subsetneqq U_m.$$

For (4) follows from (3) with $k = m - n$. Also, (4) yields

(5) $$n \leqq m \text{ implies } U_n \subset U_m.$$

Now (1) is proved indirectly. Suppose there exist $m, n \in I$ with $m \neq n$, $x_m = x_n$. Then $m > n$ or $m < n$. If $m > n$, then $m \geqq n + 1$, so that, by (5) with n replaced by $n + 1$,

(6) $$U_{n+1} \subset U_m.$$

Now $x_m \in U_{m+1} - U_m$, while $x_n \in U_{n+1}$. By (6), $x_n \in U_m$. Since $x_m = x_n$, we have $x_m \in U_m$, which is false. Hence $m \not> n$. Similarly $m \not< n$. Since we had $m > n$ or $m < n$, we have reached a contradiction, and (1) follows.

Define

$$T \equiv [x_n; n \in I].$$

The sequence $(x_n; n \in I)$ has domain I and range T and satisfies (10.2.2.b) by (1). Hence $I \sim T \subset S$, and the proof is complete.

The statement made earlier, that I is a "smallest" infinite set, must not be misinterpreted. For, as will be shown next, I has proper subsets which are infinite. However, from the "standpoint of equivalence," these subsets are not "smaller" than I but are "the same size as" I, that is, they are equivalent to I.

(13.4.4) THEOREM: *If I_e is the set of all even elements of I, that is,*

$$I_e = [2 \cdot k;\ k \in I],$$

then $I_e \sim I$.

PROOF: Define φ on I to I_e so that,

$$\text{for every } k \in I,\ \varphi(k) = 2 \cdot k.$$

Then φ has domain I and range I_e and satisfies (10.2.2.b). Hence $I_e \sim I$.

(13.4.5) COROLLARY: *There exists a proper subset of I which is equivalent to I.*

PROOF: By (13.4.4), $I_e \sim I$. Since $1 \in' I_e$, $I_e \subsetneqq I$.

REMARK: There are, of course, many other proper subsets of I equivalent to I; for example, the set $I - I_e$ of all odd elements, the set $I - [1]$, the set $I - [1, 2]$. It will now be shown that every infinite set has an equivalent proper subset.

(13.4.6) THEOREM: *If S is an infinite set, then there exists $T \subsetneqq S$ such that $T \sim S$.*

PROOF: By (13.4.3), there exists $U \subset S$ such that $U \sim I$. Hence there exists a one-to-one correspondence φ between I and U. By (13.4.5), there exists $I_0 \subsetneqq I$ with $I_0 \sim I$. Define

$$V \equiv \varphi(I_0),$$

whence $V \subsetneqq U$ by (10.2.8). Define

$$T \equiv V + (S - U).$$

Since $V = \varphi(I_0)$, it follows that $V \sim I_0$ by (10.2.6). But

$$I_0 \sim I \sim U,$$

whence $V \sim U$. We have

$$V \cdot (S - U) = \Theta,$$
$$U \cdot (S - U) = \Theta,$$

whence, by (10.2.5), $T \sim S$. Suppose $T = S$. Since $V \subsetneqq U$, there exists $x \in U - V \subset S$, whence $x \in T$. But then $x \in V$ or $x \in S - U$, which is impossible. This establishes $T \subsetneqq S$ and completes the proof. (The principle of choice is used because of reference to (13.4.3).)

Finally, we have the desired characterization of infinite sets without reference to $(I, 1, \sigma)$.

(13.4.7) THEOREM: *Let S be a set. Then S is infinite if and only if there exists $T \subsetneqq S$ such that $T \sim S$.*

PROOF: This is the conjunction of (13.4.2) and (13.4.6). (The principle of choice is involved.)

(13.4.8) THEOREM: *Let S be a set, $S \neq \Theta$. Then S is finite if and only if $T \subset S$, $T \sim S$ implies $T = S$.*

PROOF: Contrapositives of the two implications in (13.4.7) yield (13.4.8). (The principle of choice is involved.)

REMARK: Some treatments of set theory use the criteria of (13.4.8), (13.4.7) as *definitions* of finite and infinite sets. We have preferred our procedure because it seems closer to the intuitive and historical approaches. If it is assumed that a set S exists satisfying the criterion of (13.4.7), then it may be proved that the axioms for $(I, 1, \sigma)$ are consistent. From this point of view, then, the consistency of the axioms for $(I, 1, \sigma)$ is equivalent to the existence of a set S as described in (13.4.7) [see the remark after (13.4.1)].

(13.4.9) PROJECT: Prove that, if a set S is infinite and if $S \subset T$, then T is infinite.

(13.4.10) PROJECT: Prove that, if S, T are sets such that $S \subset T$, S is finite and T is infinite, then $T - S$ is infinite.

(13.4.11) PROJECT: Prove that, if S, T are infinite sets, then $S + T$ is infinite.

(13.4.12) PROJECT: Prove that, if S, T are sets such that S is infinite and $S \sim T$, then T is infinite.

(13.4.13) PROJECT: Prove that, if $n \in I$, then $I - I_n$ is infinite.

(13.4.14) PROJECT: Prove that $I - I_e$ is infinite.

(13.4.15) PROJECT: Prove that, if S, T are sets such that S is infinite, $T \neq \Theta$, then $S \times T$ is infinite.

(13.4.16) PROJECT: Let S be an infinite set, and let $\mathfrak{M}$ be the set of all subsets of S. Then prove that $\mathfrak{M}$ is infinite.

13.5. Countable Sets. For many purposes in mathematics a partial classification of infinite sets is indispensable. A first step in this direction is an analysis of the non-empty subsets of I. It is clear from (13.4.5) that I possesses proper subsets which are equivalent to I. Such subsets are then infinite, since I is infinite. Of course, I has finite subsets also. Our first major result is that every non-empty subset of I is either finite or (if infinite) equivalent to I. Sets equivalent to I play an important role, and for this reason they are given a special designation.

The adoption of a special name for infinite sets which are equivalent to I would be unnecessary if there did not exist infinite sets not equivalent to I. Proof of the existence of infinite sets not equivalent to I appears in (17.5.5).

(13.5.1) DEFINITION: A set S is called *denumerably infinite* if $S \sim I$; S is called *countable* if S is either finite or denumerably infinite.

REMARK: Since I is infinite, it follows that any denumerably infinite set is infinite. The term *countable* is somewhat unfortunate, since it might seem desirable to apply it only to sets to which the counting process is applicable, that is, to finite sets. However, it is used because of custom.

(13.5.2) THEOREM: *Let* $S \subset I$, $S \neq \Theta$. *Then either* S *is finite or* $S \sim I$.

PROOF: Let us suppose that $S \subset I$, and that S is infinite. It is our task to construct a sequence $(k_n; n \in I)$ in S such that

(1) $$m \neq n \text{ implies } k_m \neq k_n.$$

The existence of such a sequence will establish that $S \sim I$.

For every $n \in S$, the set

(2) $$[p \in S; p > n]$$

is non-empty. For otherwise $m \in S$ implies $m \leqq n$, whence $S \subset I_n$, and S is finite by (10.4.5). By (9.3.9), the set (2) has a least element. Define a function F on S to S so that, for every $n \in S$, $F(n)$ is the least element in (2). If n_0 is the least element in S, let $(k_n; n \in I)$ be the sequence in S inductively defined by n_0 and F. Then

(3) $k_1 = n_0$;
(4) $n \in I$ implies k_{n+1} is the least element in $[p \in S; p > k_n]$.

It is immediate that

(5) $$n \in I \text{ implies } k_n < k_{n+1}.$$

Before proving (1), let us prove that, for every $m \in I$,

$$H \equiv [l \in I; k_m < k_{m+l}] = I.$$

Clearly $1 \in H$ by (5). If $q \in H$, then

$$k_m < k_{m+q} < k_{(m+q)+1} = k_{m+(q+1)},$$

and $q + 1 \in H$. Therefore $H = I$. Now let $m \neq n$. Then $m < n$ or $m > n$. If $m < n$, then $l \equiv n - m \in H$, whence

$$k_m < k_{m+(n-m)} = k_n,$$

so that $k_m \neq k_n$. Similarly, $m > n$ yields $k_m \neq k_n$. The proof of (1) is complete.

The sequence $(k_n; n \in I)$ has domain I and satisfies (10.2.2.b) by (1). Therefore it is a one-to-one correspondence between I and the set

$[k_n; n \in I] \subset S$. Thus $[k_n; n \in I] \subset S \subset I$, and $[k_n; n \in I] \sim I$. That $S \sim I$ follows from (13.3.3). (The principle of choice is used through (13.3.3), although $[k_n; n \in I] = S$ may be proved and the principle of choice avoided.)

(13.5.3) Theorem: *Let S be a countable set, and let $T \subset S$, $T \neq \Theta$. Then T is countable.*

Proof: If T is finite, T is countable. Suppose T is infinite. Then S is infinite by (10.4.7), so that $S \sim I$. There exists a one-to-one correspondence φ between S and I, whence $T \sim \varphi(T) \subset I$ by (10.2.6). By (10.4.4.a), $\varphi(T)$ is infinite, whence $\varphi(T) \sim I$ by (13.5.2). Thus $T \sim I$, and T is denumerably infinite. This proves that T is countable.

(13.5.4) Theorem: *A set S is countable if and only if there exists a subset $I_0 \neq \Theta$ of I such that $S \sim I_0$.*

Proof: Suppose S is countable. If S is infinite, define $I_0 \equiv I \neq \Theta$, whence $S \sim I_0$. If S is finite, we may define $I_0 \equiv I_{n(S)} \neq \Theta$. Again $S \sim I_0$. Conversely, if $S \sim I_0 \subset I$, $I_0 \neq \Theta$, then by (13.5.2), either I_0 is finite, whence S is finite and therefore countable, or $I_0 \sim I$, so that $S \sim I$, whence S is denumerably infinite and therefore countable.

(13.5.5) Theorem: *Let S be a countable set. Then there exists a sequence in S whose range is S.*

Proof: Suppose, first, that S is denumerably infinite, so that $S \sim I$. Then, by the definition of equivalence, there exists a one-to-one correspondence φ between I and S. But then $(\varphi(n); n \in I)$ is a sequence whose range is S. On the other hand, if S is finite, then there is a one-to-one correspondence ψ between $I_{n(S)}$ and S. Define a sequence $(k_n; n \in I)$ by the requirement that $k_n = \psi(n)$ if $n \in I_{n(S)}$ and $k_n = \psi(1)$ if $n \in' I_{n(S)}$. Then it is easily seen that the range of the sequence $(k_n; n \in I)$ is S; details are left for the reader. This completes the proof.

(13.5.6) Project: Prove that, if S is a countable set and if T is a set with $S \sim T$, then T is countable.

(13.5.7) Project: Complete the proof of (13.5.5).

(13.5.8) Project: Prove that, if S is a set for which there exists a sequence in S whose range is S, then S is countable. (This is a converse of (13.5.5).)

13.6. Countable Sums. It is our aim now to prove that the set-theoretic sum of a "countable number" of countable sets is a countable set. This will extend (10.4.8), (10.4.10), which dealt with two finite sets. A preliminary result is that $I \times I$ is denumerably infinite. This is proved with the help of some properties of I_e [see (13.4.4)].

(13.6.1) LEMMA: *If* $n \in I$, *then* $n \cdot (n + 1) \in I_e$.

PROOF: If n is even, then $n \cdot (n + 1)$ is even by (9.5.6). If n is odd, then, since 1 is odd, $n + 1$ is even by (9.5.5.c), whence $n \cdot (n + 1)$ is even by (9.5.6).

(13.6.2) LEMMA: *Define a sequence* $(S_n; n \in I)$ *of subsets of* I_e *so that, for every* $n \in I$,

$$S_n = \begin{cases} [2] & \text{if } n = 1 \\ [k \in I_e;\ (n - 1) \cdot n < k \leqq (n + 1) \cdot n] & \text{if } n > 1. \end{cases}$$

Then

(a) $$\sum S_n = I_e;$$

(b) $$m \neq n \text{ implies } S_m \cdot S_n = \Theta.$$

REMARK: The reader should write down the first few of the sets S_n. For example, $S_2 = [4, 6]$. It is seen that S_1 has 1 element, S_2 has 2 elements, and it may be proved that S_n has n elements, although this fact is not explicitly needed.

PROOF OF (a): Evidently $\sum S_n \subset I_e$. Let $p \in I_e$. If $p = 2$, then $p \in S_1$, and $p \in \sum S_n$. Suppose $p \neq 2$, whence $p > 2$. Define

$$H \equiv [n \in I;\ n > 1,\ (n - 1) \cdot n < p].$$

Now $2 \in H$, so that $H \neq \Theta$. Moreover, for every $n \in H$,

$$\begin{aligned} n = 1 \cdot n &\leqq (n - 1) \cdot n \qquad [\text{since } n > 1] \\ &< p, \end{aligned}$$

whence $H \subset I_p$. Therefore H has a greatest element m by (9.3.7). Since $m \in H$, $m > 1$ and

$$(m - 1) \cdot m < p.$$

If

$$(m + 1) \cdot m < p,$$

then $m + 1 \in H$, which is impossible. Hence

$$(m + 1) \cdot m \geqq p;$$

consequently $p \in S_m$. Thus $p \in \sum S_n$. This establishes $I_e \subset \sum S_n$ and completes the proof of (a).

PROOF OF (b): Let $m \neq n$. Then $m > n$ or $m < n$. Suppose first that $m > n$. If $n = 1$, then $m > 1$. If $S_m \cdot S_1 \neq \Theta$, then there exists $p \in S_m \cdot S_1$, whence $p = 2$, and

(1) $$(m - 1) \cdot m < 2 \leqq (m + 1) \cdot m.$$

But since $m > 1$, $(m - 1) \cdot m \geqq m$ by (9.2.19), whence $(m - 1) \cdot m > 1$. Then by (9.2.10.b), $(m - 1) \cdot m \geqq 2$, contrary to (1). This proves

$S_m \cdot S_1 = \Theta$. Now let $n \neq 1$, whence $m, n > 1$. If $S_m \cdot S_n \neq \Theta$, there exists $p \in S_m, S_n$, and

$$(2) \qquad (m-1) \cdot m < p \leqq (m+1) \cdot m;$$

$$(3) \qquad (n-1) \cdot n < p \leqq (n+1) \cdot n.$$

We prove now that $(n+1) \cdot n \leqq (m-1) \cdot m$. Since $m > n$, we have $m \geqq n+1$ by (9.2.10.b) and $m - 1 \geqq n$ by (9.2.10.a). Thus, by (9.2.22),

$$(n+1) \cdot n \leqq m \cdot (m-1).$$

By (2), (3),

$$p \leqq (n+1) \cdot n \leqq (m-1) \cdot m < p,$$

so that, by (9.2.6), $p < p$, which is impossible. This contradiction proves $S_m \cdot S_n = \Theta$. The case $m < n$ is similarly treated.

(13.6.3) Lemma: *Define a sequence* $(T_n; n \in I)$ *of subsets of* $I \times I$ *so that, for every* $n \in I$,

$$T_n = [(p, q) \in I \times I; p + q = n + 1].$$

Then

(a) $$\sum T_n = I \times I;$$

(b) $$m \neq n \textit{ implies } T_m \cdot T_n = \Theta.$$

Remark: A convenient way of picturing the sets T_n is by means of the following diagram:

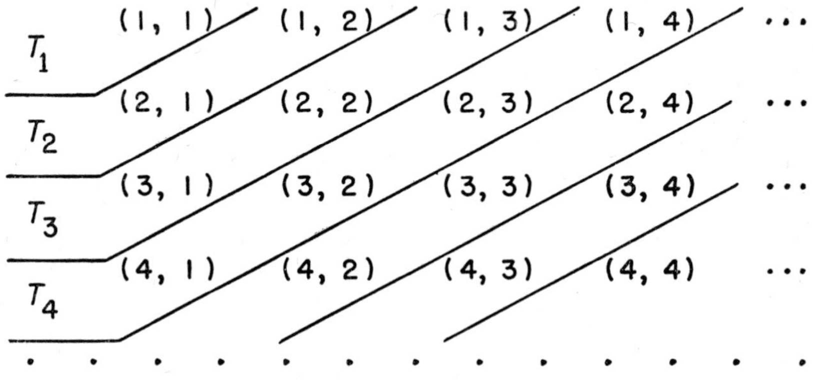

Each set T_1, T_2, and so on, consists of the pairs lying between adjacent diagonal lines. It is seen that T_1 has 1 element, T_2 has 2 elements, and so on. It may be proved that, for every $n \in I$, T_n has n elements, although this fact is not explicitly needed.

Proof of (a): Obviously $\sum T_n \subset I \times I$. If $(p, q) \in I \times I$, then $p + q \geqq 1 + 1 = 2$, whence $p + q > 1$, and $(p, q) \in T_{p+q-1}$. Hence $(p, q) \in \sum T_n$.

Proof of (b): Let $m \neq n$. If $(p, q) \in T_m$, then $p + q = m + 1 \neq n + 1$, whence $(p, q) \in' T_n$. Thus $T_m \cdot T_n \neq \Theta$.

(13.6.4) THEOREM: *The sets I and $I \times I$ are equivalent.*

PROOF: We shall first prove $I \times I \sim I_e$. Define

$$\mathfrak{M} \equiv [\text{all subsets of } I_e] + [\text{all subsets of } I \times I],$$

and define sequences $(S_n; n \in I)$, $(T_n; n \in I)$ in $\mathfrak{M}$ as in (13.6.2) and (13.6.3). It will be shown that

(1) $$n \in I \text{ implies } T_n \sim S_n.$$

It is clear that $T_1 \sim S_1$, since $S_1 = [2]$, $T_1 = [(1, 1)]$. Let $n \in I$, $n > 1$, and define a function φ on T_n to I_e so that,

$$\text{for every } (p, q) \in T_n,\ \varphi(p, q) = (n - 1) \cdot n + 2 \cdot p.$$

The domain of φ is, of course, T_n. It is now shown that the range of φ is S_n. If $(p, q) \in T_n$, then $p + q = n + 1$, whence $p < n + 1$, and [by (9.2.10.a)] $p \leqq n$. Therefore $2 \cdot p \leqq 2 \cdot n$, and

$$\begin{aligned}(n - 1) \cdot n < (n - 1) \cdot n + 2 \cdot p \leqq (n - 1) \cdot n + 2 \cdot n &= ((n - 1) + 2) \cdot n \\ &= (n + 1) \cdot n.\end{aligned}$$

Thus $\varphi(p, q) \in S_n$. Therefore range of $\varphi \subset S_n$. To prove the reverse inclusion, let $k \in S_n$. Since $k > (n - 1) \cdot n$, there exists $l \in I$ such that $k = (n - 1) \cdot n + l$. By (13.6.1), $(n - 1) \cdot n$ is even. If l is odd, then, by (9.5.5.b), k is odd, contrary to $k \in I_e$. Thus l is even, and there exists $p \in I$ with $l = 2 \cdot p$, so that

(2) $$k = (n - 1) \cdot n + 2 \cdot p.$$

We prove that $p < n + 1$. If $p \geqq n + 1$, then $2 \cdot p \geqq 2 \cdot (n + 1)$, whence

$$\begin{aligned} k &= (n - 1) \cdot n + 2 \cdot p \\ &\geqq (n - 1) \cdot n + 2 \cdot (n + 1) \\ &= (n - 1) \cdot n + 2 \cdot n + 2 \\ &= ((n - 1) + 2) \cdot n + 2 \\ &= (n + 1) \cdot n + 2 \\ &> (n + 1) \cdot n. \end{aligned}$$

Thus $k > (n + 1) \cdot n$, contrary to $k \in S_n$. Now, since $p < n + 1$, we may define $q \equiv (n + 1) - p$. Then $p + q = n + 1$, so that $(p, q) \in T_n$. Moreover, by the definition of φ and (2),

$$\varphi(p, q) = (n - 1) \cdot n + 2 \cdot p = k.$$

Thus $S_n \subset$ range of φ.

It will now be shown that

$$(p, q), (r, s) \in T_n,\ (p, q) \neq (r, s) \text{ implies } \varphi(p, q) \neq \varphi(r, s).$$

Let $(p, q) \neq (r, s)$. If $p = r$, then

$$q = (n + 1) - p = (n + 1) - r = s,$$

whence $(p, q) = (r, s)$. This contradiction shows that $p \neq r$. Thus $2 \cdot p \neq 2 \cdot r$, and

$$\varphi(p, q) = (n - 1) \cdot n + 2 \cdot p \neq (n - 1) \cdot n + 2 \cdot r = \varphi(r, s).$$

We have proved that φ has domain T_n and range S_n, and satisfies (10.2.2.b). Hence φ is a one-to-one correspondence between T_n and S_n, so that $T_n \sim S_n$. By (1), (13.6.3.b), (13.6.2.b), the hypotheses of (13.3.1) hold. Thus we conclude that $\sum T_n \sim \sum S_n$. By (13.6.3.a), (13.6.2.a), this yields $I \times I \sim I_e$. Finally, by (13.4.4), $I_e \sim I$. Hence $I \times I \sim I$, and the proof is complete. (Application of (13.3.1) entails use of the principle of choice, although the proof could be rephrased so as to avoid the principle of choice.)

Before proceeding to the main theorem, we prove a useful general result.

(13.6.5) THEOREM: *If S and T are (non-empty) sets such that there exists a function φ with domain S and range T, then there exists a subset U of S such that $U \sim T$.*

PROOF: We employ the principle of choice. The relation φ^* has domain T and range S. By (11.5.2), there exists a function ψ on T to S with $\psi \subset \varphi^*$. Define $U \equiv \psi(T)$. It is now shown that ψ is a one-to-one correspondence between T and U. Clearly ψ has domain T and range U. Let $x_1, x_2 \in T$, $x_1 \neq x_2$. Define

$$y_1 \equiv \psi(x_1), \quad y_2 \equiv \psi(x_2).$$

Suppose $y_1 = y_2$. We have

$$x_1 \, \psi \, y_1, \quad x_2 \, \psi \, y_2,$$

whence, since $\psi \subset \varphi^*$,

$$x_1 \, \varphi^* \, y_1, \quad x_2 \, \varphi^* \, y_2,$$

or

$$y_1 \, \varphi \, x_1, \quad y_2 \, \varphi \, x_2.$$

Thus

$$x_1 = \varphi(y_1) = \varphi(y_2) = x_2,$$

contrary to $x_1 \neq x_2$. This proves $y_1 \neq y_2$. By (10.2.2), $T \sim U$.

(13.6.6) THEOREM: *Let $\mathfrak{M}$ be a countable set of sets, each member of $\mathfrak{M}$ being a countable set. Then $\sum \mathfrak{M}$ is countable.*

PROOF: Since $\mathfrak{M}$ is countable, there exists [by (13.5.4)] a subset $I_0 \neq \Theta$ of I and a function

$$(S_n; n \in I_0)$$

with

$$\mathfrak{M} = [S_n; n \in I_0].$$

Furthermore, since every member of $\mathfrak{M}$ is a countable set, we apply (13.5.4), obtaining

(1) for every $n \in I_0$ there exists $H \subset I$ such that $H \neq \Theta$ and $S_n \sim H$.

In order to apply the principle of choice, define

$$A \equiv I_0 \neq \Theta, \quad B \equiv [\text{all subsets of } I] \neq \Theta,$$
$$R \equiv [(n, H) \in A \times B;\, S_n \sim H].$$

Then the relation R on $A \times B$ has domain A by (1). By (11.5.2), there exists a function on A to B which is contained in R. Such a function may be denoted by $(H_n;\, n \in I_0)$, and we have

(2) for every $n \in I_0$, $S_n \sim H_n$ and $H_n \subset I$.

Another formulation of (2) is this:

(3) for every $n \in I_0$, there exists a one-to-one correspondence φ between H_n and S_n.

Again we prepare to use the principle of choice by defining

$$A_* \equiv I_0 \neq \Theta, \quad B_* \equiv [\text{all functions on } I \times \textstyle\sum\mathfrak{M}],$$
$$R_* \equiv [(n, \varphi) \in A_* \times B_*;\, \varphi \text{ is a one-to-one correspondence between } H_n \text{ and } S_n].$$

Of course $B_* \neq \Theta$, since $\sum\mathfrak{M} \neq \Theta$. Also, by (3), the domain of R_* is A_*, whence (11.5.2) applies, yielding a function on A_* to B_* which is contained in R_*. Such a function is denoted by $(\varphi_n;\, n \in I_0)$, and we have

(4) for every $n \in I_0$, φ_n is a one-to-one correspondence between H_n and S_n.

Define a subset J of $I \times I$ thus:

$$J \equiv [(m, n);\, m \in I_0,\, n \in H_m].$$

Moreover, define a function F on J to $\sum\mathfrak{M}$ so that,

(5) for every $(m, n) \in J$, $F(m, n) = \varphi_m(n)$.

(Since $(m, n) \in J$, we have $m \in I_0$, $n \in H_m$, so that $\varphi_m(n) \in S_m$ and $\varphi_m(n) \in \sum\mathfrak{M}$.) It is shown now that the range of F is $\sum\mathfrak{M}$. Let $x \in \sum\mathfrak{M}$. Then there exists $m \in I_0$ with $x \in S_m$. Define $n \equiv \varphi_m^*(x)$, whence $n \in H_m$. Then $(m, n) \in J$, and

$$F(m, n) = \varphi_m(n) = \varphi_m(\varphi_m^*(x)) = x$$

by (10.2.1.b).

Now (13.6.5) is applied with S, T replaced by J, $\sum\mathfrak{M}$; thus there exists $K \subset J$ such that $K \sim \sum\mathfrak{M}$. By (13.5.3), J is countable, whence also K is countable. Since $K \sim \sum\mathfrak{M}$, it follows that $\sum\mathfrak{M}$ is countable [by (13.5.4)]. The proof is complete.

REMARK: In (13.6.6), if $\mathfrak{M}$ is finite, and if every member of $\mathfrak{M}$ is a finite set, then, of course $\sum\mathfrak{M}$ is countable. But the proof of (13.6.6) does not show that a stronger conclusion, that $\sum\mathfrak{M}$ is finite, also follows. Hence we state this result as a separate theorem.

(13.6.7) THEOREM: *Let $\mathfrak{M}$ be a finite set of sets, each member of $\mathfrak{M}$ being a finite set. Then $\sum\mathfrak{M}$ is finite.*

PROOF: The proof is merely outlined. Details may be supplied by the reader. Define

$$H \equiv [m \in I; \text{ for every set } \mathfrak{M} \text{ with } m \text{ elements, each element being a finite set, } \textstyle\sum\mathfrak{M} \text{ is finite}].$$

Then $1 \in H$, since if $\mathfrak{M} = [S]$, with S finite, then $\sum\mathfrak{M} = S$, and $\sum\mathfrak{M}$ is finite. Suppose $q \in H$, and let $\mathfrak{M}$ have $q + 1$ elements, each being a finite set. Hence $I_{q+1} \sim \mathfrak{M}$, so that there exists a one-to-one correspondence

$$(S_n;\ n \in I_{q+1})$$

between I_{q+1} and $\mathfrak{M}$. Define

$$\mathfrak{N} \equiv [S_n;\ n \in I_q],$$

so that $\mathfrak{N}$ has q elements. It follows that $\sum\mathfrak{N}$ is finite (since $q \in H$). We have

$$\textstyle\sum\mathfrak{M} = \sum\mathfrak{N} + S_{q+1},$$

so that we apply (10.4.8), (10.4.10), obtaining that $\sum\mathfrak{M}$ is finite. Thus $q + 1 \in H$. The proof is complete, since $H = I$.

(13.6.8) PROJECT: Prove that, in (13.6.6), if $\mathfrak{M}$ is infinite, and if $S, T \in \mathfrak{M}$, $S \neq T$ implies $S \cdot T = \Theta$, then $\sum\mathfrak{M}$ is (denumerably) infinite.

(13.6.9) PROJECT: Prove that, in (13.6.6), if there exists a member of $\mathfrak{M}$ which is infinite, then $\sum\mathfrak{M}$ is (denumerably) infinite.

(13.6.10) PROJECT: Prove that, if S, T are countable sets, then $S \times T$ is countable. Moreover, show that $S \times T$ is infinite if and only if one of S, T is infinite.

(13.6.11) PROJECT: Complete the proof of (13.6.7).

13.7. Conclusion. The portions of set theory given in this chapter and in Chapter 10 constitute only a beginning of the subject. We have selected those results which for various reasons will prove useful in later developments. However, if the reader should investigate the various treatises on set theory, he will find that the theorems proved here are the really basic theorems, and that they will serve as excellent background for further study in the subject.

Chapter 14

ISOMORPHISM AND CATEGORICAL SYSTEMS OF AXIOMS

[No Basis]

14.1. Introduction. At the end of the discussion of systems of axioms [(7.4)], the term *categorical* appeared with a brief intuitive description of its meaning. Further clarification of this concept requires the development of an idea called *isomorphism* of two mathematical systems. Accordingly, we devote the present chapter to an explanation of isomorphism and to a detailed discussion of categoricalness of systems of axioms.

14.2. Isomorphisms. It is our purpose here to discuss a generalization of the concept of equivalence of sets. It will be recalled that equivalence of finite sets is a concept which enables one to give a precise meaning to sets, "having the same number of elements." Two finite sets have the same number of elements if and only if they are equivalent, according to (10.4.4.b). Thus equivalence, at least for finite sets, is a mathematical counterpart of the intuitive idea of "resemblance." The question to be discussed in this section is the existence of a similar concept of "resemblance" applicable to systems more general than a single abstract set.

We have seen that a mathematical theory is a discourse, not as a rule on *one* set, but rather on a system consisting of *several* sets, relations, functions, and so on. It is desirable to seek an extension of the mathematical concept of equivalence, or the intuitive concept of "resemblance," which is applicable to such more general systems. In order to indicate the procedure to be adopted, we consider first an example of the type of system involved in group theory. Let G_1 be a set of three pairwise distinct elements designated by p, q, r, and let G_2 be another set of three pairwise distinct elementsdesi gnated by 1, 2, 3 (not to be confused with the positive integers 1, 2, 3). Define operations $\circ_1$, $\circ_2$ by the following tables:

$\circ_1$:

	p	q	r
p	p	q	r
q	q	r	p
r	r	p	q

$\circ_2$:

	1	2	3
1	1	2	3
2	2	3	1
3	3	1	2

It follows that o_1 is on $G_1 \times G_1$ to G_1, o_2 is on $G_2 \times G_2$ to G_2, and that (G_1, o_1) and (G_2, o_2) are both groups [see (7.2.2)]. Moreover, it will be seen that these groups bear to each other a close resemblance, even though the sets G_1, G_2 may be different, and indeed may even have no elements in common. First, it is noted that G_1 and G_2 are equivalent sets. For the function φ represented by the table

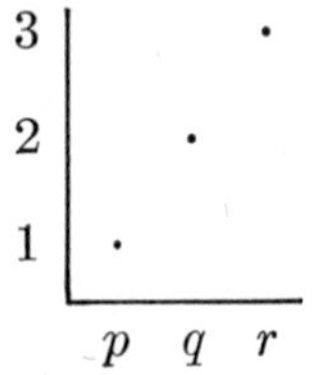

is evidently a one-to-one correspondence between G_1 and G_2, since it satisfies the criterion (10.2.2.b).

But there is more "resemblance" than the equivalence of the sets. If one defines an operation p_2 by the table

	$\varphi(p)$	$\varphi(q)$	$\varphi(r)$
$\varphi(p)$	$\varphi(p)$	$\varphi(q)$	$\varphi(r)$
$\varphi(q)$	$\varphi(q)$	$\varphi(r)$	$\varphi(p)$
$\varphi(r)$	$\varphi(r)$	$\varphi(p)$	$\varphi(q)$

obtained from the table for o_1 by replacing every entry by its φ-correspondent, one sees that p_2 is on $G_2 \times G_2$ to G_2, and, moreover, that $\mathsf{p}_2 = \mathsf{o}_2$. Some mathematicians would say that we have succeeded in passing from (G_1, o_1) to (G_2, o_2) by merely changing the names of the elements p, q, r to 1, 2, 3, respectively. They would say that therefore the systems (G_1, o_1), (G_2, o_2) are "abstractly identical." [See (14.3) for a similar discussion.]

Mathematical formulation of the connection just described between two arbitrary groups may be given thus: Let (G_1, o_1), (G_2, o_2) be two groups. We shall say that these groups are *isomorphic* if there exists a one-to-one correspondence φ between the sets G_1 and G_2 such that,

(14.2.1) for every $a, b \in G_1$, $\varphi(a) \mathsf{o}_2 \varphi(b) = \varphi(a \mathsf{o}_1 b)$.

It is convenient to abbreviate (14.2.1) by saying that φ *carries* o_1 *into* o_2. Hence isomorphism means the existence of a one-to-one correspondence between G_1 and G_2 which carries o_1 into o_2. The reader should convince himself that (14.2.1) asserts in the example exactly that $\mathsf{p}_2 = \mathsf{o}_2$.

An important observation is that the criterion for isomorphism is meaningful even if the systems (G_1, o_1), (G_2, o_2) are not necessarily groups, indeed, even if they satisfy no axioms whatever. With this in mind, we make a formal definition.

(14.2.2) DEFINITION: Let the systems $(G_1, \circ_1)$, $(G_2, \circ_2)$ be given, G_1, G_2 being sets, $\circ_1$ a binary operation on $G_1 \times G_1$ to G_1 and $\circ_2$ a binary operation on $G_2 \times G_2$ to G_2. Then $(G_1, \circ_1)$ is *isomorphic* to $(G_2, \circ_2)$ (in symbols, $(G_1, \circ_1) \sim (G_2, \circ_2)$) if there exists a one-to-one correspondence φ between G_1 and G_2 such that (14.2.1) holds. Such a correspondence φ is called an *isomorphism* between $(G_1, \circ_1)$ and $(G_2, \circ_2)$.

It will be recalled [see (10.2.4)] that set-theoretic equivalence has three important properties:

$$S \sim S;$$
$$S \sim T \text{ implies } T \sim S;$$
$$S \sim T,\ T \sim U \text{ implies } S \sim U.$$

Corresponding properties hold for isomorphism as defined in (14.2.2), as is now shown.

(14.2.3) COROLLARY: *Let* $(G_1, \circ_1)$, $(G_2, \circ_2)$, $(G_3, \circ_3)$ *be systems as described in* (14.2.2). *Then*
(a) $(G_1, \circ_1) \sim (G_1, \circ_1)$;
(b) $(G_1, \circ_1) \sim (G_2, \circ_2)$ *implies* $(G_2, \circ_2) \sim (G_1, \circ_1)$;
(c) *if* $(G_1, \circ_1) \sim (G_2, \circ_2)$ *and* $(G_2, \circ_2) \sim (G_3, \circ_3)$, *then* $(G_1, \circ_1) \sim (G_3, \circ_3)$.

PROOF OF (a): Define φ as the identity relation E on $G_1 \times G_1$. Then φ is a one-to-one correspondence, and, if $a, b \in G_1$, then

$$\varphi(a) \circ_1 \varphi(b) = a \circ_1 b = \varphi(a \circ_1 b),$$

whence (14.2.1) is proved.

PROOF OF (b): Let φ be an isomorphism between $(G_1, \circ_1)$ and $(G_2, \circ_2)$. Then φ^* is a one-to-one correspondence between G_2 and G_1. It remains to prove that

$$c, d \in G_2 \text{ implies } \varphi^*(c) \circ_1 \varphi^*(d) = \varphi^*(c \circ_2 d).$$

Let $c, d \in G_2$. Since the range of φ is G_2, there exist $a, b \in G_1$ such that $c = \varphi(a)$, $d = \varphi(b)$. Hence

$$\begin{aligned} \varphi^*(c) \circ_1 \varphi^*(d) &= \varphi^*(\varphi(a)) \circ_1 \varphi^*(\varphi(b)) \\ &= a \circ_1 b && \text{[by (10.2.1.a)]} \\ &= \varphi^*(\varphi(a \circ_1 b)) && \text{[by (10.2.1.a)]} \\ &= \varphi^*(\varphi(a) \circ_2 \varphi(b)) && \text{[by (14.2.1)]} \\ &= \varphi^*(c \circ_2 d), \end{aligned}$$

and the proof is complete.

PROOF OF (c): Let φ be an isomorphism between $(G_1, \circ_1)$ and $(G_2, \circ_2)$, and let ψ be an isomorphism between $(G_2, \circ_2)$ and $(G_3, \circ_3)$. Then (14.2.1) applies to φ, ψ, yielding

$$(1) \qquad a, b \in G_1 \text{ implies } \varphi(a) \circ_2 \varphi(b) = \varphi(a \circ_1 b);$$
$$(2) \qquad c, d \in G_2 \text{ implies } \psi(c) \circ_3 \psi(d) = \psi(c \circ_2 d).$$

Define a function ρ on G_1 to G_3 so that

$$\text{for } a \in G_1,\ \rho(a) = \psi(\varphi(a)).$$

It is easily proved that ρ is a one-to-one correspondence between G_1 and G_3 [see the proof of (10.2.4.c)]. If $a, b \in G_1$, then

$$\begin{aligned} \rho(a) \circ_3 \rho(b) &= \psi(\varphi(a)) \circ_3 \psi(\varphi(b)) \\ &= \psi(\varphi(a) \circ_2 \varphi(b)) && \text{[by (2)]} \\ &= \psi(\varphi(a \circ_1 b)) && \text{[by (1)]} \\ &= \rho(a \circ_1 b), \end{aligned}$$

and (14.2.1) holds for ρ. The proof is complete.

In (14.2.2), we have defined isomorphism for systems $(G_1, \circ_1)$, $(G_2, \circ_2)$. It would be desirable to have a similar notion of isomorphism for any mathematical systems that are to be dealt with. Now it is clear that a mathematical system may involve much more than a given set and operation. There may be included (as for the basic system of positive integers $(I, 1, \sigma)$), one or more particular elements of a basic set in the basis. Also, there may be many basic sets, rather than just one. Hence the basis of a mathematical system may involve many sets, subsets of these sets, relations, operations, and so on. The problem of including "all possible" mathematical systems in a general definition is one which we do not attempt to treat. In fact, it is doubtful that this problem is meaningful. Such a treatment, if possible at all, would have to be made within the framework of logic, since it would deal with arbitrary mathematical systems as entities. Accordingly, we shall be content with an attempt to make the concept of isomorphism intuitively meaningful by giving the definition in a number of special cases. The reader should, in each case, study carefully the statements corresponding to (14.2.1); he will materially aid his understanding by carrying out the proofs of the corollaries like (14.2.3). Such corollaries always hold, and will not be stated after each definition. Motivation for each definition lies in demanding that the sets involved be equivalent, and that the tables (real or conceptual) representing the relations and functions involved be related as they were in the example given for groups. An asterisk indicates the existence of simple instances; the reader should construct such examples and study the intuitive similarity between the systems and its connection with the precise concept being defined. The symbol $\sim$ is understood to mean "is isomorphic to" in each sense introduced.

(14.2.4) DEFINITION:* If I_1, I_2 are sets and 1_1, 1_2 are respective elements of I_1, I_2, then $(I_1, 1_1)$ is *isomorphic* to $(I_2, 1_2)$ if there exists a one-to-one correspondence φ between I_1 and I_2 such that

$$\varphi(1_1) = 1_2.$$

REMARK: Here φ *carries* 1_1 *into* 1_2.

(14.2.5) DEFINITION:* If I_1, I_2 are sets and R_1 and R_2 are relations on $I_1 \times I_1$ and on $I_2 \times I_2$ respectively, then (I_1, R_1) is *isomorphic* to (I_2, R_2) if there exists a one-to-one correspondence φ between I_1 and I_2 such that

$$\text{if } a, b \in I_1, \text{ then } a\ R_1\ b \text{ if and only if } \varphi(a)\ R_2\ \varphi(b).$$

REMARK: Here φ *carries* R_1 *into* R_2.

(14.2.6) THEOREM:* *If* I_1, I_2 *are sets and* σ_1 *and* σ_2 *are functions on* I_1 *to* I_1 *and on* I_2 *to* I_2 *respectively, then* $(I_1, \sigma_1) \sim (I_2, \sigma_2)$ *if and only if there exists a one-to-one correspondence* φ *between* I_1 *and* I_2 *such that*

$$a \in I_1 \textit{ implies } \varphi(\sigma_1(a)) = \sigma_2(\varphi(a)).$$

PROOF: If $(I_1, \sigma_1) \sim (I_2, \sigma_2)$, then, since the functions σ_1, σ_2 are also relations on $I_1 \times I_1$, and $I_2 \times I_2$, (14.2.5) applies, yielding a one-to-one correspondence φ between I_1 and I_2 such that, if $a, b \in I_1$, then

$$a\ \sigma_1\ b \text{ if and only if } \varphi(a)\ \sigma_2\ \varphi(b).$$

But if $a \in I_1$, then $b \equiv \sigma_1(a)$ yields $a\ \sigma_1\ b$, whence $\varphi(a)\ \sigma_2\ \varphi(\sigma_1(a))$, or $\varphi(\sigma_1(a)) = \sigma_2(\varphi(a))$. Conversely, if the condition of the theorem holds, let $a, b \in I_1$, preparatory to verifying the condition of (14.2.5). If $a\ \sigma_1\ b$, we have $b = \sigma_1(a)$, so that

$$\sigma_2(\varphi(a)) = \varphi(\sigma_1(a)) = \varphi(b),$$

whence $\varphi(a)\ \sigma_2\ \varphi(b)$. On the other hand, if $\varphi(a)\ \sigma_2\ \varphi(b)$, then

$$\varphi(b) = \sigma_2(\varphi(a)) = \varphi(\sigma_1(a)).$$

But φ is a one-to-one correspondence. Hence by (10.2.2), $b = \sigma_1(a)$, and $a\ \sigma_1\ b$. This completes the proof.

(14.2.7) DEFINITION:* If I_1, I_2 are sets, if $1_1 \in I_1$, $1_2 \in I_2$ and if σ_1 and σ_2 are functions on I_1 to I_1 and on I_2 to I_2, respectively, then $(I_1, 1_1, \sigma_1)$ is *isomorphic* to $(I_2, 1_2, \sigma_2)$ if there exists a one-to-one correspondence φ between I_1 and I_2 such that

(a) $\qquad \varphi(1_1) = 1_2;$
(b) $\qquad a \in I_1 \text{ implies } \varphi(\sigma_1(a)) = \sigma_2(\varphi(a)).$

REMARK: Note that (14.2.7) is constructed from (14.2.4) and (14.2.6), the conditions of these two definitions being simultaneously imposed on the same φ. That is, φ carries 1_1 into 1_2 *and* σ_1 into σ_2. One use of (14.2.7) is to give meaning to the idea of isomorphism of two basic systems of positive integers [see (14.4)].

A simple extension of (14.2.4) is this:

(14.2.8) DEFINITION: * If I_1, I_2, J_1, J_2 are sets with $J_1 \subset I_1$, $J_2 \subset I_2$, then (I_1, J_1) is *isomorphic* to (I_2, J_2) if there exists a one-to-one correspondence φ between I_1 and I_2 such that

$$\varphi(J_1) = J_2.$$

REMARK: Here φ *carries* J_1 *into* J_2. It follows from $\varphi(J_1) = J_2$ that $J_1 \sim J_2$ by (10.2.6).

A generalization of (14.2.5) follows.

(14.2.9) DEFINITION: * If I_1, I_2 are sets, and if R_1, S_1 are relations on $I_1 \times I_1$ and R_2, S_2 are relations on $I_2 \times I_2$, then (I_1, R_1, S_1) is *isomorphic* to (I_2, R_2, S_2) if there exists a one-to-one correspondence φ between I_1 and I_2 such that,

if $a, b \in I_1$, then $a\, R_1\, b$ if and only if $\varphi(a)\, R_2\, \varphi(b)$;
if $a, b \in I_1$, then $a\, S_1\, b$ if and only if $\varphi(a)\, S_2\, \varphi(b)$.

REMARK: Here φ carries R_1 into R_2 *and* S_1 into S_2.

A generalization of (14.2.2) follows.

(14.2.10) DEFINITION: * If G_1, G_2 are sets, and if o_1, p_1 are operations on $G_1 \times G_1$ to G_1 and o_2, p_2 are operations on $G_2 \times G_2$ to G_2, then $(G_1, \mathsf{o}_1, \mathsf{p}_1)$ is *isomorphic* to $(G_2, \mathsf{o}_2, \mathsf{p}_2)$ if there exists a one-to-one correspondence φ between G_1 and G_2 such that,

for every $a, b \in G_1$, $\varphi(a)\, \mathsf{o}_2\, \varphi(b) = \varphi(a\, \mathsf{o}_1\, b)$;
for every $a, b \in G_1$, $\varphi(a)\, \mathsf{p}_2\, \varphi(b) = \varphi(a\, \mathsf{p}_1\, b)$.

REMARK: Here φ carries o_1 into o_2 *and* p_1 into p_2.

The next definition is of considerable importance since it deals with a case that occurs frequently. A particular application of (14.2.11) is to define isomorphism of two algebraic systems of positive integers.

(14.2.11) DEFINITION: If G_1, G_2 are sets, if $u_1 \in G_1$, $u_2 \in G_2$, if $<_1$ is a relation on $G_1 \times G_1$ and $<_2$ is a relation on $G_2 \times G_2$, and if $+_1$, $\times_1$ are operations on $G_1 \times G_1$ to G_1 and $+_2$, $\times_2$ are operations on $G_2 \times G_2$ to G_2, then $(G_1, u_1, <_1, +_1, \times_1)$ is *isomorphic to* $(G_2, u_2, <_2, +_2, \times_2)$ if there exists a one-to-one correspondence φ between G_1 and G_2, such that

(a) $\varphi(u_1) = u_2$;
(b) for every $a, b \in G_1$, $a <_1 b$ if and only if $\varphi(a) <_2 \varphi(b)$;
(c) for every $a, b \in G_1$, $\varphi(a) +_2 \varphi(b) = \varphi(a +_1 b)$;
(d) for every $a, b \in G_1$, $\varphi(a) \times_2 \varphi(b) = \varphi(a \times_1 b)$.

REMARK: Here φ carries u_1 into u_2, $<_1$ into $<_2$, $+_1$ into $+_2$ and $\times_1$ into $\times_2$.

In all the preceding definitions the systems involved consist of a single basic set, together with certain elements or subsets of the basic set and certain functions, relations or operations defined on cartesian products built up from the given set. A rather subtle question arises when it is desired to define isomorphism for systems which include two or more basic sets. For example, one may ask, what will be the definition of isomorphism between (A_1, B_1) and (A_2, B_2), where A_1, B_1, A_2, B_2 are sets? Two possibilities suggest themselves:

(14.2.12.a) $(A_1 B_1)$ is isomorphic to (A_2, B_2) if there exists a one-to-one correspondence φ between A_1 and A_2 and a one-to-one correspondence ψ between B_1 and B_2.

(14.2.12.b) (A_1, B_1) is isomorphic to (A_2, B_2) if there exists a one-to-one correspondence φ between $A_1 + B_1$ and $A_2 + B_2$ such that

$$\varphi(A_1) = A_2 \quad \text{and} \quad \varphi(B_1) = B_2.$$

In (14.2.12.a), the two sets are treated entirely separately, while in (14.2.12.b) it is required that a single correspondence between the set-theoretic sums should carry each of the given sets, considered as a subset of the first sum, into its corresponding subset of the second sum.

These two notions are quite different, as can be seen by considering the case $A_1 \subset B_1$. Here the first definition (14.2.12.a) of isomorphism would not require that $A_2 \subset B_2$ while the second definition (14.2.12.b) would. In loose terminology, isomorphism in the sense of (14.2.12.b) "preserves any set-theoretic interconnections between A_1 and B_1," while isomorphism in the sense of (14.2.12.a) treats the possibility of set-theoretic interconnections between A_1 and B_1 as extraneous. Actually both of these notions are important. There are mathematical systems for which set-theoretic interconnections between basic sets constitute an essential feature of the systems themselves; there are other systems in which such interconnections, if they exist, are completely irrelevant. Fortunately, a simple convention suffices to deal with this situation. Isomorphism between (A_1, B_1) and (A_2, B_2), in the case when set-theoretic interconnections are irrelevant, is defined by (14.2.12.a). However, when set-theoretic interconnections constitute an integral part of the description of the system (A, B), we effect an implicit statement of this fact by denoting the system thus:

$$(C, A, B), \text{ where } A, B, C \text{ are sets with } C = A + B,$$

rather than by the simple notation (A, B). Isomorphism between two systems (C_1, A_1, B_1) and (C_2, A_2, B_2), where $C_1 = A_1 + B_1$ and $C_2 = A_2 + B_2$, is then defined by the condition of (14.2.12.b), namely, that there exists a one-to-one correspondence φ between C_1 and C_2 such that $\varphi(A_1) = A_2$ and $\varphi(B_1) = B_2$. The next two definitions describe the two types of isomorphism just discussed.

(14.2.13) DEFINITION:* If A_1, B_1, A_2, B_2 are sets, then (A_1, B_1) is *isomorphic* to (A_2, B_2) if there exists a one-to-one correspondence φ_1 between A_1 and A_2, and a one-to-one correspondence φ_2 between B_1 and B_2.

(14.2.14) DEFINITION:* If C_1, A_1, B_1 are sets with $C_1 = A_1 + B_1$, and C_2, A_2, B_2 are sets with $C_2 = A_2 + B_2$, then (C_1, A_1, B_1) is *isomorphic* to (C_2, A_2, B_2) if there exists a one-to-one correspondence φ between C_1 and C_2 such that

$$\varphi(A_1) = A_2, \quad \varphi(B_1) = B_2.$$

REMARK: Here φ carries A_1 into A_2 *and* B_1 into B_2. It should be noted that (14.2.14) is an extension of (14.2.8).

An important example of a system containing two basic sets in which set-theoretic interconnections between the sets are not pertinent is the system consisting of a group and a basic system of positive integers. The following definition applies.

(14.2.15) DEFINITION: Let $(G_1, I_1, 1_1, \sigma_1, \circ_1)$, $(G_2, I_2, 1_2, \sigma_2, \circ_2)$ be systems in which $(G_1, \circ_1)$ and $(G_2, \circ_2)$ are groups, and $(I_1, 1_1, \sigma_1)$, $(I_2, 1_2, \sigma_2)$ are basic systems of positive integers. Then the given systems are isomorphic if there exists a one-to-one correspondence φ between G_1 and G_2, and a one-to-one correspondence ψ between I_1 and I_2, such that

(a) $\psi(1_1) = 1_2$;
(b) $n \in I_1$ implies $\psi(\sigma_1(n)) = \sigma_2(\psi(n))$;
(c) $a, b \in G_1$ implies $\varphi(a) \circ_2 \varphi(b) = \varphi(a \circ_1 b)$.

REMARK: It should be verified that (14.2.15) amounts to requiring that $(G_1, \circ_1)$ and $(G_2, \circ_2)$ be isomorphic in the sense of (14.2.2), and independently requiring that $(I_1, 1_1, \sigma_1)$ and $(I_2, 1_2, \sigma_2)$ be isomorphic in the sense of (14.2.7).

Of course it is not always possible to divide an assertion of isomorphism between systems containing more than one basic set into the independent assertions of isomorphism between "subsystems," since functions or relations involving more than one of the basic sets may be included in the system. The next definition affords a typical example.

(14.2.16) Definition: Let $(S_1, I_1, 1_1, \sigma_1, F_1)$, $(S_2, I_2, 1_2, \sigma_2, F_2)$ be systems in which S_1, S_2 are sets, $(I_1, 1_1, \sigma_1)$, $(I_2, 1_2, \sigma_2)$ are basic systems of positive integers, and F_1 and F_2 are functions on I_1 to S_1 and on I_2 to S_2, respectively. Then the given systems are *isomorphic* if there exists a one-to-one correspondence φ between S_1 and S_2, and a one-to-one correspondence ψ between I_1 and I_2 such that

(a) $\psi(1_1) = 1_2$;
(b) $n \in I_1$ implies $\psi(\sigma_1(n)) = \sigma_2(\psi(n))$;
(c) $n \in I_1$ implies $\varphi(F_1(n)) = F_2(\psi(n))$.

Remark: If in (14.2.16) it had been asserted that $S_1 \subset I_1$ and $S_2 \subset I_2$, then no function φ would have been required; ψ would have replaced φ in (c), and the condition $\psi(S_1) = S_2$ would have been added. This shows how definitions of isomorphisms may be essentially affected by introducing the set-theoretic interrelations among the objects comprising the systems.

As has been stated, no "general" definition of isomorphism will be given. It is hoped that the material given and suggested will aid the reader in securing a reasonable grasp of the intuitive principles which underlie the construction of specific definitions of isomorphism. Henceforth, whenever a new type of mathematical system is introduced (through basis and axioms), we shall state precisely what is meant by isomorphism of two systems of the specified type.

(14.2.17) Project: Show that (14.2.1) is equivalent to $\mathsf{p}_2 = \mathsf{o}_2$ in the example preceding the statement of (14.2.1).

(14.2.18) Project: Construct appropriate examples and prove the corollaries to each of the definitions (14.2.4) to (14.2.10), (14.2.13) to (14.2.16).

(14.2.19) Project: Formulate a definition of isomorphism of two systems of this form: $(G, \mathsf{o}, \mathsf{p}, H, +, \times)$, where G, H are sets, o, p are operations on $G \times G$ to G, $+$ is an operation on $H \times H$ to H, and $\times$ is an operation on $G \times H$ to H.

(14.2.20) Project: Let (G_1, o_1), (G_2, o_2) be isomorphic systems, in which G_1, G_2 are sets and o_1, o_2 are operations on $G_1 \times G_1$ to G_1 and $G_2 \times G_2$ to G_2, respectively. Prove that, if (G_1, o_1) is a group, then (G_2, o_2) is a group.

(14.2.21) PROJECT: Let $(G_1, \circ_1)$, $(G_2, \circ_2)$ be groups. Define $G \equiv G_1 \times G_2$, and $\circ$ on $G \times G$ to G so that, for (a, b), $(c, d) \in G$,

$$(a, b) \circ (c, d) = (a \circ_1 c, b \circ_2 d).$$

Prove that $(G, \circ)$ is a group. ($(G, \circ)$ is called the *direct product* of $(G_1, \circ_1)$ and $(G_2, \circ_2)$.)

14.3. Categorical Systems of Axioms. In (7.4) certain properties of systems of axioms were described. One of these properties was designated by the term *categorical*; in terms of the concept of isomorphism, categorical systems of axioms may now be more fully discussed.

Let us consider a mathematical system, that is, a basis for a mathematical theory, together with a system of axioms concerning the basis. Let us assume that the concept of isomorphism of two systems of the type under consideration has been defined. Then we shall say that the system of axioms is *categorical*, if any two mathematical systems satisfying the axioms are isomorphic.

It should be noted that we have not actually *defined* the concept *categorical*; we have only *described* what its definition would be in the case of mathematical systems for which isomorphism has been defined. Since it has not been found possible for us to give a universally applicable definition of isomorphism, we must recognize that categoricalness becomes meaningful in any particular case only after isomorphism has been defined.

Some mathematicians would say that a mathematical system described by categorical axioms is "abstractly unique." For, they would argue, since any two instances must be isomorphic, such instances are "abstractly identical," that is, are the "same so far as 'essentials' are concerned." From this point of view, categoricalness bears the same relation to consistency [see (7.4)] as uniqueness bears to existence. While such statements may be intuitively suggestive, we find them somewhat objectionable in the absence of a precise idea concerning something like the "set of all mathematical systems" or "the set of all instances" of a given mathematical theory. Moreover, it is not clear how "essentials" mentioned above differ from "unessentials," so that "abstractly identical" is a hazy concept. In view of our agreement to define isomorphism for each type of mathematical system that arises, we shall be led immediately to a precise meaning in each case for categoricalness, and proof or disproof of such categoricalness is in order. Thus, although our lack of universal concepts of isomorphism and categoricalness may incur the displeasure of logicians, it results in no practical handicap.

Since the definitions of isomorphism in (14.2) were motivated by an intuitive idea of similarity or resemblance of systems, it follows (intuitively) that instances of a mathematical theory differ much less from one another when the axioms are categorical than when they are not. Possible fields for application are thus narrower when the categorical feature is present; content of the theorems within the theory is accordingly less. However, the development of mathematics and its uses has shown that certain systems—usually those most widely employed, such as the positive integers and the real numbers—came to be known intuitively as though they were unique and specific. Axioms for these particular systems may be expected, then, to be categorical. Both categorical and noncategorical types of mathematical theory play essential roles in the overall growth of the subject; it would be foolish to attempt to rate them as to their relative importance or usefulness.

The following theorem asserts that the axioms for a group are not categorical [see (7.4)].

(14.3.1) **Theorem**: *There exist groups* $(G_1, \circ_1)$, $(G_2, \circ_2)$ *such that* $(G_1, \circ_1) \sim' (G_2, \circ_2)$.

Proof: Define $(G_1, \circ_1)$ as in (7.2.1), $(G_2, \circ_2)$ as in (7.2.2). Then the set G_1 has 2 elements and G_2 has 3 elements, so that $G_1 \sim' G_2$ by (10.4.4.b). Now, if $(G_1, \circ_1) \sim (G_2, \circ_2)$, there exists a one-to-one correspondence between G_1 and G_2 by (14.2.2), whence $G_1 \sim G_2$. This contradiction completes the proof.

Remark: It is natural to ask whether for groups $(G_1, \circ_1)$, $(G_2, \circ_2)$ it is true that

$$G_1 \sim G_2 \text{ implies } (G_1, \circ_1) \sim (G_2, \circ_2).$$

Negative answer is given by this example:

$$G \equiv G_1 \equiv G_2 \equiv [a, b, c, d] \quad (a \neq b, c, d; b \neq c, d; c \neq d);$$

$\circ_1$:

	a	b	c	d
a	a	b	c	d
b	b	c	d	a
c	c	d	a	b
d	d	a	b	c

$\circ_2$:

	a	b	c	d
a	a	b	c	d
b	b	a	d	c
c	c	d	a	b
d	d	c	b	a

We leave to the reader the task of proving that $(G_1, \circ_1)$, $(G_2, \circ_2)$ are groups. Clearly $G_1 \sim G_2$. But, as we shall now show, $(G_1, \circ_1) \sim' (G_2, \circ_2)$. Suppose $(G_1, \circ_1) \sim (G_2, \circ_2)$, whence there exists a one-to-one correspondence φ between G_1 and G_2 such that

(1) $$x, y \in G \text{ implies } \varphi(x) \circ_2 \varphi(y) = \varphi(x \circ_1 y).$$

It should be observed that a is the identity element of each group. Hence it follows that $\varphi(a) = a$. For if $x \in G_2$,

$$\begin{aligned} x \circ_2 \varphi(a) &= \varphi(\varphi^*(x)) \circ_2 \varphi(a) && \text{[by (10.2.1.b)]} \\ &= \varphi(\varphi^*(x) \circ_1 a) && \text{[by (1)]} \\ &= \varphi(\varphi^*(x)) && \text{[since } a \text{ is the identity element]} \\ &= x = x \circ_2 a; \end{aligned}$$

if we put $x = a$, we obtain

$$\varphi(a) = a \circ_2 \varphi(a) = a \circ_2 a = a. \tag{2}$$

Now it is seen from the table defining $\circ_2$ that $x \in G_2$ implies $x \circ_2 x = a$. In particular,

$$\begin{aligned} a = \varphi(b) \circ_2 \varphi(b) &= \varphi(b \circ_1 b) && \text{[by (1)]} \\ &= \varphi(c). \end{aligned} \tag{3}$$

Hence

$$\begin{aligned} a = \varphi^*(\varphi(a)) &= \varphi^*(a) && \text{[by (2)]} \\ &= \varphi^*(\varphi(c)) && \text{[by (3)]} \\ &= c, \end{aligned}$$

which is impossible, since $a \neq c$. This contradiction completes the proof. The group $(G_1, \circ_1)$ is called the *cyclic group of order* 4; $(G_2, \circ_2)$ is called the 4-*group*.

(14.3.2) PROJECT: Prove that $(G_1, \circ_1)$ in the remark is a commutative group.

(14.3.3) PROJECT: Prove that $(G_2, \circ_2)$ in the remark is a commutative group.

(14.3.4) PROJECT: Prove that, in (14.2.4), if $I_1 \sim I_2$, then $(I_1, 1_1) \sim (I_2, 1_2)$.

14.4. Categoricalness for the Positive Integers. In this section it is shown that the axioms for the positive integers are categorical.

(14.4.1) THEOREM: *Every two basic systems* $(I_1, 1_1, \sigma_1)$, $(I_2, 1_2, \sigma_2)$ *of positive integers (satisfying Axioms* I, II, III *of Chapter* 8) *are isomorphic.*

PROOF: We recognize first that in the theory of $(I_1, 1_1, \sigma_1)$ there is an operation $+_1$, and in the theory of $(I_2, 1_2, \sigma_2)$ there is an operation $+_2$. The axioms III′ referring to the respective systems are denoted by III_1', III_2'. The principle of inductive definition (11.4.5) when employing $(I_1, 1_1, \sigma_1)$ is referred to as $(11.4.5_1)$, while that based on $(I_2, 1_2, \sigma_2)$ is $(11.4.5_2)$.

In order to prove the desired isomorphism we must establish, in accordance with (14.2.7), the existence of a one-to-one correspondence φ between I_1 and I_2, such that

$$\varphi(1_1) = 1_2; \tag{1}$$

$$m_1 \in I_1 \text{ implies } \varphi(\sigma_1(m_1)) = \sigma_2(\varphi(m_1)). \tag{2}$$

We apply ($11.4.5_1$) with $A \equiv I_2$, $x \equiv 1_2$, $F \equiv \sigma_2$. Let φ be the sequence defined inductively by 1_2 and σ_2. Then (1) holds, and

$$m_1 \in I_1 \text{ implies } \varphi(m_1 +_1 1_1) = \sigma_2(\varphi(m_1)),$$

so that (2) holds. Moreover, φ is on I_1 to I_2.

It remains to show that φ has range I_2 and that (10.2.2.c) holds. Let us apply ($11.4.5_2$) with $A \equiv I_1$, $x \equiv 1_1$, $F \equiv \sigma_1$, obtaining a function ψ on I_2 to I_1 such that

(3) $$\psi(1_2) = 1_1;$$
(4) $$m_2 \in I_2 \text{ implies } \psi(\sigma_2(m_2)) = \sigma_1(\psi(m_2)).$$

It will be shown that

(5) $$m_1 \in I_1 \text{ implies } \psi(\varphi(m_1)) = m_1;$$
(6) $$m_2 \in I_2 \text{ implies } \varphi(\psi(m_2)) = m_2.$$

Define

$$H_1 \equiv [m_1 \in I_1;\ \psi(\varphi(m_1)) = m_1].$$

Clearly $1_1 \in H_1$, since

$$\begin{aligned} \psi(\varphi(1_1)) &= \psi(1_2) && \text{[by (1)]} \\ &= 1_1 && \text{[by (3)].} \end{aligned}$$

Suppose $q_1 \in H_1$. Then

$$\begin{aligned} \psi(\varphi(q_1 +_1 1_1)) &= \psi(\varphi(\sigma_1(q_1))) \\ &= \psi(\sigma_2(\varphi(q_1))) && \text{[by (2)]} \\ &= \sigma_1(\psi(\varphi(q_1))) && \text{[by (4)]} \\ &= \sigma_1(q_1) && \text{[since } q_1 \in H_1\text{]} \\ &= q_1 +_1 1_1. \end{aligned}$$

Thus $q_1 +_1 1_1 \in H_1$, and $H_1 = I_1$ by III_1'. This proves (5); the proof of (6) is similar.

Now if $m_2 \in I_2$, we may define $m_1 = \psi(m_2)$, whence, by (6), $\varphi(m_1) = m_2$. This establishes that the range of φ is I_2. The function φ satisfies the hypotheses of (10.2.2) and has the property (10.2.2.c) in view of (5), (6); therefore φ is a one-to-one correspondence between I_1 and I_2. The proof is complete.

(14.4.2) PROJECT: Let $(I_1, 1_1, \sigma_1)$, $(I_2, 1_2, \sigma_2)$ be two basic systems of positive integers, and let φ, ψ be two isomorphisms between them. Prove that $\varphi = \psi$.

(14.4.3) PROJECT: Let $(I_1, 1_1, \sigma_1)$ and $(I_2, 1_2, \sigma_2)$ be basic systems of positive integers and let $(I_1, 1_1, <_1, +_1, \times_1)$ and $(I_2, 1_2, <_2, +_2, \times_2)$ be the corresponding algebraic systems of positive integers. Prove that the latter systems are isomorphic.

14.5. Subsystems. Just as the idea of isomorphism of two mathematical systems is a generalization of the concept of equivalence of sets, a notion of *subsystems* of a given mathematical system is available which extends the idea of subsets of a set. The same considerations which prevent our defining isomorphism in general are effective in barring a universal definition of subsystem. However, we shall briefly present a few examples.

Let G be a set, and let $\circ$ be an operation on $G \times G$ to G. Let H be any non-empty subset of G. We might be led to consider a system of this type:

(14.5.1) $$(H, (x \circ y; (x, y) \in H \times H)),$$

in which the "reduced" operation appearing is on $H \times H$ to G and is a subset of the operation $\circ$ (thought of as a subset of $(G \times G) \times G$). Such a system might be called a *subsystem* of $(G, \circ)$. It is convenient to specialize the terminology somewhat so that the system shall have the same character as $(G, \circ)$; specifically, it is required that the range of the operation should be contained in H, that is, the operation should be on $H \times H$ to H.

The requirement just described may be stated thus:

(14.5.2) $$x, y \in H \text{ implies } x \circ y \in H.$$

Before stating a formal definition, let us agree to abbreviate (14.5.1) by the notation $(H, \circ)$; no ambiguity can possibly arise from this multiple use of the symbol $\circ$, and great convenience results, particularly when many sets H are under consideration.

(14.5.3) Definition: If $(G, \circ)$ is a system in which G is a set and $\circ$ an operation on $G \times G$ to G, then $(H, \circ)$ is called a *subsystem* of $(G, \circ)$ if $H \subset G$ and (14.5.2) holds.

In the example $(G, \circ)$, with $G = [a, b, c, d]$, and $\circ$ given by

$\circ$:

	a	b	c	d
a	a	b	c	d
b	b	a	d	c
c	c	d	a	b
d	d	c	b	a

possible subsystems are $(H, \circ)$ with $H = [a, b], [a, c], [a, d], [a]$. Thus, if $H = [a, b]$ the operation $(x \circ y; (x, y) \in H \times H)$ is given by

	a	b
a	a	b
b	b	a

and satisfies (14.5.2). It is of interest to note that here (G, o) is a group, as are the various subsystems. Subsystems of groups which are also groups are called *subgroups*; it is not generally true that all subsystems of a group are necessarily groups, as the example might tend to indicate.

The reader might formulate for himself definitions like (14.5.3) for various other systems, for example, those appearing in (14.2). For a system $(I, 1)$ where $1 \in I$, a subsystem $(J, 1)$ would be subject to the requirements that $J \subset I$, $1 \in J$. For (I, σ) as in (14.2.6), a subsystem (J, σ) would satisfy $J \subset I$ and

$$a \in J \text{ implies } \sigma(a) \in J.$$

If another operation p is appended to (G, o), then both o, p would satisfy (14.5.2). In the case of (I, R), where R is a relation on $I \times I$, it is interesting to note that no condition like (14.5.2) is needed, since, for $J \subset I$, the "reduced" relation

$$[(a, b) \in R; (a, b) \in J \times J] = R \cdot (J \times J)$$

has the proper character, that is, is on $J \times J$.

While subsystems are of considerable interest in mathematics generally, we shall not be required to make extensive use of them in this book; hence further discussion of them will not be necessary.

(14.5.4) PROJECT: Formulate definitions of subsystems for systems of the types in (14.2.7), (14.2.8), (14.2.9), (14.2.10), (14.2.13), (14.2.14), (14.2.15), (14.2.16).

(14.5.5) PROJECT: Prove that a basic system $(I, 1, \sigma)$ of positive integers is its only subsystem.

Chapter 15

EQUIVALENCE AND ORDER RELATIONS

[No Basis]

15.1. Introduction. This chapter will be devoted to the discussion of particular types of relations that are of frequent occurrence and great importance in mathematics. The discussion will serve, on the one hand, to unify many results that have been or will be obtained concerning specific relations, and, on the other hand, to provide some necessary tools for later applications.

The first relations to be discussed are referred to as *equivalence relations* because they constitute a generalization of the identity relation. The word "equivalent" has intuitively the force of "equal in some particular respect," or "possessive of some common attribute." It may be recalled that at the time we first discussed equality in (4.5) we promised a discussion of "equivalence" of elements. Clearly any precise concept of "equivalence" between elements of a set A would have to appear as a relation on $A \times A$. Equivalence relations as defined in (15.2.3) will be found to be appropriate mathematical counterparts of those intuitive relations which express "equivalence of elements."

Order relations, on the other hand, satisfy requirements suggested by the intuitive relations "is to the left of," "is shorter than," "is younger than," "is older than," and the like. These relations, in contrast to equivalence relations, express intuitively the idea "superior (or inferior) in some particular respect."

It is rather curious that one of the most important properties of relations is to be required for both equivalence relations and order relations. The property is called *transitivity*.

(15.1.1) Definition: Let A be a set and R a relation on $A \times A$. Then R is *transitive* if, for every $a, b \in A$ for which there exists $c \in A$ such that $a \; R \; c$ and $c \; R \; b$, it is true that $a \; R \; b$.

It is intuitively clear that the intuitive relations "is to the left of," "is younger than," and the like, do possess this property. For if a "is to the left of" c, and c "is to the left of" b, then certainly a "is to the left of" b. It is equally acceptable intuitively that, if each of two elements is "equal in a certain respect" to a third, then they are "equal in this respect" to each other. Thus this chapter may be regarded as a study of certain types of transitive relations.

(15.1.2) PROJECT: Let $A \equiv [p_1, p_2]$, $p_1 \neq p_2$. Determine all transitive relations R on $A \times A$. (Do not neglect those relations for which the condition in (15.1.1) is vacuously true.)

15.2. Equivalence Relations. Let A be a set and $\mathcal{R}_A$ the set of all relations on $A \times A$. Let us look for properties of relations $R \in \mathcal{R}_A$ that seem to hold for intuitive instances of relations of "equivalence."

The first of these properties is evident. Two elements x, y are certainly "equivalent" in any respect if they are equal. Hence we require, for an *equivalence relation* R,

(15.2.1) for every $x \in A$, $x \, R \, x$.

This requirement may also be stated in the form $R \supset E$, where E is the identity relation on $A \times A$ [see (5.3)]. A relation R satisfying (15.2.1) is called *reflexive.*

A second property is also apparent. "Equivalence" should not depend on the "order" in which the elements "appear." Hence we insist that,

(15.2.2) for every x, $y \in A$, $x \, R \, y$ implies $y \, R \, x$.

This may also be stated in the form $R = R^*$, where R^* is the transpose relation to R [see (5.3)]. A relation R satisfying (15.2.2) is called *symmetric.*

The third property, transitivity, has already been discussed.

These three properties are all that will be required; that is, a relation on $A \times A$ will be called an *equivalence relation* if it is reflexive, symmetric and transitive. For convenience of reference we state these definitions formally.

(15.2.3) DEFINITION: If A is a set and R is a relation on $A \times A$, then R is *reflexive* if,

(a) for every $x \in A$, $x \, R \, x$;

R is *symmetric* if,

(b) for every x, $y \in A$, if $x \, R \, y$ then $y \, R \, x$;

R is *transitive* if,

(c) for every x, $z \in A$, if there exists $y \in A$ such that $x \, R \, y$ and $y \, R \, z$, then $x \, R \, z$.

Moreover, R is an *equivalence relation* if R is reflexive, symmetric and transitive. The set of all equivalence relations on $A \times A$ is denoted by $\mathcal{E}_A$.

The consideration of a few intuitive relations might help to clarify the meaning of an equivalence relation. The relation "has the same parents as" is an equivalence relation. For, clearly, any person has the same parents as himself; if a "has the same parents as" b then b "has the same parents as" a; and finally, if a and c have the same parents, and if c and b have the same parents, then a and b have the same parents. On the other hand, "is a friend of" is not an equivalence relation. For transitivity is certainly not valid; symmetry is quite dubious; and by a stretch of the imagination, even reflexivity may be doubted in this case. The relation "was born in the same calendar year as" is (intuitively) an equivalence relation. But the relation "was born within one year of" is not an equivalence relation, since it is not transitive, although it is reflexive and symmetric.

(15.2.4) PROJECT: Note that (15.2.2) states actually that $R \subset R^*$. Why does this imply $R = R^*$?

(15.2.5) PROJECT: What can be said of the domain and range of an equivalence relation?

(15.2.6) PROJECT: If A is a set, and R is a relation on $A \times A$, prove that R is an equivalence relation if and only if (a) $E \subset R$, and (b) if x, $z \in A$ such that there exists $y \in A$ with $x \, R \, y$, $z \, R \, y$, then $x \, R \, z$. Does (b) imply (a)?

15.3. Equivalence Classes and Partitions. A consideration of intuitive examples of equivalence relations suggests an extremely important feature of such relations. The main difference between the equivalence relation "was born in the same calendar year as" and the non-equivalence relation "was born within one year of" is that the first suggests a "partition" or "grouping" of all people into sets, depending on the calendar year of their birth, while the second does not suggest such a "partition." Similarly, the relation "has the same parents as" suggests a "partition" into "families," while "is a friend of" does not lead to such a grouping. In this section, it will be shown that equivalence relations on $A \times A$ always lead to a "partition" of A, and, conversely, that any "partition" of A leads to an equivalence relation.

(15.3.1) DEFINITION: Let A be a set and R an equivalence relation on $A \times A$. For every $x \in A$, define

$$A_R(x) \equiv [y \in A; x \, R \, y];$$
$$\mathfrak{A}_R \equiv [A_R(x); x \in A].$$

The elements of $\mathfrak{A}_R$ are called *equivalence classes.*

REMARK: In defining $A_R(x)$, we have simply considered all elements of A which are equivalent ("similar") to the given element x and collected them into a single set. The equivalence classes which are the elements of $\mathfrak{A}_R$ are clearly certain subsets of A.

(15.3.2) COROLLARY: *Let A be a set and R an equivalence relation on $A \times A$. Then, for every $x, y \in A$,*

(a) $x \in A_R(x)$;

(b) $A_R(x) = A_R(y)$ *if and only if* $x \; R \; y$;

(c) $A_R(x) \cdot A_R(y) = \Theta$ *if and only if* $x \; R' \; y$;

(d) $A_R(x) \cdot A_R(y) \neq \Theta$ *if and only if* $A_R(x) = A_R(y)$.

PROOF OF (a): Since $x \; R \; x$ by (15.2.3.a), $x \in A_R(x)$ by (15.3.1).

PROOF OF (b): If $A_R(x) = A_R(y)$, we have $y \in A_R(y)$ by (a), so that $y \in A_R(x)$. Hence $x \; R \; y$ by (15.3.1). Conversely, suppose $x \; R \; y$, whence $y \in A_R(x)$. If $z \in A_R(y)$, then $y \; R \; z$. Thus

$$x \; R \; y \quad \text{and} \quad y \; R \; z,$$

and, by (15.2.3.c), $x \; R \; z$. Hence $z \in A_R(x)$. This proves $A_R(y) \subset A_R(x)$. To show the reverse inclusion, let $w \in A_R(x)$, whence $x \; R \; w$. Since $x \; R \; y$, we have $y \; R \; x$ by (15.2.3.b), so that

$$y \; R \; x, \quad x \; R \; w.$$

By (15.2.3.c), $y \; R \; w$, and $w \in A_R(y)$. This proves $A_R(x) \subset A_R(y)$, and the proof is complete.

PROOF OF (c): Suppose $A_R(x) \cdot A_R(y) = \Theta$. If $x \; R \; y$, then, by (b), $A_R(x) = A_R(y)$, and, by (a), $x \in A_R(x) \cdot A_R(y)$, contrary to the hypothesis. Hence $x \; R' \; y$. Conversely, if $x \; R' \; y$, and if $A_R(x) \cdot A_R(y) \neq \Theta$, there exists $z \in A_R(x) \cdot A_R(y)$. Then $x \; R \; z$ and $y \; R \; z$, whence also $z \; R \; y$ by (15.2.3.b). Thus $x \; R \; y$ by (15.2.3.c), contrary to the assumption. This completes the proof.

PROOF OF (d): This is left to the reader [use (c), (b)].

(15.3.3) COROLLARY: *If A is a set and R an equivalence relation on $A \times A$, then*

(a) $\sum \mathfrak{A}_R = A$;

(b) $B, C \in \mathfrak{A}_R$, $B \neq C$ *implies* $B \cdot C = \Theta$.

PROOF OF (a): Evidently $\sum \mathfrak{A}_R \subset A$. If $x \in A$, then $x \in A_R(x)$ by (15.3.2), whence $x \in \sum \mathfrak{A}_R$. This proves the reverse inclusion.

PROOF OF (b): Let $B, C \in \mathfrak{A}_R$, $B \neq C$. Then there exist $x, y \in A$ with $B = A_R(x)$, $C = A_R(y)$. If $x \; R \; y$, then, by (15.3.2.b), $B = C$, contrary to the hypothesis. Hence $x \; R' \; y$, and $B \cdot C = \Theta$ by (15.3.2.c).

(15.3.4) Definition: If A is a set, then a *partition* of A is a set $\mathfrak{A}$ of non-empty subsets of A such that

(a) $$\sum \mathfrak{A} = A;$$

(b) $$\text{if } B, C \in \mathfrak{A}, \text{ then } B \neq C \text{ implies } B \cdot C = \Theta.$$

(15.3.5) Theorem: *If A is a set and R an equivalence relation on $A \times A$, then $\mathfrak{A}_R$ is a partition of A.*

Proof: By (15.3.3), it is sufficient to verify that every $B \in \mathfrak{A}_R$ is non-empty. This follows from (15.3.2.a).

We have shown that for every equivalence relation R on $A \times A$, $\mathfrak{A}_R$ is a partition of A. It will now be shown that *every* partition of A arises in this way.

(15.3.6) Theorem: *If A is a set, and $\mathfrak{A}$ is a partition of A, then* (a) *there exists a unique equivalence relation R on $A \times A$ such that $\mathfrak{A} = \mathfrak{A}_R$. Moreover,* (b) *$x \, R \, y$ if and only if there exists $B \in \mathfrak{A}$ with $x, y \in B$.*

Proof of Existence in (a): Since $\sum \mathfrak{A} = A$, we see that for every $x \in A$ there exists $B \in \mathfrak{A}$ such that $x \in B$. That B is unique follows since $x \in B$, C implies $B \cdot C \neq \Theta$, whence $B = C$ by the contrapositive of (15.3.4.b). If $x \in A$, denote the unique $B \in \mathfrak{A}$ such that $x \in B$ by $B(x)$. Define

(1) $$R \equiv [(x, y) \in A \times A; B(x) = B(y)].$$

Let us observe first that R is an equivalence relation. The reflexive and symmetric properties are obvious; if $B(x) = B(y)$ and $B(y) = B(z)$, then $B(x) = B(z)$, and R is transitive.

It remains to prove

(2) $$\mathfrak{A}_R = \mathfrak{A}.$$

Note first that

(3) $$A_R(x) = [y \in A; x \, R \, y] = [y \in A; B(x) = B(y)].$$

Now let $B \in \mathfrak{A}_R$. Then there exists $x \in A$ such that $B = A_R(x)$. If $y \in A_R(x)$, then $B(x) = B(y)$, whence $y \in B(x)$; conversely, if $y \in B(x)$, then $B(x) = B(y)$, and $y \in A_R(x)$. Therefore

$$B = A_R(x) = B(x),$$

whence $B \in \mathfrak{A}$. This proves

(4) $$\mathfrak{A}_R \subset \mathfrak{A}.$$

To prove the reverse inclusion, let $B \in \mathfrak{A}$. Since $B \neq \Theta$ by (15.3.4), there exists x such that $x \in B$. Hence $B = B(x)$. Now if $y \in B$, we have

$$B(y) = B = B(x),$$

and, by (3), $y \in A_R(x)$; this proves $B \subset A_R(x)$. And, if $y \in A_R(x)$, then, by (3), $B(x) = B(y)$, whence $y \in B(x) = B$; hence $A_R(x) \subset B$. It follows then that $A_R(x) = B$. Since $A_R(x) \in \mathfrak{A}_R$, we have $B \in \mathfrak{A}_R$. This establishes

$$(5) \qquad \mathfrak{A} \subset \mathfrak{A}_R.$$

Now (4) and (5) yield (2).

PROOF OF UNIQUENESS IN (a): Suppose R, S are equivalence relations such that $\mathfrak{A}_R = \mathfrak{A}$, $\mathfrak{A}_S = \mathfrak{A}$. It will be proved that $R \subset S$ and $S \subset R$. Suppose $x\ R\ y$, whence $y \in A_R(x)$. Since $\mathfrak{A}_R = \mathfrak{A}_S$, it follows that $A_R(x) \in \mathfrak{A}_S$, whence there exists $z \in A$ with $A_R(x) = A_S(z)$. By (15.3.2.b), $A_R(x) = A_R(y)$, so that $x, y \in A_R(x)$. Therefore $x, y \in A_S(z)$. It follows that $z\ S\ x$, $z\ S\ y$. By the symmetry of S, we have

$$x\ S\ z, \quad z\ S\ y,$$

whence $x\ S\ y$ by the transitivity of S. We have proved that $R \subset S$; similarly, $S \subset R$. Consequently $R = S$, and the proof is complete.

PROOF OF (b): Since R is unique, and since the relation R defined by (1) is effective, it follows that this R is the only relation which satisfies the condition $\mathfrak{A} = \mathfrak{A}_R$. We shall prove that

(6) $x\ R\ y$ if and only if there exists $B \in \mathfrak{A}$ such that $x, y \in B$.

If $x\ R\ y$, then define $B \equiv B(x)$. It follows that $B(x) = B(y)$, so that $x, y \in B$. Conversely, if there exists $B \in \mathfrak{A}$ such that $x, y \in B$, we have $B = B(x)$, $B = B(y)$, whence $B(x) = B(y)$ and $x\ R\ y$. Therefore (6) holds, and the proof is complete.

The results of this section indicate that an equivalence relation as defined by (15.2.3) is a reasonable mathematical counterpart of the intuitive concept "is equal in a certain respect." For, in the case of any intuitive relation of "equality in a certain respect," one can conceive of lumping together all objects which are equal in the particular respect. The sets into which all the objects under consideration fall constitute a partition in the sense of (15.3.4). But, by (15.3.6), such a partition leads to an equivalence relation. The sets constituting the partition are the equivalence classes, so that two objects are "equal in the given respect" exactly when they lie in the same set.

(15.3.7) PROJECT: Prove (15.3.2.d).

(15.3.8) PROJECT: If A is a set, prove that E, $A \times A$ are equivalence relations on $A \times A$. For each, determine the set of equivalence classes.

(15.3.9) PROJECT: If A is a set, define $\mathcal{P}_A$ as the set of all partitions of A: $\mathcal{P}_A \equiv [\mathfrak{A}_R;\ R \in \mathcal{E}_A]$. Prove that $\mathcal{E}_A \sim \mathcal{P}_A$, an appropriate one-to-one correspondence being $(\mathfrak{A}_R;\ R \in \mathcal{E}_A)$.

(15.3.10) PROJECT: Determine $\mathcal{E}_A$, $\mathcal{P}_A$ for the sets $A = [p_1, p_2]$, $[p_1, p_2, p_3]$.

15.4. Order Relations. As has already been mentioned, order relations are relations satisfying properties suggested by the intuitive relations "is to the left of," "is younger than," and the like. These relations seem to lend themselves to description by the term "order of precedence." They share with equivalence relations the property of being transitive. But with respect to reflexivity and symmetry they are the exact antithesis of equivalence relations. For no element "is to the left of" itself, and, further, if a "is to the left of" b then b "is *not* to the left of" a. It is thus suggested that we require, for an order relation R,

(15.4.1) for every $x \in A$, $x\ R'\ x$.

This requirement may also be stated in the form $R \cdot E = \Theta$. A relation R satisfying (15.4.1) is called *irreflexive*. It should be noted that irreflexivity is not the simple negation of reflexivity; a relation may be neither reflexive nor irreflexive.

It is also suggested that we require

(15.4.2) for every $x, y \in A$, $x\ R\ y$ implies $y\ R'\ x$.

This may also be stated in the form $R \cdot R^* = \Theta$. A relation R satisfying (15.4.2) is called *asymmetric*. Again, asymmetry is not the simple negation of symmetry.

Actually it is not necessary to require both irreflexivity and asymmetry in addition to transitivity for an order relation, since it happens that asymmetry is a consequence of irreflexivity and transitivity. Thus we shall define a (*partial*) *ordering relation* as a relation which is irreflexive and transitive. For reference, these suggested definitions are formalized.

(15.4.3) DEFINITION: If A is a set and R is a relation on $A \times A$, then R is *irreflexive* if

(a) for every $x \in A$, $x\ R'\ x$;

R is *asymmetric* if

(b) for every $x, y \in A$, if $x\ R\ y$ then $y\ R'\ x$.

Moreover, R is a *partial ordering of* A (or A is *partially ordered by* R) if R is irreflexive and transitive.

(15.4.4) THEOREM: *Let A be a set and R a partial ordering of A. Then R is asymmetric.*

PROOF: Suppose the theorem false so that there exist $x, y \in A$ such that $x\ R\ y$ and $y\ R\ x$. Then, by transitivity, $x\ R\ x$. But this contradicts irreflexivity.

The reason for the term *partial* ordering is that such a relation R does not necessarily establish an "order of precedence" for any two elements of A, that is, there may exist $x, y \in A$ such that $x \neq y$, $x\, R'\, y$, $y\, R'\, x$. A relation which does establish an "order of precedence" for any two elements more closely approximates the simple intuitive concept of a "single succession" and is called a *linear ordering*. Partial orderings serve to describe systems composed of many (possibly interlaced) "successions."

(15.4.5) DEFINITION: If A is a set and R is a relation on $A \times A$, then R is a *linear ordering of* A (or A is *linearly ordered by* R) if

(a) R is a partial ordering of A;
(b) for every $x, y \in A$, it is true that $x = y$ or $x\, R\, y$ or $y\, R\, x$.

Intuitively it is clear that both "is younger than" and "is older than" constitute linear orderings (if it is assumed that no two distinct persons are ever exactly the same age). Similarly linear orderings are established by both "is to the left of" and "is to the right of." It is suggested that, if R is a partial or linear ordering, then R^* is also a partial or linear ordering. That this is so will be shown next.

(15.4.6) THEOREM: *If A is partially (linearly) ordered by a relation R, then A is partially (linearly) ordered by R^*.*

PROOF: If $x \in A$, then $x\, R'\, x$ by (15.4.3.a), whence $x\, R^{*\prime}\, x$. Suppose $x, z \in A$ such that there exists $y \in A$ with $x\, R^*\, y$, $y\, R^*\, z$. Then $z\, R\, y$, $y\, R\, x$, and $z\, R\, x$, since R is transitive. Hence $x\, R^*\, z$, so that R^* is transitive. If R is a linear ordering, then R^* is a partial ordering by the proof just given. But (15.4.5.b) immediately follows for R^* since it holds for R. Thus R^* is a linear ordering, and the proof is complete.

(15.4.7) DEFINITION: If A is a set and R is a relation on $A \times A$, then R is a *well-ordering of* A (or A is *well-ordered by* R) if
(a) R is a linear ordering;
(b) for every $B \subset A$ with $B \neq \Theta$ there exists $b \in A$ such that

(1) $b \in B$;
(2) $c \in B$, $c \neq b$ implies $b\, R\, c$.

REMARK: An element b as in (15.4.7.b) may be called a *least* element of B [see (15.5.1)].

(15.4.8) THEOREM: *If A is a set and R is a partial ordering of A, then $S \equiv R + E$ has the properties*

(a) *S is reflexive;*
(b) *S is transitive;*
(c) *if $x, y \in A$ such that $x\, S\, y$ and $y\, S\, x$, then $x = y$.*

Conversely, if S is any relation on $A \times A$ such that (a), (b), (c) *hold, then $R \equiv S - E$ is a partial ordering of A.*

PROOF: Since $x \in A$ implies $(x, x) \in E \subset R + E$, it follows that (a) holds. Suppose $x\, S\, y$, $y\, S\, z$. Then four possibilities exist:

$$\begin{array}{ll} x = y, & y\, R\, z; \\ x\, R\, y, & y = z; \\ x = y, & y = z; \\ x\, R\, y, & y\, R\, z. \end{array}$$

In the first two cases, it is obvious that $x\, R\, z$, whence $x\, S\, z$. In the third, $x = z$, whence $x\, S\, z$. In the last, $x\, R\, z$ by the transitivity of R, whence again $x\, S\, z$. Thus S is transitive, and (b) holds. Suppose $x\, S\, y$ and $y\, S\, x$. If $x \neq y$, then $x\, R\, y$ and $y\, R\, x$. But this contradicts the asymmetry of R [see (15.4.4)]. Therefore $x = y$, and (c) is proved.

Proof of the converse part is left for the reader.

(15.4.9) EXAMPLES:

(a) In the theory of $(I, 1, \sigma)$, the relation $|$ on $I \times I$ has the properties (15.4.8.a), (15.4.8.b), (15.4.8.c) by (9.4.3), (9.4.4), (9.4.6), respectively. Hence $| - E$ is a partial ordering of I by (15.4.8). The discussion following (9.4.7) shows that $| - E$ is not a linear ordering, since (15.4.5.b) fails. Consequently not every partial ordering is a linear ordering.

(b) If $\mathbf{A}$ is the set of all subsets of a given set A, then the inclusion relation c, where

$$\mathsf{c} \equiv [(B, C) \in \mathbf{A} \times \mathbf{A};\, B \subset C],$$

satisfies (a), (b), (c) of (15.4.8). Hence $\mathsf{c} - E$ is a partial ordering of $\mathbf{A}$. Moreover, $\mathsf{c} - E$ is not a linear ordering unless A has only one element, since, if $a, b \in A$, $a \neq b$, then $[a], [b] \in \mathbf{A}$, and $[a] \neq [b]$, $[a] \not\subset [b]$, $[b] \not\subset [a]$.

(c) In the theory of $(I, 1, \sigma)$, the relation $<$ is a partial ordering of I by (9.2.4), (9.2.5). By (9.2.14), $<$ is in addition a linear ordering, and, by (9.3.9), $<$ is even a well-ordering. The reader should show that $<^* (= >)$ is not a well-ordering [use (9.3.8)]. It will be seen [Chapters 16, 17, 18, 19] that relations also denoted by $<$ occur in the theories of positive rational, positive real and real numbers; these relations will be linear orderings but not well-orderings.

(15.4.10) PROJECT: Prove that there exists a relation which is neither reflexive nor irreflexive.

(15.4.11) PROJECT: Prove that there exists a relation which is neither symmetric nor asymmetric. Prove that Θ on $A \times A$ (A being a set) is both symmetric and asymmetric.

(15.4.12) Project: Prove the converse of (15.4.8).

(15.4.13) Project: Prove that, in the theory of $(I, 1, \sigma)$, $>$ is not a well-ordering.

(15.4.14) Project: Determine for $A \equiv [p_1, p_2, p_3]$ all partial orderings, all linear orderings, and all well-orderings.

15.5. Least and Greatest Elements. Associated with the intuitive concepts "is to the left of" and "is younger than," are corresponding concepts "leftmost" and "youngest." In this section it is shown that any partial ordering leads to a concept of *least* element of a given subset.

Because of the intuitive flavor of an ordering relation, it is usual to employ the symbol $<$ for such relations. This practice will be followed in the present section. Moreover, $< + E$ is denoted by $\leqq$, $<^*$ by $>$, and $> + E$ by $\geqq$. It is important to remember, however, that $<$ is a notation for *any* partial ordering of any set A and not necessarily the specific relation $<$ on $I \times I$ treated in Chapter 9.

(15.5.1) Definition: If A is a set, if $<$ is a partial ordering of A, and if $S \subset A$, $x \in A$, then x is a *least* (*element*) of S if

(a) $x \in S$;

(b) $y \in S$ implies $x \leqq y$.

Moreover, x is a *greatest* (*element*) of S if

(c) $x \in S$;

(d) $y \in S$ implies $x \geqq y$.

(15.5.2) Theorem: *If A is a set, and if $<$ is a partial ordering of A, then two least (greatest) elements of any subset S of A are equal.*

Proof: Let x, y be least elements of S. Then $x \leqq y$ by (15.5.1.b), since x is a least. Similarly, $y \leqq x$. Hence $x = y$ by (15.4.8.c). The alternate reading follows by replacing $<$ by $>$.

Remark: It may happen that subsets S exist which have no leasts (greatests). However, if a least (greatest) exists, it is unique by (15.5.2).

(15.5.3) Theorem: *If A is a set and $<$ is a linear ordering of A, then every (non-empty) finite subset of A has a least.*

Proof: Define

$$H \equiv [m \in I; \text{every (non-empty) finite } S \subset A \text{ with } n(S) = m \text{ has a least}].$$

It is trivial that $1 \in H$, since, if $n(S) = 1$, S is of the form $[x]$, whence x is a least element of S. Suppose $q \in H$, and let $S \subset A$ such that S is finite with $n(S) = q + 1$. Let x be any element of S, and define $T \equiv S - [x]$.

If $T = \Theta$, we have $S = [x]$, $n(S) = 1$, contrary to $n(S) = q + 1$. Also, $T \subset S$, so that T is finite by (10.4.7). We have

$$T + [x] = S, \quad T \cdot [x] = \Theta,$$

whence, by (10.4.8),

$$q + 1 = n(S) = n(T) + n([x]) = n(T) + 1,$$

and $n(T) = q$. Since $q \epsilon H$, T has a least element y. By (15.4.5.b), $y < x$ or $x < y$, the possibility $x = y$ being ruled out because $y \epsilon T$, $x \epsilon' T$. Suppose first that $y < x$. Since $y \leqq z$ for every $z \epsilon T$, and since $S = T + [x]$, it follows that $y \leqq w$ for every $w \epsilon S$. And, since $y \epsilon S$, y is a least element of S. Now suppose $x < y$. If $z \epsilon S$, and if $z \neq x$, then $z \epsilon T$, whence $x < y$, $y \leqq z$. By the transitivity of $<$, $x < z$. Hence $x \leqq w$ for every $w \epsilon S$, and, since $x \epsilon S$, x is a least element of S. This proves that S has a least and hence that $q + 1 \epsilon H$. By III′, $H = I$, and the proof is complete.

(15.5.4) Remark: The concepts "least" and "greatest" have generalizations of considerable importance. If A is partially ordered by $<$, then a *lower bound* of a set $S \subset A$ is an element $x \epsilon A$ such that

$$\text{for every } y \epsilon S,\ x \leqq y.$$

An *upper bound* is similarly defined, with $>$ replacing $<$. Denote by S^+ (S^-) the set of all upper (lower) bounds of S. If S^+ (S^-) has a least (greatest), then it has only one by (15.5.2). The least of S^+ (greatest of S^-), if existent, is called the *least upper bound* (*greatest lower bound*) of S. It is denoted by l.u.b. S (g.l.b. S). Now if a set S has a least (greatest) element x, then g.l.b. S (l.u.b. S) exists, and

$$\text{g.l.b. } S \text{ (l.u.b. } S) = x.$$

Moreover, if $x =$ g.l.b. S (l.u.b. S) exists *and if* $x \epsilon S$, then x is a least (greatest) of S. (These statements should be proved by the reader.) However, sets may have greatest lower bounds (least upper bounds) without having leasts (greatests). In (15.4.9.b), every subset $\boldsymbol{B}$ of $\boldsymbol{A}$ has a g.l.b. (l.u.b.), namely, $\prod \boldsymbol{B}$ ($\sum \boldsymbol{B}$) (note that, if $\boldsymbol{B} = \Theta$, then $\prod \boldsymbol{B} = A$, $\sum \boldsymbol{B} = \Theta$, and if $\boldsymbol{B} = A$, then $\prod \boldsymbol{B} = \Theta$, $\sum \boldsymbol{B} = A$). But, if $a, b \epsilon A$, $a \neq b$, then $\boldsymbol{B} = [[a], [b]]$ has neither least nor greatest.

(15.5.5) Project: Let A be a set, and $<$ a linear ordering of A. Prove that every finite subset of A has a greatest.

(15.5.6) Project: Let A be a finite set, and $<$ a linear ordering of A. Prove that $<$ is a well-ordering.

(15.5.7) Project: Let A be a set, well-ordered by relation $<$. Prove the following principle of *transfinite induction*: *Let $H \subset A$ be such that, if $x \in A$ such that*

$$y \in A,\ y < x \textit{ implies } y \in H,$$

then $x \in H$. Then $H = A$.

(15.5.8) Project: Let A be partially ordered by a relation $<$. If $S \subset A$, define S^+, S^- as in (15.5.4), and denote by S^{+-} the set $(S^+)^-$, and by S^{-+} the set $(S^-)^+$. Prove that, if $S, T \subset A$, then
(a) $S \subset T$ implies $S^+ \supset T^+$ and $S^- \supset T^-$;
(b) $S^{+-} \supset S$, $S^{-+} \supset S$;
(c) $S^{+-+} = S^+$, $S^{-+-} = S^-$;
(d) $S^{+-+-} = S^{+-}$, $S^{-+-+} = S^{-+}$.

(15.5.9) Project: Continuing the ideas in (15.5.8), let $\mathfrak{M}$ be a set of subsets of A such that

$$S \in \mathfrak{M} \text{ implies } S^{+-} = S.$$

Then $\left(\prod \mathfrak{M}\right)^{+-} = \prod \mathfrak{M}$.

(15.5.10) Project: Prove the assertions in (15.5.4) connecting leasts (greatests) with greatest lower (least upper) bounds.

15.6. Well-Ordering and the Principle of Choice. We conclude this chapter with a brief discussion of a connection between well-ordering and the principle of choice. If the reader will review the proof of (11.5.1), he will note that a special case of the principle of choice was proved with the help of the well-ordering relation $<$ on $I \times I$. A generalization follows.

(15.6.1) Theorem: *If for every set S there exists a relation by which S is well-ordered, then the principle of choice* (11.5.2) *is true.*

Proof: As in (11.5.2), let A, B be non-empty sets and R a relation on $A \times B$ with domain A. By the hypothesis, with $S = B$, there exists a relation $<$ on $B \times B$ which is a well-ordering of B. For every $a \in A$, the set

$$R(a) \equiv [b \in B;\ a\ R\ b]$$

is a non-empty subset of B. Hence for every $a \in A$ there exists a unique least element of $R(a)$. The relation

$$F \equiv [(a, b) \in A \times B;\ b \text{ is the least element of } R(a)]$$

is clearly a function, and since $a\ F\ b$ implies $b \in R(a)$, whence $a\ R\ b$, we have $F \subset R$.

A converse of (15.6.1) also holds, although we shall not give the proof here.

(15.6.3) THEOREM: *If the principle of choice is true, then, for every non-empty set* S, *there exists a relation on* $S \times S$ *which is a well-ordering of* S.

It follows that the principle of choice may be replaced by an equivalent principle demanding that every non-empty set possess a well-ordering relation.

Chapter 16

THE POSITIVE RATIONAL NUMBERS

16.1. Introduction. [No Basis.] The *positive rational numbers*, also called the *positive fractions*, are the entities introduced early in the history of mathematics to answer the question "how long?" They are the measuring numbers, or rather, they were introduced in the hope that they would be the measuring numbers. Subsequent to their invention, it was found that in this respect they failed partially, in that they did not make possible a perfect answer to the question "how long?" in all cases.

For example, it was found [see (16.6.7) and (17.1)] that the question "how long is the diagonal of a square of unit side?" cannot be answered exactly by means of a rational number. To provide precise, mathematically perfect answers to the question "how long?" it has been found necessary to invent still another system of numbers known as the *positive real numbers*. However, the rational numbers do provide a sufficiently good "approximate" answer to the question "how long?" for most purposes, and thus they have enormous practical importance. And they have a clear advantage over the real numbers, in that it is possible to invent a symbolism or nomenclature for them so that each individual rational number has its own designation; such a symbolism has not been evolved for the real numbers.

The name *rational number* is somewhat misleading since it is apt to suggest the word "rational," meaning "reasonable." Actually the origin of the term *rational number* is connected with the word "ratio," so that the term should be thought of as ratio-nal, that is, ratio-like.

As in the case of the positive integers, there is considerable choice in the formulation of a basis and axioms for the positive rational numbers. The formulation to be used is chosen for two reasons; first, it closely follows the (intuitive) historical pattern, and secondly, it seems to involve a minimum of axioms, while yielding the desired end result. It will be noted that, in our approach, operations $+$, $\cdot$ (mathematical counterparts of the processes of "adding" and "multiplying" fractions) do not appear in the basis, but are *defined* later in the theory.

16.2. Axioms for the Positive Rational Numbers. [No Basis.] Let us recall that the fractions were introduced intuitively to represent broken (fractured) segments of a measuring stick of "unit length." Thus, when one measures the length of an object by applying a unit stick, and it happens that the unit stick does not "go" an integral number of times into the given length, one breaks the unit stick into a number (such as two, three, and so on) of equally long pieces and applies these shorter pieces to the deficit (or to the entire length). Therefore the fractions should consist, intuitively, of all the "lengths" obtainable by "breaking" the "unit length" into a number of pieces and then "putting together" any number of these pieces.

How shall we arrive at a mathematical formulation of this intuitive process? First, the rational numbers should constitute a set to be denoted by $\boldsymbol{F}$ whose elements are the mathematical counterparts of the "lengths" arising in the intuitive description. Secondly, a specific element of $\boldsymbol{F}$, to be denoted by $\boldsymbol{u}$, is to be singled out and called the *unit* element. This $\boldsymbol{u}$ represents the "unit length." Let us overlook for the moment the process of "breaking" the unit, and turn to the "putting together" of any number of (equally long) pieces. Any such piece is itself a "length" and hence is represented by an element of $\boldsymbol{F}$. The intuitive "number" (of pieces) is to be represented by a positive integer, or element of I. The "putting together" leads to another "length," represented again by an element of $\boldsymbol{F}$. Our process thus associates with every element of I and every element of $\boldsymbol{F}$ another element of $\boldsymbol{F}$. Mathematically, such a process is described as a binary operation on $I \times \boldsymbol{F}$ to $\boldsymbol{F}$, to be denoted by $\odot$ (read "dotto").

We can now easily analyze the process of "breaking" the unit length. An element $f \in \boldsymbol{F}$ represents the result of "breaking" the unit $\boldsymbol{u}$ into a certain number of equally long parts, provided $\boldsymbol{u}$ represents the result of "putting together" the same number of equally long fractions represented by f. Thus we have simply

$$\boldsymbol{u} = n \odot f,$$

if $n \in I$ represents the "number of parts" involved.

We shall now formulate the intuitively acceptable property that every fraction may be obtained by putting together a suitable number of equally long pieces resulting from the breaking of the unit length. This is intuitively equivalent to the requirement that any fraction has the property that, by putting it together with itself a suitable number of times, one arrives at the result of putting the unit together with itself a suitable number of times. This last statement becomes, in mathematical terms, the following:

(16.2.1) for every $f \in \boldsymbol{F}$, there exist $m, n \in I$ such that

$$m \odot f = n \odot \boldsymbol{u}.$$

Another fundamental property insures that the unit length may be "broken" into *any* number of (equally long) pieces. Clearly this appears mathematically thus:

(16.2.2) for every $m \in \boldsymbol{I}$, there exists $g \in \boldsymbol{F}$ such that $m \odot g = \boldsymbol{u}$.

The intuitive counterpart of $\odot$ has various other properties, any of which might be chosen as additional potential axioms. How many of these properties one needs to *assume* can be determined only by experiment. We have selected the following three, each of which should be examined in intuitive terms to check its acceptability:

(16.2.3) if $m, n \in \boldsymbol{I}$, $m \neq n$, and $f \in \boldsymbol{F}$, then $m \odot f \neq n \odot f$;
(16.2.4) if $m \in \boldsymbol{I}$, and $f, g \in \boldsymbol{F}$, $f \neq g$, then $m \odot f \neq m \odot g$;
(16.2.5) if $m, n \in \boldsymbol{I}$ and $f \in \boldsymbol{F}$, then $m \odot (n \odot f) = (m \cdot n) \odot f$.

We now state the full foundation for the positive rational numbers.

Basis: $(\boldsymbol{F}, \boldsymbol{u}, \odot)$, where $\boldsymbol{F}$ is a set, $\boldsymbol{u}$ an element of $\boldsymbol{F}$, and $\odot$ is an operation on $\boldsymbol{I} \times \boldsymbol{F}$ to $\boldsymbol{F}$.

Axioms:

I. (a) For every $f \in \boldsymbol{F}$, there exist $m, n \in \boldsymbol{I}$ such that $m \odot f = n \odot \boldsymbol{u}$.
(b) For every $m \in \boldsymbol{I}$, there exists $g \in \boldsymbol{F}$ such that $m \odot g = \boldsymbol{u}$.
II. For every $m, n \in \boldsymbol{I}$ and $f \in \boldsymbol{F}$, $m \neq n$ implies $m \odot f \neq n \odot f$.
III. For every $m \in \boldsymbol{I}$ and $f, g \in \boldsymbol{F}$, $f \neq g$ implies $m \odot f \neq m \odot g$.
IV. For every $m, n \in \boldsymbol{I}$ and $f \in \boldsymbol{F}$, $m \odot (n \odot f) = (m \cdot n) \odot f$.

Any system $(\boldsymbol{F}, \boldsymbol{u}, \odot)$ satisfying Axioms I, II, III, IV is called a *basic system of positive rational numbers*. Elements of $\boldsymbol{F}$ are called *positive rational numbers*.

Remark: Axiom IV is suggestive of associativity. True associativity is of course impossible here, since the meaningless symbol $m \odot n$ would be involved.

16.3. Consistency of the Axioms. [No Basis.] It will be recalled that we were not able to demonstrate in clear-cut fashion that the axioms for positive integers are consistent. All we could do was to assert that the intuitive "counting numbers" seem to form an instance of positive integers. If one believes that the concept of "counting numbers" is a valid intuitive notion and that this notion, together with the idea of a successor, is an instance of positive integers, then one must believe that the axioms for positive integers are consistent.

In the case of the positive rational numbers, we do not have to depend on a belief in the existence of intuitive "fractions" as an instance, in order to settle the matter of consistency. In fact, we are able to *define* an instance of positive rational numbers in terms of the positive integers. This reduces the question of consistency to the previous question of the consistency of the positive integers. If one "believes in" the positive integers, one must also "believe in" the positive rationals. Thus no fresh doubts concerning the question of the consistency of our system are introduced at this point.

In order to construct an instance of the positive rational numbers, we shall employ directly the system $(I, 1, <, +, \cdot)$ of positive integers. The set $I \times I$ might be thought appropriate for our construction. For, by Axiom I(a), every $f \in F$ in a system $(F, u, \odot)$ gives rise to a pair $(m, n) \in I \times I$. The difficulty here is that this pair is not unique. For, if $k \in I$, and if (m, n) is an appropriate pair, then $(k \cdot m, k \cdot n)$ is another effective pair, since

$$\begin{aligned}(k \cdot m) \odot f &= k \odot (m \odot f) && \text{[by IV]}\\ &= k \odot (n \odot u)\\ &= (k \cdot n) \odot u && \text{[by IV].}\end{aligned}$$

This heuristic consideration indicates that certain subsets of $I \times I$ may be chosen so as to constitute a set F for which u, $\odot$ may be introduced so that Axioms I–IV hold. The subsets will be certain equivalence classes, corresponding to an equivalence relation on $(I \times I) \times (I \times I)$, which relation we now define.

(16.3.1) Definition:

$$\sim \equiv [((m, n), (p, q)) \in (I \times I) \times (I \times I); m \cdot q = n \cdot p].$$

Thus, if (m, n), $(p, q) \in I \times I$, then $(m, n) \sim (p, q)$ if and only if $m \cdot q = n \cdot p$.

(16.3.2) Theorem: *The relation $\sim$ is an equivalence relation.*

Proof: By the definition (15.2.3) of an equivalence relation, we are to show that the relation $\sim$ is reflexive, symmetric and transitive. The reflexive law is obvious, that is, $(m, n) \sim (m, n)$, since $m \cdot n = n \cdot m$ by the commutative law for $\cdot$. The symmetric law is also very easy. Suppose $(m, n) \sim (p, q)$, so that $m \cdot q = n \cdot p$. Then, by the commutative law, $p \cdot n = q \cdot m$, whence $(p, q) \sim (m, n)$. To prove the transitive law, assume

(1) $$(m_1, n_1) \sim (m_2, n_2) \quad \text{and} \quad (m_2, n_2) \sim (m_3, n_3).$$

Then

(2) $$m_1 \cdot n_2 = n_1 \cdot m_2,$$

and

(3) $$m_2 \cdot n_3 = n_2 \cdot m_3.$$

From (2) and (3), we have

$$(4) \qquad (m_1 \cdot n_2) \cdot (m_2 \cdot n_3) = (n_1 \cdot m_2) \cdot (n_2 \cdot m_3).$$

But, by the commutative and associative laws for $\cdot$, (4) may be written

$$(5) \qquad (m_1 \cdot n_3) \cdot (m_2 \cdot n_2) = (n_1 \cdot m_3) \cdot (m_2 \cdot n_2),$$

and, by the cancellation law (9.2.17),

$$(6) \qquad m_1 \cdot n_3 = n_1 \cdot m_3,$$

so that

$$(7) \qquad (m_1, n_1) \sim (m_3, n_3).$$

Thus (1) implies (7), and the transitive law for $\sim$ has been demonstrated. This completes the proof.

(16.3.3) Definition: If $(m, n) \in I \times I$, define $\{m, n\}$ to be the equivalence class of (m, n), that is,

$$\text{(a)} \qquad \{m, n\} \equiv [(p, q) \in I \times I; (m, n) \sim (p, q)].$$

Also, define

$$\text{(b)} \qquad \boldsymbol{F} \equiv [\{m, n\}; (m, n) \in I \times I].$$

Remark: The general concepts leading to these definitions are found in (15.3.1). However, the notation there is too cumbersome for our present application. Note that (15.3.2), (15.3.3) apply to $I \times I$ and $\sim$; these properties will be used freely.

(16.3.4) Definition: Define $\boldsymbol{u} \equiv \{1, 1\}$.

The set $\boldsymbol{F}$ and element $\boldsymbol{u} \in \boldsymbol{F}$ will serve as the basic set and unit element in the instance of $(\boldsymbol{F}, \boldsymbol{u}, \odot)$ being constructed. We turn now to the definition of $\odot$.

(16.3.5) Lemma: *Let* $m_1, n_1, m_2, n_2 \in I$. *If* $(m_1, n_1) \sim (m_2, n_2)$, *then, for every* $p \in I$,

$$(p \cdot m_1, n_1) \sim (p \cdot m_2, n_2).$$

Proof: By (16.3.1), $(m_1, n_1) \sim (m_2, n_2)$ yields $m_1 \cdot n_2 = n_1 \cdot m_2$. Hence

$$\begin{aligned}(p \cdot m_1) \cdot n_2 &= p \cdot (m_1 \cdot n_2) = p \cdot (n_1 \cdot m_2) \\ &= p \cdot (m_2 \cdot n_1) = (p \cdot m_2) \cdot n_1 = n_1 \cdot (p \cdot m_2),\end{aligned}$$

whence the conclusion follows.

(16.3.6) Lemma: *For every* $f \in \boldsymbol{F}$, *and* $p \in I$, *there exists a unique* $g \in \boldsymbol{F}$ *such that, for every* $(m, n) \in f$, $(p \cdot m, n) \in g$.

PROOF OF EXISTENCE: Since $f \in F$, by (16.3.3.b) there exists $(m_1, n_1) \in I \times I$ such that $f = \{m_1, n_1\}$. Define $g \equiv \{p \cdot m_1, n_1\}$. Now suppose $(m, n) \in f$. By (16.3.3.a), $(m_1, n_1) \sim (m, n)$. Hence, by (16.3.5), $(p \cdot m_1, n_1) \sim (p \cdot m, n)$. Thus $(p \cdot m, n) \in g$ by (16.3.3.a).

PROOF OF UNIQUENESS: Suppose g_1, g_2 satisfy the condition of the lemma. Again let $f = \{m_1, n_1\}$. Then, by the assumption concerning g_1, g_2, we have

$$(p \cdot m_1, n_1) \in g_1, \quad (p \cdot m_1, n_1) \in g_2.$$

Now there exists $(q, r) \in I \times I$ such that $g_1 = \{q, r\}$. Thus

$$(q, r) \sim (p \cdot m_1, n_1),$$

whence, by (15.3.2.b),

$$\{q, r\} = \{p \cdot m_1, n_1\}.$$

It follows that

$$g_1 = \{p \cdot m_1, n_1\}.$$

Similarly,

$$g_2 = \{p \cdot m_1, n_1\},$$

whence $g_1 = g_2$.

(16.3.7) DEFINITION: If $f \in F$, $p \in I$, define $p \odot f$ as the unique $g \in F$ given by (16.3.6). The operation $\odot$ on $I \times F$ to F is then defined thus:

$$\odot \equiv (p \odot f;\ (p, f) \in I \times F).$$

REMARK: An alternate form of the definition of $\odot$ is the following:

$$\odot \equiv [((p, f), g) \in (I \times F) \times F;\ \text{for every } (m, n) \in f,\ (p \cdot m, n) \in g].$$

This form shows that $\odot$ is a relation on $(I \times F) \times F$; (16.3.6) says that the relation is a function whose domain is $I \times F$, whence the relation is an operation on $I \times F$ to F.

The reader should study carefully the process embodied in (16.3.5), (16.3.6), (16.3.7), since it is a very common one in mathematics. It defines $p \odot f$ as $\{p \cdot m, n\}$, where (m, n) may be *any* pair such that $\{m, n\} = f$, the result being independent of what "representative" pair is chosen.

(16.3.8) THEOREM: *The system* $(F, u, \odot)$ *defined by* (16.3.3), (16.3.4), (16.3.7) *is a basic system of positive rational numbers, that is, satisfies Axioms* I–IV.

PROOF: To prove I(a), let $f \in F$, so that $f = \{p, q\}$. It is to be shown that there exist $m, n \in I$ such that

$$m \odot \{p, q\} = n \odot u = n \odot \{1, 1\}.$$

Define $m \equiv q$, $n \equiv p$. Then

$$m \odot \{p, q\} = q \odot \{p, q\} = \{q \cdot p, q\}.$$

But it is evident that $(q \cdot p, q) \sim (p, 1)$, since $(q \cdot p) \cdot 1 = q \cdot p$. Hence, by (15.3.2.b), $\{q \cdot p, q\} = \{p, 1\}$. Thus

$$m \odot \{p, q\} = \{p, 1\} = \{p \cdot 1, 1\} = p \odot \{1, 1\} = n \odot \boldsymbol{u}.$$

To show I(b), let $m \in I$. Then it is to be shown that there exists $g \in \boldsymbol{F}$ such that

$$m \odot g = \{1, 1\}.$$

But this is true with $g = \{1, m\}$, since

$$m \odot \{1, m\} = \{m, m\} = \{1, 1\},$$

the last equality holding because obviously $(m, m) \sim (1, 1)$.

To prove II, we shall show that, if $m, n \in I$, and if $f \in \boldsymbol{F}$ such that $m \odot f = n \odot f$, then $m = n$. Let $f = \{p, q\}$. Then from

$$m \odot \{p, q\} = n \odot \{p, q\}$$

we have

$$\{m \cdot p, q\} = \{n \cdot p, q\}.$$

Therefore

$$(m \cdot p, q) \sim (n \cdot p, q),$$

or

$$m \cdot p \cdot q = q \cdot n \cdot p,$$

whence $m \cdot (p \cdot q) = n \cdot (p \cdot q)$, and $m = n$ by the cancellation law.

To prove III, we show that, if $m \in I$, and $f, g \in \boldsymbol{F}$ such that $m \odot f = m \odot g$, then $f = g$. Let $f = \{p, q\}$, $g = \{r, s\}$. Then from

$$m \odot \{p, q\} = m \odot \{r, s\}$$

we have

$$\{m \cdot p, q\} = \{m \cdot r, s\},$$

whence

$$m \cdot p \cdot s = q \cdot m \cdot r.$$

Therefore $p \cdot s = q \cdot r$, and $\{p, q\} = \{r, s\}$.

The proof of IV is the simplest of all, since

$$m \odot (n \odot \{p, q\}) = \{m \cdot n \cdot p, q\} = (m \cdot n) \odot \{p, q\}.$$

This completes the proof.

Having produced an instance of positive rational numbers in (16.3.8), we have established the consistency of our axioms, assuming consistency of the axioms for $(I, 1, \sigma)$.

16.4. Categoricalness, and Symbolism for Positive Rational Numbers. [No Basis.] In this section it will be shown that the special instance of positive rational numbers, given in the preceding section, is not really very special. In fact, it will be shown that any basic system of positive rational numbers is isomorphic to this instance. This means, in particular, that the axioms for positive rational numbers are categorical. The existence of such an isomorphism makes possible a symbolism for positive rational numbers (in terms of pairs of positive integers), which is very useful both in the theory of positive rational numbers and in practical computations involving these numbers. The convenience of this symbolism explains the fact that positive rational numbers are used almost universally to give practical answers to questions involving measurement, even though, from a theoretical point of view, they are not really adequate for this purpose. The unfortunate fact is that the positive real numbers [see Chapter 18], which are theoretically adequate for measuring purposes, appear not to admit a convenient universal symbolism (system of labels), and so are not well suited for practical computations involving individual numbers.

In (16.4.1)–(16.4.6), $(\boldsymbol{F}, \boldsymbol{u}, \odot)$ is *any* system satisfying Axioms I–IV. A result of primary importance is now proved.

(16.4.1) THEOREM: *Let $m, n \in \boldsymbol{I}$. Then there exists a unique element $f \in \boldsymbol{F}$ such that*

$$n \odot f = m \odot \boldsymbol{u}.$$

PROOF OF EXISTENCE: By I(b), there exists $g \in \boldsymbol{F}$ such that

$$n \odot g = \boldsymbol{u}.$$

Define $f \equiv m \odot g$. Then

$$\begin{aligned} n \odot f &= n \odot (m \odot g) \\ &= (n \cdot m) \odot g && \text{[by IV]} \\ &= (m \cdot n) \odot g \\ &= m \odot (n \odot g) && \text{[by IV]} \\ &= m \odot \boldsymbol{u}. \end{aligned}$$

PROOF OF UNIQUENESS: Let $f_1, f_2 \in \boldsymbol{F}$ such that $n \odot f_1 = m \odot \boldsymbol{u}$, $n \odot f_2 = m \odot \boldsymbol{u}$. Then $n \odot f_1 = n \odot f_2$, whence $f_1 = f_2$ by III.

(16.4.2) DEFINITION: Let $m, n \in \boldsymbol{I}$. Then denote by $\frac{m}{n}$ or m/n the unique element $f \in \boldsymbol{F}$ such that $n \odot f = m \odot \boldsymbol{u}$ (existence and uniqueness having been guaranteed by (16.4.1)).

REMARK: It is seen that, if $m, n \in \boldsymbol{I}$, then m/n is a positive rational number. It is next shown that every element of $\boldsymbol{F}$ is obtainable in this fashion.

(16.4.3) THEOREM: *For every $f \in \boldsymbol{F}$, there exist $m, n \in \boldsymbol{I}$ such that $m/n = f$.*

PROOF: This is a restatement of I(a).

The reader should prove that $\boldsymbol{u} = 1/1 = m/m$ for every $m \in I$. This fact shows that the elements m, n in (16.4.3) are not unique. The next theorem tells exactly when m_1/n_1 and m_2/n_2 are equal.

(16.4.4) THEOREM: *Let m_1, n_1, m_2, $n_2 \in I$. Then*

$$\frac{m_1}{n_1} = \frac{m_2}{n_2}$$

if and only if

$$m_1 \cdot n_2 = n_1 \cdot m_2.$$

PROOF: Assume first that $m_1/n_1 = m_2/n_2$, and define f to be this element. Then, by (16.4.2),

(1) $$n_1 \odot f = m_1 \odot \boldsymbol{u},$$

and

(2) $$n_2 \odot f = m_2 \odot \boldsymbol{u}.$$

We have

(3) $$m_2 \odot (n_1 \odot f) = m_2 \odot (m_1 \odot \boldsymbol{u}) \qquad \text{[by (1)]},$$

and

(4) $$m_1 \odot (n_2 \odot f) = m_1 \odot (m_2 \odot \boldsymbol{u}) \qquad \text{[by (2)]}.$$

But, by IV and familiar arguments, (3) and (4) yield

$$(n_1 \cdot m_2) \odot f = (m_1 \cdot m_2) \odot \boldsymbol{u},$$

and

$$(m_1 \cdot n_2) \odot f = (m_1 \cdot m_2) \odot \boldsymbol{u},$$

so that

$$(n_1 \cdot m_2) \odot f = (m_1 \cdot n_2) \odot f.$$

But then, by II,

$$n_1 \cdot m_2 = m_1 \cdot n_2.$$

The remaining half of the proof, that from $m_1 \cdot n_2 = n_1 \cdot m_2$ it follows that $m_1/n_1 = m_2/n_2$, is left for the reader. It should be noted that this half of the proof requires Axiom III in much the same way as the first half requires Axiom II.

(16.4.5) COROLLARY: *Let m, n, $p \in I$. Then*

$$\frac{m \cdot p}{n \cdot p} = \frac{m}{n}.$$

PROOF: This follows from (16.4.4), since $m \cdot p \cdot n = n \cdot p \cdot m$.

REMARK: This corollary expresses another of the so-called "cancellation laws" of elementary arithmetic.

The next theorem shows the connection between the operations $\odot$ on $I \times F$ to F and $\cdot$ on $I \times I$ to I.

(16.4.6) THEOREM: *If $p \in I$, $f \in F$, then, for every m, $n \in I$ such that $f = m/n$,*

$$p \odot f = \frac{p \cdot m}{n}.$$

PROOF: By (16.4.2), it is to be shown that

$$(1) \qquad n \odot (p \odot f) = (p \cdot m) \odot \boldsymbol{u}.$$

By IV,

$$\begin{aligned} n \odot (p \odot f) &= (n \cdot p) \odot f \\ &= (p \cdot n) \odot f \\ &= p \odot (n \odot f), \end{aligned}$$

whence

$$(2) \qquad n \odot (p \odot f) = p \odot (n \odot f).$$

Also, by IV,

$$(3) \qquad (p \cdot m) \odot \boldsymbol{u} = p \odot (m \odot \boldsymbol{u}).$$

Since $f = m/n$, we have

$$(4) \qquad n \odot f = m \odot \boldsymbol{u}.$$

Hence (1) follows from (2), (3), in view of (4).

We have now succeeded in introducing the promised symbolism for the individual elements of F. By (16.4.3), every $f \in F$ is equal to m/n for suitable positive integers m, n. In terms of any method of labeling individual positive integers, we thus arrive at a designation for each individual $f \in F$. For example, $\boldsymbol{u} = 1/1$, $2 \odot \boldsymbol{u} = 2/1$, the element $f \in F$ with the property $2 \odot f = \boldsymbol{u}$ is $1/2$, and so forth. The universal arabic notation for positive integers yields the best known system of labels for the positive rational numbers.

Categoricalness of the axioms I–IV is now considered. We need first a definition of isomorphism of two basic systems of positive rational numbers.

(16.4.7) DEFINITION: Let $(F_1, \boldsymbol{u}_1, \odot_1)$, $(F_2, \boldsymbol{u}_2, \odot_2)$ be basic systems of positive rational numbers. They are called *isomorphic* if there exists a one-to-one correspondence φ between F_1 and F_2 such that

(a) $\varphi(\boldsymbol{u}_1) = \boldsymbol{u}_2$;
(b) for every $f_1 \in F_1$, and every $p \in I$, $\varphi(p \odot_1 f_1) = p \odot_2 \varphi(f_1)$.

REMARK: The reader should state and prove the analogue here of (14.2.3).

In order to prove categoricalness, we shall consider the instance of (16.3). Denote this system by $(\boldsymbol{F}_0, \boldsymbol{u}_0, \odot_0)$.

(16.4.8) THEOREM: *If* $(\boldsymbol{F}, \boldsymbol{u}, \odot)$ *is any basic system of positive rational numbers, then* $(\boldsymbol{F}, \boldsymbol{u}, \odot)$ *is isomorphic to* $(\boldsymbol{F}_0, \boldsymbol{u}_0, \odot_0)$.

PROOF: Let $f \in \boldsymbol{F}$. We shall show that there exists a unique element $f_0 \in \boldsymbol{F}_0$ such that

$$(1) \qquad \text{for every } (m, n) \in f_0,\ f = m/n.$$

By (16.4.3), there exists $(m', n') \in I \times I$ with $f = m'/n'$. Define $f_0 \equiv \{m', n'\}$. Then, if $(m, n) \in f_0$, we have $(m, n) \sim (m', n')$, so that $m \cdot n' = n \cdot m'$. Thus, by (16.4.4), $m/n = m'/n' = f$, and existence is established. If f_0, f_0' are two effective elements of $\boldsymbol{F}_0$, then again let $f = m'/n'$. It follows that any pair $(m, n) \in f_0$ has the property $m/n = f = m'/n'$, whence $m \cdot n' = n \cdot m'$, and $(m, n) \sim (m', n')$. Thus $\{m', n'\} = f_0$; similarly, $\{m', n'\} = f_0'$. Uniqueness therefore follows.

Now define a function φ on $\boldsymbol{F}$ to $\boldsymbol{F}_0$ such that, for every $f \in \boldsymbol{F}$, $\varphi(f)$ is the unique f_0 just introduced. An immediate consequence is

$$(2) \qquad \varphi(m/n) = \{m, n\}.$$

To prove that φ has range $\boldsymbol{F}_0$, let $f_0' \in \boldsymbol{F}_0$, so that $f_0' = \{m', n'\}$. Then define $f \equiv m'/n'$. By (2), $\varphi(f) = f_0'$, and the range of φ is $\boldsymbol{F}_0$. Suppose now that $f, g \in \boldsymbol{F}$, $f \neq g$. It will be shown that $\varphi(f) \neq \varphi(g)$. Let $f = m/n$, $g = p/q$. By (16.4.4), $m \cdot q \neq n \cdot p$. Hence $(m, n) \sim' (p, q)$. But $\varphi(f) = \{m, n\}$, $\varphi(g) = \{p, q\}$, so that $\varphi(f) = \varphi(g)$ is impossible. This completes the proof that φ is a one-to-one correspondence.

Now

$$\varphi(\boldsymbol{u}) = \varphi(1/1) = \{1, 1\} = \boldsymbol{u}_0,$$

and (16.4.7.a) holds.

Let $f \in \boldsymbol{F}$ and $p \in I$. Then, by (16.4.6), if $f = m/n$,

$$(3) \qquad p \odot f = (p \cdot m)/n.$$

Now, for every $f \in \boldsymbol{F}$ and $p \in I$,

$$\begin{aligned} \varphi(p \odot f) &= \varphi((p \cdot m)/n) && \text{[by (3)]} \\ &= \{p \cdot m, n\} && \text{[by (2)]} \\ &= p \odot_0 \{m, n\} && \text{[by (16.3.7)]} \\ &= p \odot_0 \varphi(f). \end{aligned}$$

This proves (16.4.7.b) and completes the proof of the theorem.

(16.4.9) THEOREM: *If* $(F_1, u_1, \odot_1)$, $(F_2, u_2, \odot_2)$ *are basic systems of positive rational numbers, then they are isomorphic.*

PROOF: By (16.4.8), $(F_1, u_1, \odot_1)$ is isomorphic to $(F_0, u_0, \odot_0)$ and $(F_2, u_2, \odot_2)$ is also isomorphic to $(F_0, u_0, \odot_0)$. Hence it follows that $(F_1, u_1, \odot_1)$ is isomorphic to $(F_2, u_2, \odot_2)$.

REMARK: The proof of categoricalness of the axioms I–IV for positive rational numbers is now complete.

(16.4.10) PROJECT: Prove that, for every $m \epsilon I$, $m/m = 1/1 = u$.

(16.4.11) PROJECT: Prove that, in (16.4.4), $m_1 \cdot n_2 = n_1 \cdot m_2$ implies $m_1/n_1 = m_2/n_2$.

(16.4.12) PROJECT: State and prove the analogue of (14.2.3) for isomorphism as defined in (16.4.7).

16.5. Countability of the Positive Rational Numbers. [BASIS: $(F, u, \odot)$; AXIOMS: I, II, III, IV.] We shall now prove the rather surprising fact that F is countable. We shall need (13.6.5), (16.4.2) and (16.4.3). Use of the principle of choice is implicit in the application of (13.6.5).

(16.5.1) THEOREM: *The set* F *is countable.*

PROOF: Define a function φ on $I \times I$ to F such that, for every $(m, n) \epsilon I \times I$, $\varphi(m, n) = m/n$. Now (16.4.3) shows that the range of φ is F. In (13.6.5), we take S, T to be $I \times I$ and F, respectively. Then the hypothesis holds, namely, that a function on S to T with range T exists, whence there exists a subset J of $I \times I$ such that $J \sim F$. By (13.6.4), $I \times I$ is countable. Thus, by (13.5.3), since clearly $J \neq \Theta$, J is countable. It follows then that F is countable, since $J \sim F$. (The principle of choice is used through (13.6.5).)

REMARK: The question whether F is finite or infinite is not settled by (16.5.1). This matter is easily treated in (16.9.5).

The proof of (16.5.1) does not actually display a one-to-one correspondence between I or a subset of I and F. Many such correspondences exist, but there is one of particular interest which we shall describe. We shall not give a complete definition of the correspondence but shall list the correspondents of the first few positive integers 1, 2, 3, · · ·. The first listed corresponds to 1, the second to 2, and so on:

$$\frac{1}{1}; \frac{1}{2}, \frac{2}{1}; \frac{1}{3}, \frac{3}{1}; \frac{1}{4}, \frac{2}{3}, \frac{3}{2}, \frac{4}{1}; \frac{1}{5}, \frac{5}{1};$$

$$\frac{1}{6}, \frac{2}{5}, \frac{3}{4}, \frac{4}{3}, \frac{5}{2}, \frac{6}{1}; \cdots.$$

Intuitive description of the method of determining the entry in the partial table in any specified position is as follows. The numbers m/n are grouped according to the value of $m + n$. Thus, in the first group, $m + n = 2$; this group has the one number $1/1$. In the second group, $m + n = 3$, so that $1/2$, $2/1$ are included. The third group includes $1/3$, $2/2$, $3/1$, but $2/2$ is omitted since $2/2 = 1/1$, and $1/1$ has already appeared. Within each group two numbers m/n and p/q are placed so that m/n precedes p/q if $m < p$. Semicolons separate the various groups in the table. It is intuitively clear that every positive rational number occupies a place in the (extended) table, and there is reasonable indication that the one-to-one correspondence will be between I and F, so that F is infinite.

A complete mathematical definition of the correspondence described in the previous paragraph would yield a proof of (16.5.1) not involving the principle of choice.

16.6. Operations with the Positive Rational Numbers. [BASIS: $(F, u, \odot)$; AXIOMS: I, II, III, IV.] Just as there are two important operations $+$, $\cdot$ for the positive integers (both are on $I \times I$ to I), there are two similar operations on $F \times F$ to F. The notations for these will be $\oplus$, $\otimes$, at least at first. Before defining these operations, we prove two preliminary theorems.

(16.6.1) THEOREM: *Let $f, g \in F$. Then there exists a unique $h \in F$ such that, if $m, n, p, q \in I$ such that*

(a) $$f = \frac{m}{n}, \quad g = \frac{p}{q},$$

then

(b) $$h = \frac{m \cdot q + n \cdot p}{n \cdot q}.$$

PROOF OF EXISTENCE: Let $m_1, n_1, p_1, q_1 \in I$ such that

$$f = \frac{m_1}{n_1}, \quad g = \frac{p_1}{q_1}.$$

Existence of these positive integers is guaranteed by (16.4.3). Define

$$h \equiv \frac{m_1 \cdot q_1 + n_1 \cdot p_1}{n_1 \cdot q_1},$$

so that $h \in F$. Now suppose $m, n, p, q \in I$ satisfy (a); we shall prove that (b) holds. By (16.4.4), we have, since $m_1/n_1 = m/n$, $p_1/q_1 = p/q$,

(1) $$m_1 \cdot n = n_1 \cdot m, \quad p_1 \cdot q = q_1 \cdot p.$$

Hence, by the properties of $+$, $\cdot$ for positive integers,

$$\begin{aligned}(m_1 \cdot q_1 + n_1 \cdot p_1) \cdot (n \cdot q) &= (m_1 \cdot q_1) \cdot (n \cdot q) + (n_1 \cdot p_1) \cdot (n \cdot q) \\ &= (m_1 \cdot n)(q_1 \cdot q) + (p_1 \cdot q)(n_1 \cdot n) \\ &= (n_1 \cdot m)(q_1 \cdot q) + (q_1 \cdot p)(n_1 \cdot n) \qquad \text{[by (1)]} \\ &= (n_1 \cdot q_1)(m \cdot q) + (n_1 \cdot q_1)(n \cdot p) \\ &= (n_1 \cdot q_1) \cdot (m \cdot q + n \cdot p).\end{aligned}$$

Then (16.4.4) yields

$$h = \frac{m_1 \cdot q_1 + n_1 \cdot p_1}{n_1 \cdot q_1} = \frac{m \cdot q + n \cdot p}{n \cdot q}.$$

This completes the proof of existence of $h \in F$ satisfying (b).

PROOF OF UNIQUENESS: Suppose $h_1, h_2 \in F$ have the desired property. Let m, n, p, q satisfy (a) [use (16.4.3) for existence]. Then

$$h_1 = \frac{m \cdot q + n \cdot p}{n \cdot q} = h_2,$$

and the proof is complete.

(16.6.2) THEOREM: *Let $f, g \in F$. Then there exists a unique $k \in F$ such that, if $m, n, p, q \in I$ such that*

(a) $$f = \frac{m}{n}, \quad g = \frac{p}{q},$$

then

$$k = \frac{m \cdot p}{n \cdot q}.$$

PROOF: The proof is similar to that of (16.6.1), and is left to the reader.

(16.6.3) DEFINITION: Define two operations $\oplus$, $\otimes$ on $F \times F$ to F so that, for every $(f, g) \in F \times F$, the $\oplus$-correspondent is the unique $h \in F$ of (16.6.1), and the $\otimes$-correspondent is the unique $k \in F$ of (16.6.2).

REMARK: It follows that, if $f, g \in F$, and if m, n, p, q are any elements of I such that $f = m/n$, $g = p/q$, then

$$f \oplus g = \frac{m \cdot q + n \cdot p}{n \cdot q}, \quad f \otimes g = \frac{m \cdot p}{n \cdot q}.$$

The next theorem shows that $\oplus$, $\otimes$ have the same properties of commutativity, associativity and distributivity which hold for $+$, $\cdot$ on $I \times I$ to I.

(16.6.4) THEOREM: *Let $f, g, h \in F$. Then*

(a) $f \oplus g = g \oplus f$;

(b) $(f \oplus g) \oplus h = f \oplus (g \oplus h)$;

(c) $f \otimes g = g \otimes f$;

(d) $(f \otimes g) \otimes h = f \otimes (g \otimes h)$;

(e) $f \otimes (g \oplus h) = (f \otimes g) \oplus (f \otimes h)$.

PROOF: By (16.4.3), there exist $m, n, p, q, r, s \in I$ such that

$$f = \frac{m}{n}, \quad g = \frac{p}{q}, \quad h = \frac{r}{s}.$$

To prove (a), we have, by (16.6.3),

$$f \oplus g = \frac{m \cdot q + n \cdot p}{n \cdot q} = \frac{p \cdot n + q \cdot m}{q \cdot n} = g \oplus f.$$

Thus the commutativity of $+, \cdot$ is the essential tool used. To prove (b), we have

$$\begin{aligned}(f \oplus g) \oplus h &= \frac{(m \cdot q + n \cdot p) \cdot s + (n \cdot q) \cdot r}{(n \cdot q) \cdot s} \\ &= \frac{m \cdot q \cdot s + n \cdot p \cdot s + n \cdot q \cdot r}{n \cdot q \cdot s} \\ &= \frac{m \cdot (q \cdot s) + n \cdot (p \cdot s + q \cdot r)}{n \cdot (q \cdot s)} \\ &= f \oplus (g \oplus h).\end{aligned}$$

Note that the distributive law for $+, \cdot$ is required in this proof. The proofs of (c), (d), (e) are equally straightforward and are left for the reader.

The next theorem marks a difference between the properties of $\oplus, \otimes$ and those of $+, \cdot$.

(16.6.5) THEOREM: $(F, \otimes)$ *is a group.*
PROOF: The axioms for a group are to be established, namely,

(1) for every $f, g, h \in F$,

$$(f \otimes g) \otimes h = f \otimes (g \otimes h);$$

(2) for every $f, g \in F$, there exists $h \in F$ such that $f \otimes h = g$;
(3) for every $f, g \in F$, there exists $k \in F$ such that $k \otimes f = g$.

Now (1) holds by (16.6.4.d). To prove (2), let $f = m/n$, $g = p/q$. Define

$$h \equiv \frac{n \cdot p}{m \cdot q}.$$

Then

$$\begin{aligned}f \otimes h &= \frac{m \cdot n \cdot p}{n \cdot m \cdot q} && \text{[by (16.6.2)]} \\ &= \frac{p}{q} && \text{[by (16.4.5)]} \\ &= g.\end{aligned}$$

Finally, (3) follows from (2) and the commutative property of $\otimes$.

(16.6.6) COROLLARY: *The identity of the group* $(\boldsymbol{F}, \otimes)$ *is* $\boldsymbol{u}$. *Moreover, if* $f = m/n$, *then* n/m *is the inverse of* f.

PROOF: The proof is left to the reader.

REMARK: The inverse of f is also called the *reciprocal* of f. The property (16.6.4.c) shows the group to be commutative.

The next theorem is rather special, but it will prove useful later. For example, it will clarify our earlier statement that the positive rational numbers do not provide a perfect answer to the question "how long?"

(16.6.7) THEOREM: *There does not exist* $f \in \boldsymbol{F}$ *such that* $f \otimes f = 2/1$.

REMARK: The "negative" form of the statement of the theorem was chosen for emphasis. What is meant, of course, is that, for every $f \in \boldsymbol{F}$, $f \otimes f \neq 2/1$.

PROOF: Suppose the theorem is false, that is, suppose there exists $f \in \boldsymbol{F}$ such that $f \otimes f = 2/1$. There exist $m, n \in \boldsymbol{I}$ such that $m/n = f$. Hence the set

$$\boldsymbol{I}_0 \equiv [m \in \boldsymbol{I};\ \text{there exists } n \in \boldsymbol{I} \text{ such that } m/n = f]$$

is not empty, whence $\boldsymbol{I}_0$ has a least element p. Thus there exists $q \in \boldsymbol{I}$ with $f = p/q$. Now p, q are not both even. For otherwise, by (9.5.4.a), there exist $k, l \in \boldsymbol{I}$ with

$$p = 2 \cdot k, \quad q = 2 \cdot l,$$

and, since $f = p/q = k/l$, we have $k \in \boldsymbol{I}_0$; but $k < p$, contrary to the fact that p is a least in $\boldsymbol{I}_0$. Since $f \otimes f = 2/1$,

$$\frac{p \cdot p}{q \cdot q} = \frac{2}{1},$$

so that

$$(1) \qquad p \cdot p = 2 \cdot q \cdot q.$$

It is next shown that (1) implies that p is even. Suppose that p is odd. Then, by (9.5.6.c), $p \cdot p$ is odd, contrary to (1). Since p is even, there exists $s \in \boldsymbol{I}$ with $p = 2 \cdot s$. Then (1) yields

$$2 \cdot (2 \cdot s \cdot s) = 2 \cdot (q \cdot q),$$

so that, by cancellation,

$$(2) \qquad 2 \cdot s \cdot s = q \cdot q.$$

Next, the proof just given to show that (1) implies p to be even may be used to show that (2) implies q to be even. Hence p, q are both even, in violation of the earlier assertion to the contrary. This contradiction completes the proof.

(16.6.8) PROJECT: Prove (16.6.2).

(16.6.9) PROJECT: Prove (c), (d), (e) of (16.6.4).

(16.6.10) PROJECT: Prove that $m, n, p \in I$ implies $(m/p) \oplus (n/p) = (m + n)/p$.

(16.6.11) PROJECT: Prove (16.6.6).

(16.6.12) PROJECT: Evaluate (express in the form m/n) each of the following, justifying the results:

$$\frac{2}{3} \oplus \frac{1}{2}, \quad \frac{3}{4} \otimes \frac{5}{6}, \quad \frac{5}{4} \otimes \frac{4}{5}.$$

16.7. The Order Relation. [BASIS: $(F, u, \odot)$; AXIOMS: I, II, III, IV.] We shall introduce a relation on $F \times F$ analogous to the relation $<$ on $I \times I$. The definition will depend on the relation $<$ and its properties, although (16.7.5) shows that the same definition might have been used here as was used for $<$ in the theory of $(I, 1, \sigma)$. A preliminary lemma and theorem are required.

(16.7.1) LEMMA: *If* $m, n, p, q, m_1, n_1, p_1, q_1 \in I$ *such that*

$$\frac{m}{n} = \frac{m_1}{n_1}, \quad \frac{p}{q} = \frac{p_1}{q_1},$$

then

(a) $m \cdot q < n \cdot p$ *if and only if* $m_1 \cdot q_1 < n_1 \cdot p_1$;

(b) $m \cdot q = n \cdot p$ *if and only if* $m_1 \cdot q_1 = n_1 \cdot p_1$.

PROOF: Suppose $m \cdot q < n \cdot p$. Then there exists $k \in I$ such that

(1) $$n \cdot p = m \cdot q + k.$$

Now, by the hypothesis,

(2) $$m \cdot n_1 = n \cdot m_1, \quad p \cdot q_1 = q \cdot p_1.$$

We shall prove that

(3) $$n \cdot q \cdot n_1 \cdot p_1 = n \cdot q \cdot m_1 \cdot q_1 + n_1 \cdot q_1 \cdot k.$$

We have

$$\begin{aligned} n \cdot q \cdot m_1 \cdot q_1 + n_1 \cdot q_1 \cdot k &= m \cdot n_1 \cdot q \cdot q_1 + n_1 \cdot q_1 \cdot k && \text{[by (2)]} \\ &= n_1 \cdot q_1 \cdot (m \cdot q + k) \\ &= n_1 \cdot q_1 \cdot n \cdot p && \text{[by (1)]} \\ &= n \cdot q \cdot n_1 \cdot p_1 && \text{[by (2)],} \end{aligned}$$

and (3) holds. But (3) yields

$$(n \cdot q) \cdot (m_1 \cdot q_1) < (n \cdot q) \cdot (n_1 \cdot p_1).$$

By (9.2.21), it follows that

$$m_1 \cdot q_1 < n_1 \cdot p_1.$$

The converse is proved by interchanging m with m_1, n with n_1, p with p_1, q with q_1 and applying the same argument. This proves (a). The proof of (b) is quite similar and is left to the reader.

(16.7.2) THEOREM: *Let* $f, g \in F$. *Then*

(a) *if* $m, n, p, q \in I$ *such that* $m/n = f$, $p/q = g$, *then* $m \cdot p < n \cdot q$,

or

(b) *if* $m, n, p, q \in I$ *such that* $m/n = f$, $p/q = g$, *then* $m \cdot p \nless n \cdot q$.

REMARK: The possibility that $m \cdot p < n \cdot q$ for certain positive integers m, n, p, q and $m \cdot p \nless n \cdot q$ for others is thus ruled out.

PROOF: Let $m_1, n_1, p_1, q_1 \in I$ be specific positive integers such that

$$f = \frac{m_1}{n_1}, \quad g = \frac{p_1}{q_1}.$$

Then there are three possibilities:

$$(1) \quad m_1 \cdot q_1 < n_1 \cdot p_1, \quad m_1 \cdot q_1 = n_1 \cdot p_1 \quad \text{or} \quad n_1 \cdot p_1 < m_1 \cdot q_1.$$

Let $m, n, p, q \in I$ be *any* positive integers such that

$$f = \frac{m}{n}, \quad g = \frac{p}{q}.$$

In the first case under (1), it follows from (16.7.1.a) that

$$m \cdot q < n \cdot p,$$

and possibility (a) holds. In the second case under (1), it follows from (16.7.1.b) that

$$m \cdot q = n \cdot p;$$

and in the third case, (16.7.1.a) yields

$$n \cdot p < m \cdot q.$$

The last two cases thus lead to (b), and the proof is complete.

(16.7.3) DEFINITION: Define a relation $\otimes$ on $F \times F$ as follows:

$$\otimes \equiv [(f, g) \in F \times F;\ \text{there exist } m, n, p, q \in I \text{ with } f = m/n,\ g = p/q \text{ such that } m \cdot q < n \cdot p].$$

(16.7.4) COROLLARY:

$$\otimes = [(f, g) \in F \times F;\ \text{for every } m, n, p, q \in I \text{ with } f = m/n,\ g = p/q, \text{ it is true that } m \cdot q < n \cdot p].$$

PROOF: This is immediate from (16.7.3) and (16.7.2).

REMARK: It follows that, if $f = m/n$, $g = p/q$, then $f \mathbin{\textcircled{<}} g$ if and only if $m \cdot q < n \cdot p$.

(16.7.5) THEOREM: *If $f, g \in \boldsymbol{F}$, then $f \mathbin{\textcircled{<}} g$ if and only if there exists $h \in \boldsymbol{F}$ such that $g = f \oplus h$.*

PROOF: Suppose $f \mathbin{\textcircled{<}} g$, and let $m, n, p, q \in I$ such that

$$f = \frac{m}{n}, \quad g = \frac{p}{q}.$$

Since $f \mathbin{\textcircled{<}} g$,

(1) $$m \cdot q < n \cdot p.$$

Hence there exists $r \in I$ such that

(2) $$n \cdot p = m \cdot q + r.$$

Define

$$h \equiv \frac{r}{n \cdot q}.$$

Then

$$\begin{aligned} f \oplus h = \frac{m}{n} \oplus \frac{r}{n \cdot q} &= \frac{m \cdot n \cdot q + n \cdot r}{n \cdot n \cdot q} \\ &= \frac{n \cdot (m \cdot q + r)}{n \cdot n \cdot q} \\ &= \frac{n \cdot n \cdot p}{n \cdot n \cdot q} \qquad \text{[by (2)]} \\ &= \frac{p}{q} = g. \end{aligned}$$

The converse is left to the reader.

The notations $\textcircled{\leqq}$ and $\textcircled{>}$ are used to designate $\textcircled{<} + E$, and the transpose of $\textcircled{<}$, respectively. We denote the negatives of $\textcircled{<}$, $\textcircled{>}$, $\textcircled{\leqq}$ by $\textcircled{<}'$, $\textcircled{>}'$, $\textcircled{\leqq}'$, respectively. The properties of $\textcircled{<}$ are similar to those of $<$ on $I \times I$. The next theorem lists a number of them.

(16.7.6) THEOREM: *Let $f, g, h, k \in \boldsymbol{F}$. Then*

(a) $f \mathbin{\textcircled{<}'} f$ *(irreflexive law);*
(b) $f \mathbin{\textcircled{<}} g$ *implies* $g \mathbin{\textcircled{<}'} f$ *(asymmetric law);*
(c) $f \mathbin{\textcircled{<}} g$, $g \mathbin{\textcircled{<}} h$ *implies* $f \mathbin{\textcircled{<}} h$ *(transitive law);*
(d) $f \mathbin{\textcircled{<}} g$ *implies* $f \oplus h \mathbin{\textcircled{<}} g \oplus h$;
(e) $f \oplus h \mathbin{\textcircled{<}} g \oplus h$ *implies* $f \mathbin{\textcircled{<}} g$;
(f) *either* $f = g$ *or* $f \mathbin{\textcircled{<}} g$ *or* $g \mathbin{\textcircled{<}} f$;
(g) $f \mathbin{\textcircled{<}} g$ *implies* $f \otimes h \mathbin{\textcircled{<}} g \otimes h$;
(h) $f \otimes h \mathbin{\textcircled{<}} g \otimes h$ *implies* $f \mathbin{\textcircled{<}} g$;
(i) $f \mathbin{\textcircled{<}} g$, $h \mathbin{\textcircled{\leqq}} k$ *implies* $f \otimes h \mathbin{\textcircled{<}} g \otimes k$.

PROOF: All properties are straightforward consequences of the definition of $\otimes$ and properties of $<$ on $I \times I$. We prove only (c), leaving the remainder to the reader. Let

$$f = \frac{m}{n}, \quad g = \frac{p}{q}, \quad h = \frac{r}{s},$$

with $m, n, p, q, r, s \in I$. By the hypothesis,

$$(1) \qquad m \cdot q < n \cdot p, \quad p \cdot s < q \cdot r.$$

Then (1) yields

$$m \cdot q \cdot s < n \cdot p \cdot s, \quad n \cdot p \cdot s < n \cdot q \cdot r,$$

whence by the transitivity of $<$,

$$m \cdot q \cdot s < n \cdot q \cdot r.$$

It then follows that $m \cdot s < n \cdot r$, whence $f \otimes h$.

(16.7.7) COROLLARY: *The set* F *is linearly ordered by* $\otimes$.
PROOF: This follows from (16.7.6.a), (16.7.6.c), (16.7.6.f).

(16.7.8) PROJECT: Prove (16.7.1.b).

(16.7.9) PROJECT: Complete the proof of (16.7.5).

(16.7.10) PROJECT: Complete the proof of (16.7.6).

(16.7.11) PROJECT: Prove that $3/4 \otimes 4/5$.

16.8. Least and Greatest Elements. [BASIS: $(F, u, \odot)$; AXIOMS: I, II, III, IV.] It was proved earlier that I possesses a least element 1; indeed it was found that I is well-ordered, in that every non-empty subset has a least. This property is not possessed by F, as is now shown.

(16.8.1) THEOREM: *Let* $f \in F$. *Then there exists* $g \in F$ *such that* $g \otimes f$.
PROOF: Let $f \in F$, and let $m, n \in I$ with $f = m/n$. Define

$$g \equiv \frac{m}{2 \cdot n}.$$

Then $g \otimes f$, since

$$m \cdot n < 2 \cdot n \cdot m = m \cdot n + m \cdot n.$$

More generally, the elements of F are "dense" with respect to the relation $\otimes$. This means that there are elements lying "between" any two elements of F.

(16.8.2) THEOREM: *Let* $f_1, f_2 \in F$ *and* $f_1 \otimes f_2$. *Then there exists* $g \in F$ *such that* $f_1 \otimes g$ *and* $g \otimes f_2$.

PROOF: Let $f_1 = m_1/n_1$, $f_2 = m_2/n_2$ and $f_1 \otimes f_2$. Define

$$g \equiv \frac{m_1 \cdot n_2 + n_1 \cdot m_2}{2 \cdot n_1 \cdot n_2}.$$

It is left for the reader to show that $f_1 \otimes g$ and $g \otimes f_2$.

A further fact is that, if $f \in \boldsymbol{F}$, then there exists $g \in \boldsymbol{F}$ such that $f \otimes g$. This implies in particular that $\boldsymbol{F}$ has no greatest element. The reader may carry out a proof of these statements using the methods of the two preceding proofs.

(16.8.3) PROJECT: Complete the proof of (16.8.2).

(16.8.4) PROJECT: Prove that $\boldsymbol{F}$ has no greatest.

16.9. The Integral Positive Rational Numbers. [BASIS: $(\boldsymbol{F}, \boldsymbol{u}, \odot)$; AXIOMS: I, II, III, IV.]

(16.9.1) DEFINITION: Define

$$\boldsymbol{I} \equiv [f;\text{ there exists } m \in I \text{ with } f = m/1].$$

Elements of $\boldsymbol{I}$ are called *integral positive rational numbers.* Define a function φ on $\boldsymbol{I}$ to $\boldsymbol{F}$ such that, for every $f \in \boldsymbol{I}$, $\varphi(f) = f \oplus \boldsymbol{u}$.

(16.9.2) COROLLARY: *If $f \in \boldsymbol{I}$, then there exists a unique $m \in I$ such that $f = m/1$. The function φ is on $\boldsymbol{I}$ to $\boldsymbol{I}$. If $f \in \boldsymbol{I}$, $f = m/1$ with $m \in I$, then $\varphi(f) = (m + 1)/1$. Finally, $\boldsymbol{u} \in \boldsymbol{I}$.*

The proof is left to the reader.

It will now be shown that $(\boldsymbol{I}, \boldsymbol{u}, \varphi)$ is a basic system of positive integers; from this it follows that $(\boldsymbol{I}, \boldsymbol{u}, \varphi)$ is isomorphic to $(I, 1, \sigma)$.

(16.9.3) THEOREM: *$(\boldsymbol{I}, \boldsymbol{u}, \varphi)$ satisfies Axioms* I, II, III *for positive integers.*

PROOF: It is to be shown that

(1) $f, g \in \boldsymbol{I}$, $f \neq g$ implies $\varphi(f) \neq \varphi(g)$;
(2) $f \in \boldsymbol{I}$ implies $\varphi(f) \neq \boldsymbol{u}$;
(3) if $\boldsymbol{H} \subset \boldsymbol{I}$ such that $\boldsymbol{u} \in \boldsymbol{H}$, and such that $f \in \boldsymbol{H}$ implies $\varphi(f) \in \boldsymbol{H}$, then $\boldsymbol{H} = \boldsymbol{I}$.

Let $f, g \in \boldsymbol{I}$, $f \neq g$, $f = m/1$, $g = n/1$. Then

$$\varphi(f) = \frac{m+1}{1}, \quad \varphi(g) = \frac{n+1}{1}.$$

If $\varphi(f) = \varphi(g)$, then $m + 1 = n + 1$, and $m = n$, so that $f = g$. This contradiction proves (1).

Suppose there exists $f \in \boldsymbol{I}$ such that $\varphi(f) = \boldsymbol{u}$. Let $f = m/1$. Hence

$$\varphi(f) = \frac{m+1}{1} = \boldsymbol{u} = \frac{1}{1},$$

whence $m + 1 = 1$, which is impossible. This proves (2).

Let $\boldsymbol{H} \subset \boldsymbol{I}$ satisfy the hypotheses of (3). Define

$$H \equiv [m \in I;\, m/1 \in \boldsymbol{H}].$$

Since $\boldsymbol{u} \in \boldsymbol{I}$, that is, $1/1 \in \boldsymbol{H}$, it follows that $1 \in H$. Suppose $q \in H$, that is, $q/1 \in \boldsymbol{H}$. Then, by the hypothesis on $\boldsymbol{H}$,

$$\frac{q+1}{1} = \varphi\left(\frac{q}{1}\right) \in \boldsymbol{H},$$

and $q + 1 \in H$. By III′, $H = I$. Now let $f \in \boldsymbol{I}$, whence there exists $m \in I$ with $f = m/1$. Since $H = I$, that is, $m \in I$ implies $m/1 \in \boldsymbol{H}$, it follows that $f \in \boldsymbol{H}$. Thus $\boldsymbol{I} \subset \boldsymbol{H}$, and we have $\boldsymbol{H} = \boldsymbol{I}$. This completes the proof of (3).

(16.9.4) Theorem: *The system* $(\boldsymbol{I}, \boldsymbol{u}, \varphi)$ *is isomorphic to* $(I, 1, \sigma)$.

Proof: This is immediate from the fact that the axioms for positive integers are categorical [see (14.4.1)], in view of (16.9.3).

(16.9.5) Theorem: *The set* $\boldsymbol{F}$ *is denumerably infinite.*

Proof: That $\boldsymbol{F}$ is infinite follows from (10.4.7), in view of $\boldsymbol{I} \subset \boldsymbol{F}$, $\boldsymbol{I} \sim I$ and the fact that I is infinite. But, by (16.5.1), $\boldsymbol{F}$ is countable. Hence the conclusion follows. (The principle of choice is used through (16.5.1).)

(16.9.6) Project: Prove (16.9.2).

16.10. Conclusion. [No Basis.] It will be recalled that in (9.7) distinction was made between basic and algebraic systems of positive integers. A similar distinction will now be made for positive rational number systems. Let $(\boldsymbol{F}, \boldsymbol{u}, \odot)$ satisfy Axioms I, II, III, IV; then $(\boldsymbol{F}, \boldsymbol{u}, \otimes\!\!\!<, \oplus, \otimes)$ is called the associated *algebraic system of positive rational numbers.* Again the desirability of introducing the algebraic system stems from the important role that $\otimes\!\!\!<$, $\oplus$, $\otimes$ play in the theory.

In further work with a positive rational number system, the operation $\odot$ may be dispensed with, since,

$$\text{for every } m \in I, f \in \boldsymbol{F},\ m \odot f = \frac{m}{1} \otimes f,$$

in view of (16.4.6).

It is possible now to sharpen (16.9.3).

(16.10.1) THEOREM: *Let* $(F, u, \otimes\!\!\!<, \oplus, \otimes)$ *be an algebraic system of positive rational numbers. Then* $(I, u, ⧀, \oplus, \otimes)$ *is a subsystem of* $(F, u, ⧀, \oplus, \otimes)$, *in the sense that*

(a) $m, n \in I$ *implies* $\dfrac{m+n}{1} = \dfrac{m}{1} \oplus \dfrac{n}{1}$;

(b) $m, n \in I$ *implies* $\dfrac{m \cdot n}{1} = \dfrac{m}{1} \otimes \dfrac{n}{1}$;

(c) *if* $m, n \in I$, *then* $m < n$ *if and only if* $\dfrac{m}{1} ⧀ \dfrac{n}{1}$.

Moreover, $(I, u, ⧀, \oplus, \otimes)$ *is the algebraic system of positive integers associated with the basic system* (I, u, φ).

PROOF: Statements (a), (b) follow directly from the definitions (16.6.3). Also, (c) is immediate from (16.7.3). This proves the first part.

Let $(I, u, ⧀_0, \oplus_0, \otimes_0)$ be the algebraic system of positive integers associated with (I, u, φ). It is to be proved that

(1) $a, b \in I$ implies $a \oplus b = a \oplus_0 b$;
(2) $a, b \in I$ implies $a \otimes b = a \otimes_0 b$;
(3) if $a, b \in I$, then $a ⧀ b$ if and only if $a ⧀_0 b$.

It is immediately verified that

$$\psi \equiv \left(\frac{m}{1};\ m \in I\right)$$

is an isomorphism between $(I, 1, \sigma)$ and (I, u, φ). From this it follows [see (14.4.3)] that ψ is an isomorphism between $(I, 1, <, +, \times)$ and $(I, u, ⧀_0, \oplus_0, \otimes_0)$. But then, if $a, b \in I$, and if $a = m/1$, $b = n/1$, then

$$a \oplus b = \frac{m}{1} \oplus \frac{n}{1} = \frac{m+n}{1} \qquad \text{[by (a)]}$$

$$= \psi(m+n) = \psi(m) \oplus_0 \psi(n) = \frac{m}{1} \oplus_0 \frac{n}{1} = a \oplus_0 b.$$

Hence (1) holds. Similar arguments prove (2), (3). Details are left to the reader.

At this point it is convenient to effect a change in notation in order to free the symbols $\oplus$, $\otimes$, $⧀$ for use in connection with the system to be treated in Chapter 18. It will be noted that, if $a, b \in F$ (even if $a, b \in I$), then $a + b$ has no meaning. Therefore we may agree to use the notation $a + b$ henceforth to designate $a \oplus b$. A similar agreement is made to replace $\otimes$ by $\times$ or $\cdot$, and $⧀$ by $<$. While each of the symbols $+$, $\cdot$, $<$ will then be used to represent different things, no ambiguity will result, since the context will clearly show what meaning is intended. These replacements are particularly appropriate in view of (16.10.1).

We conclude this section with a theorem on isomorphic systems of positive rational numbers.

(16.10.2) THEOREM: *Let* $(\boldsymbol{F}_1, \boldsymbol{u}_1, \odot_1)$, $(\boldsymbol{F}_2, \boldsymbol{u}_2, \odot_2)$ *be two basic systems of positive rational numbers, and let* $(\boldsymbol{F}_1, \boldsymbol{u}_1, <_1, +_1, \times_1)$ *and* $(\boldsymbol{F}_2, \boldsymbol{u}_2, <_2, +_2, \times_2)$ *be the corresponding algebraic systems of positive rational numbers. Let* ψ *be an isomorphism between* $(\boldsymbol{F}_1, \boldsymbol{u}_1, \odot_1)$ *and* $(\boldsymbol{F}_2, \boldsymbol{u}_2, \odot_2)$. *Then* ψ *is also an isomorphism between* $(\boldsymbol{F}_1, \boldsymbol{u}_1, <_1, +_1, \times_1)$ *and* $(\boldsymbol{F}_2, \boldsymbol{u}_2, <_2, +_2, \times_2)$.

PROOF: In view of (14.2.11), it must be shown that,

(1) for every $f, g \in \boldsymbol{F}_1$, $\psi(f) <_2 \psi(g)$ if and only if $f <_1 g$;
(2) for every $f, g \in \boldsymbol{F}_1$, $\psi(f) +_2 \psi(g) = \psi(f +_1 g)$;
(3) for every $f, g \in \boldsymbol{F}_1$, $\psi(f) \times_2 \psi(g) = \psi(f \times_1 g)$.

We prove only (2), leaving the proofs of (1) and (3) for the reader. By I(a), there exist $m, n, p, q \in I$ such that

(4) $$n \odot_1 f = m \odot_1 \boldsymbol{u}_1,$$

and

(5) $$q \odot_1 g = p \odot_1 \boldsymbol{u}_1.$$

Since ψ is an isomorphism between $(\boldsymbol{F}_1, \boldsymbol{u}_1, \odot_1)$ and $(\boldsymbol{F}_2, \boldsymbol{u}_2, \odot_2)$, we have, for every $r, s \in I$, $h \in \boldsymbol{F}_1$,

(6) $$r \odot_1 f = s \odot_1 \boldsymbol{u}_1 \text{ implies } r \odot_2 \psi(f) = s \odot_2 \boldsymbol{u}_2.$$

Thus, by (4) and (5),

(7) $$n \odot_2 \psi(f) = m \odot_2 \boldsymbol{u}_2,$$

and

(8) $$q \odot_2 \psi(g) = p \odot_2 \boldsymbol{u}_2.$$

By (4), (5), (16.6.3), $f +_1 g$ is the unique element of $\boldsymbol{F}_1$ such that

$$(n \cdot q) \odot_1 (f +_1 g) = (m \cdot q + n \cdot p) \odot_1 \boldsymbol{u}_1,$$

whence, by (6),

(9) $$(n \cdot q) \odot_2 \psi(f +_1 g) = (m \cdot q + n \cdot p) \odot_2 \boldsymbol{u}_2.$$

But, by (7), (8), (16.6.3), $\psi(f) +_2 \psi(g)$ is the unique element of $\boldsymbol{F}_2$ such that

(10) $$(n \cdot q) \odot_2 (\psi(f) +_2 \psi(g)) = (m \cdot q + n \cdot p) \odot_2 \boldsymbol{u}_2.$$

Hence, by (9), (10) and the uniqueness in (16.4.1),

$$\psi(f +_1 g) = \psi(f) +_2 \psi(g),$$

and (2) is proved.

(16.10.3) COROLLARY: *Any two algebraic systems of positive rational numbers are isomorphic.*

PROOF: This is immediate from (16.4.9) and (16.10.2).

(16.10.4) PROJECT: Complete the proof of (16.10.1).

(16.10.5) PROJECT: Complete the proof of (16.10.2).

(16.10.6) PROJECT: Prove (16.10.3) in detail.

Chapter 17

ONE–DIMENSIONAL CONTINUA

17.1. The Positive Number Scale. [NO BASIS.] In this section we shall discuss, on an intuitive basis, the widely used geometric interpretation of positive rational numbers, and shall indicate why a further extension of this number system is sought.

As we have seen, the positive rational numbers were designed to serve as lengths of objects. However, it is equally possible, intuitively, to think of positive rational numbers as "corresponding" to "positions on a ruler"; the connection between this interpretation and the preceding is that the positive rational number "corresponding" to a particular "position" would also serve to indicate the "length of the ruler" up to that "position." From this point of view, the positive rational numbers should constitute a sort of abstract measuring device. Let us indicate to what extent this interpretation is reasonable by carrying out an imaginary construction of a three-inch ruler with the help of an algebraic system $(F, u, <, +, \cdot)$ of rational numbers.

We begin with a "straightedge" of adequate "length." (It is emphasized that this entire discussion is intuitive; accordingly, we do not investigate the meaning of "straight.") We now designate various "positions" along the straightedge as follows. It is assumed that a method is available for verifying that the length of a "segment" of the straightedge is "one inch." The point terminating the one-inch segment starting at the left end of the straightedge is marked $1/1$ $(= u)$. Next, $2/1$ designates a position one inch from the position marked $1/1$. Similarly, $3/1$ corresponds to the end of a further one-inch interval. Henceforth that portion of the straightedge lying beyond the point marked $3/1$ is disregarded. We now have the situation indicated in (17.1.1).

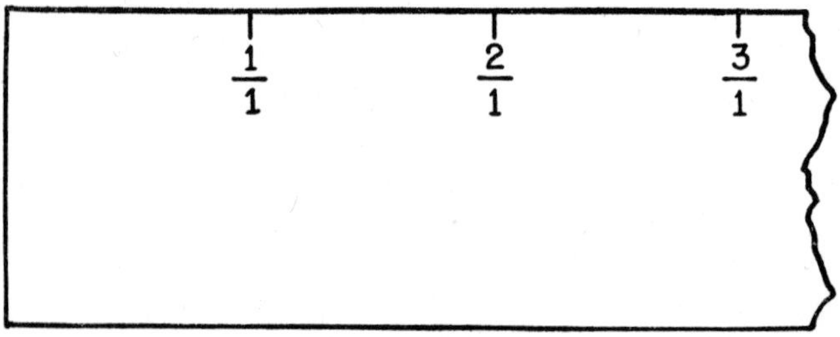

(17.1.1) FIGURE

Now equally spaced positions are marked 1/2, 2/2, 3/2, 4/2, 5/2, 6/2; the spacing is chosen in such a way that 2/2 falls on the same position as 1/1, and, similarly, 4/2 coincides with 2/1 and 6/2 with 3/1. Then 1/2, 2/3, 3/3, and so on, up to 9/3 are marked in a similar way, equally spaced, with 3/3 falling at 1/1. This leads to (17.1.2).

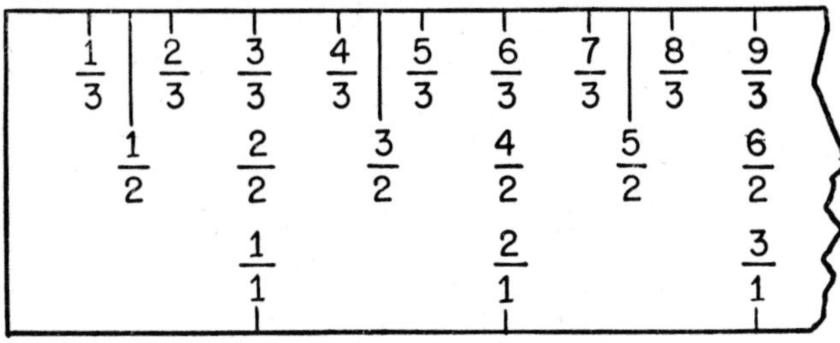

(17.1.2) FIGURE

It is to be imagined that the process just outlined is continued indefinitely, so that every positive rational number of the set

$$F_3 \equiv \left[\frac{m}{n};\ m \leqq 3 \cdot n\right]$$

designates exactly one position on the straightedge. There are three intuitively verifiable "facts" to be noted. First, m/n and p/q designate the same point when $m \cdot q = n \cdot p$, that is, when m/n and p/q are the same. This indicates that our procedure leads to an intuitive one-to-one correspondence between those positive rational numbers employed and the designated positions on the straightedge. Secondly, the relation $<$ is reflected in the intuitive relation "is to the left of," that is, the position designated f "is to the left of" the position designated g if $f < g$. This may be checked for special cases by the reader. Finally, the leftmost point (the left end) of the straightedge has no designation, as might be expected from (16.8.1), which says that $\boldsymbol{F}$ has no least element (whence $\boldsymbol{F}_3$ has no least element).

The fact that there is no designation for the leftmost point is not a serious matter. It would be easy to modify $\boldsymbol{F}$ by appending to it a single element which could designate this point. However, such an extension of $\boldsymbol{F}$ is unnecessary for our purposes. The presence of one undesignated point suggests a question that is much more serious and quite deep. Are there any points other than the leftmost one that are not designated by positive rational numbers? In other words, do the points occupied by elements of $\boldsymbol{F}_3$ constitute a full "solid line" of the three-inch ruler edge, or do they constitute merely a "dotted line"? (This question is meaningful only to the extent that our intuitive understanding of the nature of a straightedge is clear.) A pertinent fact here is (16.8.2), which yields that, between *any* two positions of the scale which are designated by elements of F_3, there is another designated position. This result indicates that a very large number of positions are occupied by elements of F_3, but it does not really furnish an answer to our question.

The following intuitive construction does indicate the answer. Let us draw a "right triangle" with the two sides AB, BC each one inch in

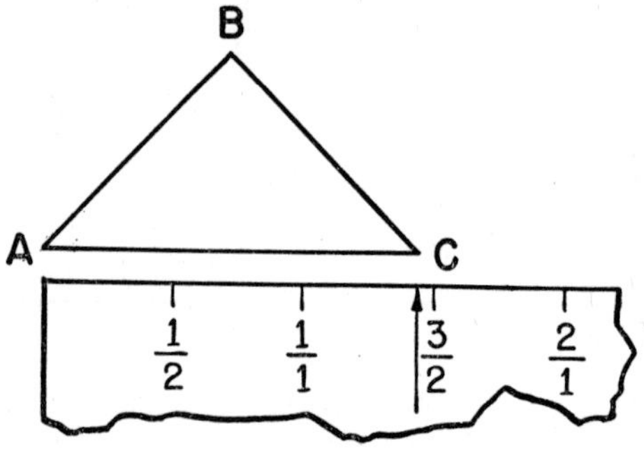

length and with the "right angle" at B. Let us imagine the "hypotenuse" of this right triangle placed along our straightedge with A at the left end. Then the position at which C falls on the straightedge may be marked. It is easily seen that C will fall between 1/1 and 2/1. But it will now be indicated, on the basis of the "pythagorean theorem," that C does not fall on a point designated by an element of F_3. In fact, from the "pythagorean theorem," the length, in inches, of the hypotenuse AC should be a "number" x for which $x^2 = x \cdot x = 2$. If the point C were designated by an element $f \in F_3$ we should expect that $f^2 = 2/1$. But no such element exists in F (or in F_3) by (16.6.7). Thus we have located one vacancy (undesignated position) on our straightedge. From this vacancy we could find many others; indeed, deeper analysis indicates that for every designated point there are myriads of undesignated points, so that the elements of F_3 occupy but a scant portion of the straightedge. The designated points constitute a very dotted line indeed.

It is now clear that the positive rational numbers do not provide a designation for every position on a straightedge and thus do not provide a length for every segment. It is not surprising, then, that mathematicians were not content with the positive rational numbers but proceeded to the construction of a system whose elements (intuitively) correspond to *all* the positions on a complete straightedge. The remainder of this chapter and the next will be devoted to the development of such a system.

The project now before us is the construction of a mathematical counterpart of the intuitive measuring scale. In our treatment we do not limit ourselves to the three-inch ruler but imagine it to "extend indefinitely" to the right.

Positions on the straightedge will be thought of mathematically as simply elements of a set, to be denoted by K. Moreover, the intuitive relation "is to the left of" will be replaced, in the mathematical theory, by a basic relation $<$ on $K \times K$. A natural first axiom is that $(K, <)$ should be a linearly ordered system [see (15.4.5)], that is, if $a, b, c \in K$, then

$$a \nless a;$$
$$a < b, b < c \text{ implies } a < c;$$
$$a \neq b \text{ implies } a < b \text{ or } b < a.$$

A second axiom, intuitively evident, is required for technical reasons: K possesses at least two distinct elements. A third axiom, also intuitively acceptable, expresses a "density" requirement similar to (16.8.2), namely, if $a, c \in K$, then there exists $b \in K$ with $a < b$ and $b < c$ (b is "between" a and c). However, these three axioms are not enough to insure anything like "solidity" of our number scale. For, if $(F, u, <, +, \cdot)$ is an algebraic system of positive rational numbers, then $(F, <)$ satisfies all three of these axioms. Hence we shall have to search for some further requirement which will insure "solidity." The concept of "solidity" is a rather subtle one, and it is correspondingly difficult to formulate an appropriate requirement. In order to arrive at such a formulation, it will be desirable to discuss first some concepts concerning linearly ordered systems. Accordingly, the next section will be devoted to the discussion of these concepts; the material will supplement (15.5) and will lead to the formulation of the final axiom.

17.2. Intervals and Bounds. [Basis and Axioms: see text.] Let $(L, <)$ be a "linearly ordered system," that is, let L be a set and $<$ a relation on $L \times L$ such that L is linearly ordered by $<$ [see (15.4.5)]. Certain subsets of L play an important role in many theories involving such a system $(L, <)$. These will now be defined.

(17.2.1) Definition: Let $S \subset L$. Then S is called

(a) a *closed interval* if there exist $a, b \in L$ such that $a \leqq b$ and

$$S = [x \in L; a \leqq x, x \leqq b]$$

(that is, S consists of all elements "between" two particular elements, including the particular elements);

(b) an *open interval* if there exist $a, b \in L$ such that $a < b$ and

$$S = [x \in L; a < x, x < b]$$

(that is, S consists of all elements "between" two particular elements, excluding the particular elements);

(c) a *closed initial half-interval* if there exists $b \in L$ such that

$$S = [x \in L; x \leqq b]$$

(that is, S consists of all elements $\leqq$ a particular element);

(d) an *open initial half-interval* if there exists $b \in L$ such that

$$S = [x \in L; x < b]$$

(that is, S consists of all elements $<$ a particular element);

(e) a *lower set* if for every $x \in S$ and every $y \in L$ such that $y < x$, it is true that $y \in S$ (that is, S contains with each of its elements all elements of $L \leqq$ that element).

In (a) and (b), the elements a, b are called *lower* and *upper endpoints*, respectively, of S. In (c) and (d), the element b is called an *upper endpoint* of S.

(17.2.2) Corollary: *Let* $S \subset L$. *Then,*

(a) *if* S *is a closed interval, then its lower and upper endpoints are unique;*

(b) *if* S *is an open interval and* $S \neq \Theta$, *then its lower and upper endpoints are unique;*

(c) *if* S *is a closed initial half-interval, then its upper endpoint is unique;*

(d) *if* S *is an open initial half-interval, then its upper endpoint is unique.*

Proof: We first prove part (a). Let S be a closed interval, and let a, b and a', b' be two pairs of endpoints, so that

(1) $$S = [x \in L; a \leqq x, x \leqq b]$$

and

(2) $$S = [y \in L; a' \leqq y, y \leqq b'].$$

Now $a \in S$ by (1), whence, by (2), $a' \leqq a$. Similarly, $a' \in S$ by (2), whence, by (1), $a \leqq a'$. But $a' \leqq a$, $a \leqq a'$ implies $a = a'$ by (15.4.8.c). In the same way, $b = b'$. This completes the proof of (a).

To prove (b), let S be an open interval, $S \neq \Theta$, and let a, b and a', b' be two pairs of endpoints, so that

(3) $$S = [x \in L; a < x, x < b]$$

and

(4) $$S = [y \in L; a' < y, y < b'].$$

There are three possibilities, $a < a'$, $a' < a$, $a = a'$. It will be shown that the first two possibilities lead to contradictions.

Suppose $a < a'$. Since $S \neq \Theta$, there exists $z \in S$. By (3),

(5) $$z < b,$$

and, by (4),

(6) $$a' < z.$$

From (5) and (6) it follows that $a' < b$. But since $a < a'$, we have $a' \in S$ by (3). Hence, by (4), $a' < a'$, which is a contradiction. The possibility $a' < a$ leads to a contradiction in a similar way. Hence $a = a'$.

The proof that $b = b'$ is similar. This proves (b).

The proofs of (c) and (d) are left for the reader.

(17.2.3) Corollary: *Every open or closed initial half-interval is a lower set.*

Proof: Let S be an open or closed initial half-interval with upper endpoint b. Let $x \in S$ so that $x \leqq b$. Let $y \in L$ such that $y < x$. Then $y < b$, whence $y \in S$. Thus S is a lower set.

(17.2.4) Definition: Let $S \subset L$, $b \in L$. Then

(a) b is a *lower bound* of S if, for every $x \in S$, it is true that $b \leqq x$;

(b) b is an *upper bound* of S if, for every $x \in S$, it is true that $x \leqq b$;

(c) b is a *greatest lower bound* of S if b is a lower bound of S and if, for every lower bound c of S, it is true that $c \leqq b$;

(d) b is a *least upper bound* of S if b is an upper bound of S and if, for every upper bound c of S, it is true that $b \leqq c$.

(17.2.5) Definition: Let $S \subset L$. Then

(a) S is *bounded below* if there exists $b \in L$ such that b is a lower bound of S;

(b) S is *bounded above* if there exists $b \in L$ such that b is an upper bound of S;

(c) S is *bounded* if S is bounded below and bounded above.

Remark: The reader should compare (17.2.4) and (17.2.5) with (15.5.4). It should be noted that a set S need not have either an upper or a lower bound. Furthermore, if b is an upper bound, then $c > b$ is also an upper bound, so that upper bounds (similarly, lower bounds) are not necessarily unique. A greatest lower bound or least upper bound is unique, if existent, by (15.5.2). In this case, g.l.b. S (l.u.b. S) denotes the unique greatest lower bound of S (least upper bound of S). Every closed or open interval is bounded, and its endpoints are bounds. Indeed, for a closed interval the lower and upper endpoints are the greatest lower bound and the least upper bound, respectively. For a closed initial half-interval the upper endpoint is the least upper bound. From these examples and others readily constructed, it is seen that a least upper bound or greatest lower bound of a set S may be (but need not be) an element of S. If the least upper bound (greatest lower bound) of S is in S, then S has a greatest (least) element. Thus a closed interval has a least element and a greatest element, while an open interval need not have either a least or a greatest element. The empty set Θ is bounded, any element of L serving as both upper and lower bound of Θ. Finally, the entire set L may be but need not be bounded above or below; for example, $(I, <)$ has a lower bound, 1, but no upper bound.

It might be asked whether the existence of an upper bound of a non-empty set implies the existence of a least upper bound. It should be recalled that this is the case for the system $(I, <)$ [see (9.3.7)]. However, it will be shown later [(17.3.3)] that not every system $(L, <)$ has this property, that is, there exist systems $(L, <)$ in which there are subsets of L which are bounded above but have no least upper bound. The next theorem shows that, in order to determine if a system $(L, <)$ has this property, it is sufficient to examine the special kinds of subsets called lower sets.

(17.2.6) THEOREM: *If every non-empty lower set $T \subset L$ which is bounded above has a least upper bound, then every non-empty set $S \subset L$ which is bounded above has a least upper bound.*

PROOF: Let $S \subset L$, $S \neq \Theta$, and let $b \in L$ be an upper bound of S. Define

$$T \equiv [x \in L; \text{ there exists } y \in S \text{ with } x \leqq y].$$

We shall show first that T is bounded above, in fact, that b is an upper bound. Let $x \in T$. Then there exists $y \in S$ such that $x \leqq y$. But $y \in S$ yields $y \leqq b$. Hence $x \leqq b$, and b is an upper bound of T. Clearly $T \neq \Theta$; in fact, $S \subset T$ and $S \neq \Theta$. Next we show that T is a lower set. Let $x \in T$, so that there exists $y \in S$ such that $x \leqq y$. Let $z \in L$ such that $z < x$. Then $z < y$, whence $z \in T$. Thus T is a lower set. Since T is a non-empty lower set and is bounded above, by the hypothesis there is a least upper bound c of T. It will be shown that c is a least upper bound of S. Clearly c is an upper bound of S since $S \subset T$. To prove that c is a *least* upper bound of S, let d be any upper bound of S. For every $x \in T$, there exists $y \in S$ with $x \leqq y$. But $y \leqq d$. Hence $x \leqq d$, and d is an upper bound of T. Since c is the least upper bound of T, $c \leqq d$. This completes the proof.

(17.2.7) PROJECT: Prove (c), (d) in (17.2.2).

(17.2.8) PROJECT: Prove that least upper and greatest lower bounds need not exist in linearly ordered systems.

(17.2.9) PROJECT: Let S be an open interval. Are the endpoints least upper and greatest lower bounds of S? Why?

(17.2.10) PROJECT: Let S be an open initial half-interval. Is the upper endpoint the least upper bound of S? Why?

17.3. Axioms for One-Dimensional Continua. [NO BASIS.] Let us now return to our attempt to ascertain what axiom should be added to the three already proposed for a system $(K, <)$ to insure "solidity" of the number scale. Such an axiom is suggested most readily by finding out what properties are associated with a "lack of solidity." In other words, in order to rule out the possibility of "missing points," we first find what property is brought about by the "removal" of a "point." Let us imagine our intuitive "solid" line to be before us and then consider that a single "point" P is removed from the line. The system $(K - [P], <)$ would still satisfy the three requirements of (17.1), that is, $K - [P]$ would be linearly ordered by $<$, $K - [P]$ would have at least two elements, and the "density" property would remain valid. (Verification of these intuitive facts is left for the reader.) Now consider the set S of all "points" to the left of P. This set S could be described mathematically as an open initial half-interval in K but would not be such in $K - [P]$; nevertheless, in $K - [P]$, S would be a lower set. In K, S would be bounded above and indeed would possess a least upper bound P. In $K - [P]$, however, S would be bounded above (by any point Q to the right of P) but would not possess a least upper bound. The removal of a point P seems to lead to the existence of a set S which is bounded above without having a least upper bound. And the process of passing from $K - [P]$ to K, namely, the addition of $[P]$, appears as the process of supplying the set S (bounded above) with a least upper bound.

The heuristic discussion just given indicates that, in order to guard against the "broken" character of the line $K - [P]$, we might insist that every non-empty set $S \subset K$ which is bounded above must have a least upper bound. This requirement may be considerably less acceptable intuitively than the three axioms proposed in (17.1). Certainly we cannot *prove* that the property is valid for an intuitive "solid" line. However, it is hoped that we have succeeded in making such a requirement seem reasonable. Actually, in view of (17.2.6), it is sufficient to require that every non-empty *lower* set which is bounded above has a least upper bound. This will be the desired axiom to insure "solidity."

A system $(K, <)$ possessing this "solidity" property, together with the three requirements discussed in (17.1), is called a *one-dimensional continuum*. Its foundation is as follows.

Basis: $(K, <)$, where K is a set and $<$ is a relation on $K \times K$.

Axioms:

I. There exist $a, b \in K$ with $a \neq b$.

II. The set K is linearly ordered by $<$, that is,

(a) $<$ is irreflexive;

(b) $<$ is transitive;

(c) for every $a, b \in K$, it is true that $a = b$ or $a < b$ or $b < a$.

III. For every $a, b \in K$ such that $a < b$, there exists $x \in K$ such that $a < x$ and $x < b$.

IV. Every non-empty lower subset of K which is bounded above has a least upper bound.

REMARK: In view of (17.2.6), IV implies the following:

IV′. Every non-empty subset of K which is bounded above has a least upper bound.

We were led to the adoption of Axiom IV by considerations connected with the intuitive concept of "solidity." And we were led to the consideration of "solidity" by indications that the positive rational number system does not possess such "solidity." Hence it is to be expected that the system $(\boldsymbol{F}, <)$ associated with an algebraic system $(\boldsymbol{F}, \boldsymbol{u}, <, +, \cdot)$ of positive rational numbers does not satisfy Axiom IV and hence is not a one-dimensional continuum. Before proceeding with the discussion of one-dimensional continua we shall devote the remainder of this section to *proving* (without recourse to intuition) that this is the case. Hence it will be seen that Axiom IV really imposes a restriction, that is, that Axiom IV is independent of Axioms I, II, III.

The proof will be carried out with the assistance of two lemmas, one concerning $(I, 1, <, +, \cdot)$ and the other concerning $(\boldsymbol{F}, \boldsymbol{u}, <, +, \cdot)$.

(17.3.1) LEMMA: *Let $a, b \in I$ such that $4 \cdot b \leqq a$. Then there exists $n \in I$ such that*

$$a \cdot b \leqq n^2 \quad \textit{and} \quad n^2 \leqq a \cdot (b + 1).$$

PROOF: Let $a, b \in I$ and

(1) $$4 \cdot b \leqq a.$$

Define

$$J \equiv [k \in I;\ k^2 < a \cdot b].$$

Now $k \in I$ implies $k \leqq k^2 \leqq a \cdot b$, whence $J \subset I_{a \cdot b}$. Moreover, $J \neq \Theta$, since $1 \in J$ by virtue of the fact that $a \cdot b = 1$ contradicts (1). Thus, by (9.3.7), there is a greatest element m in J, whence

(2) $$m^2 < a \cdot b,$$

and

(3) $$a \cdot b \leqq (m + 1)^2.$$

From (2), we have

(4) $$4 \cdot m^2 < 4 \cdot a \cdot b.$$

But, by (1),

(5) $$4 \cdot a \cdot b \leqq a^2.$$

By (4) and (5),

(6) $$4 \cdot m^2 < a^2.$$

We now establish indirectly that $2 \cdot m < a$. Assume $a \leqq 2 \cdot m$. Then $a^2 \leqq 2 \cdot m \cdot a \leqq (2 \cdot m) \cdot (2 \cdot m) = 2^2 \cdot m^2 = 4 \cdot m^2$, whence $a^2 \leqq 4 \cdot m^2$, contrary to (6). Thus

$$(7) \qquad 2 \cdot m < a.$$

By (2) and (7),

$$m^2 + 2 \cdot m < m^2 + a, \quad m^2 + a < a \cdot b + a,$$

whence

$$m^2 + 2 \cdot m < a \cdot (b + 1).$$

By (9.2.10.b),

$$(8) \qquad m^2 + 2 \cdot m + 1 \leqq a \cdot (b + 1).$$

It will be shown that $m^2 + 2 \cdot m + 1 = (m + 1)^2$ [see Project (8.7.7.c)]. Indeed,

$$\begin{aligned} (m + 1)^2 &= (m + 1) \cdot (m + 1) \\ &= m \cdot (m + 1) + 1 \cdot (m + 1) \\ &= m^2 + m + m + 1 \\ &= m^2 + (1 + 1) \cdot m + 1 \\ &= m^2 + 2 \cdot m + 1. \end{aligned}$$

Hence, by (8),

$$(9) \qquad (m + 1)^2 \leqq a \cdot (b + 1).$$

From (3) and (9), it is seen that the requirements of (17.3.1) are satisfied by $n \equiv m + 1$. The proof is complete.

(17.3.2) LEMMA: *Suppose* $(\boldsymbol{F}, \boldsymbol{u}, <, +, \cdot)$ *is an algebraic system of positive rational numbers. Let* $f_1, f_2 \in \boldsymbol{F}$ *such that* $f_1 < f_2$. *Then there exists* $x \in \boldsymbol{F}$ *such that*

$$f_1 < x^2 \quad \textit{and} \quad x^2 < f_2.$$

PROOF: First, by (16.8.2), there exist $g_1, g_2 \in \boldsymbol{F}$ such that

$$(1) \qquad f_1 < g_1, \quad g_1 < g_2, \quad g_2 < f_2.$$

By (16.4.3), there exist $p_1, q_1, p_2, q_2 \in \boldsymbol{I}$ such that

$$g_1 = \frac{p_1}{q_1}, \quad g_2 = \frac{p_2}{q_2}.$$

Since $g_1 < g_2$, it follows that

$$p_1 \cdot q_2 < q_1 \cdot p_2,$$

whence, by (9.2.10.b),

$$(2) \qquad p_1 \cdot q_2 + 1 \leqq q_1 \cdot p_2.$$

By (16.4.5),

(3) $$g_1 = \frac{4 \cdot p_1^2 \cdot q_1 \cdot q_2 \cdot (p_1 \cdot q_2)}{4 \cdot p_1^2 \cdot q_1^2 \cdot q_2^2},$$

and

(4) $$g_2 = \frac{4 \cdot p_1^2 \cdot q_1 \cdot q_2 \cdot (q_1 \cdot p_2)}{4 \cdot p_1^2 \cdot q_1^2 \cdot q_2^2}.$$

If we define

$$a \equiv 4 \cdot p_1^2 \cdot q_1 \cdot q_2, \quad b \equiv p_1 \cdot q_2,$$

we have $a, b \in I$, and

$$4 \cdot b = 4 \cdot p_1 \cdot q_2 \leqq 4 \cdot p_1 \cdot q_2 \cdot (p_1 \cdot q_1) = a.$$

By (17.3.1), there exists $n \in I$ such that

(5) $$4 \cdot p_1^2 \cdot q_1 \cdot q_2 \cdot (p_1 \cdot q_2) = a \cdot b \leqq n^2,$$

and

(6) $$n^2 \leqq a \cdot (b + 1) = 4 \cdot p_1^2 \cdot q_1 \cdot q_2 \cdot (p_1 \cdot q_2 + 1).$$

From (6) and (2), we have

(7) $$n^2 \leqq 4 \cdot p_1^2 \cdot q_1 \cdot q_2 \cdot (q_1 \cdot p_2).$$

Define

$$x \equiv \frac{n}{2 \cdot p_1 \cdot q_1 \cdot q_2}.$$

Then

(8) $$x^2 = \frac{n^2}{4 \cdot p_1^2 \cdot q_1^2 \cdot q_2^2}.$$

Thus, by (3), (8), (5), (9.2.15) and (16.7.3),

$$g_1 \leqq x^2,$$

and, by (4), (8), (7), (9.2.15) and (16.7.3),

$$x^2 \leqq g_2.$$

It follows from (1) that

$$f_1 < x^2, \quad x^2 < f_2,$$

and the proof is complete.

(17.3.3) THEOREM: *Let* $(\boldsymbol{F}, \boldsymbol{u}, <, +, \cdot)$ *be an algebraic system of positive rational numbers. Then there exists a subset* S *of* $\boldsymbol{F}$ *such that* $S \neq \Theta$, S *is bounded above, and* S *has no least upper bound.*

PROOF: Define

$$S \equiv \left[x \in \boldsymbol{F};\, x^2 < \frac{2}{1}\right].$$

First, $S \neq \Theta$ since $\boldsymbol{u} = 1/1 \in S$. Also, S is bounded above; for example, $2/1$ is an upper bound of S. For if $y \in \boldsymbol{F}$ is such that $y > 2/1$, then

$y^2 > (2/1)^2 > 2/1$, and $y \epsilon' S$. It remains to be shown that S has no least upper bound. This is proved indirectly.

Suppose S has a least upper bound c. Then either $c^2 < 2/1$ or $c^2 > 2/1$ or $c^2 = 2/1$. These three cases are considered separately. Suppose first $c^2 < 2/1$. By (17.3.2), there exists $y \in F$ such that

$$c^2 < y^2 \quad \text{and} \quad y^2 < \frac{2}{1}.$$

Hence $y \in S$. But from $c^2 < y^2$ it follows that $c < y$. This contradicts the fact that c is an upper bound of S. Next, suppose $2/1 < c^2$. By (17.3.2), there exists $z \in F$ such that

$$\frac{2}{1} < z^2 < c^2.$$

Now, for every $x \in S$, we have $x^2 < 2/1$. Hence, from $2/1 < z^2$, it follows that $x^2 < z^2$ and $x < z$. Thus z is an upper bound of S. But $z < c$. This contradicts the fact that c is the *least* upper bound of S. Since $c^2 < 2/1$ and $2/1 < c^2$ lead to contradictions, we have shown that $c^2 = 2/1$. But this contradicts (16.6.7). This contradiction completes the proof.

(17.3.4) COROLLARY: *Let* $(F, u, <, +, \cdot)$ *be an algebraic system of positive rational numbers. Then* $(F, <)$ *is not a one-dimensional continuum.*

PROOF: Every one-dimensional continuum satisfies IV′. But $(F, <)$ does not satisfy IV′ by (17.3.3).

REMARK: It is easily seen that the set S defined in the proof of (17.3.3) is actually a lower set, so that (17.3.3) is a direct denial of IV for the system $(F, <)$.

The remainder of this chapter will be devoted to the study of one-dimensional continua. Since $(F, <)$ has been shown not to be a one-dimensional continuum, the question of consistency remains open, and this will be treated as usual before the study of consequences of Axioms I–IV.

17.4. Consistency of the Axioms. [NO BASIS.] The consistency of the axioms for a one-dimensional continuum is proved, as usual, by the construction of an instance. In this case, the set K in the instance will consist of certain subsets of a set of positive rational numbers, and the order relation will be defined by means of set-theoretic inclusion. Thus the question of consistency for one-dimensional continua is reduced to the question of consistency for positive rational numbers; this, in turn, has been reduced to the question of consistency for positive integers.

In short, if one "believes in" the positive integers, one should "believe in" one-dimensional continua also.

In the remainder of this section, $(F, u, <, +, \cdot)$ is an algebraic system of positive rational numbers. Then the subsets of F that will constitute the elements of our set K are those indicated by the following definition.

(17.4.1) DEFINITION: A subset J of F is called a *lower cut* if

(a) $J \neq \Theta$;
(b) J is a lower set;
(c) J is bounded above;
(d) J has no greatest element.

The set K is defined by

$$K \equiv [J \subset F;\ J \text{ is a lower cut}].$$

(17.4.2) DEFINITION: A relation $<$ on $K \times K$ is defined by

$$< \ \equiv [(J_1, J_2) \in K \times K;\ J_1 \subsetneqq J_2].$$

Thus $J_1 < J_2$ if and only if $J_1 \subset J_2$ and $J_1 \neq J_2$.

It will now be shown, with the help of several lemmas, that $(K, <)$ as defined in (17.4.1), (17.4.2) is a one-dimensional continuum.

(17.4.3) LEMMA: *If J is an open initial half-interval in F, then J is a lower cut, and $J \in K$.*

PROOF: By (17.2.1.d), there exists $b \in F$ such that

$$J = [x \in F;\ x < b].$$

Then, by (16.8.1), $J \neq \Theta$. By (17.2.3), J is a lower set. Clearly J is bounded above, since b is an upper bound of J. Finally, suppose J has a greatest element c. Then, since $c \in J$, $c < b$. Then, by (16.8.2), there exists $x \in F$ such that $c < x$ and $x < b$. Since $x < b$, $x \in J$. But then $c < x$ contradicts the fact that c is a greatest element in J. This contradiction shows that J has no greatest element. We have established the four conditions (a), (b), (c), (d) of (17.4.1), and the proof is complete.

(17.4.4) COROLLARY: *There exist $J_1, J_2 \in K$ such that $J_1 \neq J_2$.*

PROOF: Define

$$J_1 \equiv \left[x \in F;\ x < \frac{1}{1}\right], \quad J_2 \equiv \left[x \in F;\ x < \frac{2}{1}\right].$$

Then, by (17.4.3), $J_1, J_2 \in K$. But $J_1 \neq J_2$ since $1/1 \notin J_1$, $1/1 \in J_2$.

(17.4.5) LEMMA: *The set K is linearly ordered by $<$.*

PROOF: It is easily shown that $<$ is irreflexive and transitive; the proof is left for the reader. Thus K is partially ordered by $<$. It remains to be shown that, if $J_1, J_2 \in K$, then

(1) $\qquad J_1 = J_2 \quad \text{or } J_1 < J_2 \quad \text{or } J_2 < J_1.$

Suppose the contrary, so that there exist J_1, J_2 such that $J_1 \not\subset J_2$, $J_2 \not\subset J_1$. Since $J_1 \not\subset J_2$, there exists $x \in \boldsymbol{F}$ such that

$$(2) \qquad x \in J_1 \quad \text{and} \quad x \in' J_2.$$

Since $x \in' J_2$,

$$(3) \qquad \text{for every } y \in J_2,\ y \leqq x;$$

for otherwise there would exist $y \in J_2$ with $x < y$, whence $x \in J_2$ by (17.4.1.b), contrary to (2). But, since J_1 is a lower set, (2) and (3) show that $y \in J_2$ implies $y \in J_1$; thus $J_2 \subset J_1$. This contradicts $J_2 \not\subset J_1$. The proof is complete.

(17.4.6) Lemma: *For every J_1, $J_2 \in K$ with $J_1 < J_2$, there exists $J_3 \in K$ such that $J_1 < J_3$ and $J_3 < J_2$.*

Proof: Since $J_2 \not\subset J_1$, there exists $x \in J_2$ with $x \in' J_1$. But, by (17.4.1.d), J_2 has no greatest element; in particular, x is not a greatest. Therefore there exists $y \in J_2$ such that $x < y$. If $y \in J_1$, then, since J_1 is a lower set, $x \in J_1$, contrary to $x \in' J_1$. Thus $y \in' J_1$. Define

$$J_3 \equiv [z \in \boldsymbol{F};\ z < y],$$

so that $J_3 \in K$ by (17.4.3). It is now easily proved that $J_1 < J_3$ and $J_3 < J_2$; details are left to the reader.

(17.4.7) Lemma: *Let S be a non-empty subset of K which is bounded above. Then $\sum S \in K$, and $\sum S$ is a least upper bound of S.*

Proof: Define $J_0 \equiv \sum S$. We prove first that $J_0 \in K$, that is, that J_0 is a lower cut. Since $S \neq \Theta$, there exists $J \in S$. But $J \neq \Theta$ (since J is a lower cut), so that there exists an element $x \in J$. Then $x \in J_0$, and $J_0 \neq \Theta$; thus (17.4.1.a) is true for J_0. Now let $x \in J_0$, and let $y \in \boldsymbol{F}$ such that $y \leqq x$. Then there exists $J \in S$ such that $x \in J$. Hence, since J is a lower set, $y \in J$, whence also $y \in J_0$. This establishes (17.4.1.b). Now, since S is bounded above, there exists $J_1 \in K$ such that

$$J \in S \text{ implies } J \leqq J_1.$$

Thus $J_0 \subset J_1$. Since J_1 is bounded above, being a lower cut, there exists $f \in \boldsymbol{F}$ such that $w \in J_1$ implies $w \leqq f$. But then $w \in J_0$ implies $w \leqq f$, so that f is an upper bound of J_0. This establishes (17.4.1.c). Finally, (17.4.1.d) is proved indirectly. Suppose J_0 has a greatest element g. Then, since $g \in J_0$, there exists $J \in S$ with $g \in J$. But $z \in J_0$ implies $z \leqq g$; hence $z \in J$ implies $z \leqq g$. It follows that g is a greatest element of J, contrary to the fact that J satisfies (17.4.1.d). This completes the proof that $J_0 \in K$.

It remains to prove that J_0 is a least upper bound of S. Evidently

$$J \in S \text{ implies } J \leqq J_0,$$

so that J_0 is an upper bound. Suppose J_0' is another upper bound of S. Then

$$J \in S \text{ implies } J \subset J_0',$$

whence $J_0 \subset J_0'$. Hence $J_0 \leqq J_0'$, so that J_0 is a least upper bound of S.

(17.4.8) THEOREM: *The system* $(K, <)$ *defined in* (17.4.1), (17.4.2) *is a one-dimensional continuum.*

PROOF: Axioms I, II, III, IV are immediate from (17.4.4), (17.4.5), (17.4.6), (17.4.7), respectively.

The treatment of the question of consistency is complete. The question of categoricalness remains. The definition of isomorphism of one-dimensional continua is contained in (14.2.5); thus categoricalness is defined. Actually it is possible, though by no means easy, to construct non-isomorphic instances of one-dimensional continua, so that, in fact, the axioms are not categorical. However, this fact will not be demonstrated here and will not be required in subsequent developments.

We conclude this section with two results concerning isomorphism of partially ordered systems.

(17.4.9) THEOREM: *Let* $(L, <)$, $(L^\dagger, <^\dagger)$ *be isomorphic partially ordered systems, with* φ *an isomorphism between them. Let* $S \subset L$, *and let* $p \in L$ *be a least upper bound of* S. *Then* $\varphi(p) \in L^\dagger$ *is a least upper bound of* $\varphi(S) \subset L^\dagger$.

PROOF: Since $p = \text{l.u.b. } S$,

(1) $x \in S$ implies $x \leqq p$;

(2) if $q \in L$ such that $x \in S$ implies $x \leqq q$, then $p \leqq q$.

Let $y \in \varphi(S)$, so that there exists $x \in S$ with $y = \varphi(x)$. Hence, by (1), $x \leqq p$, so that

(3) $$y = \varphi(x) \leqq^\dagger \varphi(p)$$

[use (14.2.5), treating the cases $x = p$ and $x < p$ separately]. Let $r \in L^\dagger$ such that $y \in \varphi(S)$ implies $y \leqq^\dagger r$. Then $x \in S$ implies $\varphi(x) \leqq^\dagger r$, so that $x \leqq \varphi^*(r)$. By (2), $p \leqq \varphi^*(r)$, whence $\varphi(p) \leqq^\dagger r$. This together with (3) completes the proof that $\varphi(p)$ is a least upper bound of $\varphi(S)$.

(17.4.10) THEOREM: *Let* K_1, K_2 *be sets and let* $<_1$, $<_2$ *be relations on* $K_1 \times K_1$ *and on* $K_2 \times K_2$, *respectively. If* $(K_1, <_1)$ *is isomorphic to* $(K_2, <_2)$ *and if* $(K_1, <_1)$ *is a one-dimensional continuum, then* $(K_2, <_2)$ *is a one-dimensional continuum.*

PROOF: Let φ be a one-to-one correspondence between K_1, K_2 such that, if $a, b \in K_1$,

$$(1) \qquad a <_1 b \text{ if and only if } \varphi(a) <_2 \varphi(b).$$

It is to be shown that $(K_2, <_2)$ satisfies I, II, III, IV. Evidently, if $a, b \in K_1$, $a \neq b$, then $\varphi(a) \neq \varphi(b)$, whence $(K_2, <_2)$ satisfies I. If there exists $c \in K_2$, with $c <_2 c$, then $\varphi^*(c) <_1 \varphi^*(c)$ by (1), contrary to the irreflexive property of $<_1$; thus II(a) holds. Similarly II(b) and II(c) are proved. If $c, d \in K_2$ with $c <_2 d$, then $\varphi^*(c) <_1 \varphi^*(d)$ by (1), whence there exists $x \in K_1$ with $\varphi^*(c) <_1 x$, $x <_1 \varphi^*(d)$. Hence, by (1), $c <_2 \varphi(x)$, $\varphi(x) <_2 d$. This proves III. Now, by virtue of the fact that $(K_2, <_2)$ satisfies II, the hypotheses of (17.4.9) hold for $(K_1, <_1)$, $(K_2, <_2)$. If $T \subset K_2$, $T \neq \Theta$, then $S \equiv \varphi^*(T) \subset K_1$, $S \neq \Theta$, and $\varphi(S) = T$. If T is bounded above by q, then S is bounded above by $\varphi^*(q)$. But then S has a least upper bound p, by IV applied to $(K_1, <_1)$, so that, by (17.4.9), $\varphi(p)$ is a least upper bound of T. This establishes IV for $(K_2, <_2)$ and completes the proof.

(17.4.11) PROJECT: In the proof of (17.4.5), show that $<$ is irreflexive and transitive.

(17.4.12) PROJECT: Complete the proof of (17.4.6).

17.5. Properties of One-Dimensional Continua. [BASIS: $(K, <)$; AXIOMS: I, II, III, IV.] In this section there will be derived a few of the consequences of Axioms I–IV. It is emphasized that $(K, <)$ is *any* system satisfying Axioms I–IV and no use is made of material pertaining to the specific instance defined in (17.4).

The first theorem removes an apparent lack of symmetry in the statements of IV and IV′ by showing that the assertion obtained from IV′ by replacing $<$ by $>$ is a consequence of Axioms I–IV.

(17.5.1) THEOREM: *Every non-empty subset of K which is bounded below has a greatest lower bound.*

PROOF: Let $S \subset K$ be bounded below and $S \neq \Theta$. Define

$$T \equiv [k \in K; k \text{ is a lower bound of } S] \subset K.$$

Then T is bounded above; for example, any element of S (existent since $S \neq \Theta$) is an upper bound of T. Also, $T \neq \Theta$ since S is bounded below. Hence, by IV′, T has a least upper bound $g \in K$. Then it is easily shown that g is a greatest lower bound of S; details are left for the reader.

It is easily seen that (17.5.1) could have been used to replace IV as an axiom for a one-dimensional continuum. To facilitate formulation of the next theorem, we first give a definition.

(17.5.2) DEFINITION: Let $(C_n; n \in I)$ be a sequence of closed intervals in K. Then $(C_n; n \in I)$ is called a *nested* sequence if, for every $n \in I$, $C_{n+1} \subset C_n$.

The appositeness of the word *nested* is clear but should not lead the reader astray. A closed interval of a nested sequence is not required to be "properly interior" to its "predecessor." All intervals might, for example, have a common endpoint. Or, since set-theoretic inclusion does not exclude equality, some or all intervals C_n might be the same.

The next theorem to be proved states that every nested sequence of closed intervals contains a common element ("point"). This theorem is a rather good indication that, intuitively, a one-dimensional continuum represents a "solid line." However the intuitive reasonableness of the theorem is somewhat misleading. For example, the untrained intuition usually fails to perceive that the theorem becomes false if restated for open rather than closed intervals. In many proofs, the use of this theorem is more convenient than use of Axiom IV.

(17.5.3) THEOREM: *Let $(C_n; n \in I)$ be a nested sequence of closed intervals. Then there exists $k \in K$ such that, for every $n \in I$, $k \in C_n$.*

PROOF: Let S be the set of all lower endpoints of intervals C_n, that is,

(1) $$S \equiv [p \in K;\ \text{there exist } q \in K,\ n \in I \text{ such that } C_n = [x \in K;\ p \leqq x,\ x \leqq q]].$$

Now S is bounded above; for example, the upper endpoint of C_1 is an upper bound of S. Since $S \neq \Theta$, IV′ yields that there exists a least upper bound k of S. It will be shown indirectly that, for every $n \in I$, $k \in C_n$. Suppose this statement is false, so that there exists $m \in I$ such that $k \in' C_m$. Let p^*, q^* be, respectively, the lower and upper endpoints of C_m. Since k is an upper bound of S, and $p^* \in S$, we have $p^* \leqq k$. If $k \leqq q^*$, then $k \in C_m$, contrary to $k \in' C_m$. Thus, $k \nleqq q^*$, whence, by II, $q^* < k$. Then, by III, there exists $h \in K$ such that

(2) $$q^* < h, \quad h < k.$$

Now it is easily shown from (2) and the definition of a nested sequence that h is an upper bound of S; details are left for the reader. Hence (2) contradicts the definition of k as a least upper bound of S. This completes the proof.

The use of (17.5.3) in proofs is illustrated by proving the very important result that K is infinite but not countable. First, a lemma is demonstrated. We shall call an interval *proper* if its endpoints are distinct.

(17.5.4) LEMMA: *Let C be a proper closed interval in K and let $k \in K$. Then there exists a proper closed interval $D \subset K$ such that $D \subset C$ and $k \in' D$.*

PROOF: Let p and q be respectively the lower and upper endpoints of C, so that $p < q$ and

$$C = [x \in K; p \leqq x, x \leqq q].$$

Now if $k \epsilon' C$ the conclusion of the lemma is true with $D = C$. Suppose $k \in C$, so that $p \leqq k$, $k \leqq q$. We consider the cases $p = k$, $p < k$ separately. If $p = k$, then $k < q$ since $p < q$. Then, by III, there exists $h \in K$ such that $k < h$, $h < q$. Define

$$D \equiv [x \in K; h \leqq x, x \leqq q].$$

Then D is proper and $D \subset C$, since $p = k < h < q$. Also $k \epsilon' D$ since $k < h$. Hence, if $p = k$, the conclusion of the lemma is true. Finally, suppose $p < k$. Then, by III, there exists $g \in K$ such that $p < g$, $g < k$. Define

$$D \equiv [x \in K; p \leqq x, x \leqq g].$$

Then again D is proper, $D \subset C$ and $k \epsilon' D$.

(17.5.5) THEOREM: *The set K is infinite but not countable.*

PROOF: The principle of choice is employed. It is first proved that K is infinite. By I, there exist a, $b \in K$ with $a \neq b$. By II(c), $a < b$ or $b < a$. We treat the case $a < b$ only, the treatment for the case $b < a$ being similar. Define

$$A \equiv [y \in K; a < y, y < b].$$

Then by III, $A \neq \Theta$; let x be any particular element of A. Define a relation R on $A \times A$ thus:

$$R \equiv [(y, z) \in A \times A; y < z].$$

Since $y \in A$ implies $y < b$, whence, by III, there exists z with $y < z$, $z < b$, it follows that $y \in A$ implies the existence of $z \in A$ such that $y \, R \, z$. Hence A = domain of R. By the principle (11.6.1) of general inductive definition, there exists a sequence α in A such that

(1) $\alpha(1) = x$;

(2) for every $n \in I$, $\alpha(n) \, R \, \alpha(n + 1)$.

But (2) yields

(3) for every $n \in I$, $\alpha(n) < \alpha(n + 1)$.

It may now be proved that

(4) $m, n \in I, m \neq n$ implies $\alpha(m) \neq \alpha(n)$;

details are left to the reader [use (3) and induction]. Now, by (4) and (10.2.2), α is a one-to-one correspondence between I and the set

$$B \equiv [\alpha(n); n \in I] \subset A \subset K.$$

If K is finite, then B is finite by (10.4.7); but then $I \sim B$ yields that I is finite by (10.4.4). This contradiction shows that K is infinite (since $K \neq \Theta$).

Now it is shown indirectly that K is not countable. If K is countable, then K is denumerably infinite, since K has been proved infinite. Now by (13.5.5) there exists a sequence $(k_n; n \in I)$ in K such that

$$[k_n; n \in I] = K.$$

Let $\mathcal{C}$ be the set of all proper closed intervals in K, so that $\mathcal{C} \neq \Theta$ by I. Define a sequence $(R_n; n \in I)$ of relations on $\mathcal{C} \times \mathcal{C}$ so that, for every $n \in I$,

(5) $$R_n = [(C, D) \in \mathcal{C} \times \mathcal{C}; D \subset C, k_n \in' D].$$

Now, by (17.5.4), for every $C \in \mathcal{C}$ there exists $D \in \mathcal{C}$ such that $C \, R_n \, D$; hence R_n has domain $\mathcal{C}$. Let C be any proper closed interval in K (any element of $\mathcal{C}$) and let $(C_n; n \in I)$ be a sequence of closed intervals defined inductively by C and $(R_n; n \in I)$ [see (11.6.2)]. Then $C_1 = C$ and, for every $n \in I$,

(6) $$C_n \, R_n \, C_{n+1}.$$

From (5) and (6), we have

(7) $$\text{for every } n \in I, \; C_{n+1} \subset C_n, \; k_n \in' C_{n+1}.$$

By (7), the sequence $(C_n; n \in I)$ is a nested sequence of closed intervals, whence, by (17.5.3), there exists $k \in K$ such that, for every $n \in I$, $k \in C_n$. But

$$k \in K = [k_n; n \in I],$$

whence there exists $m \in I$ such that $k = k_m$. Then, for every $n \in I$, $k_m \in C_n$; in particular, $k_m \in C_{m+1}$. But this contradicts (7). The proof is complete.

Theorem (17.5.5) provides the first demonstration of the existence of infinite non-countable sets. It should also be noticed that (17.5.5) provides an alternate proof of the corollary (17.3.4) stating that the system $(F, <)$ is not a one-dimensional continuum. For it was shown earlier, in (16.5.1), that F is countable, whence $(F, <)$ cannot be a one-dimensional continuum by (17.5.5).

(17.5.6) PROJECT: Complete the proof of (17.5.1).

(17.5.7) PROJECT: Complete the proof of (17.5.3).

(17.5.8) PROJECT: In the proof of (17.5.5), prove (4).

(17.5.9) Project: Prove that (17.5.1) may be used as an axiom to replace IV in the foundation of a one-dimensional continuum.

(17.5.10) Project: Let $(K, <)$ be the system defined in (17.4). Define a nested sequence of open intervals by the same condition as is employed for closed intervals. Prove the existence of a nested sequence $(C_n; n \in I)$ of non-empty open intervals such that no $J \in K$ exists with $J \in C_n$ for every $n \in I$.

Chapter 18

THE POSITIVE REAL NUMBERS

18.1. Axioms for the Positive Real Numbers. [No Basis.] The preceding chapter treated the problem of describing mathematically a measuring scale. But the treatment is still far from complete. For, even if it is agreed that the positive rational number system cannot serve the purpose of providing an adequate measuring scale, and if it is accepted that a satisfactory scale must have the property that every non-empty subset bounded above has a least upper bound, it does not follow that any one-dimensional continuum satisfies all the requirements on which one might wish to insist. Moreover, it is not at all clear how one might use a one-dimensional continuum for practical purposes involving measurement.

Now it is reasonable to expect that, in any mathematical system capable of serving as a measuring scale, operations analogous to $+$, $\cdot$, which appear in the theory of positive rational numbers, ought to be available. The need for something like $+$ is evident if one wishes to be able to measure the result of placing two measured segments end to end. The need for an analogue of $\cdot$, or at least of $\odot$, is clear from (16.2). Hence this chapter continues the task begun in the preceding, aiming, in particular, at the introduction of suitable operations.

Deeper analysis than we shall attempt to give shows that it would be erroneous to attempt to define operations like $+$, $\cdot$, within the theory of any one-dimensional continuum. In fact, it seems to be necessary to discard from further consideration most one-dimensional continua, and to limit discussion to certain ones having further properties. In other words, it will be necessary to restrict one-dimensional continua by imposing further basic material and axioms in order to obtain the desired measuring scale. Introduction of this further material is accomplished in a manner which parallels the approach to the positive rational number system [(16.2)].

The basis for our system, to be called a *basic system of positive real numbers*, is $(\mathcal{P}, \otimes, v, \odot)$, where $(\mathcal{P}, \otimes)$ is a one-dimensional continuum [(17.3)], $v \in \mathcal{P}$, and $\odot$ is an operation on $I \times \mathcal{P}$ to $\mathcal{P}$. Of course, the additional axioms cannot consist of those employed in (16.2) for the positive rational number system. For by (17.3.4) these axioms contradict those for a one-dimensional continuum, so that our totality of axioms would be inconsistent. We shall employ a much weakened form of (16.2.I) and slightly strengthened forms of (16.2.II) and (16.2.III).

The foundation of the theory of positive real numbers is as follows:

BASIS: $(\mathcal{P}, \otimes, v, \odot)$, where $\mathcal{P}$ is a set, $\otimes$ is a relation on $\mathcal{P} \times \mathcal{P}$, v is an element of $\mathcal{P}$, and $\odot$ is an operation on $I \times \mathcal{P}$ to $\mathcal{P}$.

AXIOMS:

I. $(\mathcal{P}, \otimes)$ is a one-dimensional continuum, that is,
  (a) there exist $a, b \in \mathcal{P}$ with $a \neq b$;
  (b) the set $\mathcal{P}$ is linearly ordered by $\otimes$;
  (c) for every $a, b \in \mathcal{P}$ such that $a \otimes b$, there exists $x \in \mathcal{P}$ such that $a \otimes x$ and $x \otimes b$;
  (d) every non-empty (lower) subset of $\mathcal{P}$ which is bounded above has a least upper bound.

II. (a) For every $a, b \in \mathcal{P}$ for which $a \otimes b$, there exist $x \in \mathcal{P}$ and $m, n \in I$ such that $a \otimes x$, $x \otimes b$, $m \odot x = n \odot v$;
  (b) for every $m \in I$ there exists $x \in \mathcal{P}$ such that $m \odot x = v$.

III. For every $m, n \in I$ and $a \in \mathcal{P}$, $m < n$ implies $m \odot a \otimes n \odot a$.

IV. For every $m \in I$ and $a, b \in \mathcal{P}$, $a \otimes b$ implies $m \odot a \otimes m \odot b$.

V. For every $m, n \in I$ and $a \in \mathcal{P}$, $m \odot (n \odot a) = (m \cdot n) \odot a$.

Any system $(\mathcal{P}, \otimes, v, \odot)$ satisfying Axioms I–V is called a *basic system of positive real numbers*. Elements of $\mathcal{P}$ are called *positive real numbers*.

The notations $\underline{\otimes}$ and $\oslash$ are used to designate $\otimes + E$ and the transpose of $\otimes$, respectively.

REMARK: The reader should note carefully the relation between these axioms and those in (16.2). In particular, II(a) should be compared with (16.2.I.a); instead of requiring $m \odot x = n \odot v$ for *every* $x \in \mathcal{P}$, we have required that, for every $a, b \in \mathcal{P}$ with $a \otimes b$, such an element x should exist "between" them. Also, it should be noted in what way III, IV strengthen (16.2.II), (16.2.III). Finally, it is seen that II(b) and V are identical respectively with (16.2.I.b) and (16.2.IV), aside from obvious differences in notation.

REMARK: It should be observed that I(a) is implied by II(b) in view of III and I(b). For in II(b) let $m = 1$ and $m = 2$, so that there exist $x_1, x_2 \in \mathcal{P}$ such that $1 \odot x_1 = v$, $2 \odot x_2 = v$. If $x_1 = x_2$, we have $1 \odot x_1 \otimes 2 \odot x_2$ by III, whence $v \otimes v$, contrary to I(b). Moreover, I(c) is an immediate consequence of II(a). Hence in the interest of independence of the axioms, we might have omitted I(a) and I(c) from the list.

18.2. Consistency of the Axioms. [No BASIS.] In order to establish consistency of our axioms, we shall, as usual, construct an instance.

The validity of the instance to be constructed will depend on the consistency of the axioms for the positive rational numbers; thus ultimately the consistency of the axioms for the positive integers is required. The situation here is similar to that described in (16.3) and so requires no further discussion. We shall employ the same instance as that introduced in (17.4.1), (17.4.2) to prove consistency of the axioms for a one-dimensional continuum; of course, v and $\odot$ must be suitably defined. Hence, for (18.2.1)–(18.2.9), $(\boldsymbol{F}, \boldsymbol{u}, \odot)$ is a basic system of positive rational numbers. Definitions leading to a full description of the instance will now be restated for reference.

(18.2.1) Definition: A *lower cut in* $\boldsymbol{F}$ is a subset J of $\boldsymbol{F}$ such that
(a) $J \neq \Theta$;
(b) J is a lower set, that is,

$$x \in J,\ y \in \boldsymbol{F},\ y < x \text{ implies } y \in J;$$

(c) J is bounded above;
(d) J has no greatest element.

(18.2.2) Definition: Denote by $\mathcal{P}$ the set of all lower cuts in $\boldsymbol{F}$.

(18.2.3) Definition: Define a relation $\otimes$ on $\mathcal{P} \times \mathcal{P}$ so that $J_1 \otimes J_2$ if and only if $J_1 \subsetneqq J_2$; thus,

$$\otimes \equiv [(J_1, J_2) \in \mathcal{P} \times \mathcal{P};\ J_1 \subsetneqq J_2].$$

(18.2.4) Lemma: *The set* $[f \in \boldsymbol{F}; f < \boldsymbol{u}]$ *is an element of* $\mathcal{P}$.
Proof: This follows from (17.4.3), which states that every open initial half-interval in $\boldsymbol{F}$ is a lower cut.

(18.2.5) Definition: Define $v \equiv [f \in \boldsymbol{F}; f < \boldsymbol{u}] \in \mathcal{P}$.

The next theorem paves the way for an appropriate definition of $\odot$.

(18.2.6) Theorem: *If* $J \in \mathcal{P}$ *and* $m \in I$, *and if*

$$\begin{aligned} K &\equiv [m \cdot h;\ h \in J] \\ &= \left[j \in \boldsymbol{F};\ \text{there exists } h \in J \text{ with } j = m \cdot h \left(= \frac{m}{1} \cdot h \right) \right], \end{aligned}$$

then $K \in \mathcal{P}$.

Proof: First, since $J \neq \Theta$, it follows that $K \neq \Theta$, since $h \in J$ yields $m \cdot h \in K$; thus (18.2.1.a) holds. To prove (18.2.1.c), we note that J has an upper bound f, whence $m \cdot f$ is an upper bound of K, in view of (16.7.6.g). We prove (18.2.1.d) indirectly. Suppose K has a greatest element j_0; since $j_0 \in K$, there exists $h_0 \in J$ with $j_0 = m \cdot h_0$. Now J has no greatest element, whence there exists $h \in J$ with $h > h_0$. Hence, by (16.7.6.g), $m \cdot h > m \cdot h_0 = j_0$. But $m \cdot h \in K$, contrary to the fact that

j_0 is a greatest element in K. Finally, let $j_1 \in K$, $j_2 \in F$, $j_2 < j_1$; it is to be proved that $j_2 \in K$. Now there exist $h \in J$ and $p, q, r, s \in I$ such that

$$j_1 = m \cdot h, \quad h = \frac{r}{s}, \quad j_2 = \frac{p}{q}.$$

Since $j_2 < j_1$,

$$\frac{p}{q} < \frac{m \cdot r}{s},$$

whence

$$p \cdot s < m \cdot q \cdot r,$$

so that

$$\frac{p}{q \cdot m} < \frac{r}{s} = h.$$

Define $h_1 \equiv p/(q \cdot m)$, whence $h_1 < h$. By (18.2.1.b) applied to J, $h_1 \in J$, whence $m \cdot h_1 \in K$. But

$$m \cdot h_1 = m \cdot \frac{p}{q \cdot m} = \frac{p \cdot m}{q \cdot m} = \frac{p}{q} = j_2.$$

Thus $j_2 \in K$, and the proof of (18.2.1.b) is complete. This establishes that $K \in \mathcal{P}$.

(18.2.7) Definition: Define an operation $\odot$ on $I \times \mathcal{P}$ to $\mathcal{P}$ so that, for every $(m, J) \in I \times \mathcal{P}$,

$$m \odot J = [m \cdot h; h \in J] \in \mathcal{P}.$$

The construction of a system $(\mathcal{P}, \otimes, v, \odot)$ is complete. It remains to prove that Axioms I–V are satisfied.

(18.2.8) Lemma: *If $J \in \mathcal{P}$ is an open initial half-interval with upper endpoint h, and if $m \in I$, then $m \odot J$ is an open initial half-interval with upper endpoint $m \cdot h$.*

Proof: Let

$$J = [j \in F; j < h],$$

and define

$$K \equiv [k \in F; k < m \cdot h].$$

It is to be proved that $m \odot J = K$. Clearly any element $m \cdot j$ of $m \odot J$, where $j \in J$, has the property

$$m \cdot j < m \cdot h$$

by (16.7.6.g), since $j < h$. Hence $m \odot J \subset K$. Now let $k \in K$, whence $k < m \cdot h$. If $k = p/q$, with $p, q \in I$, then define $j = p/(q \cdot m)$. Since $k < m \cdot h$, it follows easily that $j < h$, so that $j \in J$. Moreover,

$$m \cdot j = m \cdot \frac{p}{q \cdot m} = \frac{m \cdot p}{m \cdot q} = \frac{p}{q} = k,$$

and $k \in m \odot J$. This shows that $K \subset m \odot J$ and completes the proof.

(18.2.9) THEOREM: *The system* $(\mathcal{P}, \otimes, v, \odot)$ *is a basic system of positive real numbers.*

PROOF: By (17.4.8), $(\mathcal{P}, \otimes)$ is a one-dimensional continuum, whence I holds.

Let us prove II(a) next. Suppose $J_1, J_2 \in \mathcal{P}$ such that $J_1 \otimes J_2$. Since $J_1 \subset J_2$, $J_1 \neq J_2$, there exists $k \in \boldsymbol{F}$ such that $k \in J_2$, $k \in' J_1$. By (18.2.1.d), k is not a greatest element in J_2, whence there exists $h \in J_2$ such that $k < h$. Define

$$J_3 \equiv [f \in \boldsymbol{F}; f < h].$$

By (18.2.1.b), $J_3 \subset J_2$. Also $J_3 \neq J_2$ since $h \in J_2$, $h \in' J_3$. Thus $J_3 \otimes J_2$. Moreover, it is immediate that $J_1 \subset J_3$; also, $J_1 \neq J_3$ since $k \in J_3$, $k \in' J_1$. Hence $J_1 \otimes J_3$. Now, by (16.2.I.a), there exist $m, n \in \boldsymbol{I}$ such that

(1) $$m \cdot h = n \cdot \boldsymbol{u}.$$

But, by (18.2.8),

$$m \odot J_3 = [g \in \boldsymbol{F}; g < m \cdot h],$$
$$n \odot v = [g \in \boldsymbol{F}; g < n \cdot \boldsymbol{u}].$$

Hence, by (1),

$$m \odot J_3 = n \odot v,$$

and II(a) holds.

To prove II(b), let $m \in \boldsymbol{I}$. By (16.2.I.b) there exists $g \in \boldsymbol{F}$ with

$$m \cdot g = \boldsymbol{u}.$$

Define

$$J \equiv [f \in \boldsymbol{F}; f < g].$$

Then, by (18.2.8), $m \odot J$ is an open initial half-interval with upper endpoint $m \cdot g = \boldsymbol{u}$, that is,

$$m \odot J = [h \in \boldsymbol{F}; h < \boldsymbol{u}] = v.$$

The proof of III is somewhat more difficult. First we show that,

(2) if $m, n \in \boldsymbol{I}$ with $m \leqq n$, and if $J \in \mathcal{P}$, then $m \odot J \subset n \odot J$.

By (18.2.7),

$$m \odot J = [m \cdot h; h \in J];$$
$$n \odot J = [n \cdot h; h \in J].$$

Let $k \in m \odot J$, so that there exists $h_1 \in J$ with $k = m \cdot h_1$. Then $n \cdot h_1 \in n \odot J$. But $m \leqq n$ yields $k = m \cdot h_1 \leqq n \cdot h_1$. Since $n \odot J$ is a lower set, it follows that $k \in n \odot J$. This completes the proof of (2).

Next it is shown that,

(3) for every $m \in \boldsymbol{I}$, $m \odot J \neq (m + 1) \odot J$.

To this end, let $f_0 \in J$. Since $f_0 \in F$, there exist $k, l \in I$ such that $f_0 = k/l$. Define

$$(4) \qquad h \equiv k/(l \cdot (m + 1)),$$

so that

$$(5) \qquad (m + 1) \cdot h = f_0 \in J.$$

Now it is shown that

$$(6) \qquad [f + h; f \in J] \not\subset J.$$

For if (6) is false, then, for every $f \in J$, it is true that $f + h \in J$. From this it is easily shown, by induction, that for every $t \in I$, and every $f \in J$, $f + t \cdot h \in J$ (the proof of this is left for the reader). Now let a be an upper bound of (the lower set) J and let $p, q \in I$ such that $a = p/q$. Since $f + t \cdot h \in J$ for every $t \in I$, we have

$$(7) \qquad f + (p \cdot l \cdot (m + 1)) \cdot h \in J.$$

But from (4) and $a = p/q$ it follows that

$$(8) \qquad (p \cdot l \cdot (m + 1)) \cdot h \geqq a,$$

since

$$p \cdot l \cdot (m + 1) \cdot k \cdot q \geqq p \cdot l \cdot (m + 1).$$

By (8),

$$f + (p \cdot l \cdot (m + 1)) \cdot h > a,$$

so that (7) contradicts the fact that a is an upper bound of J. This contradiction establishes (6).

By (6) there exists $f_1 \in J$ such that $f_1 + h \in' J$. Since J is a lower set, $f_1 + h \in' J$ implies that $f_1 + h$ is an upper bound of J. In particular, since $f_0 \in J$,

$$f_0 < f_1 + h,$$

or, by (5),

$$(m + 1) \cdot h < f_1 + h,$$

whence

$$m \cdot h < f_1,$$

so that

$$(9) \quad m \cdot (f_1 + h) = m \cdot f_1 + m \cdot h < m \cdot f_1 + f_1 = (m + 1) \cdot f_1.$$

But, since $f_1 + h$ is an upper bound of J, it follows that $m \cdot (f_1 + h)$ is an upper bound of $m \odot J$, whence $m \cdot (f_1 + h) \in' m \odot J$. On the other hand, $f_1 \in J$, whence $(m + 1) \cdot f_1 \in (m + 1) \odot J$, and, by (9), $m \cdot (f_1 + h) \in (m + 1) \odot J$. This completes the proof of (3).

Now, to prove III, let $J \in \mathcal{P}$, and let $m, n \in I$ with $m < n$. Then, by (3), $m \odot J \neq (m + 1) \odot J$. But, by (2), $m \odot J \subset (m + 1) \odot J$. Hence $m \odot J \subsetneqq (m + 1) \odot J$. But from $m < n$ it follows that

$m + 1 \leqq n$, so that, by (2), $(m + 1) \odot J \subset n \odot J$. Hence $m \odot J \subsetneqq n \odot J$, or $m \odot J \circledless n \odot J$. This completes the proof of III.

The proofs of IV, V are quite easy and are left for the reader.

The proof of (18.2.9) is complete.

It is evident from (18.2.9) that Axioms I–V are consistent.

(18.2.10) PROJECT: Complete the proof of (18.2.9).

18.3. The Rational Positive Real Numbers. [BASIS: $(\mathcal{P}, \circledless, v, \odot)$; AXIOMS: I–V.] Before investigating the categoricalness of the axioms, we develop some of their consequences. No use is to be made of the material pertaining to the specific instance of the last section.

In the theory of positive rational numbers it was found possible to define a subsystem of an algebraic system of positive rational numbers which is an algebraic system of positive integers [see (16.9), (16.10)]. We prepare for a corresponding result in the theory of positive real numbers by showing first that there is a subset $\mathcal{F}$ of $\mathcal{P}$ such that $(\mathcal{F}, v, \odot)$ is a basic system of positive rational numbers. Here the use of the notation $(\mathcal{F}, v, \odot)$ is based on the suppositions that $v \in \mathcal{F}$ and that

$$m \in I, f \in \mathcal{F} \text{ implies } m \odot f \in \mathcal{F},$$

so that the "reduced" operation $(m \odot f; m \in I, f \in \mathcal{F})$ is on $I \times \mathcal{F}$ to $\mathcal{F}$. (This is similar to the requirement (14.5.2) in the discussion of subsystems.)

(18.3.1) THEOREM: *For every $a \in \mathcal{P}$, $1 \odot a = a$.*

PROOF: By V,

$$(1) \qquad 1 \odot (1 \odot a) = (1 \cdot 1) \odot a = 1 \odot a.$$

Now we have, by I(b),

$$(2) \qquad 1 \odot a \circledless a \quad \text{or} \quad a \circledless 1 \odot a \quad \text{or} \quad 1 \odot a = a.$$

If $1 \odot a \circledless a$, then, by IV,

$$1 \odot (1 \odot a) \circledless 1 \odot a,$$

contrary to (1). Hence $1 \odot a \circledless' a$. Similarly, $a \circledless' 1 \odot a$. Hence $1 \odot a = a$ by (2).

(18.3.2) DEFINITION: Define

$$\mathcal{F} \equiv [x \in \mathcal{P}; \text{there exist } m, n \in I \text{ such that } m \odot x = n \odot v].$$

Elements of $\mathcal{F}$ are called *rational positive real numbers*.

(18.3.3) THEOREM: *The system $(\mathcal{F}, v, \odot)$ is a basic system of positive rational numbers.*

PROOF: First $v \in \mathfrak{F}$, since $1 \odot v = 1 \odot v$. Next it is shown that

(1) $$m \in I,\ a \in \mathfrak{F} \text{ implies } m \odot a \in \mathfrak{F}.$$

Since $a \in \mathfrak{F}$, there exist $p, q \in I$ with

(2) $$p \odot a = q \odot v.$$

Hence

$$\begin{aligned} p \odot (m \odot a) &= (p \cdot m) \odot a && \text{[by V]} \\ &= (m \cdot p) \odot a \\ &= m \odot (p \odot a) && \text{[by V]} \\ &= m \odot (q \odot v) && \text{[by (2)]} \\ &= (m \cdot q) \odot v && \text{[by V]}, \end{aligned}$$

whence $m \odot a \in \mathfrak{F}$, and (1) is proved. Now Axioms (16.2.II) and (16.2.III) for $(\mathfrak{F}, v, \odot)$ follow from III and IV in view of I(b). Axiom (16.2.IV) holds by virtue of V. Axiom (16.2.I.a) holds by (18.3.2). To prove (16.2.I.b), let $m \in I$. By II(b), there exists $x \in \mathcal{P}$ such that $m \odot x = v$. But, by (18.3.1),

$$m \odot x = v = 1 \odot v,$$

whence $x \in \mathfrak{F}$. The proof is complete.

The reader should compare (18.3.3) with its analogue (16.9.3). In view of (18.3.3), $(\mathfrak{F}, v, \odot)$ is a system to which all the results of Chapter 16 pertaining to such systems apply. In particular, the notations $\frac{m}{n}$ (or m/n) (with $m, n \in I$) for all elements of $(\mathfrak{F}, v, \odot)$ may be employed, and the definitions and theorems of (16.4)–(16.10) may be used. Furthermore, there is an algebraic system $(\mathfrak{F}, v, <, +, \cdot)$ of positive rational numbers which possesses a subsystem $(\mathcal{I}, v, <, +, \cdot)$ which is an algebraic system of positive integers. Application of this result is now made.

(18.3.4) DEFINITION: Define

$$\mathcal{I} \equiv \left[x \in \mathfrak{F};\ \text{there exists } m \in \text{I with } x = \frac{m}{1} \right].$$

Elements of $\mathcal{I}$ are called *integral positive real numbers.*

(18.3.5) COROLLARY: $v = 1/1 \in \mathcal{I}$.
PROOF: This is immediate from (16.4.2) applied to $(\mathfrak{F}, v, \odot)$.

It is natural to ask what connection exists between the relation $<$ in $(\mathfrak{F}, v, <, +, \cdot)$ and the relation $\otimes$ in our basis; the next theorem answers this question.

(18.3.6) THEOREM: *If $x, y \in \mathfrak{F}$, then $x < y$ if and only if $x \circledless y$.*

PROOF: Since $x, y \in \mathfrak{F}$, there exist $m, n, p, q \in I$ such that

$$(1) \qquad m \odot x = n \odot v, \quad p \odot y = q \odot v,$$

or equivalently

$$x = \frac{n}{m}, \quad y = \frac{q}{p}.$$

Suppose $x < y$. Then $n \cdot p < m \cdot q$, so that, by III,

$$(2) \qquad (n \cdot p) \odot v \circledless (m \cdot q) \odot v.$$

But

$$\begin{aligned} (n \cdot p) \odot v &= p \odot (n \odot v) && [\text{by V}] \\ &= p \odot (m \odot x) && [\text{by (1)}] \\ &= (p \cdot m) \odot x && [\text{by V}], \end{aligned}$$

and, similarly,

$$(m \cdot q) \odot v = (p \cdot m) \odot y.$$

Hence (2) becomes

$$(3) \qquad (p \cdot m) \odot x \circledless (p \cdot m) \odot y.$$

Now if $x \circledless' y$, we have $y \circledless x$ or $y = x$ by I(b); if $y = x$, (3) is obviously contradicted, and, if $y \circledless x$, then, by IV,

$$(p \cdot m) \odot y \circledless (p \cdot m) \odot x,$$

contrary to (3). Therefore $x \circledless y$. Conversely, let $x \circledless y$. To prove $x < y$, suppose the contrary, whence $x = y$ or $y < x$ by (16.7.6.f). But $x = y$ contradicts $x \circledless y$ by I(b), and $y < x$ implies, by the proof just given, that $y \circledless x$, contrary to $x \circledless y$. Hence $x < y$.

REMARK: In view of (18.3.6), the notation $<$ may be used interchangeably with $\circledless$ for elements in $\mathfrak{F}$. In other words, when $x, y \in \mathfrak{F}$, so that $x = n/m$, $y = q/p$, the assertion $x \circledless y$ is equivalent to $n \cdot p < m \cdot q$.

(18.3.7) THEOREM: *Let $a, b \in \mathcal{P}$, $a \circledless b$. Then there exists $f \in \mathfrak{F}$ such that $a \circledless f$, $f \circledless b$.*

PROOF: This is a restatement of II(a), in view of the definition (18.3.2) of $\mathfrak{F}$.

(18.3.8) THEOREM: *Let $a \in \mathcal{P}$, and define*

$$S_a \equiv [x \in \mathfrak{F}; x \circledless a].$$

Then a is the least upper bound of S_a.

PROOF: Clearly a is an upper bound of S_a. Let b be any upper bound of S_a. It is to be shown that $a \circledleq b$. Assume the contrary, namely, by I(b), that $b \circledless a$. Then, by (18.3.7), there exists $f \in \mathfrak{F}$ such that

$b \circledless f, f \circledless a$. But $f \in S_a$, so that $f \circledleq b$, since b is an upper bound of S_a. But $f \circledleq b$ contradicts $b \circledless f$ by I(b), and the proof is complete.

(18.3.9) Lemma: *The set $\mathcal{P}$ has no upper bound and no lower bound.*

Proof: Suppose there exists an upper bound a. Then by (18.3.1), III,

(1) $$a = 1 \odot a \circledless 2 \odot a.$$

But $2 \odot a \circledleq a$, since a is an upper bound of $\mathcal{P}$, contrary to (1). Suppose there exists a lower bound b. Then by (18.3.1), III,

$$b = 1 \odot b \circledless 2 \odot b,$$

so that, by (18.3.7), there exists $f \in \mathfrak{F}$ with $b \circledless f, f \circledless 2 \odot b$. Let $f = m/n$ with $m, n \in I$. Then $m/(2 \cdot n) \in \mathfrak{F}$, and we have

(2) $$2 \odot \frac{m}{2 \cdot n} = 2 \cdot \frac{m}{2 \cdot n} = \frac{m}{n} = f \circledless 2 \odot b.$$

It follows from (2), IV, I(b) that

$$\frac{m}{2 \cdot n} \circledless b.$$

But this contradicts $b \circledleq m/(2 \cdot n)$, which holds since b is a lower bound. The proof is complete.

(18.3.10) Theorem: *Let $a \in \mathcal{P}$. Then there exist $f, g \in \mathfrak{F}$ such that $f \circledless a, a \circledless g$.*

Proof: Since a is not an upper bound of $\mathcal{P}$ by (18.3.9), there exists $b \in \mathcal{P}$ such that $a \circledless b$. By (18.3.7), there exists $g \in \mathfrak{F}$ such that $a \circledless g$, $g \circledless b$. The existence of f is similarly proved.

Remark: The results expressed in (18.3.7), (18.3.10) show how the elements of $\mathfrak{F}$ are "distributed" in $\mathcal{P}$. In terms of the measuring scale which we are trying to describe, they yield that every "point" (element of $\mathcal{P}$) has "rational points" (elements of $\mathfrak{F}$) as "near" to it as we please.

(18.3.11) Project: Let $a, b \in \mathcal{P}$ with $a \circledless b$. Prove that the set $[x \in \mathfrak{F}; a \circledless x, x \circledless b]$ is infinite.

18.4. Categoricalness of the Axioms. [No Basis.] In this section, isomorphism for basic systems of positive real numbers is defined, and it is shown that the axioms for positive real numbers are categorical. A preliminary theorem is first proved; for it and its corollary, $(\mathcal{P}, \circledless, v, \odot)$ is any basic system of positive real numbers.

(18.4.1) Theorem: *Let S be a lower cut in $\mathfrak{F}$. Then there exists a unique $a \in \mathcal{P}$ such that*

$$S = S_a \equiv [x \in \mathfrak{F}; x \circledless a].$$

Proof of Existence: Since S is a subset of $\mathcal{P}$ bounded above, it follows from I(d) that S has a least upper bound $a \in \mathcal{P}$. Hence $x \in S$ implies $x \leqq a$. Moreover, if there exists $x \in S$ such that $x = a$, then $a \in S$, whence a is a greatest element of S, contrary to the definition of lower cut [(18.2.1.d)]. Thus

$$x \in S \text{ implies } x < a,$$

whence, since $S \subset \mathfrak{F}$, $S \subset S_a$. Conversely, if $x \in S_a$, then $x \in \mathfrak{F}$, $x < a$. Suppose that $x \in' S$, and let $y \in S$. By I(b), $y = x$ or $x < y$ or $y < x$. But $y = x$ is impossible since $y \in S$, $x \in' S$. If $x < y$, then $x \in S$ by (18.2.1.b), contrary to $x \in' S$. Hence $y < x$. We have thus proved that

$$y \in S \text{ implies } y < x,$$

that is, x is an upper bound of S. But a is a least upper bound of S, whence $a \leqq x$, contrary to $x < a$. This contradiction shows that $x \in' S$ is impossible, so that $x \in S$, and we have established that

$$x \in S_a \text{ implies } x \in S,$$

that is, $S_a \subset S$. The proof is complete.

Proof of Uniqueness: Let $a, b \in \mathcal{P}$ such that $S = S_a$, $S = S_b$, whence $S_a = S_b$. If $a \neq b$, then $a < b$ or $b < a$ by I(b). If $a < b$, there exists $x \in \mathfrak{F}$ with $a < x$, $x < b$ by (18.3.7). Hence $x \in S_b$; but then $x \in S_a$ (since $S_a = S_b$), so that $x \leqq a$, contrary to $a < x$. Thus $a < b$ is impossible; similarly $b < a$ is impossible. This proves that $a \neq b$ cannot hold, so that $a = b$ follows, and the proof is complete.

(18.4.2) Corollary: *The domain of the function*

$$(S_a;\, a \in \mathcal{P})$$

is $\mathcal{P}$ and the range is the set of all lower cuts in $\mathfrak{F}$.

Proof: The first statement is obvious. The reader may easily verify that, if $a \in \mathcal{P}$, then S_a is a lower cut in $\mathfrak{F}$ (conditions (a), (b), (c), (d) of (18.2.1) are all easily proved). Hence the range is a subset of the set of all lower cuts in $\mathfrak{F}$. Finally, in view of (18.4.1), every lower cut is in the range.

(18.4.3) Definition: If $\mathcal{P}_1$, $\mathcal{P}_2$ are sets, if $<_1$, $<_2$ are relations on $\mathcal{P}_1 \times \mathcal{P}_1$ and on $\mathcal{P}_2 \times \mathcal{P}_2$, respectively, if $v_1 \in \mathcal{P}_1$, $v_2 \in \mathcal{P}_2$, and if $\odot_1$, $\odot_2$ are operations on $I \times \mathcal{P}_1$ to $\mathcal{P}_1$ and on $I \times \mathcal{P}_2$ to $\mathcal{P}_2$, respectively, then $(\mathcal{P}_1, <_1, v_1, \odot_1)$ is *isomorphic* to $(\mathcal{P}_2, <_2, v_2, \odot_2)$ if there exists a one-to-one correspondence φ between $\mathcal{P}_1$ and $\mathcal{P}_2$ such that

(a) if $a, b \in \mathcal{P}_1$, then $a <_1 b$ if and only if $\varphi(a) <_2 \varphi(b)$;

(b) $\varphi(v_1) = v_2$;

(c) for every $a \in \mathcal{P}_1$ and $m \in I$, $\varphi(m \odot_1 a) = m \odot_2 \varphi(a)$.

REMARK: The reader should state and prove the analogue here of (14.2.3).

For the purposes of the following theorem, $(\mathcal{P}, \otimes, v, \odot)$ is a basic system of positive real numbers; $(\mathfrak{F}, v, \odot)$ is the corresponding basic system of rational positive real numbers as defined in (18.3.2). Finally, $(\mathcal{P}^\dagger, \otimes^\dagger, v^\dagger, \odot^\dagger)$ is the basic system of positive real numbers defined in terms of $(\mathfrak{F}, v, \odot)$ [as in (18.2.2), (18.2.3), (18.2.5), (18.2.7)].

(18.4.4) THEOREM: *The system* $(\mathcal{P}, \otimes, v, \odot)$ *is isomorphic to the system* $(\mathcal{P}^\dagger, \otimes^\dagger, v^\dagger, \odot^\dagger)$.

PROOF: As in (18.4.1), define, for every $a \in \mathcal{P}$,

$$S_a \equiv [x \in \mathfrak{F};\, x \otimes a],$$

and define

$$\varphi \equiv (S_a;\, a \in \mathcal{P}).$$

Then φ is a function on $\mathcal{P}$ to $\mathcal{P}^\dagger$. By (18.4.2), the range of φ is $\mathcal{P}^\dagger$, in view of (18.2.2). We shall prove first that φ is a one-to-one correspondence between $\mathcal{P}$ and $\mathcal{P}^\dagger$. For this purpose, let $a, b \in \mathcal{P}$, $a \neq b$, with the aim of proving $\varphi(a) \neq \varphi(b)$, that is, $S_a \neq S_b$. Suppose $S_a = S_b$; by the uniqueness in (18.4.1), $a = b$, contrary to our assumption. This verifies the criterion (10.2.2.b). We turn now to the proof of conditions (a), (b), (c) of (18.4.3).

PROOF OF (a): Let $a, b \in \mathcal{P}$, $a \otimes b$. Then clearly

$$\varphi(a) = S_a \subset S_b = \varphi(b).$$

But, by (18.3.7), there exists $f \in \mathfrak{F}$ with $a \otimes f$, $f \otimes b$. Thus $f \in S_b$, $f \in' S_a$, and $S_a \neq S_b$. Hence $S_a \subsetneqq S_b$, so that

(1) $$a \otimes b \text{ implies } \varphi(a) \otimes^\dagger \varphi(b).$$

Conversely, if $\varphi(a) \otimes^\dagger \varphi(b)$, we have, by I(b), $a = b$ or $a \otimes b$ or $b \otimes a$. Obviously $a = b$ is impossible, and $b \otimes a$ cannot hold, since otherwise $\varphi(b) \otimes^\dagger \varphi(a)$ by (1) with a, b interchanged. Hence $a \otimes b$ follows, so that the converse of (1) is also true.

PROOF OF (b): Clearly

$$\varphi(v) = [x \in \mathfrak{F};\, x \otimes v] = v^\dagger$$

by (18.2.5) (note that the present symbols v, $v^\dagger$ replace $\mathbf{u}$, v in (18.2)).

PROOF OF (c): Let $a \in \mathcal{P}$, $m \in I$. It is to be proved that

(2) $$\varphi(m \odot a) = m \odot^\dagger \varphi(a).$$

Let $x \in \varphi(m \odot a)$, so that

(3) $$x \in \mathfrak{F}, \quad x \otimes m \odot a.$$

Since $x \in \mathcal{F}$, there exist $p, q \in I$ with $x = p/q$. Define $y \equiv p/(q \cdot m) \in \mathcal{F}$, whence

(4)
$$m \odot y = m \cdot \frac{p}{q \cdot m} = \frac{p}{q} = x.$$

It is now proved that $y \olessthan a$. If $y = a$, then

$$x = m \odot y = m \odot a,$$

contrary to (3). If $a \olessthan y$, then, by IV,

$$m \odot a \olessthan m \odot y = x,$$

contrary to (3). Hence, by I(b), $y \olessthan a$, and we have, by (4),

$$x \in [m \odot y; y \in S_a] = m \odot^{\dagger} \varphi(a),$$

the last equality holding by (18.2.7). Therefore

(5)
$$\varphi(m \odot a) \subset m \odot^{\dagger} \varphi(a).$$

Conversely, let $x \in m \odot^{\dagger} \varphi(a)$, so that there exists $y \in \mathcal{F}$ with

$$y \olessthan a, \quad x = m \odot y.$$

Then, by IV,

$$x = m \odot y \olessthan m \odot a,$$

and $x \in \varphi(m \odot a)$. This proves

(6)
$$m \odot^{\dagger} \varphi(a) \subset \varphi(m \odot a).$$

Now (2) follows from (5) and (6).

(18.4.5) THEOREM: *If* $(\mathcal{P}_1, \olessthan_1, v_1, \odot_1)$, $(\mathcal{P}_2, \olessthan_2, v_2, \odot_2)$ *are basic systems of positive real numbers, then* $(\mathcal{P}_1, \olessthan_1, v_1, \odot_1)$ *is isomorphic to* $(\mathcal{P}_2, \olessthan_2, v_2, \odot_2)$.

PROOF: Let $(\mathcal{F}_1, v_1, \odot_1)$, $(\mathcal{F}_2, v_2, \odot_2)$ be the corresponding basic systems of rational positive real numbers as defined in (18.3.2), and let $(\mathcal{P}_1^{\dagger}, \olessthan_1^{\dagger}, v_1^{\dagger}, \odot_1^{\dagger})$, $(\mathcal{P}_2^{\dagger}, \olessthan_2^{\dagger}, v_2^{\dagger}, \odot_2^{\dagger})$ be the corresponding systems of positive real numbers as defined in (18.2). (This notation is parallel to that used in (18.4.4).) By (18.4.4),

(1) $(\mathcal{P}_1, \olessthan_1, v_1, \odot_1)$ is isomorphic to $(\mathcal{P}_1^{\dagger}, \olessthan_1^{\dagger}, v_1^{\dagger}, \odot_1^{\dagger})$,
(2) $(\mathcal{P}_2, \olessthan_2, v_2, \odot_2)$ is isomorphic to $(\mathcal{P}_2^{\dagger}, \olessthan_2^{\dagger}, v_2^{\dagger}, \odot_2^{\dagger})$.

By (16.4.9),

$$(\mathcal{F}_1, v_1, \odot_1) \text{ is isomorphic to } (\mathcal{F}_2, v_2, \odot_2),$$

so that, by (16.4.7), there exists a one-to-one correspondence φ between $\mathcal{F}_1$ and $\mathcal{F}_2$ such that

$$\varphi(v_1) = v_2;$$
$$f \in \mathcal{F}_1,\ m \in I \text{ implies } \varphi(m \odot_1 f) = m \odot_2 \varphi(f).$$

The remainder of the proof will be outlined, details being left to the reader. Define a function Φ with domain $\mathcal{P}_1^\dagger$ so that, for every $J_1 \in \mathcal{P}_1^\dagger$, that is, for every lower cut J_1 in $\mathfrak{F}_1$,

$$\Phi(J_1) = [\varphi(x_1);\, x_1 \in J_1].$$

Note first that the range of Φ is $\mathcal{P}_2^\dagger$. For let J_2 be any lower cut in $\mathfrak{F}_2$, and define

$$J_1 \equiv [\varphi^*(x_2);\, x_2 \in J_2];$$

it is easily verified that J_1 is a lower cut in $\mathfrak{F}_1$ and that $\Phi(J_1) = J_2$. One proves next that Φ satisfies the conditions (10.2.2.b), (18.4.3.a), (18.4.3.b), (18.4.3.c); it follows that

$$(\mathcal{P}_1^\dagger, \oslash_1^\dagger, v_1^\dagger, \odot_1^\dagger) \text{ is isomorphic to } (\mathcal{P}_2^\dagger, \oslash_2^\dagger, v_2^\dagger, \odot_2^\dagger).$$

From this, together with (1), (2), we obtain the desired result.

Categoricalness of the axioms is now established by virtue of (18.4.5). This section is concluded with another result concerning isomorphism of positive real number systems.

(18.4.6) THEOREM: *Let* $(\mathcal{P}_1, \oslash_1, v_1, \odot_1)$, $(\mathcal{P}_2, \oslash_2, v_2, \odot_2)$ *be basic systems of positive real numbers, with* φ *an isomorphism between them. Let* $(\mathfrak{F}_1, v_1, \odot_1)$, $(\mathfrak{F}_2, v_2, \odot_2)$ *be their respective basic systems of rational positive real numbers, and define*

$$\psi \equiv (\varphi(f);\, f \in \mathfrak{F}_1).$$

Then ψ *is an isomorphism between* $(\mathfrak{F}_1, v_1, \odot_1)$ *and* $(\mathfrak{F}_2, v_2, \odot_2)$.

PROOF: Since φ is an isomorphism between $(\mathcal{P}_1, \oslash_1, v_1, \odot_1)$ and $(\mathcal{P}_2, \oslash_2, v_2, \odot_2)$, it follows from (18.4.3) that φ is a one-to-one correspondence between $\mathcal{P}_1$ and $\mathcal{P}_2$, and that

(1) $\varphi(v_1) = v_2$;

(2) for every $m \in I$, $p \in \mathcal{P}_1$, $\varphi(m \odot_1 p) = m \odot_2 \varphi(p)$.

Now, if $f \in \mathfrak{F}_1$, it follows from (18.3.2) that there exist $m, n \in I$ such that

(3) $$m \odot_1 f = n \odot_1 v_1.$$

Thus

$$\begin{aligned} m \odot_2 \varphi(f) &= \varphi(m \odot_1 f) && \text{[by (2)]} \\ &= \varphi(n \odot_1 v_1) && \text{[by (3)]} \\ &= n \odot_2 \varphi(v_1) && \text{[by (2)]} \\ &= n \odot_2 v_2 && \text{[by (1)]}, \end{aligned}$$

and

(4) $$m \odot_2 \varphi(f) = n \odot_2 v_2.$$

By (4), (18.3.2), $\varphi(f) \in \mathfrak{F}_2$. This proves $\varphi(\mathfrak{F}_1) \subset \mathfrak{F}_2$. The reverse inclusion is easily proved; details are left to the reader. Hence $\varphi(\mathfrak{F}_1) = \mathfrak{F}_2$, so that, by (10.2.6), ψ is a one-to-one correspondence between $\mathfrak{F}_1$ and $\mathfrak{F}_2$. Moreover, (1), (2) yield (since $v_1 \in \mathfrak{F}_1$)

$$\psi(v_1) = v_2;$$
$$\text{for every } m \in I, f \in \mathfrak{F}_1, \psi(m \odot_1 f) = m \odot_2 \psi(f).$$

In view of (16.4.7), ψ is an isomorphism between $(\mathfrak{F}_1, v_1, \odot_1)$ and $(\mathfrak{F}_2, v_2, \odot_2)$.

(18.4.7) PROJECT: State and prove the analogue of (14.2.3) for isomorphism as defined in (18.4.3).

(18.4.8) PROJECT: Complete the proof of (18.4.5).

18.5. Operations for Positive Real Numbers. [BASIS: $(\mathcal{P}, \otimes, v, \odot)$; AXIOMS: I–V.] It was indicated in (18.1) that an essential part of the theory of positive real numbers would be the introduction and study of operations analogous to $+$, $\cdot$ already available for positive rational numbers. Now if $(\mathcal{P}, \otimes, v, \odot)$ is a basic system of positive real numbers, then $(\mathfrak{F}, v, \odot)$ is a basic system of positive rational numbers. Let $(\mathfrak{F}, v, <, +, \cdot)$ be the corresponding algebraic system of positive rational numbers; we shall in this section employ the operations $+$, $\cdot$ to obtain similar operations on $\mathcal{P} \times \mathcal{P}$ to $\mathcal{P}$.

(18.5.1) THEOREM: *Let $a, b \in \mathcal{P}$. Then there exist unique elements c, $d \in \mathcal{P}$ such that c is a least upper bound of the set*

$$S \equiv [f + g; f, g \in \mathfrak{F}, f \otimes a, g \otimes b],$$

and d is a least upper bound of the set

$$T \equiv [f \cdot g; f, g \in \mathfrak{F}, f \otimes a, g \otimes b].$$

PROOF: It suffices by I(d) to prove that the sets in question have upper bounds. (These sets are non-empty by (18.3.10).) By (18.3.10), there exist $h, k \in \mathfrak{F}$ such that $a \otimes h$, $b \otimes k$. Now let $x \in S$. Then there exist f, $g \in \mathfrak{F}$ with

$$f \otimes a, \quad g \otimes b, \quad x = f + g.$$

It follows that $f \otimes h$, $g \otimes k$ by I(b), whence $f < h$, $g < k$ by (18.3.6). Thus, by (16.7.6.d),

$$f + g < h + g < h + k,$$

so that $x = f + g < h + k$, whence $x \otimes h + k$. Thus $h + k$ is an upper bound of S. Similarly T is shown to have upper bound $h \cdot k$.

(18.5.2) DEFINITION: Define operations $\oplus$, $\otimes$ on $\mathcal{P} \times \mathcal{P}$ to $\mathcal{P}$ so that, for every $a, b \in \mathcal{P}$, $a \oplus b$ is the unique c of (18.5.1) and $a \otimes b$ is the unique d of (18.5.1).

REMARK: It follows [see the remark after (17.2.5)] from (18.5.2) that, for $a, b \in \mathcal{P}$,

$$a \oplus b = \text{l.u.b.}\,[f + g; f, g \in \mathfrak{F}, f \textcircled{<} a, g \textcircled{<} b],$$
$$a \otimes b = \text{l.u.b.}\,[f \cdot g; f, g \in \mathfrak{F}, f \textcircled{<} a, g \textcircled{<} b].$$

We now investigate properties of the operations $\oplus$, $\otimes$ on $\mathcal{P} \times \mathcal{P}$ to $\mathcal{P}$ and their connection with the operations $+$, $\cdot$ on $\mathfrak{F} \times \mathfrak{F}$ to $\mathfrak{F}$.

(18.5.3) LEMMA: *Let $f_1, f_2, f \in \mathfrak{F}$. Then,*
(a) *if $f < f_1 + f_2$, there exist $g_1, g_2 \in \mathfrak{F}$ such that $f = g_1 + g_2$, $g_1 < f_1$, $g_2 < f_2$;*
(b) *if $f < f_1 \cdot f_2$, there exist $h_1, h_2 \in \mathfrak{F}$ such that $f = h_1 \cdot h_2$, $h_1 < f_1$, $h_2 < f_2$.*

PROOF OF (a): Define z as the reciprocal of $f_1 + f_2$, that is, the inverse of $f_1 + f_2$ in the group $(\mathfrak{F}, \cdot)$ [see (16.6.5), (16.6.6)], so that $(f_1 + f_2) \cdot z = v$. Define

$$g_1 \equiv f_1 \cdot (z \cdot f), \quad g_2 \equiv f_2 \cdot (z \cdot f).$$

Hence

$$\begin{aligned} g_1 + g_2 &= (f_1 + f_2) \cdot (z \cdot f) && \text{[by (16.6.4.e)]} \\ &= ((f_1 + f_2) \cdot z) \cdot f && \text{[by (16.6.4.d)]} \\ &= v \cdot f = f && \text{[by (16.6.6)].} \end{aligned}$$

Moreover, since $f < f_1 + f_2$,

$$z \cdot f < z \cdot (f_1 + f_2) = v$$

by (16.7.6.g), whence, by (16.7.6.g),

$$g_1 = f_1 \cdot (z \cdot f) < f_1 \cdot v = f_1.$$

Hence $g_1 < f_1$; similarly $g_2 < f_2$. This completes the proof.

PROOF OF (b): Define z as the reciprocal of f_1, so that $z \cdot f_1 = v$. Since $f < f_1 \cdot f_2$,

(1) $$z \cdot f < z \cdot f_1 \cdot f_2 = v \cdot f_2 = f_2$$

by (16.7.6.g). By (1) and (18.3.7), there exists $h_2 \in \mathfrak{F}$ with

(2) $$z \cdot f < h_2, \quad h_2 < f_2.$$

Define w as the reciprocal of h_2, and define $h_1 \equiv f \cdot w$. Then

(3) $$h_1 \cdot h_2 = f \cdot w \cdot h_2 = f \cdot v = f.$$

It remains to prove $h_1 < f_1$. By (2), $z \cdot f < h_2$, whence

(4) $$f = v \cdot f = f_1 \cdot z \cdot f < f_1 \cdot h_2 \qquad \text{[by (16.7.6.g)].}$$

Thus, by (4), (16.7.6.g),

(5) $$h_1 = f \cdot w < f_1 \cdot h_2 \cdot w = f_1 \cdot v = f_1.$$

The proof is complete, in view of (2), (3), (5).

(18.5.4) THEOREM: *Let $f_1, f_2 \in \mathfrak{F}$. Then*

(a) $$f_1 \oplus f_2 = f_1 + f_2;$$
(b) $$f_1 \otimes f_2 = f_1 \cdot f_2.$$

PROOF OF (a): Define

$$S \equiv [x_1 + x_2;\ x_1,\ x_2 \in \mathfrak{F},\ x_1 < f_1,\ x_2 < f_2].$$

By (18.5.2), $f_1 \oplus f_2 =$ l.u.b. S. It will be shown that also $f_1 + f_2 =$ l.u.b. S. Let $y \in S$, whence there exist $x_1, x_2 \in \mathfrak{F}$ such that

$$y = x_1 + x_2, \quad x_1 < f_1, \quad x_2 < f_2.$$

Then, by (16.7.6.d),

$$y = x_1 + x_2 < x_1 + f_2 < f_1 + f_2,$$

and $f_1 + f_2$ is an upper bound of S. Now let $a \in \mathcal{P}$ be any upper bound of S; it is to be proved that $f_1 + f_2 \circledleq a$. Assuming the contrary, we have $a \circledless f_1 + f_2$, whence, by (18.3.7), there exists $f \in \mathfrak{F}$ such that

(1) $$a \circledless f, \quad f < f_1 + f_2.$$

Now (18.5.3.a) applies, yielding the existence of $g_1, g_2 \in \mathfrak{F}$ such that

$$f = g_1 + g_2, \quad g_1 < f_1, \quad g_2 < f_2.$$

Hence $f = g_1 + g_2 \in S$ so that $f \circledleq a$, inasmuch as a is an upper bound of S. This contradicts (1), and the proof that $f_1 + f_2 =$ l.u.b. S is complete. Hence $f_1 \oplus f_2 = f_1 + f_2$.

PROOF OF (b): This is similar to the proof of (a) and is left to the reader.

The connection between the basic operation $\odot$ and $\otimes$ may now be ascertained.

(18.5.5) THEOREM: *If $m \in I$, $a \in \mathcal{P}$, then*

$$m \odot a = \frac{m}{1} \otimes a.$$

PROOF: Define

$$S \equiv \left[x_1 \cdot x_2;\ x_1,\ x_2 \in \mathfrak{F},\ x_1 < \frac{m}{1},\ x_2 \circledless a\right].$$

It will be proved directly that $m \odot a =$ l.u.b. S. Let $y \in S$, so that there exist $x_1, x_2 \in \mathfrak{F}$ with

(1) $$y = x_1 \cdot x_2, \quad x_1 < \frac{m}{1}, \quad x_2 \circledless a.$$

Since $x_1 \in \mathfrak{F}$, there exist $p, q \in I$ such that $x_1 = p/q$. Then, by (1), $p/q < m/1$, whence

(2) $$p < q \cdot m.$$

By (2), III,

$$p \odot x_2 < (q \cdot m) \odot x_2.$$

Hence, by (1), IV, V,

(3) $$p \cdot x_2 = p \odot x_2 < (q \cdot m) \odot a = q \odot (m \odot a).$$

But (3) may be written

$$q \odot \left(\frac{p}{q} \cdot x_2\right) \circledless q \odot (m \odot a),$$

so that, in view of (1), IV, I(b),

$$y = x_1 \cdot x_2 = \frac{p}{q} \cdot x_2 \circledless m \odot a. \tag{4}$$

Now (4) yields that $m \odot a$ is an upper bound of S. It remains to show that if b is any upper bound of S, then $m \odot a \circleddash b$. Assuming the contrary, we have $b \circledless m \odot a$, so that there exists, by (18.3.7), $g \in \mathfrak{F}$ with

$$b \circledless g, \quad g \circledless m \odot a.$$

Moreover, by (18.3.7), there exists $f \in \mathfrak{F}$ such that $b \circledless f$, $f \circledless g$. Now define

$$f_1 \equiv \frac{m}{1}, \quad f_2 \equiv \frac{1}{m} \cdot g.$$

Then

$$f < g = \frac{m}{1} \cdot \frac{1}{m} \cdot g = f_1 \cdot f_2.$$

By (18.5.3.b), there exist $h_1, h_2 \in \mathfrak{F}$ such that

$$f = h_1 \cdot h_2, \quad h_1 < f_1, \quad h_2 < f_2.$$

Since $h_2 < f_2$, it follows that

$$m \odot h_2 = \frac{m}{1} \cdot h_2 < \frac{m}{1} \cdot f_2 = \frac{m}{1} \cdot \frac{1}{m} \cdot g = g.$$

From $m \odot h_2 \circledless g$ and $g \circledless m \odot a$ we conclude, by IV, that $h_2 \circledless a$. This, together with $h_1 \circledless f_1 = m/1$, yields that $f = h_1 \cdot h_2 \in S$. But b is an upper bound of S, so that $f \circleddash b$, contrary to $b \circledless f$. The proof is complete.

(18.5.6) THEOREM: *Let $a_1, a_2 \in \mathcal{P}$, $f \in \mathfrak{F}$. Then*
(a) *$f \circledless a_1 \oplus a_2$ if and only if there exist $g_1, g_2 \in \mathfrak{F}$ such that*

$$f = g_1 + g_2, \quad g_1 \circledless a_1, \quad g_2 \circledless a_2;$$

(b) *$f \circledless a_1 \otimes a_2$ if and only if there exist $h_1, h_2 \in \mathfrak{F}$ such that*

$$f = h_1 \cdot h_2, \quad h_1 \circledless a_1, \quad h_2 \circledless a_2.$$

PROOF OF (a): Define

$$S \equiv [x_1 + x_2;\ x_1, x_2 \in \mathfrak{F},\ x_1 \circledless a_1,\ x_2 \circledless a_2].$$

We are to prove that $f \circledless a_1 \oplus a_2$ if and only if $f \in S$. Suppose that $f \circledless a_1 \oplus a_2$. Now f is not an upper bound of S, since otherwise $a_1 \oplus a_2 = \text{l.u.b. } S \circleddash f$, contrary to the hypothesis. Hence there exists $y \in S$ such that $f < y$. But $y \in S$ means the existence of $f_1, f_2 \in \mathfrak{F}$ such that

$$y = f_1 + f_2, \quad f_1 \circledless a_1, \quad f_2 \circledless a_2.$$

Thus $f < f_1 + f_2$. By (18.5.3.a), there exist $g_1, g_2 \in \mathfrak{F}$ such that

$$f = g_1 + g_2, \quad g_1 < f_1, \quad g_2 < f_2.$$

From $g_1 \textcircled{$<$} f_1$, $f_1 \textcircled{$<$} a_1$, we obtain $g_1 \textcircled{$<$} a_1$; similarly $g_2 \textcircled{$<$} a_2$. Therefore $f \in S$.

Conversely, let $f \in S$. Then there exist $g_1, g_2 \in \mathfrak{F}$ such that

$$f = g_1 + g_2, \quad g_1 \textcircled{$<$} a_1, \quad g_2 \textcircled{$<$} a_2.$$

By (18.3.7), there exist $x_1, x_2 \in \mathfrak{F}$ such that

(1) $$g_1 \textcircled{$<$} x_1, \quad x_1 \textcircled{$<$} a_1, \quad g_2 \textcircled{$<$} x_2, \quad x_2 \textcircled{$<$} a_2.$$

Hence, by (1), (16.7.6.d),

(2) $$g_1 + g_2 < x_1 + x_2;$$

but $x_1 + x_2 \in S$ by (1), whence

(3) $$x_1 + x_2 \textcircled{$\le$} a_1 + a_2,$$

since $a_1 \oplus a_2 = \text{l.u.b. } S$. But (2) yields

(4) $$f \textcircled{$<$} x_1 + x_2;$$

and (3), (4) yield $f \textcircled{$<$} a_1 \oplus a_2$ by I(b).

Proof of (b): This is similar to the proof of (a) and is left to the reader.

We are now ready for the analogue of (16.6.4) for the present operations $\oplus$, $\otimes$, namely, the assertions of commutativity, associativity and distributivity.

(18.5.7) Theorem: *Let $a, b, c \in \mathcal{P}$. Then*

(a) $$a \oplus b = b \oplus a;$$
(b) $$(a \oplus b) \oplus c = a \oplus (b \oplus c);$$
(c) $$a \otimes b = b \otimes a;$$
(d) $$(a \otimes b) \otimes c = a \otimes (b \otimes c);$$
(e) $$a \otimes (b \oplus c) = (a \otimes b) \oplus (a \otimes c).$$

Proof: These are consequences of the definition (18.5.2) of $\oplus$, $\otimes$ together with (16.6.4) and (18.5.6). Proofs of (a), (b), (c), (d) are left to the reader; the proof of (e) which we now give, is typical of the arguments employed.

Define

$$S \equiv [x \cdot y;\ x, y \in \mathfrak{F},\ x \textcircled{$<$} a,\ y \textcircled{$<$} b \oplus c],$$
$$T \equiv [r + s;\ r, s \in \mathfrak{F},\ r \textcircled{$<$} a \otimes b,\ s \textcircled{$<$} a \otimes c],$$

whence

(1) $$a \otimes (b \oplus c) = \text{l.u.b. } S,$$
(2) $$(a \otimes b) \oplus (a \otimes c) = \text{l.u.b. } T.$$

It will be shown that $S = T$, so that the desired result will follow from (1) and (2). First let $z \in S$. Then there exist $x, y \in \mathfrak{F}$ with

(3) $$z = x \cdot y, \quad x \otimes a, \quad y \otimes b \oplus c.$$

By (18.5.6.a) applied to b, c, y (in place of a, b, f), there exist $f_1, f_2 \in \mathfrak{F}$ such that

(4) $$y = f_1 + f_2, \quad f_1 \otimes b, \quad f_2 \otimes c.$$

From (3), (4), we have

$$z = x \cdot y = x \cdot (f_1 + f_2) = x \cdot f_1 + x \cdot f_2$$

by (16.6.4.e). Define $r \equiv x \cdot f_1$, $s \equiv x \cdot f_2$, whence

(5) $$z = r + s.$$

Now by (18.5.6.b), (3), (4), $r \otimes a \otimes b$; similarly $s \otimes a \otimes c$. Hence, in view of (5), $z \in T$. This proves $S \subset T$.

Conversely, let $z \in T$, whence there exist $r, s \in \mathfrak{F}$ such that

(6) $$z = r + s, \quad r \otimes a \otimes b, \quad s \otimes a \otimes c.$$

Applying (18.5.6.b) to a, b, r and to a, c, s (in place of a, b, f) we obtain the existence of $x_1, f_1, x_2, f_2 \in \mathfrak{F}$ such that

(7) $$r = x_1 \cdot f_1, \quad s = x_2 \cdot f_2, \quad x_1, x_2 \otimes a, \quad f_1 \otimes b, \quad f_2 \otimes c.$$

By (6), (7),

(8) $$z = r + s = x_1 \cdot f_1 + x_2 \cdot f_2.$$

If $x_1 = x_2$, define $x \equiv x_1 = x_2$, $g_1 \equiv f_1$, $g_2 \equiv f_2$, whence, by (8), (16.6.4.e), (7),

(9) $$z = x \cdot (g_1 + g_2), \quad x \otimes a, \quad g_1 \otimes b, \quad g_2 \otimes c.$$

If $x_1 \otimes x_2$, define $x \equiv x_2$, let w be the reciprocal of x, and define $g_1 \equiv x_1 \cdot f_1 \cdot w$, $g_2 \equiv f_2$. Then

$$\begin{aligned} x \cdot (g_1 + g_2) &= x \cdot (x_1 \cdot f_1 \cdot w + f_2) \\ &= (x \cdot w) \cdot (x_1 \cdot f_1) + x_2 \cdot f_2 \\ &= v \cdot (x_1 \cdot f_1) + x_2 \cdot f_2 \\ &= x_1 \cdot f_1 + x_2 \cdot f_2 = z; \end{aligned}$$

moreover, $x \otimes a$, $g_2 \otimes c$ are obvious by (7), and $g_1 \otimes b$ follows since

$$g_1 \cdot x_2 = x_1 \cdot f_1 \cdot w \cdot x = x_1 \cdot f_1 < x_2 \cdot f_1 = f_1 \cdot x_2,$$

from which $g_1 \otimes f_1$ (we had $f_1 \otimes b$ by (7)). Hence again (9) holds. A similar argument establishes (9) in case $x_2 \otimes x_1$. Now, by (9), (18.5.6.a), it follows that

$$y \equiv g_1 + g_2 \otimes b \oplus c,$$

and, by (9), (18.5.6.b), it follows that $z = x \cdot y \in S$. The proof that $T \subset S$ is complete, whence also $S = T$, and the desired result follows.

Operations $\oplus$, $\otimes$ on $\mathcal{P} \times \mathcal{P}$ to $\mathcal{P}$ analogous to those introduced for previous number systems have now been defined. The system $(\mathcal{P}, v, \lessdot, \oplus, \otimes)$ is referred to as an *algebraic system of positive real numbers.* We conclude this section with a result on isomorphism of systems of positive real numbers.

(18.5.8) THEOREM: *Let* $(\mathcal{P}_1, \lessdot_1, v_1, \odot_1)$ *and* $(\mathcal{P}_2, \lessdot_2, v_2, \odot_2)$ *be basic systems of positive real numbers, and let* $(\mathcal{P}_1, v_1, \lessdot_1, \oplus_1, \otimes_1)$ *and* $(\mathcal{P}_2, v_2, \lessdot_2, \oplus_2, \otimes_2)$ *be the corresponding algebraic systems of positive real numbers. Let* φ *be an isomorphism between* $(\mathcal{P}_1, \lessdot_1, v_1, \odot_1)$ *and* $(\mathcal{P}_2, \lessdot_2, v_2, \odot_2)$. *Then* φ *is also an isomorphism between* $(\mathcal{P}_1, v_1, \lessdot_1, \oplus_1, \otimes_1)$ *and* $(\mathcal{P}_2, v_2, \lessdot_2, \oplus_2, \otimes_2)$.

PROOF: It is to be shown that, for every $r, s \in \mathcal{P}_1$,

$$(1) \qquad \varphi(r) \oplus_2 \varphi(s) = \varphi(r \oplus_1 s);$$
$$(2) \qquad \varphi(r) \otimes_2 \varphi(s) = \varphi(r \otimes_1 s).$$

We prove only (1); the proof of (2) is left for the reader. Let $(\mathfrak{F}_1, v_1, \odot_1)$ and $(\mathfrak{F}_2, v_2, \odot_2)$ be the respective basic systems of positive rational numbers. Then, by (18.4.6),

$$\psi \equiv (\varphi(f); f \in \mathfrak{F}_1)$$

is an isomorphism between $(\mathfrak{F}_1, v_1, \odot_1)$ and $(\mathfrak{F}_2, v_2, \odot_2)$. Furthermore, by (16.10.2), ψ is an isomorphism between the algebraic systems $(\mathfrak{F}_1, v_1, <_1, +_1, \times_1)$ and $(\mathfrak{F}_2, v_2, <_2, +_2, \times_2)$ of positive rational numbers corresponding to $(\mathfrak{F}_1, v_1, \odot_1)$ and $(\mathfrak{F}_2, v_2, \odot_2)$, respectively. Thus,

$$\text{for every } f, g \in \mathfrak{F}_1, \ \psi(f) +_2 \psi(g) = \psi(f +_1 g),$$

whence

$$(3) \qquad \text{for every } f, g \in \mathfrak{F}_1, \ \varphi(f) +_2 \varphi(g) = \varphi(f +_1 g).$$

Now let $r, s \in \mathcal{P}_1$, and define

$$(4) \qquad S \equiv [f +_1 g; f, g \in \mathfrak{F}_1, f \lessdot_1 r, g \lessdot_1 s],$$

so that

$$(5) \qquad r \oplus_1 s = \text{l.u.b. } S.$$

Then, by (4),

$$\varphi(S) = [\varphi(f +_1 g); f, g \in \mathfrak{F}_1, f \lessdot_1 r, g \lessdot_1 s].$$

But, by (3) and the fact that φ carries $\lessdot_1$ into $\lessdot_2$,

$$(6) \quad \varphi(S) = [\varphi(f) +_2 \varphi(g); f, g \in \mathfrak{F}_1, \varphi(f) \lessdot_2 \varphi(r), \varphi(g) \lessdot_2 \varphi(s)].$$

From (6) and the fact that ψ is a one-to-one correspondence between $\mathfrak{F}_1$ and $\mathfrak{F}_2$, it is easy to show that

(7) $$\varphi(S) = [p +_2 q;\ p, q \in \mathfrak{F}_2,\ p \oslash_2 \varphi(r),\ q \oslash_2 \varphi(s)];$$

details are left for the reader. By (7),

(8) $$\varphi(r) \oplus_2 \varphi(s) = \text{l.u.b. } \varphi(S).$$

From (5), (8), (17.4.9), we have

$$\varphi(r \oplus_1 s) = \varphi(r) \oplus_2 \varphi(s),$$

and the proof of (1) is complete.

(18.5.9) PROJECT: Prove (18.5.4.b).

(18.5.10) PROJECT: Prove (18.5.6.b).

(18.5.11) PROJECT: Prove (18.5.7.a)–(18.5.7.d).

(18.5.12) PROJECT: Let $n \in I$, let $(b_m;\ m \in I_n)$ be an n-tuple in $\mathfrak{F}$, and let $a \in \mathfrak{F}$. Prove that

$$\sum_{m=1}^{n}(a \otimes b_m) = a \otimes \left(\sum_{m=1}^{n} b_m\right).$$

18.6. The Algebra of the Positive Real Numbers. [BASIS: $(\mathcal{P}, \oslash, v, \odot)$; AXIOMS: I–V.] This section is devoted to a continuation of the theory of (18.5), with particular emphasis on interconnections between the operations $\oplus$, $\otimes$ on $\mathcal{P} \times \mathcal{P}$ to $\mathcal{P}$ and the relation $\oslash$ on $\mathcal{P} \times \mathcal{P}$. We shall find further similarities between the algebraic system of positive real numbers and its algebraic system of positive rational numbers.

(18.6.1) LEMMA:

(a) *Let $a \in \mathcal{P}$, $f \in \mathfrak{F}$. Then there exists $g \in \mathfrak{F}$ such that $g \oslash a$, $a \oslash g + f$.*

(b) *Let $a \in \mathcal{P}$, $f \in \mathfrak{F}$, $v \oslash f$. Then there exists $g \in \mathfrak{F}$ such that $g \oslash a$, $a \oslash g \cdot f$.*

PROOF OF (a): By (18.3.10), there exists $h \in \mathfrak{F}$ such that $a \oslash h$. If $f = m/n$, $h = p/q$, we have

$$\frac{p}{1} \cdot \frac{n}{1} \cdot f = \frac{p}{1} \cdot \frac{n}{1} \cdot \frac{m}{n} = \frac{p}{q} \cdot \frac{q}{1} \cdot \frac{m}{1} = \frac{q}{1} \cdot \frac{m}{1} \cdot h \geqq h.$$

Hence

(1) $$\frac{p}{1} \cdot \frac{n}{1} \cdot f \oslash a.$$

Define

$$H \equiv \left[k \in I;\ \frac{k}{1} \cdot f \oslash a\right].$$

By (1), $H \neq \Theta$, so that H has a least element k_0 by (9.3.9). Clearly

(2) $$\frac{k_0}{1} \cdot f \oslash a.$$

Suppose first that $k_0 = 1$. Then, by (2), $a \otimes f$. By (18.3.10), there exists $g \in \mathfrak{F}$ such that $g \otimes a$. Moreover, $f < g + f$ by (16.7.5), whence from $a \otimes f$ it follows that $a \otimes g + f$, and the desired result is proved. Now suppose $k_0 > 1$. Define $p \equiv k_0 - 1$, so that $p \in' H$, and

(3) $$\frac{p}{1} \cdot f \circledleq a.$$

If $(p/1) \cdot f \otimes a$, define $g \equiv (p/1) \cdot f$. Then $g \otimes a$ is obvious, and

$$g + f = \frac{p}{1} \cdot f + \frac{1}{1} \cdot f = \frac{p+1}{1} \cdot f = \frac{k_0}{1} \cdot f \circledgt a,$$

so that the desired conclusion holds. In view of (3), it remains to consider only the case $(p/1) \cdot f = a$. In this case $a \in \mathfrak{F}$. Since $1 \in' H$, it follows that $(1/1) \cdot f \circledleq a$. Thus, by (16.7.6.g),

$$\frac{1}{2} \cdot f < \frac{1}{1} \cdot f = f \leqq a,$$

since evidently $1/2 < 1/1$. Hence $(1/2) \cdot f < a$, and, by (16.7.5), there exists $g \in \mathfrak{F}$ such that

$$\frac{1}{2} \cdot f + g = a.$$

It follows that $g < a$, and that

$$g + f = g + \frac{1}{2} \cdot f + \frac{1}{2} \cdot f = a + \frac{1}{2} \cdot f > a;$$

this establishes $g \otimes a$ and $a \otimes g + f$. The proof is complete.

PROOF OF (b): Since $f > v$, there exists, by (16.7.5), $h \in \mathfrak{F}$ such that

(1) $$f = v + h.$$

Also, by (18.3.10), there exists $k \in \mathfrak{F}$ such that

(2) $$k \otimes a.$$

By (18.6.1.a), applied with f replaced by $k \cdot h$, there exists $l \in \mathfrak{F}$ such that

(3) $$l \otimes a, \quad a \otimes l + (k \cdot h).$$

Suppose first that

(4) $$l \leqq k.$$

Then define $g \equiv k$. We have $g \otimes a$ by (2), and

$$\begin{aligned} g \cdot f &= k \cdot (v + h) && \text{[by (1)]} \\ &= k \cdot v + k \cdot h \\ &= k + (k \cdot h) \\ &\geqq l + (k \cdot h) && \text{[by (4), (16.7.6.d)]} \\ &\circledgt a && \text{[by (3)]}, \end{aligned}$$

whence $a \otimes g \cdot f$. It remains only to treat the case

(5) $$k < l.$$

Here define $g \equiv l$, so that $g \mathbin{\textcircled{<}} a$ by (3). Moreover,

$$\begin{aligned} g \cdot f &= l \cdot (v + h) && \text{[by (1)]} \\ &= l + (l \cdot h) \\ &> l + (k \cdot h) && \text{[by (5), (16.7.6.g), (16.7.6.d)]} \\ &\mathbin{\textcircled{>}} a && \text{[by (3)].} \end{aligned}$$

The proof is complete.

We turn now to the proof of an analogue of (18.5.6) in which $\textcircled{<}$ is replaced by $\textcircled{>}$. The converse parts are not proved here since they will be easy consequences of a later result (18.6.6).

(18.6.2) THEOREM: *Let $a_1, a_2 \in \mathcal{P}$, $f \in \mathfrak{F}$. Then,*
(a) *if $f \mathbin{\textcircled{>}} a_1 \oplus a_2$, there exist $g_1, g_2 \in \mathfrak{F}$ such that*

$$f = g_1 + g_2, \quad g_1 \mathbin{\textcircled{>}} a_1, \quad g_2 \mathbin{\textcircled{>}} a_2;$$

(b) *if $f \mathbin{\textcircled{>}} a_1 \otimes a_2$, there exist $h_1, h_2 \in \mathfrak{F}$ such that*

$$f = h_1 \cdot h_2, \quad h_1 \mathbin{\textcircled{>}} a_1, \quad h_2 \mathbin{\textcircled{>}} a_2.$$

PROOF OF (a): Since $a_1 \oplus a_2 \mathbin{\textcircled{<}} f$, there exists, by (18.3.7), $h \in \mathfrak{F}$ such that

(1) $$a_1 \oplus a_2 \mathbin{\textcircled{<}} h, \quad h \mathbin{\textcircled{<}} f.$$

Since $h < f$, there exists $g \in \mathfrak{F}$ such that

(2) $$h + g = f$$

by (16.7.5). We now apply (18.6.1.a) with a, f replaced first by a_1, $(1/2) \cdot g$ and then by a_2, $(1/2) \cdot g$. It follows that there exist $k_1, k_2 \in \mathfrak{F}$ such that

(3) $$k_1 \mathbin{\textcircled{<}} a_1, \quad a_1 \mathbin{\textcircled{<}} k_1 + \frac{1}{2} \cdot g,$$

(4) $$k_2 \mathbin{\textcircled{<}} a_2, \quad a_2 \mathbin{\textcircled{<}} k_2 + \frac{1}{2} \cdot g.$$

By the definition (18.5.2) of $a_1 \oplus a_2$, it follows that $k_1 + k_2 \mathbin{\textcircled{\leqq}} a_1 \oplus a_2$, whence, by (1), $k_1 + k_2 \mathbin{\textcircled{<}} h$. By (16.7.6.d), (2), it follows that

(5) $$k_1 + k_2 + g < h + g = f.$$

Now, by (5), (16.7.5), there exists $l \in \mathfrak{F}$ such that

(6) $$k_1 + k_2 + g + l = f.$$

Define

$$g_1 \equiv k_1 + \frac{1}{2} \cdot g + \frac{1}{2} \cdot l,$$

$$g_2 \equiv k_2 + \frac{1}{2} \cdot g + \frac{1}{2} \cdot l,$$

whence it follows from (6) that $g_1 + g_2 = f$. But, by (16.7.5), (3), (4),

$$g_1 > k_1 + \frac{1}{2} \cdot g \oslash a_1,$$

$$g_2 > k_2 + \frac{1}{2} \cdot g \oslash a_2,$$

whence $g_1 \oslash a_1$, $g_2 \oslash a_2$. This completes the proof.

PROOF OF (b): Since $a_1 \otimes a_2 \mathbin{⧀} f$, there exists, by (18.3.7), $h \in \mathfrak{F}$ such that

(1) $$a_1 \otimes a_2 \mathbin{⧀} h, \quad h \mathbin{⧀} f.$$

Now $(\mathfrak{F}, \cdot)$ is a group [by (16.6.5)], whence there exists $g \in \mathfrak{F}$ such that

(2) $$h \cdot g = f.$$

We have, by (1),

$$h \cdot v = h < f = h \cdot g,$$

so that, by (16.7.6.h), $v < g$. Now, by (17.3.2) there exists $k \in \mathfrak{F}$ such that

(3) $$v < k^2, \quad k^2 < g.$$

Since $v^2 = v < k^2$, it follows from (16.7.6) that $v < k$. Hence we may apply (18.6.1.b) with a, f replaced first by a_1, k and then by a_2, k, obtaining the existence of $k_1, k_2 \in \mathfrak{F}$ such that

(4) $$k_1 \mathbin{⧀} a_1, \quad a_1 \mathbin{⧀} k_1 \cdot k,$$

(5) $$k_2 \mathbin{⧀} a_2, \quad a_2 \mathbin{⧀} k_2 \cdot k.$$

By the definition (18.5.2) of $\otimes$, we have, since $k_1 \mathbin{⧀} a_1$, $k_2 \mathbin{⧀} a_2$,

$$k_1 \cdot k_2 \mathbin{\underline{⧀}} a_1 \otimes a_2.$$

Thus, by (1), $k_1 \cdot k_2 < h$. Moreover, by (3), (2),

$$k_1 \cdot k_2 \cdot k^2 < h \cdot k^2 < h \cdot g = f,$$

so that

(6) $$k_1 \cdot k_2 \cdot k^2 < f.$$

The elements in (6) are in $\mathfrak{F}$, whence, again by the group property of $(\mathfrak{F}, \cdot)$, there exists $g' \in \mathfrak{F}$ such that

(7) $$k_1 \cdot k_2 \cdot k^2 \cdot g' = f.$$

It follows that $g' > v$, since otherwise

$$f = k_1 \cdot k_2 \cdot k^2 \cdot g' \leqq k_1 \cdot k_2 \cdot k^2 \cdot v = k_1 \cdot k_2 \cdot k^2 < f \qquad \text{[by (6)]},$$

whence $f < f$, contrary to the irreflexive property of $<$.

Now define

$$h_1 \equiv k_1 \cdot k, \quad h_2 \equiv k_2 \cdot k \cdot g'.$$

Then

$$h_1 \cdot h_2 = k_1 \cdot k_2 \cdot k^2 \cdot g' = f \qquad \text{[by (7)]};$$

also $h_1 \circledgtr a_1$ by (4), and

$$h_2 = k_2 \cdot k \cdot g' > k_2 \cdot k \circledgtr a_2 \qquad \text{[by (5)]},$$

so that $h_2 \circledgtr a_2$. The proof is complete.

The next result states an important group property of the system $(\mathcal{P}, \otimes)$.

(18.6.3) THEOREM: *If $a, b \in \mathcal{P}$, then there exists $c \in \mathcal{P}$ such that $b = a \otimes c$.*

PROOF: Define

$$S \equiv [g \in \mathfrak{F}; \text{there exists } f \in \mathfrak{F} \text{ such that } a \circledless f, f \cdot g \circledless b].$$

It will first be shown that S is non-empty and bounded above. By (18.3.10), there exist $f, h \in \mathfrak{F}$ with $a \circledless f$, $h \circledless b$. By (16.6.5), there exists $g \in \mathfrak{F}$ such that $f \cdot g = h$. It follows that $g \in S$, whence $S \neq \Theta$. To prove that S has an upper bound, note first that there exist k_1, $k_2 \in \mathfrak{F}$ with $k_1 \circledless a$, $b \circledless k_2$ [by (18.3.10)]. By (16.6.5), there exists $k \in \mathfrak{F}$ with $k_1 \cdot k = k_2$. Suppose that k is not an upper bound of S, that is, that there exists $g \in S$ such that $g > k$. Since $g \in S$, there exists $f \in \mathfrak{F}$ such that

(1) $$f \circledgtr a, \quad f \cdot g \circledless b.$$

It is now shown that

(2) $$a \otimes k \;\underline{\circledless}\; f \cdot g.$$

Suppose the contrary, whence $f \cdot g \circledless a \otimes k$. By (18.5.6.b), there exist $h_1, h_2 \in \mathfrak{F}$ such that

$$f \cdot g = h_1 \cdot h_2, \quad h_1 \circledless a, \quad h_2 < k.$$

It follows that $f < h_1$ (assumption of the contrary leads to an immediate contradiction in view of $g > k$). But then, by the transitivity of $\circledless$, $f \circledless a$, contrary to (1). This contradiction proves (2). Similarly [with the help of (18.6.2.b)], it is shown that

(3) $$k_1 \cdot k \;\underline{\circledless}\; a \otimes k.$$

By (2), (3) and the transitivity of $\underline{\circledless}$,

$$f \cdot g \geqq k_1 \cdot k = k_2,$$

whence, since $k_2 \circledgtr b$, $f \cdot g \circledgtr b$, contrary to (1). This contradiction proves that k is an upper bound of S.

Now, since $S \neq \Theta$ and S is bounded above, S has a least upper bound $c \in \mathcal{P}$ by I. It is to be shown that $a \otimes c = b$. To this end, we first show that $a \otimes c \textcircled{\leqq} b$, and then that $a \otimes c \textcircled{<} b$ is impossible. Define

$$T \equiv [x \cdot y;\ x, y \in \mathfrak{F}, x \textcircled{<} a, y \textcircled{<} c].$$

By the definition (18.5.2) of $\otimes$,

$$(4) \qquad a \otimes c = \text{l.u.b. } T.$$

If it is shown that b is an upper bound of T, then it is clear that $a \otimes c \textcircled{\leqq} b$. Let $x, y \in \mathfrak{F}$, $x \textcircled{<} a$, $y \textcircled{<} c$. Since $c = \text{l.u.b. } S$, and $y \textcircled{<} c$, it follows that y is not an upper bound of S; hence there exists $z \in S$ such that $y \textcircled{<} z$. The property $z \in S$ implies the existence of $w \in \mathfrak{F}$ such that

$$(5) \qquad a \textcircled{<} w, \quad w \cdot z \textcircled{<} b.$$

By (5), since $x \textcircled{<} a$, we have $x < w$, whence

$$(6) \qquad x \cdot y < w \cdot z \textcircled{<} b.$$

From (6) we infer that every element of T is $\textcircled{<} b$, so that b is an upper bound of T. By (4),

$$(7) \qquad a \otimes c \textcircled{\leqq} b.$$

Suppose now that $a \otimes c \textcircled{<} b$. There exists $t \in \mathfrak{F}$ such that

$$a \otimes c \textcircled{<} t, \quad t \textcircled{<} b$$

by (18.3.7). By (18.6.2.b), there exist $r, s \in \mathfrak{F}$ such that

$$(8) \qquad t = r \cdot s, \quad r \textcircled{>} a, \quad s \textcircled{>} c.$$

But $a \textcircled{<} r$, $r \cdot s = t \textcircled{<} b$ yield $s \in S$. Since c is an upper bound of S, $s \textcircled{\leqq} c$, contrary to (8). This contradiction, with (7), establishes $a \otimes c = b$ and completes the proof.

The familiar connection [see (16.7.5)] between $\textcircled{<}$ and $\oplus$ is now to be established.

(18.6.4) THEOREM: *If $a, b \in \mathcal{P}$, then $a \textcircled{<} b$ if and only if there exists $c \in \mathcal{P}$ such that $b = a \oplus c$.*

PROOF: First suppose that there exists $c \in \mathcal{P}$ with $b = a \oplus c$. By (18.3.10), there exists $f \in \mathfrak{F}$ such that $f \textcircled{<} c$. Now, by (18.6.1.a), there exists $g \in \mathfrak{F}$ such that

$$g \textcircled{<} a, \quad a \textcircled{<} g + f.$$

But $g + f \textcircled{\leqq} a \oplus c$ by the definition (18.5.2) of $\oplus$. It follows that

$$a \textcircled{<} a \oplus c = b$$

by the transitivity of $\textcircled{<}$.

Conversely, suppose $a \textcircled{<} b$. Define

$$S \equiv [g \in \mathfrak{F};\ \text{there exists } f \in \mathfrak{F} \text{ such that } a \textcircled{<} f, f + g \textcircled{<} b].$$

The steps of the remainder of the proof are to show that S is non-empty and bounded above, to define $c \equiv \text{l.u.b. } S$ and to prove that $b = a \oplus c$. These steps are quite similar to the corresponding parts of the proof of (18.6.3), and details are left to the reader. Note that here (18.5.6.a) and (18.6.2.a) are used instead of (18.5.6.b) and (18.6.2.b), inasmuch as we are dealing here with $\oplus$ rather than $\otimes$.

An important corollary of (18.6.3) is the following.

(18.6.5) THEOREM: *The system* $(\mathcal{P}, \otimes)$ *is a commutative group; the element* v *is the identity of* $(\mathcal{P}, \otimes)$.

PROOF: The associative property of $\otimes$ has been proved [see (18.5.7.d)]. Commutativity was shown in (18.5.7.c). The other two group axioms are immediate from (18.6.3) and commutativity. To show that v is the identity of $(\mathcal{P}, \otimes)$ let $r \in \mathcal{P}$. Then, define

$$S \equiv [f \cdot g;\ f, g \in \mathfrak{F},\ f \varolessthan r,\ g \varolessthan v],$$

so that $r \otimes v = \text{l.u.b. } S$. It will be shown that also $r = \text{l.u.b. } S$. First, if $h \in S$, then there exist $f_1, g_1 \in \mathfrak{F}$ such that $h = f_1 \cdot g_1$, $f_1 \varolessthan r$, $g_1 < v$. Then $h < f_1 \cdot v = f_1 \varolessthan r$ by (16.7.6.g), whence r is an upper bound of S. Now let s be any upper bound of S, and suppose $s \varolessthan r$. By two applications of (18.3.7), there exist $f_2, f_3 \in \mathfrak{F}$ such that $s \varolessthan f_2, f_2 < f_3, f_3 \varolessthan r$. Since $(\mathfrak{F}, \cdot)$ is a group, there exists $g_2 \in \mathfrak{F}$ such that $g_2 \cdot f_3 = f_2$. But $g_2 < v$ (since otherwise $f_2 = g_2 \cdot f_3 \geqq v \cdot f_3 = f_3$). Since furthermore $f_3 \varolessthan r$, it follows that $f_3 \cdot g_2 \in S$. But $s \varolessthan f_2 = f_3 \cdot g_2$, which contradicts the fact that s is an upper bound of S. This shows that r is the least upper bound of S, and the proof is complete.

We are now ready to assert the various interconnections among $\oplus$, $\otimes$, $\varolessthan$ similar to those proved for positive rational numbers in (16.7.6).

(18.6.6) THEOREM: *Let* $a, b, c \in \mathcal{P}$. *Then*

(a) $a \varolessthan b$ *implies* $a \oplus c \varolessthan b \oplus c$;
(b) $a \oplus c \varolessthan b \oplus c$ *implies* $a \varolessthan b$;
(c) $a \varolessthan b$ *implies* $a \otimes c \varolessthan b \otimes c$;
(d) $a \otimes c \varolessthan b \otimes c$ *implies* $a \varolessthan b$.

PROOF OF (a): If $a \varolessthan b$, there exists $d \in \mathcal{P}$ such that $a \oplus d = b$ by (18.6.4). Hence

$$\begin{aligned}(a \oplus c) \oplus d &= (a \oplus d) \oplus c \\ &= b \oplus c,\end{aligned}$$

whence $a \oplus c \varolessthan b \oplus c$ by (18.6.4).

Proof of (b): Let $a \oplus c ⧀ b \oplus c$ and suppose that $a ⧀ b$ is false, so that $b \underline{⧀} a$. It follows from (a) (with a, b interchanged) that

$$c \oplus b \underline{⧀} c \oplus a,$$

contrary to the hypothesis. Hence $a ⧀ b$.

Proof of (c): If $a ⧀ b$, there exists $d \in \mathcal{P}$ such that $a \oplus d = b$. Hence

$$\begin{aligned}(a \otimes c) \oplus (d \otimes c) &= (a \oplus d) \otimes c \qquad \text{[by (18.5.7.e)]} \\ &= b \otimes c,\end{aligned}$$

and $a \otimes c ⧀ b \otimes c$ by (18.6.4).

Proof of (d): This is similar to the proof of (b) and is left to the reader.

Corollaries of (18.6.6) are the familiar "cancellation laws":

(18.6.7) Theorem: *Let a, b, $c \in \mathcal{P}$. Then*

(a) $a \oplus c = b \oplus c$ *implies* $a = b$;
(b) $a \otimes c = b \otimes c$ *implies* $a = b$.

Proof: This is immediate from (18.6.6.b) and (18.6.6.d) in view of the fact that ⧀ is a linear ordering of $\mathcal{P}$; the detailed proof is left to the reader.

(18.6.8) Project: Let a, b, c, $d \in \mathcal{P}$ with $a ⧀ b$, $c ⧀ d$. Prove that $a \oplus c ⧀ b \oplus d$ and $a \otimes c ⧀ b \otimes d$.

(18.6.9) Project: Prove that, if a, $b \in \mathcal{P}$, then $a ⧀ b$ if and only if $a^2 ⧀ b^2$.

(18.6.10) Project: For $a \in \mathcal{P}$, let a^{-1} denote the inverse of a in the group $(\mathcal{P}, \otimes)$. Prove that, if $a ⧀ v$, then $a^{-1} ⧁ v$, and that, if $a ⧁ v$, then $a^{-1} ⧀ v$.

(18.6.11) Project: Prove the following companion to (18.6.1.b): Let $a \in \mathcal{P}$, $f \in \mathfrak{F}$, $f ⧀ v$. Then there exists $g \in \mathfrak{F}$ such that $g \cdot f ⧀ a$, $a ⧀ g$.

(18.6.12) Project: Let $a \in \mathcal{P}$, $b \in \mathfrak{F}$ with $v ⧀ b$. Prove that there exists $n \in I$ such that $a ⧀ b^n$. (Here b^n is defined as in (12.4.1).)

(18.6.13) Project: Let $a \in \mathcal{P}$, $b \in \mathfrak{F}$, $b ⧀ v$. Prove that there exists $n \in I$ such that $b^n ⧀ a$.

18.7. Conclusion. [Basis: $(\mathcal{P}, ⧀, v, \odot)$; Axioms: I–V.] At this point it is well to examine to what extent a positive real number system accomplishes its objective, namely, to furnish a mathematical measuring scale.

First, it is clear that a positive real number system is at least as satisfactory a measuring device as a positive rational number system. For, according to (18.3.3), a positive rational number system exists within every positive real number system. Hence all the "positions" on the ruler (17.1.2) which are designated by elements of $\mathfrak{F}$ are also designated by certain elements of $\mathcal{P}$, namely, those in $\mathfrak{F}$. But $\mathcal{P}$ contains many elements not included in $\mathfrak{F}$, since $\mathcal{P}$ is not countable while $\mathfrak{F}$ is countable. (Elements of $\mathcal{P} - \mathfrak{F}$ are usually called *irrational numbers.*)

In order to be certain that the number scale is represented by $\mathcal{P}$, it would be necessary to prove that $(\mathcal{P}, \bigcirc\!\!\!\!<)$ is isomorphic to (measuring scale, "is to the left of"). Since this is evidently impossible, because of the intuitive character of the latter "system," we are forced to rely on intuitive methods for gauging the extent to which the objective has been accomplished. For example, one feels that the linear ordering of $\mathcal{P}$ forces all the elements of $\mathcal{P}$ to designate points on the scale. And one can use positive real numbers as though they do represent points of the scale properly, exercising constant vigilance for discrepancies.

That positive real numbers do not possess the specific defect of positive rational numbers, namely, that no $x \in \mathfrak{F}$ exists with $x^2 = 2/1$, will now be shown. This result is but one of many tests to which $(\mathcal{P}, v, \bigcirc\!\!\!\!<, \oplus, \otimes)$ might be put in the quest for evidence on which to base our belief in the effectiveness of positive real numbers as a measuring scale. A lemma is proved first.

(18.7.1) Lemma: *Let $a, b \in \mathcal{P}$ such that $a \bigcirc\!\!\!\!< b$. Then there exists $f \in \mathfrak{F}$ such that $a \bigcirc\!\!\!\!< f^2, f^2 \bigcirc\!\!\!\!< b$.*

Proof: By (18.3.7), there exists $f_1 \in \mathfrak{F}$ such that $a \bigcirc\!\!\!\!< f_1, f_1 \bigcirc\!\!\!\!< b$. Then, again by (18.3.7), there exists $f_2 \in \mathfrak{F}$ such that $f_1 \bigcirc\!\!\!\!< f_2, f_2 \bigcirc\!\!\!\!< b$. Finally, by (17.3.2), there exists $f \in \mathfrak{F}$ such that $f_1 \bigcirc\!\!\!\!< f^2, f^2 \bigcirc\!\!\!\!< f_2$. Then, by the transitivity of $\bigcirc\!\!\!\!<$, $a \bigcirc\!\!\!\!< f^2, f^2 \bigcirc\!\!\!\!< b$.

(18.7.2) Theorem: *There exists $x \in \mathcal{P}$ such that $x^2 = 2/1$.*

Proof: Define

$$S \equiv [f \in \mathfrak{F}; f^2 < 2/1].$$

Then S is bounded; for example, 2/1 is an upper bound. Also, S is not empty, since $1/1 \in S$. Then, by I(d), there exists a least upper bound x of S. It will be shown that $x^2 = 2/1$ by proving that $x^2 \bigcirc\!\!\!\!< 2/1$ and $x^2 \bigcirc\!\!\!\!> 2/1$ are impossible. Suppose first that $x^2 \bigcirc\!\!\!\!< 2/1$. Then, by (18.7.1), there exists $g \in \mathfrak{F}$ such that $x^2 \bigcirc\!\!\!\!< g^2, g^2 \bigcirc\!\!\!\!< 2/1$. Since $g^2 < 2/1$, $g \in S$. But, since $x^2 \bigcirc\!\!\!\!< g^2$, we have $x \bigcirc\!\!\!\!< g$ [see (18.6.9)], which contradicts the fact that x is an upper bound of S. Now suppose $2/1 \bigcirc\!\!\!\!< x^2$. Then, again by (18.7.1), there exists $h \in \mathfrak{F}$ such that $2/1 \bigcirc\!\!\!\!< h^2, h^2 \bigcirc\!\!\!\!< x^2$. Now, for every $f \in S$, $f^2 < 2/1 < h^2$, whence $f^2 < h^2$, and $f < h$. Thus h

Chapter 19

THE REAL NUMBERS

19.1. Introduction. [No Basis.] It was indicated in (18.7) that a positive real number system appears to provide a satisfactory mathematical measuring scale. Yet there is one obvious shortcoming, namely, positive real numbers designate points of only a "half-line" rather than a full line. In (17.1), after the discussion of a three-inch ruler, it was stated that the scale would henceforth be considered as extending "indefinitely to the right"; simultaneous extension both to the "right" *and* to the "left" was not envisaged and is not reflected in the structure of the positive real number system.

It is quite easy to see intuitively how one might describe positions on a whole line if one has already obtained a method for describing positions on a half-line. All that is required is to choose, at random, some point on the line and note that this point divides the line into two half-lines, each extending from the chosen point indefinitely, one to the right and the other to the left. Positions on each of the two half-lines can then be described by a positive real number system; all that is necessary is to distinguish by some device positions and designations on the left of the break-point from those on the right.

This intuitive description of the considerations leading to an extension of the positive real number system is so simple that it seems now quite remarkable that it did not occur to mathematicians for many centuries. The reason seems to be that positive real numbers (or a vague approximation to them) were used primarily as designations for *lengths* of line segments, rather than for points on a line. Thus the entire motivation for devising an extension was probably lacking.

When finally an extension of the positive real number system was made, which extension was capable of representing an entire line, it was algebraic rather than geometric considerations that furnished the proper motivation. Specifically, the defect that finally became a sufficient irritant to stimulate mathematical invention is, expressed in terms of our notation, that $(\mathcal{P}, +)$ is not a group.

The reader will have observed in the preceding chapter how frequently it was convenient to introduce a new positive real number x, in terms of two existing ones, f and g, by the requirement that $f + x = g$. This process occurs repeatedly in proofs and indeed in all uses of positive real numbers. However, it is clear that such an x exists only if $f > g$. Now one objective of algebra (for example, present-day high school algebra) is to use the operations $+$, $\cdot$ with numbers whose size is not yet known; the final step in the process is the determination of the size (value) of the numbers involved. In particular, it is often desirable to determine an x in terms of f and g, without knowing in advance whether or not $f > g$ is true. Evidently this process could be carried out without exception if it were true that, for *every* f, g, there exists x such that $f + x = g$. But this would be precisely the requirement that $(\mathcal{P}, +)$ be a group (since $+$ is associative and commutative).

Now, of course, $(\mathcal{P}, +)$ is not a group, so that if the demands of algebra are to be met, it becomes necessary to devise a system similar to the positive real number system which has the group property. At the same time, it is desirable that the numbers of the new system serve as designations for points of a full line.

19.2. Axioms for Real Numbers. [No Basis.] In this section we shall set forth a system of axioms for real numbers. On this occasion it will prove more convenient to place in the basis a relation $\otimes$ and operations $\oplus$, $\otimes$, rather than a more primitive operation. Thus we choose as basis $(\mathsf{R}, \circledless, \oplus, \otimes)$ where R is a set, $\circledless$ is a relation on $\mathsf{R} \times \mathsf{R}$ and $\oplus$, $\otimes$ are operations on $\mathsf{R} \times \mathsf{R}$ to R. The axioms are chosen to retain, as far as possible, the properties of an algebraic system $(\mathcal{P}, v, <, +, \cdot)$ of positive real numbers but will impose the requirement that $(\mathsf{R}, \oplus)$ form a group.

The foundation of the theory of real numbers is as follows:

Basis: $(\mathsf{R}, \circledless, \oplus, \otimes)$, where R is a set, $\circledless$ is a relation on $\mathsf{R} \times \mathsf{R}$, and $\oplus$ and $\otimes$ are operations on $\mathsf{R} \times \mathsf{R}$ to R.

Axioms:

I. $(\mathsf{R}, \circledless)$ is a one-dimensional continuum, that is,
 (a) there exist $a, b \in \mathsf{R}$ with $a \neq b$;
 (b) the set R is linearly ordered by $\circledless$;
 (c) for every $a, b \in \mathsf{R}$ such that $a \circledless b$, there exists $x \in \mathsf{R}$ such that $a \circledless x$ and $x \circledless b$;
 (d) every non-empty (lower) subset of R which is bounded above has a least upper bound.

II. $(\mathsf{R}, \oplus)$ is a commutative group, that is,
 (a) for every $a, b \in \mathsf{R}$, $a \oplus b = b \oplus a$;
 (b) for every $a, b, c \in \mathsf{R}$, $(a \oplus b) \oplus c = a \oplus (b \oplus c)$;
 (c) for every $a, b \in \mathsf{R}$, there exists $x \in \mathsf{R}$ such that $a \oplus x = b$.

The identity element of the group $(\mathsf{R}, \oplus)$ is denoted by 0.
The set $[r \in \mathsf{R}; 0 \circledless r]$ is denoted by P.

III. $(\mathsf{P}, \otimes)$ is a subsystem of $(\mathsf{R}, \otimes)$ and is a commutative group, that is,
(a) if $a, b \in \mathsf{P}$, then $a \otimes b \in \mathsf{P}$;
(b) if $a, b \in \mathsf{P}$, then $a \otimes b = b \otimes a$;
(c) if $a, b, c \in \mathsf{P}$, then $(a \otimes b) \otimes c = a \otimes (b \otimes c)$;
(d) if $a, b \in \mathsf{P}$, then there exists $x \in \mathsf{P}$ such that $a \otimes x = b$.

IV. The operation $\otimes$ is "doubly" distributive with respect to $\oplus$, that is,
(a) if $a, b, c \in \mathsf{R}$, then $(a \oplus b) \otimes c = (a \otimes c) \oplus (b \otimes c)$;
(b) if $a, b, c \in \mathsf{R}$, then $a \otimes (b \oplus c) = (a \otimes b) \oplus (a \otimes c)$.

V. If $a, b \in \mathsf{R}$ such that $a \mathbin{\bigcirc\!\!\!\!<} b$, then, for every $c \in \mathsf{R}$, $a \oplus c \mathbin{\bigcirc\!\!\!\!<} b \oplus c$.

Any system $(\mathsf{R}, \mathbin{\bigcirc\!\!\!\!<}, \oplus, \otimes)$ satisfying Axioms I–V is called a *system of real numbers*. Elements of R are called *real numbers*.

Remark: It should be observed that $\otimes$ on $\mathsf{R} \times \mathsf{R}$ to R is not assumed to be associative or commutative; it will be proved from the weaker assumption III that $\otimes$ does have these properties. The necessity of assuming *both* distributive laws IV(a) and IV(b) is due to the absence of an axiom of commutativity for $\otimes$. It should be mentioned that the density requirement I(c) is actually a consequence of the remaining axioms, although this fact is by no means obvious. Hence, in the interest of independence, I(c) could be omitted from the above list.

19.3. Definition of an Instance. [No Basis.] The axioms are proved consistent, as usual, by the construction of an instance. Since the task is somewhat more extensive than in preceding chapters, we shall devote this and the next three sections to it. The instance will be constructed in terms of a system of positive real numbers. Again, as in (18.2), consistency will depend ultimately on consistency for positive integers. Now it would be possible to follow indications given in (19.1) for the construction of a full line from a half-line, thus obtaining a mathematical treatment of this geometrico-intuitive procedure. However, we find it algebraically more satisfying to employ equivalence classes of pairs of positive real numbers in a manner similar to that employed for the construction of an instance of positive rational numbers [see (16.3)].

For the remainder of the section, $(\mathcal{P}, <, v, \odot)$ is a basic system of positive real numbers, satisfying Axioms (18.1.I)–(18.1.V), and $(\mathcal{P}, v, <, +, \cdot)$ is the corresponding algebraic system. Before defining the set R of the instance, we introduce the appropriate equivalence relation.

(19.3.1) Definition: Define $\sim$ on $(\mathcal{P} \times \mathcal{P}) \times (\mathcal{P} \times \mathcal{P})$ thus:

$$\sim \equiv [((m, n), (p, q)) \in (\mathcal{P} \times \mathcal{P}) \times (\mathcal{P} \times \mathcal{P}); m + q = n + p].$$

Thus $(m, n) \sim (p, q)$ if and only if $m + q = n + p$.

(19.3.2) THEOREM: *The relation* $\sim$ *is an equivalence relation.*

PROOF: It is to be shown that $\sim$ is reflexive, symmetric and transitive. First, the reflexive law is obvious, that is, for every $m, n \in \mathcal{P}$, $(m, n \sim (m, n)$, since $m + n = n + m$ by the commutativity of $+$. The symmetric law also follows from the commutativity of $+$. Suppose $m, n, p, q \in \mathcal{P}$ and $(m, n) \sim (p, q)$, so that $m + q = n + p$. Then $p + n = q + m$, whence $(p, q) \sim (m, n)$. To prove $\sim$ transitive, assume $m_1, n_1, m_2, n_2, m_3, n_3 \in \mathcal{P}$ and

(1) $$(m_1, n_1) \sim (m_2, n_2) \quad \text{and} \quad (m_2, n_2) \sim (m_3, n_3).$$

Then

(2) $$m_1 + n_2 = n_1 + m_2,$$

and

(3) $$m_2 + n_3 = n_2 + m_3.$$

By (2) and (3),

(4) $$(m_1 + n_2) + (m_2 + n_3) = (n_1 + m_2) + (n_2 + m_3).$$

Since $+$ is a commutative and associative operation on $\mathcal{P} \times \mathcal{P}$ to $\mathcal{P}$, it is easy to see that (4) yields

$$(m_1 + n_3) + (m_2 + n_2) = (n_1 + m_3) + (m_2 + n_2),$$

or, by the "cancellation" rule (18.6.7.a),

$$m_1 + n_3 = n_1 + m_3.$$

Hence

$$(m_1, n_1) \sim (m_3, n_3).$$

This completes the proof.

(19.3.3) DEFINITION: If $(m, n) \in \mathcal{P} \times \mathcal{P}$, define $\{m, n\}$ to be the equivalence class of (m, n), that is,

(a) $$\{m, n\} \equiv [(p, q) \in \mathcal{P} \times \mathcal{P}; (m, n) \sim (p, q)].$$

Also, define

(b) $$\mathsf{R} \equiv [\{m, n\}; (m, n) \in \mathcal{P} \times \mathcal{P}].$$

REMARK: The general ideas and theorems pertaining to equivalence relations and equivalence classes are found in (15.3). Free use will be made of these results.

The next lemma prepares for the definition of $\oslash$ on $\mathsf{R} \times \mathsf{R}$.

(19.3.4) LEMMA: *If* $m_1, n_1, m_2, n_2, p_1, q_1, p_2, q_2 \in \mathcal{P}$ *such that*

$$(m_1, n_1) \sim (m_2, n_2), \quad (p_1, q_1) \sim (p_2, q_2),$$

and if

$$m_1 + q_1 < n_1 + p_1,$$

then

$$m_2 + q_2 < n_2 + p_2.$$

PROOF: Since $(m_1, n_1) \sim (m_2, n_2)$ and $(p_1, q_1) \sim (p_2, q_2)$,

(1) $$m_1 + n_2 = n_1 + m_2,$$

and

(2) $$p_1 + q_2 = q_1 + p_2.$$

By (1) and (2),

(3) $$(m_1 + q_1) + (n_2 + p_2) = (n_1 + p_1) + (m_2 + q_2).$$

Now

(4) $$m_1 + q_1 < n_1 + q_1.$$

Suppose

(5) $$m_2 + q_2 \not< n_2 + p_2,$$

so that, by I(b),

(6) $$n_2 + p_2 \leqq m_2 + q_2.$$

By (4), (6), (18.6.6.a),

$$(m_1 + q_1) + (n_2 + p_2) < (n_1 + p_1) + (m_2 + q_2).$$

But this contradicts (3) and shows that the assumption (5) is impossible. This completes the proof.

(19.3.5) COROLLARY: *Let* $r, s \in \mathbf{R}$. *Then one of the following is true:*

(a) *for every* $(m, n) \in r$, $(p, q) \in s$, $m + q = n + p$;
(b) *for every* $(m, n) \in r$, $(p, q) \in s$, $m + q < n + p$;
(c) *for every* $(m, n) \in r$, $(p, q) \in s$, $m + q > n + p$.

PROOF: Let $r = \{m_1, n_1\}$, $s = \{p_1, q_1\}$. Then, since $\mathcal{P}$ is linearly ordered by $<$, one of the following is true:

(1) $$m_1 + q_1 = n_1 + p_1,$$
(2) $$m_1 + q_1 < n_1 + p_1,$$
(3) $$m_1 + q_1 > n_1 + p_1.$$

In case (1), $(m_1, n_1) \sim (p_1, q_1)$, so that $r = s$, and (a) is true. For every $(m, n) \in r$, $(p, q) \in s$, it is true that $(m_1, n_1) \sim (m, n)$ and $(p_1, q_1) \sim (p, q)$. Hence, in case (2), (19.3.4) yields

$$m + q < n + p,$$

and (b) is true. Similarly (c) follows if (3) holds.

(19.3.6) DEFINITION: Define

$$\bigotimes \equiv [(r, s) \in \mathsf{R} \times \mathsf{R};\ (19.3.5.b) \text{ is true}].$$

Thus $r \bigotimes s$ if and only if, for every $(m, n) \in r$ and $(p, q) \in s$, it is true that $m + q < n + p$.

Next we turn to the definitions of operations $\oplus$, $\otimes$ on $\mathsf{R} \times \mathsf{R}$ to R. Again a preliminary lemma is proved.

(19.3.7) LEMMA: *Let $m_1, n_1, p_1, q_1, m_2, n_2, p_2, q_2 \in \mathcal{P}$ such that $(m_1, n_1) \sim (m_2, n_2)$ and $(p_1, q_1) \sim (p_2, q_2)$. Then*

(a) $(m_1 + p_1, n_1 + q_1) \sim (m_2 + p_2, n_2 + q_2)$;

(b) $(m_1 \cdot p_1 + n_1 \cdot q_1, m_1 \cdot q_1 + n_1 \cdot p_1)$
$$\sim (m_2 \cdot p_2 + n_2 \cdot q_2, m_2 \cdot q_2 + n_2 \cdot p_2).$$

PROOF: Let $(m_1, n_1) \sim (m_2, n_2)$ and $(p_1, q_1) \sim (p_2, q_2)$, so that

(1) $$m_1 + n_2 = n_1 + m_2,$$

and

(2) $$p_1 + q_2 = q_1 + p_2.$$

Then, by (1), (2),

(3) $$(m_1 + p_1) + (n_2 + q_2) = (n_1 + q_1) + (m_2 + p_2).$$

But (3) proves (a). To prove (b), note that, by (1) and the distributive law (18.5.7.e),

(4) $$m_1 \cdot p_1 + n_2 \cdot p_1 = n_1 \cdot p_1 + m_2 \cdot p_1,$$

and

(5) $$n_1 \cdot q_1 + m_2 \cdot q_1 = m_1 \cdot q_1 + n_2 \cdot q_1.$$

Hence, by (4), (5),

(6) $$(m_1 \cdot p_1 + n_1 \cdot q_1) + (n_2 \cdot p_1 + m_2 \cdot q_1) = (m_1 \cdot q_1 + n_1 \cdot p_1) + (m_2 \cdot p_1 + n_2 \cdot q_1).$$

But, by (2) and (18.5.7.e),

(7) $$m_2 \cdot p_1 + m_2 \cdot q_2 = m_2 \cdot q_1 + m_2 \cdot p_2,$$

and

(8) $$n_2 \cdot q_1 + n_2 \cdot p_2 = n_2 \cdot p_1 + n_2 \cdot q_2.$$

Then, by (7), (8),

(9) $$(m_2 \cdot q_2 + n_2 \cdot p_2) + (m_2 \cdot p_1 + n_2 \cdot q_1) = (m_2 \cdot p_2 + n_2 \cdot q_2) + (n_2 \cdot p_1 + m_2 \cdot q_1).$$

Now, by (6) and (9),

$$(10)\quad ((m_1 \cdot p_1 + n_1 \cdot q_1) + (m_2 \cdot q_2 + n_2 \cdot p_2)) + ((n_2 \cdot p_1 + m_2 \cdot q_1) + (m_2 \cdot p_1 + n_2 \cdot q_1))$$
$$= ((m_1 \cdot q_1 + n_1 \cdot p_1) + (m_2 \cdot p_2 + n_2 \cdot q_2)) + ((n_2 \cdot p_1 + m_2 \cdot q_1) + (m_2 \cdot p_1 + n_2 \cdot q_1)).$$

From (10) and the "cancellation" law (18.6.7.a), we have

$$(m_1 \cdot p_1 + n_1 \cdot q_1) + (m_2 \cdot q_2 + n_2 \cdot p_2) = (m_1 \cdot q_1 + n_1 \cdot p_1) + (m_2 \cdot p_2 + n_2 \cdot q_2),$$

and (b) is proved.

(19.3.8) COROLLARY: *Let* $r, s \in \mathsf{R}$. *Then*
(a) *there exists a unique* $x \in \mathsf{R}$ *such that, if* $(m, n) \in r$, $(p, q) \in s$, *then* $(m + p, n + p) \in x$;
(b) *there exists a unique* $y \in \mathsf{R}$ *such that, if* $(m, n) \in r$, $(p, q) \in s$, *then* $(m \cdot p + n \cdot q, m \cdot q + n \cdot p) \in y$.

PROOF: Let $m_1, n_1, q_1, p_1 \in \mathcal{P}$ such that

$$(1)\qquad r = \{m_1, n_1\}, \quad s = \{p_1, q_1\}.$$

Then define

$$(2)\qquad x \equiv \{m_1 + p_1, n_1 + q_1\};$$
$$(3)\qquad y \equiv \{m_1 \cdot p_1 + n_1 \cdot q_1, m_1 \cdot q_1 + n_1 \cdot p_1\}.$$

Now, for every m, n, p, q such that

$$(4)\qquad (m, n) \in r, \quad (p, q) \in s,$$

it is seen that (1) and (4) yield

$$(5)\qquad (m, n) \sim (m_1, n_1), \quad (p, q) \sim (p_1, q_1).$$

By (5), (19.3.7.a),

$$(m + p, n + q) \sim (m_1 + p_1, n_1 + q_1),$$

whence $(m + p, n + q) \in x$. Hence the existence is proved. Now suppose $x' \in \mathsf{R}$ satisfies (a). Then, by (1),

$$(6)\qquad (m_1 + p_1, n_1 + q_1) \in x'.$$

It follows from (6) and (2) [see (15.3.2)] that $x' = x$. This completes the proof of (a). The proof of (b) is similar and is left to the reader.

(19.3.9) DEFINITION: Define operations $\oplus$, $\otimes$ on $\mathsf{R} \times \mathsf{R}$ to R so that, for every $(r, s) \in \mathsf{R} \times \mathsf{R}$,

(a) $r \oplus s$ is the unique $x \in \mathsf{R}$ satisfying (19.3.8.a);
(b) $r \otimes s$ is the unique $y \in \mathsf{R}$ satisfying (19.3.8.b).

(The unique existence of x and y are proved in (19.3.8).)

It is to be proved in the following three sections that the system $(\mathsf{R}, \textcircled{<}, \oplus, \otimes)$, as defined in (19.3.3), (19.3.6), (19.3.9), is a system of real numbers.

19.4. The Relation $\textcircled{<}$. [Basis: $(\mathcal{P}, <, v, \odot)$; Axioms: (18.1.I)–(18.1.V).] In this section we begin the task of proving that the system $(\mathsf{R}, \textcircled{<}, \oplus, \otimes)$ defined in (19.3) is a system of real numbers. First some of the properties of the relation $\textcircled{<}$ will be determined.

(19.4.1) Theorem: R *is linearly ordered by* $\textcircled{<}$, *that is,*
(a) *for every* $r \in \mathsf{R}$, $r \textcircled{<}' r$;
(b) *if* $r, s \in \mathsf{R}$ *such that there exists* $t \in \mathsf{R}$ *with* $r \textcircled{<} t$ *and* $t \textcircled{<} s$, *then* $r \textcircled{<} s$;
(c) *for every* $r, s \in \mathsf{R}$, *it is true that* $r = s$ *or* $r \textcircled{<} s$ *or* $s \textcircled{<} r$.
Proof: This is immediate from the definition (19.3.6) of $\textcircled{<}$ and Axiom (18.1.I.b).

(19.4.2) Theorem: *Let* $r, s, t, u \in \mathsf{R}$. *Then*

(a) $r \textcircled{<} s$ *implies* $r \oplus t \textcircled{<} s \oplus t$;
(b) $r \oplus t \textcircled{<} s \oplus t$ *implies* $r \textcircled{<} s$;
(c) $r \textcircled{<} s$, $t \textcircled{<} u$ *implies* $r \oplus t \textcircled{<} s \oplus u$.

Proof: This is left for the reader; use is made of (19.3.6), (19.3.9) and (18.6.6).

(19.4.3) Corollary: *The system* $(\mathsf{R}, \textcircled{<}, \oplus, \otimes)$ *satisfies Axiom* V.
Proof: This is a restatement of (19.4.2.a).

It is convenient for later purposes to single out two specific elements of R.

(19.4.4) Definition: Define

$$0 \equiv \{v, v\}, \quad \mathsf{w} \equiv \{v + v, v\}.$$

(19.4.5) Corollary: $0 \textcircled{<} \mathsf{w}$.
Proof: This is immediate from the definition (19.3.6) of $\textcircled{<}$, since $v + v < v + v + v$.

The next definition recalls the definition of P and introduces a companion set.

(19.4.6) Definition:

$$\mathsf{P} \equiv [r \in \mathsf{R};\, 0 \textcircled{<} r];$$
$$\mathsf{N} \equiv [r \in \mathsf{R};\, r \textcircled{<} 0].$$

If $r \in \mathsf{P}$, then r is called *positive*; if $r \in \mathsf{N}$, then r is called *negative.*

(19.4.7) Corollary: $\mathsf{R} = \mathsf{P} + \mathsf{N} + [0]$.
Proof: This is obvious from (19.4.1.c).

(19.4.8) Theorem: *Let* $r \in \mathsf{R}$. *Then*
(a) $r \in \mathsf{P}$ *if and only if there exists* $m \in \mathcal{P}$ *such that* $r = \{m + v, v\}$;
(b) $r \in \mathsf{N}$ *if and only if there exists* $m \in \mathcal{P}$ *such that* $r = \{v, m + v\}$.

Proof: To prove (a) let $r = \{p, q\} \in \mathsf{P}$ with $p, q \in \mathcal{P}$. It follows that $\{p, q\} \circledcirc \{v, v\}$, whence

$$(1) \qquad p + v > q + v.$$

By (1) and (18.6.4), there exists $m \in \mathcal{P}$ such that

$$(2) \qquad p + v = (q + v) + m = q + (m + v).$$

But, by (2), $(p, q) \sim (m + v, v)$, so that

$$r = \{p, q\} = \{m + v, v\}.$$

Conversely, if $r = \{m + v, v\}$, then clearly

$$r = \{m + v, v\} \circledcirc \{v, v\} = 0$$

since $m + v + v > v + v$; hence $r \in \mathsf{P}$, and (a) is proved. The proof of (b) is left for the reader.

It will now be shown that (19.4.8) leads to an isomorphism between $(\mathcal{P}, <, +, \cdot)$ and $(\mathsf{P}, \circledcirc, \oplus, \otimes)$.

(19.4.9) Definition: Define

$$\varphi \equiv (\{m + v, v\}; m \in \mathcal{P}).$$

Thus, for every $m \in \mathcal{P}$, $\varphi(m) = \{m + v, v\}$.

(19.4.10) Theorem: φ *is a one-to-one correspondence between* $\mathcal{P}$ *and* P.
Proof: Clearly domain of $\varphi = \mathcal{P}$; it was shown in (19.4.8.a) that range of $\varphi = \mathsf{P}$. Hence it suffices to show that, if $m \neq n$, then $\{m + v, v\} \neq \{n + v, v\}$. Suppose $\{m + v, v\} = \{n + v, v\}$; then $(m + v, v) \sim (n + v, v)$, whence $m + v + v = n + v + v$, and $m = n$ by (18.6.7.a). This contradiction completes the proof.

(19.4.11) Theorem: *If* $m, n \in \mathcal{P}$, *then*

(a) $\varphi(m) \circledcirc \varphi(n)$ *if and only if* $m < n$;
(b) $\varphi(m) \oplus \varphi(n) = \varphi(m + n)$;
(c) $\varphi(m) \otimes \varphi(n) = \varphi(m \cdot n)$.

Proof: The proof of (c) is typical. It is to be shown that

$$\{m + v, v\} \otimes \{n + v, v\} = \{m \cdot n + v, v\}.$$

By (19.3.9.b),

$$\begin{aligned}\{m + v, v\} &\otimes \{n + v, v\} \\ &= \{(m + v) \cdot (n + v) + v \cdot v, (m + v) \cdot v + (n + v) \cdot v\} \\ &= \{m \cdot n + m + n + v + v, m + n + v + v\} \\ &= \{m \cdot n + v, v\}.\end{aligned}$$

The proofs of (a), (b) are left for the reader.

(19.4.12) Corollary: *The system* $(\mathsf{P}, \circledless)$ *is a one-dimensional continuum.*

Proof: By (19.4.10) and (19.4.11.a), $(\mathsf{P}, \circledless)$ is isomorphic to $(\mathcal{P}, <)$. But $(\mathcal{P}, <)$ is a one-dimensional continuum by (18.1.I). Hence $(\mathsf{P}, \circledless)$ is a one-dimensional continuum by (17.4.10).

(19.4.13) Corollary: *The system* $(\mathsf{R}, \circledless, \oplus, \otimes)$ *satisfies Axiom* III.

Proof: Let $r, s \in \mathsf{P}$. By (19.4.10), there exist $m, n \in \mathcal{P}$ such that $r = \varphi(m)$, $s = \varphi(n)$. Then, by (19.4.11.c), $r \otimes s = \varphi(m \cdot n) \in \mathsf{P}$, whence $(\mathsf{P}, \otimes)$ is a subsystem of $(\mathsf{R}, \otimes)$. Now, by (19.4.10) and (19.4.11.c), $(\mathsf{P}, \otimes)$ is isomorphic to $(\mathcal{P}, \cdot)$. But $(\mathcal{P}, \cdot)$ is a commutative group by (18.6.5). It is now easily shown that $(\mathsf{P}, \otimes)$ is a commutative group; detailed proof is left for the reader [compare with Project (14.2.20)].

(19.4.14) Project: Prove that, if $r \in \mathsf{R}$, $s \in \mathsf{P}$ then $r \circledless r + s$.

(19.4.15) Project: Prove that, if $p, q \in \mathcal{P}$, then $\{p, q\} \oplus \{q, p\} = 0$.

(19.4.16) Project: Complete the proof of (19.4.13).

(19.4.17) Project: Let $r, s \in \mathsf{R}$ with $r \circledless s$, and let $t \in \mathsf{P}$. Prove that $(r \otimes t) \circledless (s \otimes t)$.

19.5. The Operations $\oplus$, $\otimes$. [Basis: $(\mathcal{P}, <, v, \odot)$; Axioms: (18.1.I)–(18.1.V).] In this section we continue the task of proving that $(\mathsf{R}, \circledless, \oplus, \otimes)$ is an instance of a real number system, with special attention to the operations $\oplus$, $\otimes$.

(19.5.1) Theorem: *Let* $r_1, r_2, r_3 \in \mathsf{R}$. *Then*

(a) $$r_1 \oplus r_2 = r_2 \oplus r_1;$$
(b) $$(r_1 \oplus r_2) \oplus r_3 = r_1 \oplus (r_2 \oplus r_3);$$
(c) $$r_1 \otimes r_2 = r_2 \otimes r_1;$$
(d) $$(r_1 \otimes r_2) \otimes r_3 = r_1 \otimes (r_2 \otimes r_3);$$
(e) $$r_1 \otimes (r_2 \oplus r_3) = (r_1 \otimes r_2) \oplus (r_1 \otimes r_3).$$

Proof: Let

(1) $$r_1 = \{m_1, n_1\}, \quad r_2 = \{m_2, n_2\}, \quad r_3 = \{m_3, n_3\},$$

with $m_1, m_2, m_3, n_1, n_2, n_3 \in \mathcal{P}$. Then, by (19.3.9),

(2) $$r_1 \oplus r_2 = \{m_1 + m_2, n_1 + n_2\},$$
(3) $$r_2 \oplus r_1 = \{m_2 + m_1, n_2 + n_1\}.$$

But, since $+$ is commutative, it follows that $r_1 \oplus r_2 = r_2 \oplus r_1$. This proves (a). The proofs of (b), (c), (d) are similarly straightforward and are left for the reader. The most difficult part, (e), will now be proved. By (19.3.9) and (1),

$$r_2 \oplus r_3 = \{m_2 + m_3, n_2 + n_3\}.$$

Hence, again by (19.3.9),

$$(4)\ r_1 \otimes (r_2 \oplus r_3)$$
$$= \{m_1 \cdot (m_2 + m_3) + n_1 \cdot (n_2 + n_3), m_1 \cdot (n_2 + n_3) + n_1 \cdot (m_2 + m_3)\}.$$

Similarly,

$$r_1 \otimes r_2 = \{m_1 \cdot m_2 + n_1 \cdot n_2, m_1 \cdot n_2 + n_1 \cdot m_2\},$$

and

$$r_1 \otimes r_3 = \{m_1 \cdot m_3 + n_1 \cdot n_3, m_1 \cdot n_3 + n_1 \cdot m_3\}.$$

Hence

$$(5)\ (r_1 \otimes r_2) \oplus (r_1 \otimes r_3) = \{(m_1 \cdot m_2 + n_1 \cdot n_2) + (m_1 \cdot m_3 + n_1 \cdot n_3),$$
$$(m_1 \cdot n_2 + n_1 \cdot m_2) + (m_1 \cdot n_3 + n_1 \cdot m_3)\}.$$

It is easily shown, from (4), (5) and the commutative, associative and distributive laws for $+$, $\cdot$ [see (18.5.7)], that

$$r_1 \otimes (r_2 \oplus r_3) = (r_1 \otimes r_2) \oplus (r_1 \otimes r_3).$$

(19.5.2) Corollary: *The system* (R, $\otimes$, $\oplus$, $\otimes$) *satisfies Axiom* IV.
Proof: This is immediate from (19.5.1.e), (19.5.1.c).

(19.5.3) Theorem: (R, $\oplus$) *is a group.*
Proof: It is to be proved that the group axioms are satisfied for the system (R, $\oplus$). Thus it must be shown that,

(1) for every $r_1, r_2, r_3 \in \mathsf{R}$,

$$(r_1 \oplus r_2) \oplus r_3 = r_1 \oplus (r_2 \oplus r_3);$$

(2) for every $r_1, r_2 \in \mathsf{R}$ there exists $x \in \mathsf{R}$ such that

$$r_1 \oplus x = r_2;$$

(3) for every $r_1, r_2 \in \mathsf{R}$ there exists $y \in \mathsf{R}$ such that

$$y \oplus r_1 = r_2.$$

Now (1) is true by (19.5.1). To prove (2), let

$$(4)\qquad r_1 = \{m_1, n_1\}, \quad r_2 = \{m_2, n_2\}$$

with $m_1, m_2, n_1, n_2 \in \mathcal{P}$, and define

$$x \equiv \{m_2 + n_1, m_1 + n_2\} \in \mathsf{R}.$$

Then, by (19.3.9),

$$(5)\qquad r_1 \oplus x = \{m_1 + (m_2 + n_1), n_1 + (m_1 + n_2)\}.$$

Now, by (15.3.2), $r_1 \oplus x = r_2$ follows when it is proved that

$$(6)\qquad (m_2, n_2) \sim (m_1 + (m_2 + n_1), n_1 + (m_1 + n_2)).$$

But (6) is easily verified and is left for the reader. Finally, (3) follows from (2) and the fact that $\oplus$ is commutative.

(19.5.4) Corollary: *The system* $(\mathsf{R}, \otimes\!\!\!<, \oplus, \otimes)$ *satisfies Axiom* II.

Proof: The system $(\mathsf{R}, \oplus)$ is a group by (19.5.3) and is commutative by (19.5.1.a).

Since $(\mathsf{R}, \oplus)$ is a group, there is, by (7.3.3), a unique identity element in R. It will be shown that this identity element is the element 0 defined in (19.4.4).

(19.5.5) Theorem: *The element* 0 *is the identity element in* $(\mathsf{R}, \oplus)$.

Proof: It is to be shown that, for every $r \in \mathsf{R}$, $r \oplus 0 = r$. To this end, let $r = \{p, q\}$. Then

$$\begin{aligned} r \oplus 0 &= \{p, q\} \oplus \{v, v\} \\ &= \{p + v, q + v\} \\ &= \{p, q\} = r. \end{aligned}$$

Since $(\mathsf{R}, \oplus)$ is a group, each element of R has an inverse element [see (7.3.6)]. In groups in which the group operation is denoted by $+$ (or $\oplus$) it is customary to use a different notation for inverse elements from that of (7.3.6).

(19.5.6) Definition: Let $r \in \mathsf{R}$. Then the inverse of r in the group $(\mathsf{R}, \oplus)$ is denoted by $-r$.

(19.5.7) Corollary: *Let* $r \in \mathsf{R}$. *Then* $r \oplus (-r) = 0$.

Proof: This is a restatement of the definition of an inverse in view of (19.5.5).

(19.5.8) Corollary: *Let* $r \in \mathsf{R}$. *Then* $-(-r) = r$.

Proof: This is a restatement of (7.3.7) in the present notation.

(19.5.9) Project: Let $r, s \in \mathsf{R}$. Prove that

(a) $(-r) \otimes s = -(r \otimes s)$;

(b) $r \otimes (-s) = -(r \otimes s)$;

(c) $(-r) \otimes (-s) = r \otimes s$.

(19.5.10) Project: Let $r, s \in \mathsf{R}$ with $r \otimes\!\!\!< s$. Prove that $(-s) \otimes\!\!\!< (-r)$.

19.6. Consistency of the Axioms. [Basis: $(\mathcal{P}, \otimes\!\!\!<, v, \odot)$; Axioms: (18.1.I)–(18.1.V).] In this section we complete the proof of the fact that the axioms for real numbers are consistent by showing that the instance $(\mathsf{R}, \otimes\!\!\!<, \oplus, \otimes)$ as defined in (19.3) satisfies those axioms.

(19.6.1) Theorem: *The system* $(\mathsf{R}, \otimes\!\!\!<, \oplus, \otimes)$ *satisfies Axiom* I, *that is,* $(\mathsf{R}, \otimes\!\!\!<)$ *is a one-dimensional continuum.*

PROOF: Axiom I(a) is trivial since $\mathsf{R} \supset \mathsf{P}$ and $(\mathsf{P}, \circledless)$ is a one-dimensional continuum by (19.4.12). That I(b) holds has already been shown in (19.4.1). To prove I(c) let $a, b \in \mathsf{R}$ with $a \circledless b$. Define

$$a_1 \equiv a \oplus (-a) \oplus \mathsf{w} \quad \text{and} \quad b_1 \equiv b \oplus (-a) \oplus \mathsf{w}.$$

Then $a_1 = \mathsf{w}$ by (19.5.7), (19.5.5), whence $a_1 \in \mathsf{P}$ by (19.4.5). Also, by (19.4.2.a), $a_1 \circledless b_1$, whence $b_1 \in \mathsf{P}$. Since $a_1, b_1 \in \mathsf{P}$ and since $(\mathsf{P}, \circledless)$ is a one-dimensional continuum, there exists $c_1 \in \mathsf{P}$ such that $a_1 \circledless c_1$, $c_1 \circledless b_1$. But then, by (19.4.2.a), if c is defined by $c \equiv c_1 \oplus a \oplus (-\mathsf{w})$, we have $a \circledless c$, $c \circledless b$. Finally, to prove I(d), let S be a non-empty subset of R which is bounded above. Let $a \in S$ and define

$$S_1 \equiv [r \oplus (-a) \oplus \mathsf{w};\, r \in S] \cdot \mathsf{P}.$$

Then $S_1 \subset \mathsf{P}$ and S_1 is non-empty since $\mathsf{w} \in S_1$. Also S_1 is bounded above; in fact, if c is an upper bound of S, then $c \oplus (-a) \oplus \mathsf{w}$ is an upper bound of S_1, as is easily seen from (19.4.2.a). Since $(\mathsf{P}, \circledless)$ is a one-dimensional continuum, there is a least upper bound b of S_1. Then it is easily shown that $b \oplus a \oplus (-\mathsf{w})$ is a least upper bound of S; this is left for the reader.

(19.6.2) THEOREM: *The system* $(\mathsf{R}, \circledless, \oplus, \otimes)$ *is a real number system.*

PROOF: The system $(\mathsf{R}, \circledless, \oplus, \otimes)$ satisfies Axiom I by (19.6.1); Axiom II by (19.5.4); Axiom III by (19.4.13); Axiom IV by (19.5.2); and Axiom V by (19.4.3).

19.7. The Multiplicative Group. [BASIS: $(\mathsf{R}, \circledless, \oplus, \otimes)$; AXIOMS: I–V.] In this section we begin the study of the consequences of Axioms I–V for an abstract system of real numbers. No use is to be made of the material pertaining to the specific instance of (19.3)–(19.6). The set P is defined, as in the axioms, to be $[r \in \mathsf{R};\, 0 \circledless r]$.

(19.7.1) DEFINITION: Define 0 to be the identity of the group $(\mathsf{R}, \oplus)$. For every $a \in \mathsf{R}$, let $-a$ denote the inverse of a in the group $(\mathsf{R}, \oplus)$. Finally, let w be the identity of the group $(\mathsf{P}, \otimes)$.

(19.7.2) COROLLARY: *For every* $a \in \mathsf{R}$,

(a) $a \oplus (-a) = 0;$

(b) $-(-a) = a;$

(c) $0 \circledless \mathsf{w}.$

PROOF: That (c) is true follows from $\mathsf{w} \in \mathsf{P}$. Also (a), (b) are immediate from the definitions of an identity and an inverse.

(19.7.3) THEOREM: *Let* $a, b \in \mathsf{R}$. *Then* $a \circledless b$ *if and only if there exists* $x \in \mathsf{P}$ *such that* $a \oplus x = b$.

PROOF: This is immediate from II and V; details are left for the reader.

(19.7.4) THEOREM: *If* $a, b \in \mathsf{R}$ *such that* $a \mathbin{\textcircled{<}} b$, *and if* $c \in \mathsf{P}$, *then* $a \otimes c \mathbin{\textcircled{<}} b \otimes c$.

PROOF: By (19.7.3), there exists $x \in \mathsf{P}$ such that $a \oplus x = b$. Then $(a \otimes c) \oplus (x \otimes c) = b \otimes c$ by IV(a). But $x \otimes c \in \mathsf{P}$ by III(a). Then $a \otimes c \mathbin{\textcircled{<}} b \otimes c$ by (19.7.3).

(19.7.5) THEOREM: *For every* $a, b \in \mathsf{R}$, *if* $a \mathbin{\textcircled{<}} b$ *then* $-a \mathbin{\textcircled{>}} -b$.

PROOF: Suppose $a \mathbin{\textcircled{<}} b$ and $-a \mathbin{\underline{\textcircled{<}}} -b$. Then, by V,

$$a \oplus (-a) \mathbin{\textcircled{<}} b \oplus (-a),$$
$$b \oplus (-a) \mathbin{\underline{\textcircled{<}}} b \oplus (-b),$$

whence $0 \mathbin{\textcircled{<}} 0$, contrary to the irreflexive property of $\textcircled{<}$.

(19.7.6) DEFINITION: Define

$$\mathsf{N} \equiv [r \in \mathsf{R}; r \mathbin{\textcircled{<}} 0]$$

(19.7.7) COROLLARY: $\mathsf{R} = \mathsf{P} + \mathsf{N} + [0]$.

PROOF: Since $\textcircled{<}$ is a linear ordering, it follows that, for every $r \in \mathsf{R}$, $r \mathbin{\textcircled{<}} 0$ or $r = 0$ or $0 \mathbin{\textcircled{<}} r$.

(19.7.8) THEOREM: *For every* $r \in \mathsf{R}$,

(a) *if* $r \in \mathsf{P}$, *then* $-r \in \mathsf{N}$;

(b) *if* $r \in \mathsf{N}$, *then* $-r \in \mathsf{P}$;

(c) $-0 = 0$.

PROOF: First, (c) is true since the identity is its own inverse in any group. If $r \in \mathsf{P}$, then $0 \mathbin{\textcircled{<}} r$, whence, by (19.7.5), $-r \mathbin{\textcircled{<}} -0\ (= 0)$ and $-r \in \mathsf{N}$. This proves (a). The proof of (b) is similar.

(19.7.9) THEOREM: *For every* $r \in \mathsf{R}$,

(a) $0 \otimes r = 0$;

(b) $r \otimes 0 = 0$.

PROOF: From the distributive law IV(a), it follows that

$$0 \otimes r = (0 \oplus 0) \otimes r = (0 \otimes r) \oplus (0 \otimes r),$$

whence

$$\begin{aligned} 0 = (0 \otimes r) \oplus (-(0 \otimes r)) &= (0 \otimes r) \oplus ((0 \otimes r) \oplus (-(0 \otimes r))) \\ &= (0 \otimes r) \oplus 0 \\ &= 0 \otimes r. \end{aligned}$$

This proves (a). The proof of (b) follows in a similar way from IV(b) and is left for the reader. (Caution: Remember that $\otimes$ on $\mathsf{R} \times \mathsf{R}$ to R is not known to be commutative.)

(19.7.10) THEOREM: *For every* $r, s \in \mathsf{R}$,

(a) $(-r) \otimes s = -(r \otimes s)$;

(b) $r \otimes (-s) = -(r \otimes s)$.

PROOF: By (19.7.9.a),

$$\begin{aligned} 0 &= (r \oplus (-r)) \otimes s \\ &= (r \otimes s) \oplus ((-r) \otimes s) \qquad \text{[by IV(a)].} \end{aligned}$$

Then

$$\begin{aligned} -(r \otimes s) &= ((r \otimes s) \oplus (-(r \otimes s))) \oplus ((-r) \otimes s) \\ &= 0 \oplus ((-r) \otimes s) = (-r) \otimes s. \end{aligned}$$

This proves (a). The proof of (b) follows in a similar way from (19.7.9.b) and IV(b); this is left for the reader.

(19.7.11) THEOREM: *For every* $r \in \mathsf{R}$,

$$r \otimes \mathsf{w} = \mathsf{w} \otimes r = r.$$

PROOF: If $r \in \mathsf{P}$, this is true by the definition of w as the identity element of the group $(\mathsf{P}, \otimes)$. If $r = 0$ this is (19.7.9). Finally, if $r \in \mathsf{N}$, then $-r \in \mathsf{P}$. By (19.7.10.a),

$$r \otimes \mathsf{w} = -((-r) \otimes \mathsf{w}) = -(-r) = r.$$

Similarly, by (19.7.10.b),

$$\mathsf{w} \otimes r = -(\mathsf{w} \otimes (-r)) = -(-r) = r.$$

(19.7.12) THEOREM: *The system* $(\mathsf{R}, \otimes)$ *is not a group.*

PROOF: It will be shown that it is not true that, for every $r, s \in \mathsf{R}$, there exists $x \in \mathsf{R}$ such that $r \otimes x = s$. Let $s \in \mathsf{R}$, $s \neq 0$ and define $r \equiv 0$. Then there does not exist $x \in \mathsf{R}$ such that $0 \otimes x = s$, since, for every $x \in \mathsf{R}$, $0 \otimes x = 0 \neq s$ by (19.7.9).

(19.7.13) THEOREM: *The system* $(\mathsf{R} - [0], \otimes)$ *is a subsystem of* $(\mathsf{R}, \otimes)$ *and is a commutative group.*

PROOF: First it is shown that $(\mathsf{R} - [0], \otimes)$ is a subsystem, that is, that if $a, b \in \mathsf{R} - [0]$ then $a \otimes b \in \mathsf{R} - [0]$. To this end, suppose $a \otimes b = 0$. Since $a \neq 0$, it follows that $a \in \mathsf{P}$ or $a \in \mathsf{N}$. If $a \in \mathsf{P}$, then $b \in \mathsf{P}$ is impossible, since otherwise $a \otimes b \in \mathsf{P}$ by III(a), contrary to $a \otimes b = 0$. But then $b \in \mathsf{N}$, whence $-b \in \mathsf{P}$ by (19.7.8), and $a \otimes (-b) \in \mathsf{P}$, contrary to

$$a \otimes (-b) = -(a \otimes b) = -0 = 0.$$

The case $a \in \mathsf{N}$ similarly leads to a contradiction; details are left for the reader.

Now it is shown that

(1) for every $a, b \in \mathsf{R} - [0]$, $a \otimes b = b \otimes a$;

(2) for every $a, b, c \in \mathsf{R} - [0]$, $a \otimes (b \otimes c) = (a \otimes b) \otimes c$;

(3) for every $a, b \in \mathsf{R} - [0]$, there exists $x \in \mathsf{R} - [0]$ such that $a \otimes x = b$.

To prove (1), we consider separately the four cases,

$$\begin{aligned} a \in \mathsf{P}, &\quad b \in \mathsf{P}; \\ a \in \mathsf{P}, &\quad b \in \mathsf{N}; \\ a \in \mathsf{N}, &\quad b \in \mathsf{P}; \\ a \in \mathsf{N}, &\quad b \in \mathsf{N}. \end{aligned}$$

In the first case, (1) follows from the fact that $(\mathsf{P}, \otimes)$ is a commutative group [Axiom III]. In the second case, $-b \in \mathsf{P}$, whence

$$a \otimes b = -(a \otimes (-b)) = -((-b) \otimes a) = b \otimes a.$$

The other two cases are treated similarly and are left for the reader.

The proof of (3) can be accomplished by considering the same four cases and the proof of (2) by considering eight cases. Details are left for the reader.

(19.7.14) Corollary: *The element* w *is the identity of the group* $(\mathsf{R} - [0], \otimes)$.

Proof: This is immediate from (19.7.11).

(19.7.15) Definition: The inverse in the group $(\mathsf{R} - [0], \otimes)$ of an element $a \in \mathsf{R} - [0]$ is denoted by a^{-1}.

(19.7.16) Corollary: *For every* $a \in \mathsf{R} - [0]$,

$$(-a)^{-1} = -(a^{-1}).$$

Proof: This is left for the reader.

(19.7.17) Corollary: *Let* $a, b, c \in \mathsf{R}$. *Then*

(a) $$a \otimes b = b \otimes a;$$
(b) $$(a \otimes b) \otimes c = a \otimes (b \otimes c).$$

Proof: If $a \neq 0$ and $b \neq 0$ then (a) is true by (19.7.13). But, if $a = 0$ or $b = 0$, then (a) is true by (19.7.9). The proof of (b) is similar.

(19.7.18) Project: Complete the proofs of (19.7.3), (19.7.8), (19.7.9), (19.7.10), (19.7.13).

(19.7.19) Project: Prove (19.7.16).

(19.7.20) Project: Let $a, b \in \mathsf{P}$ with $a \otimes b$. Prove that $b^{-1} \otimes a^{-1}$.

19.8. The System of Positives. [Basis: $(\mathsf{R}, \otimes, \oplus, \otimes)$; Axioms: I–V.] This section will treat in some detail properties of the system $(\mathsf{P}, \otimes, \oplus, \otimes)$. The main result is that an operation $\odot$ on $I \times \mathsf{P}$ to P may be defined so that $(\mathsf{P}, \otimes, \mathsf{w}, \odot)$ is a basic system of positive real numbers.

(19.8.1) THEOREM: *The system* $(\mathsf{P}, \otimes\!\!\!\!\bigcirc, \oplus, \otimes)$ *is a subsystem of* $(\mathsf{R}, \otimes\!\!\!\!\bigcirc, \oplus, \otimes)$.

PROOF: It is to be shown that,

(1) for every $a, b \in \mathsf{P}$, $a \oplus b \in \mathsf{P}$;

(2) for every $a, b \in \mathsf{P}$, $a \otimes b \in \mathsf{P}$.

To prove (1), note that, from $0 \otimes\!\!\!\!\bigcirc a$, $0 \otimes\!\!\!\!\bigcirc b$ it follows by V that $a \otimes\!\!\!\!\bigcirc a \oplus b$, whence $0 \otimes\!\!\!\!\bigcirc a \oplus b$ by the transitivity of $\otimes\!\!\!\!\bigcirc$. Axiom III yields (2).

An operation $\odot$ will now be defined with the help of an extension of the operation $\oplus$; the notations and results of Chapter 12 will be used. In particular, the remark in (12.2.7) will serve to remind the reader of the significance of the notation to be used.

(19.8.2) DEFINITION: Define an operation $\odot$ on $I \times \mathsf{P}$ to R so that, for every $(m, r) \in I \times \mathsf{P}$,

$$m \odot r = \sum_{j=1}^{m} r.$$

(19.8.3) COROLLARY: *The operation* $\odot$ *is on* $I \times \mathsf{P}$ *to* P.

PROOF: It is to be shown that, for every $r \in \mathsf{P}$, $m \in I$, $m \odot r \in \mathsf{P}$. This is proved by induction. Let $r \in \mathsf{P}$ and define

$$H \equiv \left[m \in I; \left(\sum_{j=1}^{m} r \right) \in \mathsf{P} \right] \subset I.$$

Now $1 \in H$ since

$$\sum_{j=1}^{1} r = r \in \mathsf{P}.$$

Suppose $q \in H$, so that $\left(\sum_{j=1}^{q} r \right) \in \mathsf{P}$. Then

$$\sum_{j=1}^{q+1} r = \left(\sum_{j=1}^{q} r \right) \oplus r,$$

which is in P by (19.8.1). Thus $H = I$ and the proof is complete.

(19.8.4) THEOREM: *Let* $m, n \in I$ *and* $r, s \in \mathsf{R}$. *Then,*

(a) *if* $m < n$, *then* $m \odot r \otimes\!\!\!\!\bigcirc n \odot r$;

(b) *if* $r \otimes\!\!\!\!\bigcirc s$, *then* $m \odot r \otimes\!\!\!\!\bigcirc m \odot s$.

PROOF: By (12.4.2),

$$\sum_{j=1}^{n} r = \sum_{j=1}^{m} r \oplus \sum_{j=1}^{n-m} r \otimes\!\!\!\!\bigcirc \sum_{j=1}^{m} r.$$

This proves (a). The proof of (b) is by induction. Define

$$H \equiv [m \in I; m \odot r \otimes\!\!\!\!\bigcirc m \odot s].$$

Then $1 \in H$, since $1 \odot r = r \otimes s = 1 \odot s$. Suppose $q \in H$, whence

$$\sum_{j=1}^{q} r \otimes \sum_{j=1}^{q} s.$$

Then, since $r \otimes s$,

$$\sum_{j=1}^{q+1} r = \left(\sum_{j=1}^{q} r\right) \oplus r \otimes \left(\sum_{j=1}^{q} s\right) \oplus s = \sum_{j=1}^{q+1} s$$

by V, and $q + 1 \in H$. Then $H = I$ and the proof of (b) is complete.

(19.8.5) Corollary: *If* $m \in I$, $r, s \in \mathsf{R}$ *such that* $m \odot r = m \odot s$, *then* $r = s$.

Proof: This is immediate from (19.8.4.b).

(19.8.6) Theorem: *Let* $m, n \in I$ *and* $r, s \in \mathsf{R}$. *Then*

(a) $$m \odot (n \odot r) = (m \cdot n) \odot r;$$
(b) $$(m \odot r) \otimes s = m \odot (r \otimes s).$$

Proof: By (12.4.4),

$$\sum_{j=1}^{m}\left(\sum_{j=1}^{n} r\right) = \sum_{j=1}^{m \cdot n} r.$$

This proves (a). The proof of (b) is by induction and is very similar to the proof of (12.2.8); it is left for the reader.

(19.8.7) Theorem: *Let* $m \in I$. *Then there exists* $x \in \mathsf{P}$ *such that* $m \odot x = \mathsf{w}$.

Proof: Define $x \equiv (m \odot \mathsf{w})^{-1}$. Then

(1) $$(m \odot \mathsf{w}) \otimes x = (m \odot \mathsf{w}) \otimes (m \odot \mathsf{w})^{-1} = \mathsf{w}.$$

But, by (19.8.6.b),

(2) $$(m \odot \mathsf{w}) \otimes x = m \odot (\mathsf{w} \otimes x) = m \odot x.$$

By (1) and (2), $m \odot x = \mathsf{w}$.

(19.8.8) Theorem: *For every* $a, b \in \mathsf{P}$, *there exists* $m \in I$ *such that* $b \otimes m \odot a$.

Proof: Suppose this false, so that, for every $m \in I$, $m \odot a \,\underline{\otimes}\, b$. Then the set

$$S \equiv [m \odot a; m \in I]$$

is non-empty and bounded above by b. Hence, by I, there is a least upper bound c of S. Since c is a least upper bound, $c \oplus (-a)$ ($\otimes c$) is not an upper bound. Then there exists $j \in I$ such that

$$c \oplus (-a) \otimes j \odot a.$$

But then, by V,

$$c \otimes (j \odot a) \oplus a = (j + 1) \odot a,$$

contrary to the fact that c is an upper bound of S.

(19.8.9) THEOREM: *Let $a, b \in \mathsf{P}$ with $a \otimes b$. Then there exist $x \in \mathsf{P}$ and $m, n \in I$ such that*

$$a \circledless x, \quad x \circledless b, \quad m \odot x = n \odot \mathsf{w}.$$

PROOF: Since $a \circledless b$, there exists, by (19.7.3), $y \in \mathsf{P}$ such that

(1) $$a \oplus y = b.$$

By (19.8.8), there exists $m \in I$ such that

(2) $$\mathsf{w} \circledless m \odot y.$$

Now the set

(3) $$[j \in I; m \odot b \circledleq j \odot \mathsf{w}]$$

is not empty, by (19.8.8). Let k be the least in the set (3), so that

(4) $$m \odot b \circledleq k \odot \mathsf{w}.$$

Now $k > 1$. For, if $k = 1$, then $m \odot b \circledleq \mathsf{w}$ and, since $y \circledless b$ by (1), $m \odot y < m \odot b$ by (19.8.4.b), whence $m \odot y \circledless \mathsf{w}$ contrary to (2). Define $n \equiv k - 1$ and

(5) $$x \equiv n \odot (m \odot \mathsf{w})^{-1}.$$

It is first proved that $m \odot x = n \odot \mathsf{w}$. By (5),

$$(m \odot \mathsf{w}) \otimes x = (n \odot (m \odot \mathsf{w})^{-1}) \otimes (m \odot \mathsf{w}),$$

whence, by (19.8.6.b),

$$m \odot x = n \odot \mathsf{w}.$$

It is next shown that $x \circledless b$. Suppose $b \circledleq x$, that is

$$b \circledleq n \odot (m \odot \mathsf{w})^{-1}.$$

Then, by (19.7.4),

$$(m \odot \mathsf{w}) \otimes b \circledleq (n \odot (m \odot \mathsf{w})^{-1}) \otimes (m \odot \mathsf{w}),$$

whence, by (19.8.6.b),

$$m \odot b \circledleq n \odot \mathsf{w},$$

and n is in the set (3). But this contradicts the fact that $k = n + 1$ is the least in (3); this contradiction shows that $x \circledless b$.

Finally, it is shown that $a \circledless x$. Suppose $x \circledleq a$, that is,

$$n \odot (m \odot \mathsf{w})^{-1} \circledleq a.$$

Then, since $k = n + 1$,

(6) $$\begin{aligned} k \odot (m \odot \mathsf{w})^{-1} &= (n \odot (m \odot \mathsf{w})^{-1}) \oplus (m \odot \mathsf{w})^{-1} \\ &\circledleq a \oplus (m \odot \mathsf{w})^{-1}. \end{aligned}$$

But, by (19.8.6.b),

$$m \odot y = m \odot (\mathsf{w} \otimes y) = (m \odot \mathsf{w}) \otimes y,$$

so that, by (2),

$$\mathsf{w} \circledless (m \odot \mathsf{w}) \otimes y.$$

Then, by (19.7.4),

$$(7) \qquad (m \odot \mathsf{w})^{-1} \oslash y.$$

From (6), (7), (1), we have

$$k \odot (m \odot \mathsf{w})^{-1} \oslash a \oplus y = b,$$

whence

$$k \odot \mathsf{w} \oslash (m \odot \mathsf{w}) \otimes b = m \odot b.$$

But this contradicts (4).

(19.8.10) THEOREM: *The system* $(\mathsf{P}, \oslash)$ *is a one-dimensional continuum.*

PROOF: It is to be shown that $(\mathsf{P}, \oslash)$ satisfies (17.3.I)–(17.3.IV). Axiom (17.3.I) is obvious since $\mathsf{w} \in \mathsf{P}$ and $\mathsf{w} \oplus \mathsf{w} \in \mathsf{P}$, $\mathsf{w} \neq \mathsf{w} \oplus \mathsf{w}$. Axiom (17.3.II) is an immediate consequence of the fact that R is linearly ordered by $\oslash$. Axiom (17.3.III) is true by (19.8.9). Finally, to prove (17.3.IV), let $S \subset \mathsf{P}$ with $S \neq \Theta$ such that S is bounded above. Then, since $(\mathsf{R}, \oslash)$ is a one-dimensiona continuum, there exists a least upper bound $b \in \mathsf{R}$ of S. Since S is non-empty, there is an element $a \in S$. Then $a \underline{\oslash} b$. But $a \in S \subset \mathsf{P}$, whence $0 \oslash a$. Then $0 \oslash b$, and $b \in \mathsf{P}$. It is immediate that b is a least upper bound of S in $(\mathsf{P}, \oslash)$.

(19.8.11) THEOREM: *The system* $(\mathsf{P}, \oslash, \mathsf{w}, \odot)$ *is a basic system of positive real numbers.*

PROOF: The system $(\mathsf{P}, \oslash, \mathsf{w}, \odot)$ satisfies (18.1.I) by (19.8.10); (18.1.II.a) by (19.8.9); (18.1.II.b) by (19.8.7); (18.1.III) by (19.8.4.a); (18.1.IV) by (19.8.4.b); and (18.1.V) by (19.8.6.a).

(19.8.12) PROJECT: Prove that Axiom I(c) is dependent on the remaining axioms (and so can be removed from the list of axioms).

(19.8.13) PROJECT: Prove (19.8.6.b).

19.9. Project. [NO BASIS.] Prove the following two theorems.

(19.9.1) THEOREM: *Let* $(\mathsf{R}, \oslash, \oplus, \otimes)$ *be a system of real numbers, let* $(\mathsf{P}, \oslash, \mathsf{w}, \odot)$ *be the basic system of positive real numbers as in* (19.8), *and let* $(\mathsf{P}, \mathsf{w}, \oslash, +, \cdot)$ *be the corresponding algebraic system of positive real numbers. Then* $(\mathsf{P}, \mathsf{w}, \oslash, +, \cdot)$ *is a subsystem of* $(\mathsf{R}, \mathsf{w}, \oslash, \oplus, \otimes)$, *so that* $(\mathsf{P}, \mathsf{w}, \oslash, +, \cdot) = (\mathsf{P}, \mathsf{w}, \oslash, \oplus, \otimes)$.

OUTLINE OF PROOF: Introduce the system $(\mathsf{R}^\dagger, \oslash^\dagger, \oplus^\dagger, \otimes^\dagger)$ defined from $(\mathsf{P}, \mathsf{w}, \oslash, +, \cdot)$ as in (19.3). Let $(\mathsf{P}^\dagger, \oslash^\dagger, \oplus^\dagger, \otimes^\dagger)$ be the subsystem of "positives" in $(\mathsf{R}^\dagger, \oslash^\dagger, \oplus^\dagger, \otimes^\dagger)$. Define a function ψ on P to $\mathsf{P}^\dagger$ by defining, for every $m \in \mathsf{P}$, $\psi(m) \equiv \{m + \mathsf{w}, \mathsf{w}\}$. Then show that ψ is an isomorphism between $(\mathsf{P}, \mathsf{w}, \oslash, +, \cdot)$ and $(\mathsf{P}^\dagger, \{\mathsf{w} + \mathsf{w}, \mathsf{w}\}, \oslash^\dagger, \oplus^\dagger, \otimes^\dagger)$, [see (19.4.9), (19.4.10), (19.4.11)]. Also define a function φ on R to $\mathsf{R}^\dagger$ thus:

$$\varphi(m) = \begin{cases} \{m + \mathsf{w}, \mathsf{w}\} & \text{if } m \in \mathsf{P} \\ \{\mathsf{w}, \mathsf{w}\} & \text{if } m = 0 \\ \{\mathsf{w}, (-m) + \mathsf{w}\} & \text{if } m \in \mathsf{N}. \end{cases}$$

Then show that φ is an isomorphism between (R, $\otimes$, $\oplus$, $\otimes$) and ($\mathsf{R}^\dagger$, $\otimes^\dagger$, $\oplus^\dagger$, $\otimes^\dagger$). Note that $\psi = (\varphi(m); m \in \mathsf{P})$, so that φ carries P into $\mathsf{P}^\dagger$. Finally, since ($\mathsf{P}^\dagger$, $\otimes^\dagger$, $\oplus^\dagger$, $\otimes^\dagger$) is a subsystem of ($\mathsf{R}^\dagger$, $\otimes^\dagger$, $\oplus^\dagger$, $\otimes^\dagger$), show that (P, w, $\otimes$, $+$, $\cdot$) is a subsystem of (R, w, $\otimes$, $\oplus$, $\otimes$).

(19.9.2) THEOREM: *The axioms for a system of real numbers are categorical.*

OUTLINE OF PROOF: Given two systems of real numbers (R_1, $\otimes_1$, $\oplus_1$, $\otimes_1$) and (R_2, $\otimes_2$, $\oplus_2$, $\otimes_2$), let (P_1, w_1, $\otimes_1$, $\oplus_1$, $\otimes_1$) and (P_2, w_2, $\otimes_2$, $\oplus_2$, $\otimes_2$) be the algebraic system of positive real numbers such that (P_1, $\otimes_1$, $\oplus_1$, $\otimes_1$) and (P_2, $\otimes_2$, $\oplus_2$, $\otimes_2$) are subsystems of the original systems. Then there is an isomorphism φ between (P_1, w_1, $\otimes_1$, $\oplus_1$, $\otimes_1$) and (P_2, w_2, $\otimes_2$, $\oplus_2$, $\otimes_2$). Define ψ on R_1 to R_2 thus:

$$\psi(m) \equiv \begin{cases} \varphi(m) & \text{if } m \in \mathsf{P}_1 \\ -\varphi(-m) & \text{if } m \in \mathsf{N}_1 \\ 0_2 & \text{if } m = 0_1. \end{cases}$$

Prove that ψ is an isomorphism between the original systems.

19.10. Subsystems of a System of Real Numbers. [BASIS: (R, $\otimes$, $\oplus$, $\otimes$); AXIOMS: I–V.] Before introducing the many subsystems of (R, $\otimes$, $\oplus$, $\otimes$), we shall again simplify the notation by replacing $\otimes$, $\oplus$, $\otimes$ by $<$, $+$, $\cdot$, recognizing that the context will make the meaning clear. Moreover, in order to bring the notation closer to that in common use, we shall replace w by 1, again depending on the context to clarify the meaning.

One (algebraic) subsystem of (R, 1, $<$, $+$, $\cdot$) already studied is (P, 1, $<$, $+$, $\cdot$) [see (19.8), (19.9)]. Applying (18.3.3), (18.3.6), (18.5.4), we see that (P, 1, $<$, $+$, $\cdot$) contains a subsystem of positive rational numbers, and, applying (16.10.1), we find a further subsystem of positive integers. Hence it is to be expected that (R, 1, $<$, $+$, $\cdot$) has subsystems of these types also. We shall tabulate these together with other important subsystems after introducing the necessary subsets.

(19.10.1) DEFINITION: Define

(a) $\mathsf{I} \equiv \left[\sum_{k=1}^{n} 1; n \in I\right] = \left[n \odot 1; n \in I\right]$;

(b) $\mathsf{F} \equiv [x \cdot y^{-1}; x, y \in \mathsf{I}]$;

(c) $\mathsf{E} \equiv \mathsf{I} + [0] + [-x; x \in \mathsf{I}]$;

(d) $\mathsf{T} \equiv \mathsf{F} + [0] + [-x; x \in \mathsf{F}] = [x \cdot y^{-1}; x, y \in \mathsf{E}, y \neq 0]$.

REMARK: It should be noted that $\mathsf{I} \subset \mathsf{F} \subset \mathsf{T}$, $\mathsf{I} \subset \mathsf{E} \subset \mathsf{T}$, $\mathsf{I} \subset \mathsf{F} \subset \mathsf{P}$.

We tabulate various (algebraic) systems based on the various subsets now available.

	System	Name of System
(a)	$(\mathsf{P}, 1, <, +, \cdot)$	*system of positives*
(b)	$(\mathsf{P} + [0], 1, <, +, \cdot)$	*system of non-negative real numbers*
(c)	$(\mathsf{F}, 1, <, +, \cdot)$	*system of positive rational real numbers*
(d)	$(\mathsf{F} + [0], 1, <, +, \cdot)$	*system of non-negative rational real numbers*
(e)	$(\mathsf{I}, 1, <, +, \cdot)$	*system of positive integral real numbers*
(f)	$(\mathsf{I} + [0], 1, <, +, \cdot)$	*system of non-negative integral real numbers*
(g)	$(\mathsf{T}, 1, <, +, \cdot)$	*system of rational real numbers*
(h)	$(\mathsf{E}, 1, <, +, \cdot)$	*system of integral real numbers*

(19.10.2) TABLE

(19.10.3) THEOREM: *The systems in* (19.10.2) *are subsystems of* $(\mathsf{R}, 1, <, +, \cdot)$.

PROOF: The proof for (a) has been made [see (19.8.1)]. Proofs for the remaining systems are straightforward and are left to the reader.

(19.10.4) REMARK: It should be observed that many interrelations exist among the systems in (19.10.2). For example, (h) is a subsystem of (g). Furthermore, certain of the systems are of types considered earlier. Indeed, by (19.9.1), (a) is an algebraic system of positive real numbers. Moreover, (c) is an algebraic system of positive rational numbers, and is, in fact, that associated with $(\mathsf{F}, 1, \cdot)$, which may be proved a basic system of positive rational numbers. Finally, (e) is an algebraic system of positive integers, namely, that associated with $(\mathsf{I}, 1, (x + 1; x \in \mathsf{I}))$, which may be proved to be a basic system of positive integers. It would, of course, be possible to find appropriate axioms for each of the systems listed, although this has not been necessary for our purposes.

Once a real number system and its subsystems have been made available, it is customary to discard for purposes of future work the systems $(I, 1, <, +, \cdot)$, $(\boldsymbol{F}, \boldsymbol{u}, <, +, \cdot)$, $(\mathcal{P}, v, <, +, \cdot)$, replacing them by their counterparts (19.10.2.e), (19.10.2.c), (19.10.2.a). All the properties proved in the earlier chapters hold for the systems within $(\mathsf{R}, 1, <, +, \cdot)$. Of course, such a replacement is entirely optional, but it possesses certain advantages.

For many purposes, the systems $(\mathsf{T}, 1, <, +, \cdot)$, $(\mathsf{E}, 1, <, +, \cdot)$ are more useful than systems of positive rational numbers and of positive integers, chiefly because of the facts contained in the next theorem.

(19.10.5) Theorem: *The systems* $(\mathsf{T}, +)$, $(\mathsf{E}, +)$, $(\mathsf{T} - [0], \cdot)$ *are groups.*

Proof: This is left to the reader.

Similarly, $(\mathsf{I} + [0], 1, <, +, \cdot)$ possesses advantages over a system of positive integers. The next theorem illustrates this fact.

(19.10.6) Theorem: *If* $m \in \mathsf{I}$, $n \in \mathsf{I} + [0]$, *then there exist unique elements* $q, r \in \mathsf{I} + [0]$ *such that*

(a) $$n = m \cdot q + r \quad \textit{and} \quad r < m.$$

Proof: If $m < n$ and $m \,|'\, n$, this is a consequence of (9.4.9); in fact, $q, r \in \mathsf{I}$ in this case, so that $q \neq 0$, $r \neq 0$. If $m < n$ and $m \mid n$, then, by the definition of $|$, there exists $q \in \mathsf{I}$ such that $n = m \cdot q$, and (a) is true with $r = 0$. The uniqueness in this case is easily demonstrated and is left for the reader. If $m = n$, then $q = 1$, $r = 0$ are effective in (a), and again uniqueness is easily shown. Finally, if $n < m$ then $q = 0$, $r = n$ are effective and are again unique. This completes the proof.

Remark: The reader should note that (19.10.6) implies both (9.4.9) and (9.8.1), and thus effects a simplification in their combined statement.

(19.10.7) Project: Prove that R, P, N are uncountable, and that F, T, I, E are countable.

(19.10.8) Project: Prove (19.10.3).

(19.10.9) Project: Prove (19.10.5).

(19.10.10) Project: Prove that, if $a, b \in \mathsf{R}$ with $a < b$, then there exists $x \in \mathsf{T}$ such that $a < x$, $x < b$.

Chapter 20

FIELDS

20.1. Introduction. [No Basis.] In the preceding chapters many mathematical systems have been introduced and studied briefly. In particular, some of these systems have been referred to as "number systems." Let us briefly consider two of these, the real number system and the rational real number system [see (19.10.2.g)]. While these systems are by no means alike (isomorphic), since, for example, the set of real numbers is uncountable, while the set of rational real numbers is countable [see (19.10.7)], they do have many common properties. For example, two associative operations $+$, $\cdot$ appear in each system; $(\mathsf{R}, +)$, $(\mathsf{R} - [0], \cdot)$ and $(\mathsf{T}, +)$, $(\mathsf{T} - [0], \cdot)$ are commutative groups; also, $+$ and $\cdot$ satisfy the distributive laws (19.2.IV) in each system. It follows that mathematical systems may possess strikingly similar properties, although they are not isomorphic and so possess also strikingly different properties.

Until the beginning of the present century, most mathematical work with such systems as were known was directed toward studying the contrasts. Interest was centered on the special properties of each individual system—in particular, those properties possessed by that system and by no other (not isomorphic to it). In the past few decades, however, increasingly more attention has been devoted to the similarities between systems—the properties common to various mathematical domains.

The technique for comparative study is to accept a few of the common properties of the several systems as ax oms, thence to develop the consequences of those axioms alone. Such deductions will of course be valid for any (known or unknown) systems for which the axioms are true, in particular, for the original several systems. The resulting theory is a "unification" of the several theories with respect to their common features.

The reader has probably thought already of group theory in this connection. Several diverse examples of groups were given in (7.2) and (14.3); more instances appeared later, in the systems $(F, \cdot)$ of positive rational numbers, $(\mathcal{P}, \cdot)$ of positive real numbers, $(\mathsf{R}, +)$ of real numbers, $(\mathsf{R} - [0], \cdot)$ of non-zero real numbers. Many further instances beyond our scope here have been found to be of great importance. In the theory of groups, then, lie the common features of all these instances and still others. That such common properties are proved for all instances at one stroke, when they appear as deductions from the group axioms, is a powerful motivation for extensive study of groups. The primary purpose of the present chapter is to illustrate the principle of unification in the theory of number systems. We shall postulate a few common properties of the rational real and the real number systems, namely, those pertaining to the operations $+$, $\cdot$; subsequent deductions from the axioms will include those properties which are particularly interesting for the real (or rational real) number system. A secondary aim, namely that of extending the theory of Chapter 19, will thus be achieved. The theory to be presented is the *theory of fields*; it is the springboard for much of modern algebra.

20.2. Axioms for a Field. [No Basis.] The foundation of field theory is as follows:

Basis: $(K, +, \cdot)$, where K is a set, and $+$, $\cdot$ are operations on $K \times K$ to K.

Axioms:

I. There exist $a, b \in K$ with $a \neq b$.

II. $(K, +)$ is a commutative group:
  (a) $a, b, c \in K$ implies $(a + b) + c = a + (b + c)$;
  (b) $a, b \in K$ implies $a + b = b + a$;
  (c) if $a, b \in K$, there exists $x \in K$ with $a + x = b$.

The identity of the group $(K, +)$ is donated by 0.

III. For every $a, b, c \in K$, $(a \cdot b) \cdot c = a \cdot (b \cdot c)$ (associativity).

IV. For every $a, b \in K$, $a \cdot b = b \cdot a$ (commutativity).

V. If $a, b \in K$, $a \neq 0$, there exists $x \in K$ with $a \cdot x = b$.

VI. If $a, b, c \in K$, $(a + b) \cdot c = a \cdot c + b \cdot c$ (distributivity).

Remark: In II, the third group axiom is lacking, since it follows from (c) in view of (b). Note that III, IV, V together do *not* state that $(K, \cdot)$ is a group; the hypothesis $a \neq 0$ in V makes this trio much weaker than the group axioms. In (20.3) this matter is fully discussed. It should be noted that a generalization arises if the commutativity IV of $\cdot$ is dropped, provided mates of V and VI are appended, to the effect that $a, b \in K$, $a \neq 0$ implies the existence of $x \in K$ with $x \cdot a = b$, and that $c \cdot (a + b) = c \cdot a + c \cdot b$ for $a, b, c \in K$. The system so obtained carries the names *quasi-field* and *division ring*. We shall not study quasi-fields here, although many of the properties of fields are valid also for quasi-fields. Finally, the notational conventions of (8.7) will be adopted here.

With respect to consistency, we might readily refer to the system $(\mathsf{R}, +, \cdot)$ of real numbers, which satisfies our axioms [see (19.2.I.a),

(19.2.II), (19.7.17), (19.7.9), (19.7.13), (19.2.IV)]. However, simpler examples exist, which do not depend ultimately on consistency for the positive integers. Perhaps the simplest is the following:

(20.2.1) EXAMPLE: $K \equiv [m, n]$, $m \neq n$; $+, \cdot$ *are defined thus:*

$+$	m	n
m	m	n
n	n	m

$\cdot$	m	n
m	m	m
n	m	n

Note that $(K, +)$ is the commutative group in (7.2.1); moreover, $0 = m$. Thus II holds. Now I and IV are obvious. In V, since $a \neq 0$, we have $a = n$; if $b = m$, then $x = m$, and if $b = n$, then $x = n$. Finally, III and VI may be verified directly.

A simple proof that the axioms for a field are not categorical is obtained when one proves that the following example is a field:

(20.2.2) EXAMPLE: $K \equiv [p, q, r]$, *where* p, q, r *are pairwise distinct;* $+, \cdot$ *are defined thus:*

$+$	p	q	r
p	p	q	r
q	q	r	p
r	r	p	q

$\cdot$	p	q	r
p	p	p	p
q	p	q	r
r	p	r	q

It is left to the reader to verify the axioms for (20.2.2). Now, if this field is isomorphic to that of (20.2.1) [use (14.2.10) for the definition of isomorphism], then $[m, n] \sim [p, q, r]$, which is false.

Consequences of the axioms will be developed in the next sections.

(20.2.3) PROJECT: Verify III and VI for (20.2.1).

(20.2.4) PROJECT: Prove the axioms for (20.2.2).

(20.2.5) PROJECT: Give an alternate proof of the noncategorical feature of the axioms for a field using the real numbers and the rational real numbers. What objection might be raised to this alternate proof?

20.3. The Special Role of 0. [BASIS: $(K, +, \cdot)$; AXIOMS: I–VI.]

(20.3.1) DEFINITION: If $a \in K$, define $-a$ to be the unique inverse of a in the group $(K, +)$. The element $-a$ is called the *negative* of a. [See (7.3.6) and the remark immediately following (7.3.6).]

(20.3.2) Corollary: *Let* $a, b \in K$. *Then*

(a) $-(-a) = a$;
(b) $a \neq b$ *implies* $-a \neq -b$;
(c) $-0 = 0$;
(d) $-(a + b) = (-b) + (-a) = (-a) + (-b)$.

Proof: These results are restatements of the corresponding properties for a general group. Thus (a) is (7.3.7), (b) is (7.3.8), (c) is (7.3.12), and (d) is (7.3.13), in view of II(b).

(20.3.3) Theorem: *For every* $a \in K$, $a \cdot 0 = 0 \cdot a = 0$.

Proof: Since 0 is the unit of the group $(K, +)$, we have $0 + 0 = 0$. Hence, by VI,

$$0 \cdot a = (0 + 0) \cdot a = 0 \cdot a + 0 \cdot a.$$

Then, since $-(0 \cdot a)$ is the inverse of $0 \cdot a$,

$$\begin{aligned} 0 = 0 \cdot a + (-(0 \cdot a)) &= ((0 \cdot a) + (0 \cdot a)) + (-(0 \cdot a)) \\ &= (0 \cdot a) + ((0 \cdot a) + (-(0 \cdot a))) \quad \text{[by III]} \\ &= 0 \cdot a + 0 \\ &= 0 \cdot a. \end{aligned}$$

That $a \cdot 0 = 0$ follows from the commutativity IV.

(20.3.4) Corollary: *If* $a, b, x \in K$ *such that* $b \neq 0$ *and* $a \cdot x = b$, *then* $x \neq 0$.

Proof: If $x = 0$, then $b = a \cdot 0 = 0$, contrary to $b \neq 0$.

Remark: This strengthens V, in case $b \neq 0$, to yield $x \neq 0$.

(20.3.5) Theorem: *If* $a, b \in K$ *such that* $a \cdot b = 0$, *then* $a = 0$ *or* $b = 0$.

Proof: The proof is indirect. Suppose that $a \cdot b = 0$ and the conclusion is false, that is, $a \neq 0$ and $b \neq 0$. By V, (20.3.4), IV, there exists $x \in K$ such that $x \cdot b = b$, $x \neq 0$. By IV, V, there exists $y \in K$ such that $y \cdot a = x$. Hence, by (20.3.3),

$$0 = y \cdot 0 = y \cdot a \cdot b = x \cdot b = b,$$

contrary to $b \neq 0$.

(20.3.6) Corollary: *If* $a, b \in K$ *such that* $a \neq 0$ *and* $b \neq 0$, *then* $a \cdot b \neq 0$.

Proof: This is a contrapositive of (20.3.5).

(20.3.7) Theorem: *The system* $(K - [0], \cdot)$ *is a subsystem of* $(K, \cdot)$; *as such, it is a commutative group.*

Proof: In accordance with (14.5.3), it is first to be shown that

$$a, b \in K - [0] \text{ implies } a \cdot b \in K - [0].$$

But this is exactly the statement of (20.3.6). In view of III, IV, it remains to show that

$$\text{if } a, b \in K - [0], \text{ there exists } x \in K - [0] \text{ such that } a \cdot x = b.$$

That $x \in K$ exists follows from V; since $b \neq 0$, it follows from (20.3.4) that $x \in K - [0]$.

(20.3.8) Definition: The unique identity of the group $K - [0]$ is denoted by 1. If $a \in K - [0]$, the unique inverse of a is denoted by a^{-1} and is called the *reciprocal* of a.

(20.3.9) Corollary: *Let $a, b \in K$ such that $a, b \neq 0$. Then*

(a) $(a^{-1})^{-1} = a$;
(b) $a \neq b$ *implies* $a^{-1} \neq b^{-1}$;
(c) $1^{-1} = 1$;
(d) $(a \cdot b)^{-1} = b^{-1} \cdot a^{-1} = a^{-1} \cdot b^{-1}$.

Proof: This follows from group theory; in the present notation, (a) is (7.3.7), (b) is (7.3.8), (c) is (7.3.12), and (d) is (7.3.13) in view of IV.

(20.3.10) Corollary:

(a) $1 \neq 0$;
(b) *if* $a \in K$, *then* $a \cdot 1 = 1 \cdot a = a$.

Proof: That $1 \neq 0$ follows from the fact that $1 \in K - [0]$. Clearly (b) holds if $a \neq 0$, by the definition of 1 as an identity of $(K - [0], \cdot)$. But if $a = 0$, then, by (20.3.3), $a \cdot 1 = 0 \cdot 1 = 0 = a$ and $1 \cdot a = 1 \cdot 0 = 0 = a$.

One might naturally ask why the axioms are not formulated so that $(K, \cdot)$ is a group rather than the subsystem $(K - [0], \cdot)$. Suppose that V is strengthened to read

V′. if $a, b \in K$, there exists $x \in K$ with $a \cdot x = b$,

and that the other axioms are unmodified. It is now shown that the axioms become inconsistent. By III, IV, V′, $(K, \cdot)$ is a group. Let 1 be its identity. Moreover, (20.3.3) holds in the modified system. Now apply V′ with $a = 0$, $b = 1$, to obtain $x \in K$ with $0 \cdot x = 1$. By (20.3.3), $0 \cdot x = 0$, whence $0 = 1$. Now if $a \in K$, we have

$$0 = 0 \cdot a = 1 \cdot a = a.$$

It follows that for every $a, b \in K$, it is true that $a = b$ $(= 0)$, in direct contradiction to I. Of course, there is no objection to studying a system $(K, +, \cdot)$ in which $K = [0]$, and $(K, +)$, $(K, \cdot)$ are groups. Such a system satisfies trivially Axioms II, III, IV, V′, VI, but its theory is completely uninteresting.

The element 0 is thus seen to play a highly special role in the theory of a field; its character as a unit for $(K, +)$ precludes the possibility of its possessing an inverse in the system $(K, \cdot)$.

(20.3.11) PROJECT: Let $n \in I$ and $(a_m; m \in I_n)$ be an n-tuple in K. Prove that

(a) for every $b \in K$, $\sum_{m=1}^{n}(a_m \cdot b) = \left(\sum_{m=1}^{n} a_m\right) \cdot b$ [see (12.2)];

(b) if $a_m = 0$ for every $m \in I_n$, then $\sum_{m=1}^{n} a_m = 0$.

(20.3.12) PROJECT: Define $F \equiv (-a; a \in K)$, whence F is on K to K. Determine whether F is an isomorphism between
(a) K and K;
(b) $(K, +)$ and $(K, +)$;
(c) $(K, \cdot)$ and $(K, \cdot)$;
(d) $(K, 0)$ and $(K, 0)$;
(e) $(K, 1)$ and $(K, 1)$;
(f) $(K, +, \cdot)$ and $(K, +, \cdot)$.

(20.3.13) PROJECT: Prove that any isomorphism between $(K, +, \cdot)$ and $(K, +, \cdot)$ carries 0 into 0 and 1 into 1.

(20.3.14) PROJECT: Define a function F on I to K so that, for every $n \in I$,

$$F(n) = \sum_{k=1}^{n} 1,$$

and define $K_0 \equiv$ range of F. Prove that
(a) for every $m, n \in I$, $F(m + n) = F(m) + F(n)$;
(b) for every $m, n \in I$, $F(m \cdot n) = F(m) \cdot F(n)$.
Is F a one-to-one correspondence between I and K_0? Is 0 in K_0?

(20.3.15) PROJECT: Let $n \in I$ and $(a_m; m \in I_n)$ be an n-tuple in K such that, for every $m \in I_n$, $a_m \neq 0$. Prove that

$$\prod_{m=1}^{n} a_m \neq 0.$$

20.4. Negatives, Products and Quotients. [BASIS: $(K, +, \cdot)$; AXIOMS: I–VI.] In this section, we shall determine interconnections between the "product" operation $\cdot$, and the function $(-a; a \in K)$. We shall then study the "quotient" operation $(a \cdot b^{-1}; (a, b) \in K \times (K - [0]))$.

(20.4.1) THEOREM: *For every* $a, b \in K$, $(-a) \cdot b = -(a \cdot b)$.
PROOF: Clearly $a + (-a) = 0$, so that, by (20.3.3), VI,

$$a \cdot b + (-a) \cdot b = (a + (-a)) \cdot b = 0 \cdot b = 0.$$

But the unique $x \in K$ with $a \cdot b + x = 0$ is $-(a \cdot b)$, whence $(-a) \cdot b = -(a \cdot b)$.

REMARK: We may write $-a \cdot b$ for the common value of $(-a) \cdot b$ and $-(a \cdot b)$ without danger of ambiguity.

(20.4.2) COROLLARY: *For every* $a, b \in K$, $(-a) \cdot (-b) = a \cdot b$.
PROOF: Applying (20.4.1) twice, we have

$$(-a) \cdot (-b) = -(a \cdot (-b)) = -(-(a \cdot b)).$$

But $-(-(a \cdot b)) = a \cdot b$ by (20.3.2.a). Hence the result follows.

(20.4.3) COROLLARY: *For every* $a \in K$, $(-1) \cdot a = -a$.
PROOF: We have, by (20.4.1), $(-1) \cdot a = -(1 \cdot a) = -a$.

(20.4.4) LEMMA: *If* $a \in K$, $a \neq 0$, *then* $(-a)^{-1} = -(a^{-1})$.
PROOF: Clearly $(-a)^{-1}$ is the unique $x \in K$ such that $(-a) \cdot x = 1$. We shall show that $-(a^{-1})$ has the same property. In fact,

$$\begin{aligned} (-a) \cdot (-(a^{-1})) &= a \cdot (a^{-1}) && \text{[by (20.4.2)]} \\ &= 1. \end{aligned}$$

The result follows.

REMARK: We may write $-a^{-1}$ for the common value of $(-a)^{-1}$ and $-(a^{-1})$, without fear of being ambiguous.

(20.4.5) DEFINITION: Define an operation / (read "divided by") on $K \times (K - [0])$ so that, for every $(a, b) \in K \times (K - [0])$, $a/b = a \cdot b^{-1} = b^{-1} \cdot a$. We also write $\frac{a}{b}$ for a/b.

REMARK: We may refer to a/b as the *quotient of* a *by* b and call a the *numerator* and b the *denominator*.

(20.4.6) THEOREM: *For every* $a, b \in K$ *with* $b \neq 0$, *there exists a unique element* $x \in K$ *such that* $b \cdot x = a$; *moreover*, $x = a/b$.
PROOF: If $a = 0$, then

$$x = 0 = 0 \cdot b^{-1} = a \cdot b^{-1} = a/b$$

is effective; moreover, if $b \cdot y = a = 0$, then $y \neq 0$ contradicts (20.3.5), in view of the hypothesis $b \neq 0$. Hence $y = 0 = x$ and the uniqueness is established. Now suppose $a \neq 0$. Then $a, b \in K - [0]$, and (7.3.9) applies, yielding the desired conclusions.

REMARK: That the condition $b \neq 0$ in (20.4.6) is required is seen thus. Suppose $b = 0$. If $a \neq 0$, then x cannot exist in view of (20.3.3). But if $a = 0$, then, although x exists — for example, $x = 0$ and $x = 1$ are effective — x is evidently not unique, since $0 \neq 1$.

(20.4.7) THEOREM: *Let* $a \in K$. *Then,*

(a) *if* $a \neq 0$, *then* $1/a = a^{-1} \neq 0$;
(b) *if* $a \neq 0$, *then* $a/a = 1$;
(c) $a/1 = a$.

PROOF: Evidently $1/a = 1 \cdot a^{-1} = a^{-1}$; also, $a^{-1} \neq 0$, since a^{-1} is the inverse of a in the group $K - [0]$. This proves (a). The proofs of (b), (c) are left to the reader.

(20.4.8) THEOREM: *If* $a, b \in K$, $b \neq 0$, *then*

$$\frac{-a}{b} = -\frac{a}{b} = \frac{a}{-b}.$$

REMARK: This is an analogue of (20.4.1) for the operation /.
PROOF: We have

$$\frac{-a}{b} = (-a) \cdot b^{-1} = -(a \cdot b^{-1}) \qquad \text{[by (20.4.1)]}$$
$$= -\frac{a}{b}.$$

Also,

$$\frac{a}{-b} = a \cdot (-b)^{-1} = a \cdot (-(b^{-1})) \qquad \text{[by (20.4.4)]}$$
$$= -(a \cdot b^{-1}) \qquad \text{[by (20.4.1)]}$$
$$= -\frac{a}{b}.$$

(20.4.9) COROLLARY: *If* $a, b \in K$, $b \neq 0$, *then*

(a) $$\frac{-a}{-b} = -\frac{-a}{b} = -\frac{a}{-b} = \frac{a}{b};$$

(b) $$-\frac{-a}{-b} = -\frac{a}{b}.$$

PROOF: This follows from (20.4.8) and (20.4.1); details are left to the reader.

(20.4.10) THEOREM: *If* $a, b, c, d \in K$, *such that* $b, d \neq 0$, *then*

$$\frac{a}{b} \cdot \frac{c}{d} = \frac{a \cdot c}{b \cdot d}.$$

PROOF: We have

$$\frac{a}{b} \cdot \frac{c}{d} = (a \cdot b^{-1}) \cdot (c \cdot d^{-1})$$
$$= (a \cdot c) \cdot (b^{-1} \cdot d^{-1}) \qquad \text{[by III, IV]}$$
$$= (a \cdot c) \cdot (b \cdot d)^{-1} \qquad \text{[by (20.3.9.d)]}$$
$$= \frac{a \cdot c}{b \cdot d}.$$

(20.4.11) COROLLARY: *If $a, b, d \in K$ such that $b, d \neq 0$, then*

$$\frac{a \cdot d}{b \cdot d} = \frac{a}{b}.$$

REMARK: This is a "cancellation law" for quotients.

PROOF: We have

$$\frac{a \cdot d}{b \cdot d} = \frac{a}{b} \cdot \frac{d}{d} \qquad \text{[by (20.4.10)]}$$

$$= \frac{a}{b} \cdot 1 = \frac{a}{b} \qquad \text{[by (20.4.7.b)].}$$

(20.4.12) LEMMA: *If $a, b \in K$ such that $a, b \neq 0$, then*

$$\frac{1}{\frac{a}{b}} = \left(\frac{a}{b}\right)^{-1} = \frac{b}{a}.$$

REMARK: This states that the reciprocal of a quotient is obtained by "inverting," that is, interchanging the numerator and denominator.

PROOF: Since $b \neq 0$, we have $b^{-1} \neq 0$ by (20.4.7.a). Hence $a \neq 0$ yields $a/b = a \cdot b^{-1} \neq 0$ by (20.3.6). Now (20.4.7.a) applied to a/b yields the first equality. But

$$\left(\frac{a}{b}\right)^{-1} = (a \cdot b^{-1})^{-1} = a^{-1} \cdot (b^{-1})^{-1} \qquad \text{[by (20.3.9.d)]}$$

$$= a^{-1} \cdot b \qquad \text{[by (20.3.9.a)]}$$

$$= \frac{b}{a},$$

whence the second equality also holds.

(20.4.13) THEOREM: *If $a, b, c, d \in K$ such that $b, c, d \neq 0$, then*

$$\frac{\frac{a}{c}}{\frac{b}{d}} = \frac{a}{c} \cdot \frac{d}{b} = \frac{a \cdot d}{b \cdot c}.$$

REMARK: This states that the quotient of two quotients is obtained by "inverting" the denominator and then forming the product.

PROOF: The second equality follows from (20.4.10). To obtain the first, we use (20.4.12) to obtain

$$\frac{\frac{a}{c}}{\frac{b}{d}} = \frac{a}{c} \cdot \left(\frac{b}{d}\right)^{-1} = \frac{a}{c} \cdot \frac{d}{b}.$$

(20.4.14) Lemma: *If $a, b, c \in K$ such that $c \neq 0$, then*

$$\frac{a}{c} + \frac{b}{c} = \frac{a+b}{c}.$$

Proof: We have

$$\begin{aligned}\frac{a}{c} + \frac{b}{c} &= a \cdot c^{-1} + b \cdot c^{-1} && \text{[by (20.4.5)]}\\ &= (a+b) \cdot c^{-1} && \text{[by VI]}\\ &= \frac{a+b}{c} && \text{[by (20.4.5)].}\end{aligned}$$

(20.4.15) Theorem: *If $a, b, c, d \in K$ such that $c, d \neq 0$, then*

$$\frac{a}{c} + \frac{b}{d} = \frac{a \cdot d + c \cdot b}{c \cdot d}.$$

Proof: We have

$$\begin{aligned}\frac{a}{c} + \frac{b}{d} &= \frac{a \cdot d}{c \cdot d} + \frac{c \cdot b}{c \cdot d} && \text{[by (20.4.11)]}\\ &= \frac{a \cdot d + c \cdot b}{c \cdot d} && \text{[by (20.4.14)].}\end{aligned}$$

Remark: Appropriate rules for applying the operation + to quotients are contained in (20.4.14), (20.4.15), the former applying when the denominators are the same and the latter applying generally.

(20.4.16) Project: Prove the "laws of exponents": if $a \in K$, and $m, n \in I$, then

$$(a^m) \cdot (a^n) = a^{m+n}, \quad (a^m)^n = a^{m \cdot n},$$

by referring to Chapter 12.

(20.4.17) Project: Compare (20.4.10), (20.4.11), (20.4.13), (20.4.15) with (9.8.11.a), (9.8.9), (9.8.11.b), (9.8.11.c) [see the appendix], in which ÷ plays the role of /. Note particularly that the hypotheses in (9.8) must be more stringent than in (20.4) in order to secure that the symbols are meaningful. State and prove for / analogues of (9.8.4), (9.8.5).

(20.4.18) Project: Let $a \in K$, $n \in I$. Prove that $(-a)^n = a^n$ if n is even, and $(-a)^n = -(a^n)$ if n is odd. Also show that, if $a \neq 0$, $(1/a)^n = 1/a^n$.

(20.4.19) Project: Prove (b), (c) in (20.4.7).

(20.4.20) Project: Let $n \in I$ and $(a_m; m \in I_n)$ be an n-tuple in K. Prove that

$$\sum_{m=1}^{n}(-a_m) = -\sum_{m=1}^{n} a_m;$$

also prove that, if $a_m \neq 0$ for every $m \in I_n$, then

$$\prod_{m=1}^{n} \frac{1}{a_m} = \frac{1}{\prod_{m=1}^{n} a_m}.$$

20.5. Differences. [BASIS: $(K, +, \cdot)$; AXIOMS: I–VI.] We define an operation $-$ (*minus*) on $K \times K$ to K analogous to the operation $/$ introduced in the last section. This operation will be seen to be very much like the operation on $>$ ($\subset I \times I$) to I bearing the same name [see (9.6)]. However, the domain of the present operation is all of $K \times K$.

(20.5.1) DEFINITION: Define an operation $-$ (read "minus") on $K \times K$ to K, so that, for every $(a, b) \in K \times K$, $a - b = a + (-b)$.

REMARK: The element $a - b$ is referred to as the *difference* between a and b.

(20.5.2) THEOREM: *For every $a, b \in K$, there exists a unique element $x \in K$ such that $b + x = a$; moreover, $x = a - b$.*

PROOF: We may apply (7.3.9), since $(K, +)$ is a group; all conclusions are immediate, in view of (20.5.1).

(20.5.3) THEOREM: *Let $a, b \in K$. Then*

(a) $$-(a + b) = (-a) - b = (-b) - a;$$
(b) $$-(a - b) = (-a) + b = b - a;$$
(c) $$a - a = 0.$$

PROOF: We have, by (20.5.1),

$$\begin{aligned} (-a) - b = (-a) + (-b) &= -(a + b) && \text{[by (20.3.2.d)]} \\ &= -b + (-a) && \text{[by (20.3.2.d)]} \\ &= -b - a && \text{[by (20.5.1)]}, \end{aligned}$$

and (a) holds. By (a),

$$\begin{aligned} -(a - b) = -(a + (-b)) &= (-a) - (-b) \\ &= (-(-b)) - a \\ &= b - a && \text{[by (20.3.2.a)]}, \end{aligned}$$

so that (b) is true. Finally, (c) holds by (20.5.2), since $a + 0 = a$.

The following "associative laws" are analogous to those in (9.6.6) which refer to $-$ on $>$ to I. The reader should compare the results for the two environments, noting especially the fact that no restrictive hypotheses are necessary here.

(20.5.4) THEOREM: *Let a, b, c* ϵ *K. Then*

(a) $(a + b) - c = a + (b - c) = a - (c - b)$;
(b) $(a - b) - c = a - (b + c) = (a - c) - b$;
(c) $(a - b) + c = (a + c) - b = a - (b - c) = a + (c - b)$.

PROOF: We prove only (b), leaving (a) and (c) to the reader. We have

$$\begin{aligned}(a - b) - c &= (a + (-b)) + (-c)\\ &= a + ((-b) + (-c))\\ &= a + ((-b) - c) && \text{[by (20.5.1)]}\\ &= a + (-(b + c)) && \text{[by (20.5.3.a)]}\\ &= a - (b + c) && \text{[by (20.5.1)].}\end{aligned}$$

The other equality follows by interchanging b and c.

REMARK: As in (9.6.7) we may agree to use the symbols $m + n - p$, $m - n + p$, $m - n - p$ to represent respectively $(m + n) - p$, $(m - n) + p$, $(m - n) - p$.

(20.5.5) THEOREM: *For every a, b, c* ϵ *K,*

$$(a - b) \cdot c = (a \cdot c) - (b \cdot c).$$

PROOF: We have

$$\begin{aligned}(a - b) \cdot c = (a + (-b)) \cdot c &= (a \cdot c) + ((-b) \cdot c) && \text{[by VI]}\\ &= (a \cdot c) + (-(b \cdot c)) && \text{[by (20.4.1)]}\\ &= (a \cdot c) - (b \cdot c).\end{aligned}$$

The "distributive law" just proved leads immediately to the following theorems pertaining to differences between quotients.

(20.5.6) THEOREM: *If a, b, c* ϵ *K such that* $c \neq 0$, *then*

$$\frac{a}{c} - \frac{b}{c} = \frac{a - b}{c}.$$

REMARK: The reader should compare this with (9.8.8).

PROOF: We have

$$\begin{aligned}\frac{a}{c} - \frac{b}{c} &= (a \cdot c^{-1}) - (b \cdot c^{-1})\\ &= (a - b) \cdot c^{-1} && \text{[by (20.5.5)]}\\ &= \frac{a - b}{c}.\end{aligned}$$

(20.5.7) THEOREM: *If a, b, c, d* ϵ *K such that* $c, d \neq 0$, *then*

$$\frac{a}{c} - \frac{b}{d} = \frac{a \cdot d - c \cdot b}{c \cdot d}.$$

PROOF: This is immediate from (20.5.6) and (20.4.11). [See the proof of (20.4.15).]

Further properties of the operation—are readily obtainable from those given. Readers familiar with "college algebra" will recognize that much of that subject is devoted to applications of our theorems concerning the operations $+$, $\cdot$, $/$, $-$, and so applies to a general field.

(20.5.8) PROJECT: Complete the proof of (20.5.4).

(20.5.9) PROJECT: Define an operation $\odot$ on $I \times K$ thus:

$$\odot \equiv \left(\sum_{k=1}^{n} a;\ (n, a) \in I \times K\right).$$

Develop as many properties of this operation as you can.

(20.5.10) PROJECT: If $a, b \in K$, $n \in I$, express $(a \cdot b)^n$ in another way. Treat also $(a/b)^n$ if $b \neq 0$.

(20.5.11) PROJECT: If $a, b \in K$, $n \in I$, then $(a + b)^n$ and $(a - b)^n$ are defined. Express these in other ways for $n = 1, 2, 3, 4$. [Use the notations implied by (20.5.9) where possible.]

(20.5.12) PROJECT: If $a, b \in K$ with $a, b \neq 0$, express as simple quotients, and state all further necessary hypotheses:

$$\frac{1}{\frac{1}{a} + \frac{1}{b}}, \quad \frac{1}{\frac{1}{a} - \frac{1}{b}}, \quad \frac{1 + \frac{1}{a}}{1 + \frac{1}{b}}.$$

20.6. Conclusion. [NO BASIS.] The material presented in the preceding sections completes our treatment of number systems. If the reader has read carefully this chapter and the preceding, he should realize that all the results pertaining to a field yield many theorems concerning the real number system; he should see also that, inasmuch as the theorems on fields apply even to such bizarre systems as those introduced in (20.2.1) and (20.2.2), a kinship, distant though it may be, can exist between systems whose basic sets are respectively uncountably infinite and finite with 2 or 3 elements.

Chapter 21

CONCLUSION

21.1. The Axiomatic Method. The persistent reader should at this stage have a rather clear conception of the nature of mathematical systems and theories. Let there be no mistake concerning the breadth and depth of mathematical content contained in the preceding chapters. The thoroughness and care in presentation which our aims and point of view have demanded have severely limited both the number of theories which could be presented and the extent to which each could be developed. Nevertheless, the material presented is typical in treatment and content; constructions, procedures and proofs included are similar to those occurring in all branches of mathematics.

One virtue of the axiomatic method has been discussed in Chapter 20 and has been illustrated there by the theory of fields and throughout the book by group theory. When several non-isomorphic instances of a mathematical system exist, great economy in effort results from a unified simultaneous treatment of the various systems through deduction of their properties from the common axioms.

A second advantage of the axiomatic procedure exists which has not been stressed and which plays a role in connection with systems described by categorical axioms. In this case a particular instance, constructed, for example, in the proof of consistency, may be regarded as "typical" of all instances. It may then be argued that this instance will serve all purposes for which a system of the type under consideration is required. For example, would it not have been satisfactory to *define* a positive real number system to be the specific instance (18.2), and present no axioms at all?

Though such a procedure is logically unobjectionable, it entails a practical disadvantage. For it may well happen that, in other theories, a system will arise that is isomorphic to this positive real number system (as, for example, the subsystem $(\mathsf{P}, 1, <, +, \cdot)$ of $(\mathsf{R}, 1, <, +, \cdot)$). Then it is certainly desirable to be able to use all the results known for the specific system as valid results for the isomorphic system. However, such a procedure could be justified only by a "theorem" to the effect that "anything true of a particular mathematical system is true of every system isomorphic to it." Such a "theorem" is obviously much too broad and vague to be amenable to rigorous proof.

In the absence of a broad principle guaranteeing that isomorphic systems have identical properties, and because of the undesirability of having to reprove for the isomorphic system all properties known to be true of the specific instance, it is natural to look for a substitute procedure to achieve the same end. Now a procedure immediately suggests itself, provided a list of a few properties is available which are known to imply all others. For then the few properties may be proved directly for the isomorphic system, and any other properties already proved from the few may be concluded *without* proof. But such a list of a few properties is exactly a list of *axioms*. It should be noted that the purpose of proving [in (19.8.11)] that $(\mathsf{P}, 1, <, \odot)$ is a basic system of positive real numbers is to permit the application to $(\mathsf{P}, 1, <, \odot)$ of all the consequences of the axioms in Chapter 18 for positive real numbers. Without the equivalent of (19.8.11), any result in Chapter 18 desired for $(\mathsf{P}, 1, <, \odot)$ would have to be reproved.

21.2. The Subject Matter of Mathematics. In Chapter 3 loose descriptions of mathematics as the "science of number," the "science of measurement," the "science of space" and the "science of axiomatics" were discussed. The roles of mathematics as a study of a precise counting process and as an abstraction of measuring devices have been considered fully; axiomatic procedures have appeared as the method of development of mathematical theories.

Since the description of mathematics as the "science of space" has not been elaborated here, and since the trained reader may feel that our treatment has been largely "algebraic," a few remarks of explanation are in order.

Actually, the historical distinction between "algebra" and "geometry" has largely disappeared with the modern development of the axiomatic method. A treatment of euclidean plane geometry, for example, would look very much like the treatment we have given for any of the number systems. There might be a basis consisting of a set (whose elements might be called *points* and *lines*) together with one or more relations or functions. The axioms would be of the same general character as those which have appeared in the preceding chapters. And deductions from the axioms would be made in the same fashion, with the same type of reasoning, as proofs have been made throughout the book. "Figures" might be drawn to *illustrate* the mathematical statements and to *suggest* what theorems could be expected to be true, but the proofs would be entirely independent of such figures.

Consistency and categoricalness would be proved as usual. Indeed, it is interesting to note that an instance of euclidean plane geometry is readily constructible from a system $(\mathsf{R}, <, +, \cdot)$ of real numbers. A *point* may be defined as an element of $\mathsf{R} \times \mathsf{R}$, while a *line* may be defined as a subset of $\mathsf{R} \times \mathsf{R}$ of the following form:

$$L(a, b, c) \equiv [(x, y) \in \mathsf{R} \times \mathsf{R}; a \cdot x + b \cdot y = c],$$

where $a, b, c \in \mathsf{R}$, $(a, b) \neq (0, 0)$. A point $(x, y) \in \mathsf{R} \times \mathsf{R}$ is said to *lie on* a line L if $(x, y) \in L$. Basic relations or functions could be defined and the axioms proved. A study of this particular instance is called "analytic geometry."

It should be remarked that there is one very important number system which we have not treated. It is known as the *system of complex numbers*; an instance is readily constructed in terms of $(\mathsf{R}, <, +, \cdot)$ as follows: *Complex numbers* are elements of $\mathfrak{C} \equiv \mathsf{R} \times \mathsf{R}$; two operations $\oplus$, $\otimes$ on $\mathfrak{C} \times \mathfrak{C}$ to $\mathfrak{C}$ are defined thus:

$$\begin{aligned}(a, b) \oplus (c, d) &= (a + b, c + d)\\ (a, b) \otimes (c, d) &= (a \cdot c - b \cdot d, a \cdot d + b \cdot c).\end{aligned}$$

Whether one studies a number system or a geometry or any other mathematical system whose axioms are categorical, one uses the deductive method in the manner which has been thoroughly illustrated. The study of particular systems entails investigation more and more deeply into the interrelations among the basic objects and other objects defined in terms of them. Thus much of the "theory of numbers," which is primarily a study of $(\mathsf{E}, 1, <, +, \cdot)$ of integral real numbers, is devoted to detailed investigation of properties of $<, +, \cdot, |$ (divides), the subset of primes and many other relations and functions on $\mathsf{E} \times \mathsf{E}$. In connection with $(\mathsf{R}, 1, <, +, \cdot)$, a natural study centers about the relations and functions on $\mathsf{R} \times \mathsf{R}$, $(\mathsf{R} \times \mathsf{R}) \times \mathsf{R}$, $\mathsf{R}^n \times \mathsf{R}$, and the like; this study includes "calculus," "function theory," "differential equations," and the like. Many large volumes have been written on each of the many theories expounding the properties of these and other specific mathematical systems.

When one deals with systems whose axioms are noncategorical, one is primarily concerned with a study of the several instances, rather than of particular relations and functions pertaining to a specific instance. But the general methods are the same. In connection with fields, for example, the question of classification is of primary importance. One may ask for a complete description of those fields which are finite [see (20.2)]. It is readily seen that, in the real number field, no x exists such that $x^2 + 1 = 0$. (The reader may easily construct a proof of this fact.) Hence one may ask for a determination of those fields (if any) in which such an element x exists. The reader should check (20.2.1) for this property. It is noteworthy that the complex number system is an infinite field with the property. From what has been said, the reader might correctly infer that, while some fields serve as measuring devices, others do not. This leads to a theory of "ordered fields," such as the real number field, their classification and separation from other fields. And so it goes; every property that a field might—but need not—possess leads to a possible theory within field theory, and to questions of classification.

If the reader's curiosity has been aroused, he may profitably turn to the mathematical literature where he will find some answers to his questions. But he will find many more questions; indeed, it would be strange if the answers ever catch up with the questions. If he finds groups or fields unattractive, other general systems, like rings, semigroups, loops, lattices might possess for him greater appeal. Should he be more interested in theories which deal with specific questions pertaining to prime numbers, functions on R to R, the structure of the set R^n of all n-tuples in R, and the like, he may turn to the literature on number theory, real function theory, and topology.

To assist the reader in selecting material for further study, we include a list of titles, any of which might be regarded as an appropriate sequel to the background material which we have presented.

SUGGESTIONS FOR FURTHER READING

1. Alexandroff, P., and Hopf, H.: *Topologie*, Berlin: J. Springer, 1935.
2. Birkhoff, G., and MacLane, S.: *A Survey of Modern Algebra*, New York: The Macmillan Co., 1941.
3. Courant, R.: *Differential and Integral Calculus* (translated by E. J. McShane), New York: Nordermann Publishing Co., Inc., 1937.
4. Hardy, G. H.: *A Course of Pure Mathematics*, Cambridge: Cambridge University Press, 1944.
5. Hardy, G. H., and Wright, E. M.: *An Introduction to the Theory of Numbers*, Oxford: The Clarendon Press, 1938.
6. Hausdorff, F.: *Mengenlehre*, Leipzig: W. de Gruyter and Co., 1927. (Reprinted by Dover Publications, New York, 1944.)
7. Landau, E.: *Grundlagen der Analysis*, Leipzig: Akademische Verlagsgesellschaft, M. B. H., 1930. (Reprinted by Chelsea Publishing Co., New York, 1946.)
8. MacDuffee, C. C.: *Vectors and Matrices* (Carus Mathematical Monograph), Ithaca: The Mathematical Association of America, 1943.
9. Neumann, J. von, and Morgenstern, O.: *Theory of Games and Economic Behavior*, Princeton: Princeton University Press, 1944.
10. Pontrjagin, L.: *Topological Groups* (translated by E. Lehmer), Princeton: Princeton University Press, 1939.
11. Veblen, O., and Young, J. W.: *Projective Geometry*, Boston: Ginn and Co., 1910.

APPENDIX

SUGGESTIONS AND ANSWERS FOR THE PROJECTS

Appendix

SUGGESTIONS AND ANSWERS FOR THE PROJECTS

Chapter 4

(4.7.7) [earth, Rover], [earth], [Rover], Θ.

(4.7.8)

(a) If $A \subset B$, then every element $a \in A$ is both in A and in B, so that $A \subset A \cdot B$. But, by (4.7.5), $A \cdot B \subset A$; hence, by (4.6.4), $A \cdot B = A$.

(b) We have $A = A \cdot B \subset B$.

(c) We have $A \subset A + B = B$.

Finally, apply (a), assuming $B = C$, $A = C$, whence $A \subset B$, so that $C \cdot C = A \cdot B = A = C$.

(4.7.9) Since A, B are different sets, one of them, say A, contains an element a which is not a member of the other (B). Then $a \in A - B$. Since $a \in' B$, it follows that $a \in' B - A$. This proves that $A - B \not\subset B - A$, since we have produced an element a which is in $A - B$ but not in $B - A$. (The other possibility, that $B \not\subset A$, is similarly treated.)

(4.7.10) Suppose $a \in A - B$. Then $a \in A$ and $a \in' A \cdot B$ (since a is not even in B), whence $a \in A - A \cdot B$. This proves $A - B \subset A - (A \cdot B)$. Now suppose $a \in A - (A \cdot B)$. Then $a \in A$ and $a \in' A \cdot B$. Suppose it were true that $a \in B$. Since $a \in A$, it would follow that $a \in A \cdot B$, which is false, in view of the assertion $a \in' A \cdot B$. Hence it is *not* true that $a \in B$, whence $a \in' B$. This together with $a \in A$ yields $a \in A - B$. This proves $A - (A \cdot B) \subset A - B$.

(4.7.11) Since $A \supset B$ and $A \supset A - B$, it follows that $A \supset B + (A - B)$. But, if $a \in A$, then either $a \in B$ or $a \in' B$. In the former case, $a \in B$; in the latter, $a \in A - B$. Thus $a \in B + (A - B)$. This proves $A \subset B + (A - B)$, and completes the first part. To prove that $B \cdot (A - B)$ is empty, we verify that it has no elements. For any element in it, say a, would be in B and in $A - B$. But $a \in A - B$ yields $a \in' B$, so that a is both a member of B and not a member of B. Since no such a exists, $B \cdot (A - B) = \Theta$.

(4.8.9) $Q \times R = [(q_1, p_1), (q_1, p_2), (q_1, q_1), (q_2, p_1), (q_2, p_2), (q_2, q_1)]$;
$P \times R = [(p_1, p_1), (p_1, p_2), (p_1, q_1), (p_2, p_1), (p_2, p_2), (p_2, q_1), (p_3, p_1), (p_3, p_2), (p_3, q_1)]$.

Chapter 5

(5.2.8) In (5.2.5), $A = [q_1, q_2]$, $B = [p_1, p_2, p_3]$, $R = [(q_1, p_1), (q_1, p_3)]$. In (5.2.6), $A = B = [p_1, p_2, p_3]$, $R = [(p_1, p_1), (p_2, p_1), (p_3, p_1), (p_3, p_2)]$. In (5.2.7), $A = [p_1, p_2, p_3]$, $B = [q_1, q_2, q_3, q_4]$, $R = [(p_1, q_3), (p_2, q_1), (p_3, q_2)]$.

(5.3.8) To prove (a), (b), use (4.7.11).

(c) Let $(a, b) \epsilon (R')'$. Then $(a, b) \epsilon' R'$. Since $A \times B = R + R'$ by (a), $(a, b) \epsilon R$ or $(a, b) \epsilon R'$. Since the latter is impossible by virtue of $(a, b) \epsilon' R'$, it follows that $(a, b) \epsilon R$. Hence $(R')' \subset R$. Now suppose $(a, b) \epsilon R$. Then $(a, b) \epsilon R'$ is impossible, so that $(a, b) \epsilon' R'$. Thus $(a, b) \epsilon (A \times B) - R' = (R')'$. This proves $R \subset (R')'$.

(5.3.9) If $(b, a) \epsilon (A \times B)^*$, then $(a, b) \epsilon A \times B$, whence $(b, a) \epsilon B \times A$, so that $(A \times B)^* \subset B \times A$. Similarly, $B \times A \subset (A \times B)^*$. To prove $\Theta^* = \Theta$, it suffices to show that no pair exists in Θ^*. If there were such a pair, (b, a), then $(a, b) \epsilon \Theta$, contrary to the fact that Θ consists of no pairs. Thus it is impossible that any pair exists in Θ^*. The last part is similarly established, by showing that $E^* \subset E$, $E \subset E^*$.

(5.3.10) If $(a, b) \epsilon (R^*)^*$, then $(b, a) \epsilon R^*$, and $(a, b) \epsilon R$. Thus $(R^*)^* \subset R$. Similarly $R \subset (R^*)^*$.

(5.3.11)

(a) If $a \epsilon$ domain of R, there exists $b \epsilon B$ with $(a, b) \epsilon R$. But then $(b, a) \epsilon R^*$, whence $a \epsilon$ range of R^*. This shows domain of $R \subset$ range of R^*. The reverse inclusion is similarly established.

(b) Apply (a) to R^* in place of R, and use (5.3.10).

(c) To prove domain of $A \times B = A$, it suffices to show that $A \subset$ domain of $A \times B$. Let $b \epsilon B$. Then, for every $a \epsilon A$, $(a, b) \epsilon A \times B$, whence $a \epsilon$ domain of $A \times B$. The second part is similar.

(d) We show that domain of Θ can have no elements: if a were such an element, then there would exist $b \epsilon B$ with $(a, b) \epsilon \Theta$. This is obviously not possible.

(5.3.12) Prove $A \subset$ domain of E: Let $a \epsilon A$; then $(a, a) \epsilon E$, so that $a \epsilon$ domain of E.

(5.3.13)

(a) Sixteen relations:

$[(p_1, p_2), (p_2, p_1), (p_1, p_1), (p_2, p_2)] = A \times A$,
$[(p_1, p_2), (p_2, p_1), (p_1, p_1)]$, $[(p_1, p_2), (p_2, p_1), (p_2, p_2)]$,
$[(p_1, p_2), (p_1, p_1), (p_2, p_2)]$, $[(p_2, p_1), (p_1, p_1), (p_2, p_2)]$,
$[(p_1, p_2), (p_2, p_1)]$, $[(p_1, p_2), (p_1, p_1)]$, $[(p_1, p_2), (p_2, p_2)]$,
$[(p_2, p_1), (p_1, p_1)]$, $[(p_2, p_1), (p_2, p_2)]$, $[(p_1, p_1), (p_2, p_2)] = E$,
$[(p_1, p_2)]$, $[(p_2, p_1)]$, $[(p_1, p_1)]$, $[(p_2, p_2)]$, Θ.

(b) Eight relations:

$A \times A$, $[(p_1, p_2), (p_2, p_1), (p_1, p_1)]$, $[(p_1, p_2), (p_2, p_1), (p_2, p_2)]$, $[(p_1, p_2), (p_2, p_1)]$, E, $[(p_1, p_1)]$, $[(p_2, p_2)]$, Θ.

(c) Four relations:

$A \times A$, $[(p_1, p_2), (p_1, p_1), (p_2, p_2)]$, $[(p_2, p_1), (p_1, p_1), (p_2, p_2)]$, E.

(d) Two relations: $A \times A$, E.

(5.4.10)

$$F_1 = [(p_1, q_1), (p_2, q_1)],$$
$$F_2 = [(p_1, q_1), (p_2, q_2)],$$
$$F_3 = [(p_1, q_2), (p_2, q_1)],$$
$$F_4 = [(p_1, q_2), (p_2, q_2)].$$

Ranges are $[q_1]$, B, B, $[q_2]$, respectively. Additional functions with domain $\subset A$: $[(p_1, q_1)]$, $[(p_1, q_2)]$, $[(p_2, q_1)]$, $[(p_2, q_2)]$, Θ; domains are, respectively, $[p_1]$, $[p_1]$, $[p_2]$, $[p_2]$, Θ.

(5.4.11) If $F = G$, clearly (a) holds; if $a \in$ domain of F, then $a\,F\,F(a)$, $a\,G\,G(a)$, so that $a\,F\,G(a)$, and $F(a) = G(a)$ in view of (5.4.2). Now suppose (a) and (b) are true. To prove $F = G$, we show that $F \subset G$, $G \subset F$. Let $a\,F\,b$, whence $a \in$ domain of F, and $a \in$ domain of G by (a). But $a\,F\,b$ yields $b = F(a)$, whence, by (b), $b = G(a)$. Thus $a\,G\,b$. This shows that $F \subset G$. The reverse inclusion is proved similarly.

(5.5.4)

$$F_1 = [(p_1, p_1), (p_2, p_2), (p_3, p_3)] = E,$$
$$F_2 = [(p_1, p_1), (p_2, p_3), (p_3, p_2)],$$
$$F_3 = [(p_1, p_2), (p_2, p_1), (p_3, p_3)],$$
$$F_4 = [(p_1, p_2), (p_2, p_3), (p_3, p_1)],$$
$$F_5 = [(p_1, p_3), (p_2, p_1), (p_3, p_2)],$$
$$F_6 = [(p_1, p_3), (p_2, p_2), (p_3, p_1)].$$

(5.5.5)

$$F_1 = [(p_1, q_1), (p_2, q_1), (p_3, q_2)],$$
$$F_2 = [(p_1, q_1), (p_2, q_2), (p_3, q_1)],$$
$$F_3 = [(p_1, q_2), (p_2, q_1), (p_3, q_1)],$$
$$F_4 = [(p_1, q_2), (p_2, q_2), (p_3, q_1)],$$
$$F_5 = [(p_1, q_2), (p_2, q_1), (p_3, q_2)],$$
$$F_6 = [(p_1, q_1), (p_2, q_2), (p_3, q_2)].$$

Note that $F_1^* = [(q_1, p_1), (q_1, p_2), (q_2, p_3)]$, and that $q_1\,F_1^*\,p_1$, $q_1\,F_1^*\,p_2$, with $p_1 \neq p_2$, whence F_1^* does not satisfy the requirement for a function. Similar argument applies to the remaining. Hence no one-to-one correspondence exists between A and B.

(5.6.7) There are sixteen such operations; one has range $[q_1]$, one has range $[q_2]$, and the rest have range B.

Chapter 6

(6.5.6) If only two hats are black, all hands are raised, but no one speaks. Joe, wearing one of the black hats argues: "Suppose my hat were white. Then this would be a game with three white and one black hats, whence my black-hatted opponent would have stated immediately his color. Since he did not, my hat must be black." If three hats are black, again all hands are raised and no one speaks. Joe, seeing that one hat is white, argues that if his hat were white, the game would be one of two white and two black hats. Hence one of the two black-hatted opponents should (by the argument just given for this circumstance) have deduced his color. Since they actually remained silent, his hat must be black. Finally, if all hats are black, Joe argues that, if his hat were white, the game would involve three black and one white hats, and so one of the opponents would have applied the argument just given and deduced his color. In the absence of such deduction, Joe's hat must be black, and so he announces that fact.

Note that when Joe announces his color, he credits his opponents with ability to carry out the necessary arguments (since his own decision is based on the assumption that their failure to speak is due to the lack of appropriate color conditions rather than inability to reason); yet he demonstrates that he is more capable than the others, for otherwise they would have carried out his own identical line of reasoning and thus deduced their colors.

Chapter 7

(7.2.7) To verify Axiom I, one shows that twenty-seven equalities are true. Of these, six involve all the elements p, q, r, each of eighteen involves only two of the three elements, and each of three involves only one element. To illustrate the proof for each type, we have

$$(q \circ r) \circ p = p \circ p = p = q \circ r = q \circ (r \circ p);$$
$$(r \circ q) \circ r = p \circ r = r = r \circ p = r \circ (q \circ r);$$
$$(q \circ q) \circ q = r \circ q = p = q \circ r = q \circ (q \circ q).$$

Axioms II and III are true, since every column and every row of the table for $\circ$ contains each element of G. [See the discussion preceding (7.2.4).]

(7.2.8) Axiom I involves eight equalities, similar to those given in connection with (7.2.1). A typical verification is

$$(j \circ k) \circ j = k \circ j = j = j \circ j = j \circ (k \circ j).$$

Now II is true, since every column of the table contains all the elements of G.

(7.2.9) The proofs for Axioms I, III follow precisely the same patterns as the corresponding proofs in (7.2.8). Since no element $x \in G$ exists for which $v \circ x = w$ (in view of $v \circ v = v$, $v \circ w = v$), Axiom II fails to hold.

(7.3.14) By III, y exists such that $y \circ a = b$. Now if y is such that $y \circ a = b$, we have

$$y = y \circ e = y \circ (a \circ a') = (y \circ a) \circ a' = b \circ a'.$$

If y_1, y_2 are such that $y_1 \circ a = b$, $y_2 \circ a = b$, then it follows that $y_1 = b \circ a'$, $y_2 = b \circ a'$, whence $y_1 = y_2$.

(7.3.15)

PROOF OF (7.3.10.a): Apply (7.3.9.a) with $b = a$, so that unique existence follows. Moreover, $x = a' \circ b = a' \circ a = e$.

PROOF OF (7.3.10.b): Apply (7.3.9.b) in a similar way.

PROOF OF (7.3.11.a): Apply (7.3.9.a) with $b = e$, obtaining unique existence. Moreover, $x = a' \circ b = a' \circ e = a'$.

PROOF OF (7.3.11.b): Apply (7.3.9.b).

PROOF OF (7.3.12): By the definition (7.3.4) of e, we have $e \circ e = e$. By (7.3.11.a) with $a = e$, it follows that the only x such that $e \circ x = e$ is e'. Hence $e' = e$.

(7.3.16) No. In the example (7.2.1), $e = m$; moreover, $n \circ n = e$, whence, by (7.3.11.a) with $a = n$, $n' = n \neq e$. Note that in (7.2.2), however, the only element which is its own inverse is p $(= e)$. If $x' = x$, then $x \circ x = x \circ x' = e$; conversely, if $x \circ x = e$, then $x = x'$ by (7.3.11). Hence a criterion for existence of x with $x = x'$ is the existence of x with $x \circ x = e$.

(7.3.17) Yes. If $x \circ x = x$, then $x = e$ by (7.3.10.a) with $a = x$.

(7.3.18) Since $F = [(x, y) \in G \times G; y = a \circ x]$, it follows that $F^* = [(y, x) \in G \times G;\ y = a \circ x]$. Let $y\, F^*\, x_1$, $y\, F^*\, x_2$. Then $a \circ x_1 = y$, $a \circ x_2 = y$. By (7.3.9.a), $x_1 = x_2$, whence F^* is a function. It remains to prove that range of $F = G$. Let $y \in G$. By II, there exists $x \in G$ with $a \circ x = y$, whence $F(x) = y$. This completes the proof that F is a one-to-one correspondence between G and G. Similar argument applies to H.

Suppose $y\, K^*\, x_1$, $y\, K^*\, x_2$. Then $y = K(x_1) = K(x_2)$, whence $y = (a' \circ x_1) \circ a$, $y = (a' \circ x_2) \circ a$. It follows that $y \circ a' = a' \circ x_1$, $y \circ a' = a' \circ x_2$, whence $x_1 = x_2$ by (7.3.9.a). This establishes that K^* is a function. That range of $K = G$ is seen by showing that, if $y \in G$, then $K(x) = y$ with $x \equiv (a \circ y) \circ a'$. Note that, if $(G, \circ)$ is commutative, then K is the identity relation on $G \times G$.

To prove that L^* is a function, one shows that $y\, L^*\, x_1$, $y\, L^*\, x_2$ implies $x_1 = x_2$ by using (7.3.8). That range of $L = G$ follows from (7.3.7).

(7.3.19) $e = p$, $p' = p$, $q' = q$, $r' = r$, $s' = u$, $t' = t$, $u' = s$.

Chapter 8

(8.3.3) To prove that φ is on J to J, we note first that domain of $\varphi = J$ by the definition of φ. Now suppose $n \in J$. It is to be shown that $\varphi(n) \in J$, that is, $\varphi(n) \neq 1$. Clearly this follows from II applied to $(I, 1, \sigma)$. It remains to prove that $(J, \sigma(1), \varphi)$ satisfies I, II, III.

PROOF OF I: Let $m, n \in J$, $m \neq n$. Then $\sigma(m) \neq \sigma(n)$ by I applied to $(I, 1, \sigma)$. Hence $\varphi(m) \neq \varphi(n)$.

PROOF OF II: Let $m \in J$; it is to be proved that $\varphi(m) \neq \sigma(1)$. By I applied to $(I, 1, \sigma)$, $\sigma(m) \neq \sigma(1)$, since $m \neq 1$.

PROOF OF III: Let $H \subset J$ be such that (a) $\sigma(1) \in H$; (b) $q \in H$ implies $\varphi(q) \in H$. Define $K \equiv H + [1]$. First, $1 \in K$ is obvious. Let $k \in K$, with the aim of proving $\sigma(k) \in K$. If $k = 1$, then $\sigma(k) \in H$ by (a), so that $\sigma(k) \in K$. If $k \neq 1$, then $k \in H$, and $\sigma(k) = \varphi(k) \in H$ by (b), whence $\sigma(k) \in K$. By III applied to $(I, 1, \sigma)$, $K = I$, and therefore $H = J$.

(8.6.16)

PROOF OF (a): Immediate from (8.6.1.a).

PROOF OF (b): Let E be the identity function on I to I. Then E has the properties (a), (b) of (8.6.1) with $m = 1$: (a) $E(1) = 1$; (b) if $n \in I$, $E(n + 1) = n + 1 = E(n) + 1$. But μ_1 has these properties by its definition; hence $\mu_1 = E$ by (8.6.2). Thus $m \in I$ implies $\times(1, m) = \mu_1(m) = E(m) = m$.

(8.6.17) Let $m \in I$. Define a sequence $\lambda \in \mathcal{S}$ so that, for every $n \in I$, $\lambda(n) = \times(m, n) + n$. It will be shown that $\lambda = \mu_{m+1}$ by verifying that λ satisfies (8.6.1.a), (8.6.1.b) with m replaced by $m + 1$. First,

$$\lambda(1) = \times(m, 1) + 1 = m + 1,$$

so that (8.6.1.a) holds. Now, if $n \in I$,

$$\begin{aligned} \lambda(n + 1) &= \times(m, n + 1) + (n + 1) \\ &= (\mu_m(n + 1)) + (n + 1) && [\text{by } (8.6.4)] \\ &= (\mu_m(n) + m) + (n + 1) && [\text{by } (8.6.3)] \\ &= (\times(m, n) + m) + (n + 1) && [\text{by } (8.6.4)] \\ &= (\times(m, n) + n) + (m + 1) && [\text{by } (8.5.11)] \\ &= \lambda(n) + (m + 1), \end{aligned}$$

whence (8.6.1.b) holds. Hence $\lambda = \mu_{m+1}$, so that, for every $n \in I$,

$$\times(m + 1, n) = \mu_{m+1}(n) = \lambda(n) = \times(m, n) + n.$$

(8.7.7)

PROOF OF (a):

$$\begin{aligned} (m + n + p) \cdot q &= ((m + n) + p) \cdot q \\ &= (m + n) \cdot q + p \cdot q && [\text{by } (8.6.14)] \\ &= (m \cdot q + n \cdot q) + p \cdot q && [\text{by } (8.6.14)] \\ &= m \cdot q + n \cdot q + p \cdot q. \end{aligned}$$

PROOF OF (b):

$$(m+n)\cdot(p+q) = (m+n)\cdot p + (m+n)\cdot q \quad \text{[by (8.6.14)]}$$
$$= m\cdot p + n\cdot p + m\cdot q + n\cdot q \quad \text{[by (8.6.14)]}.$$

PROOF OF (c): Apply (b) with $p = m$, $q = n$. Then

$$(m+n)\cdot(m+n) = m\cdot m + n\cdot m + m\cdot n + n\cdot n$$
$$= m\cdot m + (1+1)\cdot m\cdot n + n\cdot n \quad \text{[by (8.6.13), (8.6.14)]}$$
$$= m\cdot m + 2\cdot m\cdot n + n\cdot n \quad \text{[by (8.7.5.a)]}.$$

PROOF OF (d):

$$((m+n)\cdot(m+n))\cdot(m+n)$$
$$= (m\cdot m + 2\cdot m\cdot n + n\cdot n)\cdot(m+n) \quad \text{[by (c)]}$$
$$= m\cdot m\cdot(m+n) + 2\cdot m\cdot n\cdot(m+n) + n\cdot n\cdot(m+n) \quad \text{[by (a)]}$$
$$= m\cdot m\cdot m + m\cdot m\cdot n + 2\cdot m\cdot n\cdot m + 2\cdot m\cdot n\cdot n + n\cdot n\cdot m + n\cdot n\cdot n \quad \text{[by (8.6.14)]}$$
$$= m\cdot m\cdot m + (1+2)\cdot m\cdot m\cdot n + (2+1)\cdot m\cdot n\cdot n + n\cdot n\cdot n \quad \text{[by (8.6.13)]}$$
$$= m\cdot m\cdot m + 3\cdot m\cdot m\cdot n + 3\cdot m\cdot n\cdot n + n\cdot n\cdot n \quad \text{[by (8.7.5.b)]}.$$

(8.7.8)

PROOF OF (a): By (8.7.5), (8.7.6),

$$3\cdot 2 = (2+1)\cdot 2 = 4+2 = 4+1+1$$
$$= 5+1 = 6.$$

PROOF OF (f): By (8.7.5),

$$6+3 = 6+1+1+1 = 7+1+1 = 8+1 = 9.$$

The others are proved similarly.

(8.8.1) It is to be shown that, if $y \in I$, then $y\cdot 2 \neq 1$. Suppose $y \in I$. Then $y = 1$, or there exists $z \in I$ with $y = z + 1$ [by (8.3.2)]. If $y = 1$, then $y\cdot 2 = 1\cdot 2 = 2 \neq 1$ [by II′]. If $y \neq 1$, then

$$y\cdot 2 = (z+1)\cdot 2 = z\cdot 2 + 1\cdot 2$$
$$= (z\cdot 2 + 1) + 1$$
$$\neq 1 \quad \text{[by II′]}.$$

Chapter 9

(9.2.23) Domain of $<$ and domain of $\leqq$ are both equal to I by the remark following (9.2.1). Since $m \in I$ implies $m \leqq m$, range of $\leqq\ = I$. Range of $<\ = I - [1]$. For, if $m < n$, then $1 \leqq m$, $m < n$ yield $1 < n$ by (9.2.6.b). Hence, if $n \in$ range of $<$, then $n \in I - [1]$. Conversely, if $n \in I$, $n \neq 1$, then, by (9.2.9), $1 < n$, so that $n \in$ range of $<$.

None of $<, >, \leqq, \geqq$ is a function. For example, $1 < 2$, $1 < 3$ and $2 \neq 3$, whence $<$ is not a function. Moreover, $3 > 1$, $3 > 2$, so that $>$ is not a function. Similar argument applies to $\leqq, \geqq$.

(9.2.24) Suppose $n \leqq q$. Then, by (9.2.12), $m + n < p + q$, which is false. If $m \leqq p$, consider separately the cases $m = p$, $m < p$. In the latter, apply the proof just given to obtain $q < n$; in the former, apply (8.5.14) to obtain $q = n$.

(9.2.25)

PROOF OF (b): If $m < q$, then $m < n$ follows from (9.2.5). If $m = q$, then $q < n$ yields $m < n$.

PROOF OF (c): If $m < q$, then $m < n$ follows from (9.2.6.a). If $m = q$, then $q \leqq n$ yields $m \leqq n$. In either case, $m \leqq n$.

(9.2.26) Proof is indirect. If $m \neq n$, then $m \leqq n$, $n \leqq m$ yield $m < n$, $n < m$. Hence, by (9.2.5), $m < m$, contrary to (9.2.4).

(9.2.27) Since $m < n$, there exists $r \in I$ with $m + r = n$. Hence $m + 1 + r = n + 1$, whence $m + 1 < n + 1$. By (9.2.10.a), $m + 1 \leqq n$. (Direct proof, similar to that of (9.2.10.a), is also possible.)

(9.3.10) Since m is a greatest, and since $n \in S$, it follows from (9.3.3.b) that $m \geqq n$. Similarly, $n \geqq m$. Hence $m = n$ by (9.2.8).

(9.3.11)

(a) Least is 1, greatest is 4, since $1, 4 \in S$, since $1 \leqq 2$, $1 \leqq 4$ and since $1 \leqq 4$, $2 \leqq 4$.

(b) Suppose m is a greatest. Since $n + 1 \neq n$, it follows that $n + 1 \in S$, whence $m \geqq n + 1$, and $m > n$. Now let $k \in I$, $k \neq n$; then $m \geqq k$. We have shown that for *every* $k \in I$, $m \geqq k$. But this implies that m is a greatest in I, which is impossible. Hence S has no greatest. If $n = 1$, then $2 \in S$, whence 2 is a least (since $1 \in' S$). Otherwise, 1 is the least, since $1 \in I$, and since $1 \leqq k$ for every $k \in S$.

(c) If $m \leqq n$, then $I_m - I_n = \Theta$. For otherwise there exists $k \in I_m$ with $k \in' I_n$. Thus $k \leqq m$, $k \nleqq n$, and we have $n < k$ by (9.2.14). Hence $n < m$ by (9.2.6.a), contrary to $m \leqq n$. In this case, $I_m - I_n$ has no least or greatest. Suppose $m > n$. Then $m \in I_m - I_n$, so that $m \in S$. But $q \in S$ implies $q \in I_m$, whence $q \leqq m$. This shows that m is a greatest in S. Moreover, since $n < m$, we have $n + 1 \leqq m$ by (9.2.10.b), so that $n + 1 \in I_m - I_n$. But $q \in S$ implies $q \nleqq n$, so that $n < q$, and $n + 1 \leqq q$ by (9.2.10.b). This proves that $n + 1$ is a least in S.

(d) Suppose m is a greatest. Then there exists $k_0 \in I$ with $m = 2 \cdot k_0$. Now $m + 2 = 2 \cdot (k_0 + 1) \in S$. Since m is a greatest, $m \geqq m + 2$; but $m < m + 2$ by (9.2.1). This contradiction shows that no greatest exists. The least is 2. For $2 = 2 \cdot 1 \in S$; and, if $m \in S$, there exists $k \in I$ with $m = 2 \cdot k$, whence $2 \leqq 2 \cdot k = m$ by (9.2.19).

(e) No greatest; least is $n + 1$ by an argument similar to that in (c).

(9.3.12)

PROOF OF (a): Clearly $\varphi(m_0) \in T$, since $m_0 \in S$. Let $q \in T$. Then there exists $m \in S$ such that $q = \varphi(m)$. Now $m \in S$ yields $m_0 \leqq m$. If $m = m_0$, then $q = \varphi(m_0)$; otherwise $m_0 < m$ yields $\varphi(m_0) < \varphi(m) = q$. In either case, $\varphi(m_0) \leqq q$.

PROOF OF (b): Similar to the proof of (a).

(9.3.13) Since $p \in S$ implies $m \geqq p$, it follows that $p \in S$ implies $m + 1 > p$. Hence $m + 1 \in T$. Let $q \in T$. Then $q > m$ by the definition of T. Hence $q \geqq m + 1$ by (9.2.10.b). Note also that $T = I - I_m$, so that the result of (9.3.11.e) might be used.

(9.4.11) Since, for every $n \in I$, $1 \cdot n = n$, it follows that $1 \mid n$, $n \mid n$; this yields the pairs

$$(1, 1), (1, 2), (1, 3), (1, 4), (1, 5), (1, 6), (1, 7), (1, 8), (1, 9);$$
$$(2, 2), (3, 3), (4, 4), (5, 5), (6, 6), (7, 7), (8, 8), (9, 9).$$

We have $2 \cdot 2 = 4$, $2 \cdot 3 = 6$, $2 \cdot 4 = 8$, $3 \cdot 3 = 9$, whence additional pairs are

$$(2, 4), (2, 6), (3, 6), (2, 8), (4, 8), (3, 9).$$

(9.4.12) Since $m \mid n$, $m \mid q$, there exist $r, s \in I$ with $m \cdot r = n$, $m \cdot s = q$. Thus

$$n + q = m \cdot r + m \cdot s = m \cdot (r + s),$$

so that $m \mid (n + q)$. This is a converse of (9.4.7).

(9.4.13) If $m \mid n$, then there exists $r \in I$ with $m \cdot r = n$. Thus $n \cdot q = m \cdot (r \cdot q)$, and $m \mid (n \cdot q)$. Similar argument applies if $m \mid q$. The converse,

$$m \mid (n \cdot q) \text{ implies } m \mid n \text{ or } m \mid q,$$

is false. For let $m = 6$, $n = 4$, $q = 3$. Then

$$4 \cdot 3 = 2 \cdot 2 \cdot 3 = 2 \cdot 6,$$

whence $m \mid (n \cdot q)$; but neither $6 \mid 4$ nor $6 \mid 3$ holds since $4 < 6$, $3 < 6$, whence $m \mid' n$, $m \mid' q$.

(9.4.14) If $m \mid 1$, there exists $r \in I$ with $m \cdot r = 1$. Hence $m = 1$ by (9.2.20).

(9.4.15) Primes: 2, 3, 5, 7. To prove that n is a prime, examine the pairs $(r, s) \in I \times I$ such that $r \cdot s = n$; if no such pair exists with $r \neq 1$ and $r \neq n$, the number is clearly a prime. To find all pairs (r, s) with

$r \cdot s = n$, use the fact that $r \leqq n$, $s \leqq n$ by (9.2.19). For example, to prove that 2 is a prime, let $r \cdot s = 2$. Then, since $r \leqq 2$, $r = 1$ or $r = 2$ [use (9.2.10.a) with $n = 1$]. Similarly, $s = 1$ or $s = 2$. Hence these possibilities occur for (r, s): (1, 1), (1, 2), (2, 1), (2, 2). The first and last are impossible, since $r \cdot s = 2$. Hence $r = 1$ and $s = 2$, or $r = 2$ and $s = 1$. This shows that 2 is a prime.

(9.4.16) Evidently $3 < 5$, $3 \nmid 5$ (since 5 is a prime). Then $q = 1$, $r = 2$, since $3 \cdot 1 + 2 = 5$. (The proof of (9.4.9) gives a method of determining q, r. Thus, in the particular case,

$$S = [s; 3 \cdot s < 5].$$

But $s \in S$ implies $s < 2$, since otherwise $3 \cdot s \geqq 3 \cdot 2 > 5$. Hence $S = [1]$, and $q = 1$. Then $r = 2$ follows.)

(9.5.7) Since $1, 2, 3 \leqq 3$, $[1, 2, 3] \subset I_3$. Suppose $m \in I_3$. It is to be proved that $m = 1$ or $m = 2$ or $m = 3$. If $m \neq 3$, then $m < 3 = 2 + 1$, whence, by (9.2.10.a), $m \leqq 2$. If $m \neq 2$, then $m < 2$. By (9.5.2), $m = 1$. Similar proof applies to the other part.

(9.5.8) 2, 4, 6, 8. Note that $3 = 2 \cdot 1 + 1$, whence 3 is odd by (9.5.4.b). Similarly 5, 7, 9 are odd.

(9.5.9)

Proof of (a): By (9.5.4.a), there exist $r, s \in I$ with $m = 2 \cdot r$, $n = 2 \cdot s$. Thus

$$m + n = 2 \cdot r + 2 \cdot s = 2 \cdot (r + s).$$

Proof of (b): There exists $r \in I$ with $m = 2 \cdot r$. If $n = 1$, then $m + n = 2 \cdot r + 1$, and $m + n$ is odd by (9.5.4.b). Otherwise $n \neq 1$, and there exists $s \in I$ with $n = 2 \cdot s + 1$ by (9.5.4.b). Then

$$m + n = 2 \cdot r + 2 \cdot s + 1 = 2 \cdot (r + s) + 1,$$

whence $m + n$ is odd.

(9.5.10) Since $2 \mid m$, there exists $r \in I$ with $m = 2 \cdot r$. Hence $m \cdot n = 2 \cdot r \cdot n$, and $m \cdot n$ is even.

(9.6.8) In application of (9.6.5), the symbols m, n, p there may need to be reinterpreted in terms of the symbols m, n, p here.

Proof of (a): By (9.6.5.a),

$$n > p \text{ implies } (m + n) - p = m + (n - p).$$

Suppose $p > n$ and $m > p - n$. Then $m + n > p$. Moreover,

$$\begin{aligned} ((m + n) - p) + (p - n) &= ((m + n) + (p - n)) - p && \text{[by (9.6.5.a)]} \\ &= (m + (n + (p - n))) - p \\ &= (m + p) - p && \text{[by (9.6.4.b)]} \\ &= m. && \text{[by (9.6.4.b)].} \end{aligned}$$

Hence

$$(m + n) - p = m - (p - n).$$

PROOF OF (b): By (9.6.5.b),

$$m > n + p \text{ implies } (m - n) - p = m - (n + p).$$

Suppose $m > p$ and $m - p > n$. Then

$$\begin{aligned}((m - p) - n) + p &= ((m - p) + p) - n \quad &[\text{by } (9.6.5.\text{a})]\\ &= m - n &[\text{by } (9.6.4.\text{b})].\end{aligned}$$

Hence

$$(m - p) - n = (m - n) - p.$$

PROOF OF (c): The first and second parts restate (9.6.5.a), (9.6.5.c). Suppose $m > n$ and $p > n$. By (9.6.6.c), first part, $p + (m - n) = (p + m) - n$. Since $p > n$, we have $(p + m) - n = m + (p - n)$ by (9.6.6.a). Thus

$$(m - n) + p = m + (p - n).$$

(9.6.9)

PROOF OF (a). If $m < n$, there exists $r \in I$ with $m + r = n$. Then

$$\begin{aligned}r + (m - p) &= (r + m) - p \quad &[\text{by } (9.6.6.\text{a})],\\ &= n - p,\end{aligned}$$

and $m - p < n - p$. Conversely, if there exists $r \in I$ with $n - p = (m - p) + r$, it is easily shown by (9.6.6) that $m + r = n$.

PROOF OF (b): If $m < n$, there exists $r \in$ I with $m + r = n$. Hence $n > r$, $m = n - r$, and

$$\begin{aligned}(p - n) + r &= p - (n - r) \quad &[\text{by } (9.6.6.\text{c})]\\ &= p - m.\end{aligned}$$

The converse is similarly proved.

PROOF OF (c): Show that $(m - n) \cdot p + n \cdot p = m \cdot p$.

(9.8) First note that the proof of (9.8.1) is immediate from (9.4.1), (9.2.17). Some theorems, together with hints concerning their proofs, are as follows.

(9.8.3) THEOREM: *If $m, n, p \in I$ such that $m \cdot n = p$, then $p \mid^* n$, and $p \div n = m$.*

PROOF: Use (9.4.1) to obtain $n \mid p$, and note that $n \cdot m = p$ yields $m = p \div n$ by (9.8.2).

(9.8.4) THEOREM:

(a) *If $m, n \in I$, then $(m \cdot n) \div n = m$;*

(b) *if $m \mid^* n$, then $(m \div n) \cdot n = m$.*

PROOF: By (9.8.3) with $p = m \cdot n$, (a) holds. By (9.8.2), (b) holds.

(9.8.5) THEOREM: *Let $m, n, p \in I$. Then,*
(a) *if $n \mid^* p$, then $(m \cdot n) \div p = m \cdot (n \div p)$;*
(b) *if $m \mid^* n \cdot p$ (or equivalently, if $m \mid^* n$ and $m \div n \mid^* p$), then $(m \div n) \div p = m \div (n \cdot p)$;*
(c) *if $m \mid^* n$ and $n \mid^* p$, then $(m \div n) \cdot p = m \div (n \div p)$.*

PROOF: To prove (a), show that

$$m \cdot (n \div p) \cdot p = m \cdot n,$$

using (9.8.4.b). To prove (b), show that

$$((m \div n) \div p) \cdot (n \cdot p) = m;$$

to prove (c), show that

$$(m \div n) \cdot p \cdot (n \div p) = m.$$

Apply (9.8.3) in each case.

Analogues of all parts of (9.6.6) may be stated and proved. [See (9.6.8).] Further results are as follows.

(9.8.6) THEOREM: *If $m \in I$, then $m \div m = 1$.*

PROOF: Obvious, since $m \cdot 1 = m$.

(9.8.7) THEOREM: *If $m, n, p \in I$ such that $m \mid^* p$, $n \mid^* p$, then $(m + n) \div p = (m \div p) + (n \div p)$.*

PROOF: Define $r \equiv m \div p$, $s \equiv n \div p$. Then

$$(r + s) \cdot p = r \cdot p + s \cdot p = m + n.$$

Apply (9.8.3).

(9.8.8) THEOREM: *If $m, n, p \in I$ such that $m > n$, $m \mid^* p$, $n \mid^* p$, then $(m - n) \div p = (m \div p) - (n \div p)$.*

PROOF: Define $r \equiv m \div p$, $s \equiv n \div p$, whence $r > s$. Easily prove that $(r - s) \cdot p = m - n$, and apply (9.8.3).

(9.8.9) THEOREM: *If $m, n, p \in I$ such that $m \mid^* n$, then $m \cdot p \mid^* n \cdot p$, and $(m \cdot p) \div (n \cdot p) = m \div n$.*

PROOF: If $m = n \cdot r$, then $m \cdot p = (n \cdot p) \cdot r$; also, it is easily shown that

$$\begin{aligned} ((m \cdot p) \div (n \cdot p)) \cdot n &= (m \cdot p \cdot n) \div (n \cdot p) \\ &= (m \cdot (p \cdot n)) \div (n \cdot p) \\ &= m. \end{aligned}$$

(9.8.10) THEOREM: *If $m, n, p \in I$, then,*
(a) *if $m \mid^* p$ and $n \mid^* p$, then $m < n$ if and only if $m \div p < n \div p$;*
(b) *if $p \mid^* m$ and $p \mid^* n$, then $m < n$ if and only if $p \div m > p \div n$.*

PROOF OF (a): Define $r \equiv m \div p$, $s \equiv n \div p$, whence $m = p \cdot r$, $n = p \cdot s$. Apply (9.2.21) and (9.2.15) to obtain $m < n$ if and only if $r < s$.

PROOF OF (b): Define $r \equiv p \div m$, $s \equiv p \div n$, whence $r \cdot m = s \cdot n$. Then prove that $m < n$ if and only if $r > s$, using indirect proofs employing (9.2.22).

Similar methods are employed to prove the following.

(9.8.11) THEOREM: *Let* $m, n, p, q \in I$. *Then,*

(a) *if* $m \mid^* n$, $p \mid^* q$, *then*

$$(m \div n) \cdot (p \div q) = (m \cdot p) \div (n \cdot q);$$

(b) *if* $m \mid^* n$, $p \mid^* q$, $(m \div n) \mid^* (p \div q)$, *then*

$$(m \div n) \div (p \div q) = (m \cdot q) \div (n \cdot p);$$

(c) *if* $m \mid^* n$, $p \mid^* q$, *then*

$$(m \div n) + (p \div q) = (m \cdot q + n \cdot p) \div (n \cdot q);$$

(d) *if* $m \mid^* n$, $p \mid^* q$, *and* $m \div n > p \div q$, *then*

$$(m \div n) - (p \div q) = (m \cdot q - n \cdot p) \div (n \cdot q).$$

Chapter 10

(10.1.6) If $S = [x]$, $T = [y]$, define φ on S to T so that $\varphi(x) = y$. Hence $x \, \varphi \, y$, and $y \, \varphi^* \, x$. If $y \, \varphi^* \, x_1$, with $x_1 \in S$, it follows that $x_1 = x$ (since no other element except x is in S). Thus φ^* is a function. Conversely, let $S = [x]$, $S \sim T$. There exists a function φ on S to T such that φ is a one-to-one correspondence, whence define $y \equiv \varphi(x)$. Since $y \in T$, $[y] \subset T$. Suppose $z \in T$. Since φ has range T, there exists $w \in S$ such that $\varphi(w) = z$. But then $w = x$, and $z = \varphi(x) = y \in [y]$. This shows that $T \subset [y]$.

(10.1.7) Since $S \sim I_3$, there exists a one-to-one correspondence φ between S and I_3. Hence φ^* is a function with domain I_3 and range S. Define $a \equiv \varphi^*(1)$, $b \equiv \varphi^*(2)$, $c \equiv \varphi^*(3)$. Then

$$S = \text{range of } \varphi^* = [a, b, c].$$

Now suppose $a = b$. We have $1 \, \varphi^* \, a$, $2 \, \varphi^* \, b$, whence $a \, \varphi \, 1$, $b \, \varphi \, 2$, so that

$$1 = \varphi(a) = \varphi(b) = 2.$$

This contradiction shows $a \neq b$. Similarly, $b \neq c$, $c \neq a$.

(10.1.8) If $S = [a, b]$, $a \neq b$, define a function φ on $[1, 2]$ to S so that $\varphi(1) = a$, $\varphi(2) = b$. Then clearly $\varphi^* = [(a, 1), (b, 2)]$, whence φ^* is a function. Inasmuch as φ has range S, φ is a one-to-one correspondence between I_2 and S, so that $I_2 \sim S$. For the proof of the converse, proceed as in (10.1.6).

(10.2.9) Prove that (10.2.2.b) holds, using the same proof as that given in the text to show (10.2.2.c) implies (10.2.2.b). (Note that the hypothesis $G(F(x)) = x$ is all that is used.) Hence (a) holds. In view of (a), F^* is a function. The proof in the text of (10.2.3) is used to establish (c), that $G = F^*$. Now, if $y \in T$, we have $F(G(y)) = F(F^*(y)) = y$ by (10.2.1.b), so that (b) holds. Our result in effect establishes that the implications

(10.2.2.c) implies (10.2.2.b),
(10.2.2.c) implies (10.2.2.a),

remain valid if the hypothesis in (10.2.2.c) is weakened by removing the requirement that $F(G(y)) = y$ for every $y \in T$. The result also shows that this same assumption can be removed from the hypothesis of (10.2.3).

(10.2.10) Let $y \in T$, and define $x \equiv G(y)$. Then $F(x) = y$, so that $y \in$ range of F. Now the hypotheses of (10.2.9) hold, so that (10.2.9.c), (10.2.9.a) yield the desired results. This theorem establishes the implications

(10.2.2.c) implies (10.2.2.b),
(10.2.2.c) implies (10.2.2.a),

as well as (10.2.3), without assuming that $T =$ range of F.

(10.2.11) Define $S \equiv [a]$, $T \equiv [b, c]$, $b \neq c$. Define F, G so that $F(a) = b$, $G(b) = a$, $G(c) = a$. Then F, G are on S to T, T to S, respectively. Also, $G(F(a)) = G(b) = a$. But note that range of $F = [b] \neq T$, so that F is not a one-to-one correspondence between S and T.

(10.2.12)

Proof of (a): Let $y \in \varphi(U + V)$. Then there exists $x \in U + V$ with $y = \varphi(x)$. If $x \in U$, then $y \in \varphi(U)$; if $x \in V$, then $y \in \varphi(V)$. Hence, in any case, $y \in \varphi(U) + \varphi(V)$. Thus $\varphi(U + V) \subset \varphi(U) + \varphi(V)$. The reverse implication is similarly proved.

Proof of (b): By (a), $\varphi(V) = \varphi(U + V) = \varphi(U) + \varphi(V)$. Thus $\varphi(U) \subset \varphi(V)$.

Proof of (c): Let $y \in \varphi(U) - \varphi(V)$. Since $y \in \varphi(U)$, there exists $x \in U$ with $y = \varphi(x)$. Now if $x \in V$, then $y \in \varphi(V)$, contrary to the assumption. Hence $x \in U - V$, and $y \in \varphi(U - V)$.

Proof of (d): Since $U \cdot V \subset U$, we have $\varphi(U \cdot V) \subset \varphi(U)$ by (b). Similarly, $\varphi(U \cdot V) \subset \varphi(V)$. Thus $\varphi(U \cdot V) \subset \varphi(U) \cdot \varphi(V)$.

If φ is a one-to-one correspondence between S and $\varphi(S)$, the inclusion signs in (c), (d) become equality signs. Let $y \in \varphi(U - V)$. Then there exists $x \in U - V$ with $y = \varphi(x)$. But $x \in U$ yields $y \in \varphi(U)$. To prove $y \notin \varphi(V)$, assume the contrary. Then there exists $x' \in V$ with $y = \varphi(x')$. But $x' \neq x$, since $x \notin V$. Hence, by (10.2.2), $y = \varphi(x') \neq \varphi(x) = y$.

This shows that $y \in \varphi(U) - \varphi(V)$, and establishes the reverse inclusion in (c). In (d), let $y \in \varphi(U) \cdot \varphi(V)$. Then there exist $x \in U$, $x' \in V$ with $y = \varphi(x) = \varphi(x')$. Thus $x = x'$ by (10.2.2), and $x \in U \cdot V$, so that $y \in \varphi(U \cdot V)$.

(10.2.13) STATEMENT: If S, T, W, U, V, Z are sets such that

$$S \cdot T = T \cdot W = W \cdot S = \Theta,$$
$$U \cdot V = V \cdot Z = Z \cdot U = \Theta,$$
$$S \sim U,\ T \sim V,\ W \sim Z,$$

then $(S + T) + W \sim (U + V) + Z$.

PROOF: Since $S \cdot T = U \cdot V = \Theta$, and $S \sim U$, $T \sim V$, we have $S + T \sim U + V$ by (10.2.5). Assume $(S + T) \cdot W \neq \Theta$. Then there exists $x \in S + T$ with $x \in W$. If $x \in S$, then $x \in W \cdot S$, contrary to $W \cdot S = \Theta$; otherwise $x \in T$, contrary to $T \cdot W = \Theta$. This proves $(S + T) \cdot W = \Theta$. Similarly, $(U + V) \cdot Z = \Theta$. Now apply (10.2.5) with S, T, U, V replaced by $S + T, W, U + V, Z$ to obtain the result.

(10.3.6) If $p = n + 1$, then $I_{n+1} - [p] = I_n$. Then the identity on I_n to I_n is effective. If $p = 1$, define φ on I_n to I_{n+1} so that, for every $q \in I_n$, $\varphi(q) = q + 1$. Then prove that range of φ is $I_{n+1} - [1]$. It is easy to verify (10.2.2.b). Finally, if $p \neq 1, n + 1$, define φ so that, if $q \in I_n$,

$$\varphi(q) = \begin{cases} q & \text{if } q < p \\ q + 1 & \text{if } q \geqq p. \end{cases}$$

Again range of φ is $I_{n+1} - [p]$, and (10.2.2.b) is easily verified.

(10.4.13) The proof of the text is complete when it is shown that

$$I_{n(T)} \sim J \equiv [n(S) + p;\ p \in I_{n(T)}],$$
$$I_{n(S)} + J = I_{n(S)+n(T)},$$
$$I_{n(S)} \cdot J = \Theta.$$

The function $\varphi \equiv (n(S) + p;\ p \in I_{n(T)})$ clearly has domain $I_{n(T)}$; by its definition, φ has range J. Now if $p_1, p_2 \in I_{n(T)}$, $p_1 \neq p_2$, then $n(S) + p_1 \neq n(S) + p_2$, so that $\varphi(p_1) \neq \varphi(p_2)$, whence (10.2.2.b) holds. This proves that $I_{n(T)} \sim J$. Now it is clear that $I_{n(S)} + J \subset I_{n(S)+n(T)}$. Let $q \in I_{n(S)+n(T)}$. If $q \leqq n(S)$, then $q \in I_{n(S)}$; otherwise $q > n(S)$, and there exists $p \in I$ with $n(S) + p = q$. But we have

$$n(S) + p = q \leqq n(S) + n(T),$$

whence $p \leqq n(T)$, so that $q \in J$. This establishes

$$I_{n(S)} + J = I_{n(S)+n(T)}.$$

Finally, suppose there exists $q \in I_{n(S)} \cdot J$. Then $q \in J$ yields the existence of $p \in I_{n(T)}$ with $q = n(S) + p$, so that $q > n(S)$. This contradicts $q \in I_{n(S)}$. Therefore $I_{n(S)} \cdot J = \Theta$.

(10.4.14) Suppose $T - S \neq \Theta$. Since $T - S \subset T$, $T - S$ is finite by (10.4.7). Now $S \cdot (T - S) = \Theta$, so that (10.4.8) applies to S, $T - S$, yielding

$$n(T) = n(S + (T - S)) = n(S) + n(T - S),$$

whence the result follows.

(10.4.15) Consider first the case $A \equiv S - S \cdot T = \Theta$. Then $S = S \cdot T \subset T$, and $S + T = T$. Hence

$$n(S + T) + n(S \cdot T) = n(S) + n(T).$$

The text proof is completed by proving $A \cdot T = \Theta$. But, if there exists $q \in A \cdot T$, then $q \in S$, $q \in' S \cdot T$; since $q \in T$, it follows that $q \in ' S$, which is false.

(10.4.16) It is shown that σ has range $T \times V$ and satisfies (10.2.2.b). If $(t, v) \in T \times V$, we have $t \in T$, $v \in V$, so that there exist $x \in S$ and $y \in U$ with $t = \varphi(x)$, $v = \psi(y)$. Then

$$\sigma(x, y) = (\varphi(x), \psi(y)) = (t, v).$$

Hence $T \times V \subset$ range of σ; the reverse inclusion is evident. Now let $(x_1, y_1), (x_2, y_2) \in S \times U$, $(x_1, y_1) \neq (x_2, y_2)$. If $\sigma(x_1, y_1) = \sigma(x_2, y_2)$, then

$$(\varphi(x_1), \psi(y_1)) = (\varphi(x_2), \psi(y_2)),$$

so that $\varphi(x_1) = \varphi(x_2)$, $\psi(y_1) = \psi(y_2)$. But then $x_1 = x_2$, $y_1 = y_2$ by (10.2.2), and $(x_1, y_1) = (x_2, y_2)$, contrary to the hypothesis.

(10.4.17) We show $I_{n(S)} \times I_{n(T)} \sim I_{n(S) \cdot n(T)}$ by proving that,

$$\text{for every } m, n \in I,\ I_m \times I_n \sim I_{m \cdot n}.$$

Let $m \in I$, and define

$$H \equiv [n \in I;\ I_m \times I_n \sim I_{m \cdot n}].$$

To prove $1 \in H$, it is shown that $I_m \times I_1 \sim I_m$. The function $((k, 1);\ k \in I_m)$ on I_m to $I_m \times [1]$ is easily shown to be an appropriate one-to-one correspondence. Now suppose $q \in H$. Then $I_m \times I_q \sim I_{m \cdot q}$. It is easily shown that

$$I_m \times I_{q+1} = (I_m \times I_q) + (I_m \times [q + 1]),$$
$$(I_n \times I_q) \cdot (I_m \times [q + 1]) = \Theta.$$

Moreover (as in the proof that $1 \in H$), it is shown that $I_m \times [q + 1] \sim I_m$; and (as in the proof of (10.4.13)) it is seen that

$$I_m \sim J \equiv [m \cdot q + r;\ r \in I_m],$$
$$I_{m \cdot (q+1)} = I_{m \cdot q} + J,$$
$$I_{m \cdot q} \cdot J = \Theta.$$

Finally, it follows that

$$I_m \times [q + 1] \sim J.$$

The hypotheses of (10.2.5) are now verified for the sets $I_m \times I_q$, $I_m \times [q + 1]$, $I_{m \cdot q}$, J, whence the conclusion,

$$I_m \times I_{q+1} \sim I_{m \cdot (q+1)},$$

follows. Hence $q + 1 \in H$, and, by III′, $H = I$.

Chapter 11

(11.1.2) We prove only the second part; the first is similar but easier. Let $\alpha \in A^2$. Define $a \equiv \alpha(1)$, $b \equiv \alpha(2)$, whence $a, b \in A$, and $(a, b) \in A \times A$. It is shown that α (as a subset of $I_2 \times A$) is equal to $[(1, a), (2, b)]$. Let $(m, x) \in \alpha$. Then $m = 1$ or $m = 2$. If $m = 1$, then $(m, x) \in \alpha$ yields $x = \alpha(1)$, so that $x = a$. But then $(m, x) = (1, a)$. Similarly, if $m = 2$, then $(m, x) = (2, b)$. Thus $\alpha \subset [(1, a), (2, b)]$. But $(1, a) \in \alpha$ since $a = \alpha(1)$; similarly $(2, b) \in \alpha$. We have shown that $[(1, a), (2, b)] = \alpha$. This yields

$$A^2 \subset [[(1, a), (2, b)];\ (a, b) \in A \times A].$$

To prove the reverse inclusion, note that, if $(a, b) \in A \times A$, $[(1, a), (2, b)] \subset I_2 \times A$ satisfies the criterion for a function, that is, it contains no two pairs $(1, a_1)$, $(1, a_2)$ with $a_1 \neq a_2$; moreover, its domain is $I_2 = [1, 2]$.

(11.1.3) By (11.1.2), $A^1 = [[(1, a)];\ a \in A]$. Now define a function φ on A to A^1 so that, for every $a \in A$, $\varphi(a) = [(1, a)]$. Evidently φ has domain A and range A^1. Suppose $a, b \in A$, $a \neq b$. Then, if $\varphi(a) = \varphi(b)$, we have $(1, a) = (1, b)$, and $a = b$. This contradiction proves (10.2.2.b).

(11.1.4) First observe that, by (11.1.2),

$$A^2 = [[(1, a), (2, b)];\ (a, b) \in A \times A].$$

Now define φ on $A \times A$ to A^2 so that, if $(a, b) \in A \times A$,

$$\varphi(a, b) = [(1, a), (2, b)].$$

It follows that φ has domain $A \times A$ and range A^2. If $(a, b), (c, d) \in A \times A$ such that $(a, b) \neq (c, d)$, then $\varphi(a, b) \neq \varphi(c, d)$. For otherwise $[(1, a), (2, b)] = [(1, c), (2, d)]$ yields $(1, a) = (1, c)$, $(2, b) = (2, d)$, since $(1, a) \neq (2, d)$, $(2, b) \neq (1, c)$; hence $a = c$, $b = d$, contrary to the assumption. This proves (10.2.2.b).

When, as in the text, we treat A^2 and $A \times A$ as if they were identical, we are simply agreeing to denote $[(1, a), (2, b)]$ by the simpler notation (a, b).

(11.4.9)

Element of I	Correspondent under α
1	x
2	$F_1(x)$
3	$F_2(F_1(x))$
4	$F_3(F_2(F_1(x)))$
5	$F_4(F_3(F_2(F_1(x))))$
6	$F_5(F_4(F_3(F_2(F_1(x)))))$

(11.4.10) $\alpha = (x;\ n \in I)$, that is, for every $n \in I$, $\alpha(n) = x$. For, define $H \equiv [n \in I,\ \alpha(n) = x]$; then evidently $1 \in H$, and, if $q \in H$, then

$$\alpha(q+1) = E(\alpha(q)) = E(x) = x.$$

(11.4.11) Let $F = (n + k;\ k \in I)$. (If $n = 1$, $F = \sigma$.) Determination of α is accomplished by making a table as in (11.4.9):

(1)

1	1
2	$n + 1$
3	$n + (n + 1) = 2 \cdot n + 1$
4	$n + (2 \cdot n + 1) = 3 \cdot n + 1.$

Now we *conjecture* that, for every $m \in I$,

$$(2) \qquad \alpha(m) = \begin{cases} 1 & \text{if } m = 1 \\ (m - 1) \cdot n + 1 & \text{if } m > 1. \end{cases}$$

The *proof* is by induction. Define $H \equiv [m \in I;\ (2) \text{ holds}]$. Clearly $1 \in H$ by (1). Let $q \in H$. If $q = 1$, then

$$\alpha(q + 1) = F(\alpha(1)) = F(1) = n + 1 = 1 \cdot n + 1 = (q + 1 - 1) \cdot n + 1,$$

whence $q + 1 \in H$. If $q > 1$, then

$$\alpha(q + 1) = F(\alpha(q)) = n + \alpha(q) = n + (q - 1) \cdot n + 1 = q \cdot n + 1 = (q + 1 - 1) \cdot n + 1,$$

and again $q + 1 \in H$. (If $F = \sigma$, $\alpha = E$.) Note that guessing is a valid method for determining answers to questions, provided the guess is proved correct; induction is frequently an appropriate mode of proof.

(11.5.4) Assume (11.5.2). Define $A \equiv \mathfrak{M}$, $B \equiv T$,

$$R \equiv [(S, x) \in \mathfrak{M} \times T;\ x \in S].$$

Evidently domain of $R = \mathfrak{M}$, since every $S \in \mathfrak{M}$ is non-empty, and so $x \in T$ exists with $S\,R\,x$. By (11.5.2), there exists a function F on $\mathfrak{M}$ to T such that $F \subset R$. Define U to be the range of F: $U \equiv [F(S);\ S \in \mathfrak{M}]$. Then $U \subset T$. If $S \in \mathfrak{M}$, then $F(S) \in U$; but $S\,F\,F(S)$ yields $S\,R\,F(S)$, so that $F(S) \in S$. Hence $[F(S)] \subset U \cdot S$. If $y \in U \cdot S$, then

$y \in U$ yields the existence of $S_1 \in \mathfrak{M}$ such that $y = F(S_1)$. But then $S_1 \, R \, y$, so that $y \in S_1$. Hence $y \in S$ implies $S = S_1$. This proves $[F(S)] \supset U \cdot S$, and hence $[F(S)] = U \cdot S$. Thus $n(U \cdot S) = 1$, and the proof is complete. The statement of (11.5.4) is closer to the intuitive idea of "simultaneous choice" than is (11.5.2). The set U consists of elements each of which is "selected" from exactly one of the sets in $\mathfrak{M}$. That the statement of (11.5.4) implies (11.5.2) can be seen by applying (11.5.4) with $T \equiv A \times B$,

$$\mathfrak{M} \equiv [[(a, b) \in A \times B; a \, R \, b]; a \in A],$$

thus obtaining $U \subset T$ consisting of pairs $(a, b) \in R$, where, for each $a \in A$, exactly one occurs. Then F is defined so that $F(a)$ is the unique $b \in B$ such that $(a, b) \in U$.

(11.6.3) Effective sequences:

$$\alpha \equiv (m + k - 1; k \in I);$$
$$\beta \equiv (m + 2 \cdot k - 2; k \in I);$$
$$\gamma \equiv (m \cdot k; k \in I).$$

If uniqueness in (11.6.1) were true, we should have $\alpha = \beta$. But $\alpha(2) = m + 1$, $\beta(2) = m + 2$, so that $\alpha \neq \beta$. Hence uniqueness fails to hold.

Chapter 12

(12.2.9) The conclusion means $\prod_{m=1}^{n} a_m = 1$, where $a_m = 1$ for every $m \in I_n$. Define $H \equiv [n \in I; \prod_{m=1}^{n} 1 = 1]$. Clearly $1 \in H$. If $q \in H$, $\prod_{m=1}^{q} 1 = 1$, whence, by (12.2.6),

$$\prod_{m=1}^{q+1} 1 = \left(\prod_{m=1}^{q} 1\right) \cdot 1 = 1 \cdot 1 = 1.$$

(12.2.10) Define $H \equiv [n \in I; 2 \cdot \sum_{m=1}^{n} m = n \cdot (n + 1)]$. Since $\sum_{m=1}^{1} m = 1$ by (12.2.5.b), $1 \in H$. Let $q \in H$, so that

$$2 \cdot \sum_{m=1}^{q} m = q \cdot (q + 1).$$

Hence

$$\begin{aligned} 2 \cdot \sum_{m=1}^{q+1} m &= 2 \cdot \left(\left(\sum_{m=1}^{q} m\right) + (q + 1)\right) \\ &= 2 \cdot \left(\sum_{m=1}^{q} m\right) + 2 \cdot (q + 1) \\ &= q \cdot (q + 1) + 2 \cdot (q + 1) \\ &= (q + 1) \cdot (q + 2), \end{aligned}$$

whence $q + 1 \in H$.

(12.3.10) Define $a \equiv (((a_1 \circ a_2) \circ a_3) \circ a_4) \circ a_5$.

$$\begin{aligned} m &= 1\colon a = a_1 \circ (((a_2 \circ a_3) \circ a_4) \circ a_5); \\ m &= 2\colon a = (a_1 \circ a_2) \circ ((a_3 \circ a_4) \circ a_5); \\ m &= 3\colon a = ((a_1 \circ a_2) \circ a_3) \circ (a_4 \circ a_5); \\ m &= 4\colon a = a. \end{aligned}$$

(12.3.11) If $m = 1$, by (12.3.3), (12.2.5.b),

$$\bigcirc_{k=1}^{n} a_k = a_1 \circ \left(\bigcirc_{k=2}^{n} a_k \right).$$

If $m = n$, by (12.2.6),

$$\bigcirc_{k=1}^{n} a_k = \left(\bigcirc_{k=1}^{n-1} a_k \right) \circ a_n = \left(\bigcirc_{\substack{k=1 \\ k \neq m}}^{n} a_k \right) \circ a_m.$$

(12.3.12) Let (b_1, b_2, b_3) be a rearrangement of (a_1, a_2, a_3). Then $b_l = a_{\varphi(l)}$ for $l \in I_3$, where φ is a one-to-one correspondence between I_3 and I_3. The possibilities for φ are these:

$\varphi(1)$:	1	1	2	2	3	3
$\varphi(2)$:	2	3	1	3	1	2
$\varphi(3)$:	3	2	3	1	2	1

Hence the possibilities for (b_1, b_2, b_3) are these:

$$\begin{aligned} &(a_1, a_2, a_3), \quad (a_2, a_1, a_3), \quad (a_3, a_1, a_2), \\ &(a_1, a_3, a_2), \quad (a_2, a_3, a_1), \quad (a_3, a_2, a_1). \end{aligned}$$

(12.3.13) Let $n = 3$, $A = [a, b]$, $a \neq b$. Then (a, a, b) is a 3-tuple whose *only* rearrangements are (a, a, b), (a, b, a), (b, a, a). But (b, b, a) is another 3-tuple for which $[b, b, a] = [a, a, b]$.

(12.3.14) For (12.3.5),

$$\begin{aligned} (a_1 \circ a_2) \circ a_3 &= a_1 \circ (a_2 \circ a_3) \\ &= a_2 \circ (a_1 \circ a_3) \\ &= a_3 \circ (a_1 \circ a_2). \end{aligned}$$

For (12.3.9),

$$\begin{aligned} (a_1 \circ a_2) \circ a_3 &= (a_1 \circ a_2) \circ a_3 \\ &= (a_1 \circ a_3) \circ a_2 \\ &= (a_2 \circ a_1) \circ a_3 \\ &= (a_2 \circ a_3) \circ a_1 \\ &= (a_3 \circ a_1) \circ a_2 \\ &= (a_3 \circ a_2) \circ a_1. \end{aligned}$$

(12.3.15) It is to be shown that I_q = range of ψ and that (10.2.2.b) holds. Let $m \in I_q$. Evidently, if $\varphi(m) < k \leqq q + 1$, then $\psi(m) = \varphi(m) \leqq q$. If $\varphi(m) > k$, then $\psi(m) = \varphi(m) - 1 \leqq q$. This proves range of $\psi \subset I_q$. Now let $r \in I_q$. If $r < k$, define $m \equiv \varphi^*(r)$; if $r \geqq k$, then $r + 1 > k$, $r + 1 \in I_{q+1}$, and we define $m \equiv \varphi^*(r + 1)$. In the first case, $\varphi(m) = r < k$, whence $\psi(m) = r$; in the second, $\varphi(m) = r + 1 > k$, whence $\psi(m) = (r + 1) - 1 = r$. This proves $I_q \subset$ range of ψ. Now let $m_1, m_2 \in I_q$, $m_1 \neq m_2$. There are four cases:

$$\varphi(m_1) < k, \quad \varphi(m_2) < k;$$
$$\varphi(m_1) > k, \quad \varphi(m_2) > k;$$
$$\varphi(m_1) < k, \quad \varphi(m_2) > k;$$
$$\varphi(m_1) > k, \quad \varphi(m_2) < k.$$

The first two immediately lead to $\psi(m_1) \neq \psi(m_2)$, since φ is a one-to-one correspondence. In the third case, $\psi(m_1) = \varphi(m_1) < k$, while $\psi(m_2) = \varphi(m_2) - 1 \geqq k$, so that again $\psi(m_1) \neq \psi(m_2)$. The fourth case is similar. Thus (10.2.2.b) holds.

(12.4.6) It suffices to show that $a^m \cdot a^{n-m} = a^n$. This follows from (12.4.3).

(12.5.5) Suppose $q_1 \mid b_1$, so that there exists $d' \in I$ such that

$$b_1 = q_1 \cdot d'. \tag{16}$$

By (13), (16), $p_1 \cdot q_1 \cdot u = a_1 \cdot q_1 \cdot d'$, whence $p_1 \cdot u = a_1 \cdot d'$, and $p_1 \mid a_1 \cdot d'$. But $d' < b_1$, since $q_1 \neq 1$ (q_1 is a prime), so that d' is not an element of (3). Hence $p_1 \mid d'$. Then $p_1 \mid q_1 \cdot d'$, and, by (16), $p_1 \mid b_1$, contrary to (4).

(12.5.6) Evidently domain of $\psi = I_n$. Let $k \in I_n$. If $k \neq g + 1 = n$, then $k \in I_g$, and there exists $j_1 \in I_g$ with $k = \varphi(j_1)$. If $j_1 < h$, then $\psi(j_1) = \varphi(j_1) = k$. If $j_1 \geqq h$, define $j \equiv j_1 + 1$, so that $\psi(j) = \varphi(j_1) = k$. This proves that range of $\psi \supset I_n$. The reverse inclusion is evident. Now suppose $j_1, j_2 \in I_n$ such that $j_1 \neq j_2$ with the aim of proving $\psi(j_1) \neq \psi(j_2)$. The definition of ψ and the fact that φ satisfies (10.2.2.b) readily yield the desired conclusion in each of the nine possible cases: $j_1 < h$, $j_1 = h$, $j_1 > h$ and independently $j_2 < h$, $j_2 = h$, $j_2 > h$.

(12.5.7) Non-primes: 4, 6, 8, 9. We have

$$4 = 2 \cdot 2, \quad 6 = 2 \cdot 3 = 3 \cdot 2, \quad 8 = 2 \cdot 2 \cdot 2, \quad 9 = 3 \cdot 3.$$

Note that in the case of 6, (3, 2) is a rearrangement of (2, 3). In each of the other cases, the tuple of primes is actually unique.

Chapter 13

(13.2.8) Define

$$S \equiv \sum[\sum\mathfrak{M}; \mathfrak{M} \in \boldsymbol{M}], \quad T \equiv \sum(\sum\boldsymbol{M}).$$

If $x \in S$, then there exists $\mathfrak{M} \in \boldsymbol{M}$ such that $x \in \sum\mathfrak{M}$. Thus there exists $A \in \mathfrak{M}$ with $x \in A$. Since $\mathfrak{M} \in \boldsymbol{M}$, it follows that $\mathfrak{M} \subset \sum\boldsymbol{M}$. Thus $A \in \sum\boldsymbol{M}$, and $A \subset \sum(\sum\boldsymbol{M})$, so that $x \in T$. Conversely, let $x \in T$. Then there exists $B \in \sum\boldsymbol{M}$ such that $x \in B$. Hence there exists $\mathfrak{M} \in \boldsymbol{M}$ such that $B \in \mathfrak{M}$. It follows that $B \subset \sum\mathfrak{M}$, whence $x \in \sum\mathfrak{M}$. But $\sum\mathfrak{M} \subset S$, so that $x \in S$.

(13.2.9) Suppose $x \in S - \sum\mathfrak{M}$, so that $x \in S$, $x \in' \sum\mathfrak{M}$. The last statement means that $A \in \mathfrak{M}$ implies $x \in' A$. Hence $A \in \mathfrak{M}$ implies $x \in S - A$, so that $x \in \prod[S - A; A \in \mathfrak{M}]$. To prove (b), define

$$\mathfrak{N} \equiv [S - A; A \in \mathfrak{M}].$$

It is immediate that $[S - B; B \in \mathfrak{N}] = \mathfrak{M}$. Hence, by (a) applied to $S, \mathfrak{N}$,

$$\prod\mathfrak{M} = S - \sum\mathfrak{N}.$$

It follows that $\sum\mathfrak{N} = S - \prod\mathfrak{M}$, whence (b) holds.

(13.2.10) Proof of (a): Since $A \in \mathfrak{M}$ implies $A \in \mathfrak{N}$, it follows that $A \in \mathfrak{M}$ implies $A \subset \sum\mathfrak{N}$. Hence $\sum\mathfrak{M} \subset \sum\mathfrak{N}$.

Proof of (b): Since $A \in \mathfrak{M}$ implies $A \in \mathfrak{N}$, it follows that $A \in \mathfrak{M}$ implies $A \supset \prod\mathfrak{N}$. Thus $\prod\mathfrak{M} \supset \prod\mathfrak{N}$.

(13.2.11) Let $x \in \prod A_n$. Then, for every $n \in I$, $x \in A_n$. Hence $x \in B_n$ for every $n \in I$, so that $x \in \prod B_n$.

(13.3.4) It is proved that, for every $n \in I$, $S'_n \sim T'_n$. If $n \in I_m$, this follows from the hypothesis of (13.3.2). Otherwise $S'_n = \Theta$, $T'_n = \Theta$, whence again $S'_n \sim T'_n$. Now let $n_1, n_2 \in I$, $n_1 \neq n_2$. In each of the four cases

$$n_1, n_2 \in I_m; \quad n_1 \in I_m, n_2 \in' I_m;$$
$$n_1, n_2 \in' I_m; \quad n_1 \in' I_m, n_2 \in I_m,$$

it is easily verified that $S'_{n_1} \cdot S'_{n_2} = T'_{n_1} \cdot T'_{n_2} = \Theta$. Hence (13.3.1) applies, yielding $\sum S'_n \sim \sum T'_n$. Evidently

$$\sum[S_n; n \in I_m] \subset \sum S'_n.$$

In proving the reverse inclusion, note that, if $x \in S'_n$, then $n \in I_m$ (since otherwise $S'_n = \Theta$), whence $x \in \sum[S_n; n \in I_m]$. Similar argument applies to $\sum T'_n$, and the desired result holds.

(13.3.5) Let φ be a one-to-one correspondence between B and C. Then $D \sim \varphi(D)$ by (10.2.6). Thus $A \sim D$, $D \sim \varphi(D)$ yield $A \sim \varphi(D)$. We have also $\varphi(D) \subset C \subset A$, whence, by (13.3.3) with S, T, U replaced by $\varphi(D)$, A, C, we have $A \sim C$. In view of $B \sim C$, it follows that $A \sim B$.

(13.4.9) Evidently $T \neq \Theta$. If T is finite, then S is finite by (10.4.7).

(13.4.10) Clearly $T - S \neq \Theta$, since otherwise $T = S$, which is impossible, since S is finite and T is infinite. Now, if $T - S$ is not infinite, it is finite, whence $T = S + (T - S)$ yields that T is finite by (10.4.8).

(13.4.11) This follows from (13.4.9) since $S \subset S + T$.

(13.4.12) Since S is infinite and $T \sim S$, $T \neq \Theta$. If T is finite, then S is finite by (10.4.4.a).

(13.4.13) Since I_n is finite, $I - I_n$ is infinite by (13.4.10).

(13.4.14) Define $\varphi \equiv (2 \cdot n + 1; n \in I)$. Then domain of $\varphi = I$, and $\varphi(I) =$ range of $\varphi \subset I - I_e$ by (9.5.4.b). It is easily proved that φ satisfies (10.2.2.b), whence $I \sim \varphi(I)$. By (13.4.12), $\varphi(I)$ is infinite, whence $I - I_e$ is infinite by (13.4.9).

(13.4.15) Let $y \in T$. Define $R \equiv [(x, y) \in S \times T; x \in S]$. It is easily shown that the function $((x, y); x \in S)$ is a one-to-one correspondence between S and R. Hence R is infinite by (13.4.12), so that $R \subset S \times T$ yields that $S \times T$ is infinite by (13.4.9).

(13.4.16) Define $\mathfrak{N} \equiv [[x]; x \in S]$. It is easily seen that $S \sim \mathfrak{N} \subset \mathfrak{M}$, whence $\mathfrak{M}$ is infinite by (13.4.12), (13.4.9).

(13.5.6) Immediate from (13.5.4).

(13.5.7) Since range of $\psi = S$, and since

$$\begin{aligned}[k_n; n \in I] &= [k_n; n \in I_{n(S)}] + [k_n; n \in I - I_{n(S)}] \\ &= \text{range of } \psi + [\psi(1)] \\ &= \text{range of } \psi,\end{aligned}$$

the result follows.

(13.5.8) Let α be a sequence in S with range S. Then α^* is a relation on $S \times I$ with domain S. By (11.5.2), there exists a function β on S to I with $\beta \subset \alpha^*$. Hence, by (10.2.6), $S \sim \beta(S) \subset I$, whence S is countable by (13.5.4).

(13.6.8) Since $\mathfrak{M}$ is denumerably infinite, $\mathfrak{M} \sim I$. Employ (11.5.4) to obtain a subset U of $\sum\mathfrak{M}$ such that $n(U \cdot S) = 1$ for every $S \epsilon \mathfrak{M}$. Define φ on $\mathfrak{M}$ to U so that, for every $S \epsilon \mathfrak{M}$, the correspondent of S under φ is the unique element of $U \cdot S$. Thus prove that φ is a one-to-one correspondence between $\mathfrak{M}$ and U by verifying (10.2.2.b). This establishes $\mathfrak{M} \sim U$. Therefore, since $\mathfrak{M} \sim I$, we have $U \sim I$, whence U is infinite. Now $\sum\mathfrak{M} \supset U$ yields that $\sum\mathfrak{M}$ is infinite by (13.4.9).

(13.6.9) Let $S \epsilon \mathfrak{M}$ be infinite. Then $\sum\mathfrak{M} \supset S$, and $\sum\mathfrak{M}$ is infinite by (13.4.9).

(13.6.10) By (13.5.4), there exist non-empty sets I_0, $J_0 \subset I$ with $S \sim I_0$, $T \sim J_0$. Hence $S \times T \sim I_0 \times J_0$ by (10.4.11). But $I_0 \times J_0 \subset I \times I \sim I$, whence $I_0 \times J_0$ is countable by (13.5.3). Thus, by (13.5.6), $S \times T$ is countable. The second part follows from (13.4.15), (10.4.12).

(13.6.11) The proof is complete except for verification of $\sum\mathfrak{M} = \sum\mathfrak{N} + S_{q+1}$. Since $\mathfrak{M} = \mathfrak{N} + [S_{q+1}]$, this follows from (13.2.3).

Chapter 14

(14.2.17) Clearly p_2 has domain $\varphi(G_1) \times \varphi(G_1) = G_2 \times G_2 =$ domain of o_2. The definition of p_2 yields that, if $x, y \epsilon [1, 2, 3]$, then

$$x \mathsf{p}_2 y = \varphi(\varphi^*(x) \mathsf{o}_1 \varphi^*(y)).$$

If (14.2.1) holds, then let $a = \varphi^*(x)$, $b = \varphi^*(y)$, whence $x, y \epsilon G_2$ implies

$$x \mathsf{p}_2 y = \varphi(a \mathsf{o}_1 b) = \varphi(a) \mathsf{o}_2 \varphi(b) = x \mathsf{o}_2 y,$$

and $\mathsf{p}_2 = \mathsf{o}_2$. If $\mathsf{p}_2 = \mathsf{o}_2$, then $a, b \epsilon G_1$ implies

$$\varphi(a) \mathsf{o}_2 \varphi(b) = \varphi(a) \mathsf{p}_2 \varphi(b) = \varphi((\varphi^*(\varphi(a))) \mathsf{o}_1 (\varphi^*(\varphi(b)))) = \varphi(a \mathsf{o}_1 b),$$

and (14.2.1) holds.

(14.2.18) Examples: (In each set, the displayed elements are assumed distinct. A possible isomorphism φ is given in each example.)

(14.2.5):

$I_1 = [p, q]$, $I_2 = [u, v]$,

$R_1 = [(q, p), (p, p)]$, $R_2 = [(v, u), (u, u)]$,

$\varphi(p) = u, \quad \varphi(q) = v;$

(14.2.7):

$I_1 = [p, q, r]$, $I_2 = [u, v, w]$,

$1_1 = q$, $1_2 = v$,

$\sigma_1 = [(p, q), (q, q), (r, p)]$, $\sigma_2 = [(u, v), (v, v), (w, u)]$,

$\varphi(p) = u, \quad \varphi(q) = v, \quad \varphi(r) = w;$

(14.2.9):

$I_1 = [p, q]$, $I_2 = [u, v]$,
$R_1 = [(q, p), (p, p)]$, $R_2 = [(v, u), (u, u)]$,
$S_1 = [(q, q)]$, $S_2 = [(v, v)]$,
$\varphi(p) = u, \quad \varphi(q) = v;$

(14.2.10):

$G_1 = [p, q]$, $G_2 = [u, v]$,

$$\text{o}_1: \begin{array}{c|cc} & p & q \\ \hline p & p & p \\ q & q & q \end{array} \qquad \text{o}_2: \begin{array}{c|cc} & u & v \\ \hline u & u & u \\ v & v & v \end{array}$$

$$\text{p}_1: \begin{array}{c|cc} & p & q \\ \hline p & p & q \\ q & q & p \end{array} \qquad \text{p}_2: \begin{array}{c|cc} & u & v \\ \hline u & u & v \\ v & v & u \end{array}$$

$\varphi(p) = u, \quad \varphi(q) = v;$

(14.2.13):

$A_1 = [p, q]$, $A_2 = [u, v]$,
$B_1 = [q, r]$, $B_2 = [w, z]$
(assume p, q, r distinct and u, v, w, z distinct),
$\varphi_1(p) = u, \quad \varphi_1(q) = v, \quad \varphi_2(q) = w, \quad \varphi_2(r) = z;$

(14.2.14):

$C_1 = [p, q, r]$, $C_2 = [u, v, w]$,
$A_1 = [p, q]$, $A_2 = [u, v]$,
$B_1 = [q, r]$, $B_2 = [v, w]$,
$\varphi(p) = u, \quad \varphi(q) = v, \quad \varphi(r) = w.$

REMARK: If in the example for (14.2.13) we define $C_1 \equiv A_1 + B_1$, $C_2 \equiv A_2 + B_2$, observe that (C_1, A_1, B_1) is not isomorphic to (C_2, A_2, B_2) in accordance with (14.2.14), since $C_1 = [p, q, r]$, $C_2 = [u, v, w, z]$, and $C_1 \sim C_2$ fails.

(14.2.18) PROOFS OF COROLLARIES:

(14.2.9): Let (I_1, R_1, S_1), (I_2, R_2, S_2), (I_3, R_3, S_3) be given systems. It is readily proved that $(I_1, R_1, S_1) \sim (I_1, R_1, S_1)$, by employing the identity on I_1 to I_1 as an isomorphism. Also, if φ is an isomorphism between (I_1, R_1, S_1) and (I_2, R_2, S_2), then φ^* is readily shown to be an isomorphism between (I_2, R_2, S_2) and (I_1, R_1, S_1). Now let φ, ψ be isomorphisms between (I_1, R_1, S_1), (I_2, R_2, S_2) and between (I_2, R_2, S_2), (I_3, R_3, S_3). Define ρ on I_1 to I_3 so that, for $a \in I_1$, $\rho(a) = \psi(\varphi(a))$. As in the proof of (14.2.3), ρ is a one-to-one correspondence between I_1 and I_3. To prove (a), let $a, b \in I_1$. If $a\, R_1\, b$, then $\varphi(a)\, R_2\, \varphi(b)$, whence $\rho(a) = \psi(\varphi(a))\, R_3\, \psi(\varphi(b)) = \rho(b)$ by (a) applied to φ, ψ. Conversely, let $\rho(a)\, R_3\, \rho(b)$. Then $\psi(\varphi(a))\, R_3\, \psi(\varphi(b))$ yields $\varphi(a)\, R_2\, \varphi(b)$, whence $a\, R_1\, b$, again by (a) applied to φ, ψ. This proves (a) for ρ. Similar proof treats (b).

(14.2.16): Let $(S_1, I_1, 1_1, \sigma_1, F_1)$, $(S_2, I_2, 1_2, \sigma_2, F_2)$, $(S_3, I_3, 1_3, \sigma_3, F_3)$ be given systems. To prove the first isomorphic to itself, define φ as the identity on S_1 to S_1 and ψ as the identity on I_1 to I_1. Then (a), (b), (c) are immediate. If the first system is isomorphic to the second, with one-to-one correspondences φ, ψ, then we have (a), (b), (c) as written in the text. These conditions, with the two systems interchanged, are to be verified, using φ^*, ψ^* in place of φ, ψ. Thus, $\psi^*(1_2) = 1_1$ is immediate from (a). Also, $n \in I_2$ implies

$$\begin{aligned}\psi^*(\sigma_2(n)) &= \psi^*(\sigma_2(\psi(\psi^*(n))))\\ &= \psi^*(\psi(\sigma_1(\psi^*(n)))) \qquad \text{[by (b)]}\\ &= \sigma_1(\psi^*(n)).\end{aligned}$$

Finally, $n \in I_2$ implies

$$\begin{aligned}\varphi^*(F_2(n)) &= \varphi^*(F_2(\psi(\psi^*(n))))\\ &= \varphi^*(\varphi(F_1(\psi^*(n)))) \qquad \text{[by (c)]}\\ &= F_1(\psi^*(n)).\end{aligned}$$

Hence (a), (b), (c) hold for φ^*, ψ^*.

Now assume the first system isomorphic to the second, with φ_1, ψ_1, and assume the second isomorphic to the third, with φ_2, ψ_2. Define φ_3 on S_1 to S_3 and ψ_3 on I_1 to I_3 so that, for every $a \in S_1$, $n \in I_1$,

$$\varphi_3(a) = \varphi_2(\varphi_1(a)), \quad \psi_3(n) = \psi_2(\psi_1(n)).$$

Then

$$\psi_3(1_1) = \psi_2(\psi_1(1_1)) = \psi_2(1_2) = 1_3.$$

Also, $n \in I_1$ implies

$$\begin{aligned}\psi_3(\sigma_1(n)) &= \psi_2(\psi_1(\sigma_1(n))) = \psi_2(\sigma_2(\psi_1(n)))\\ &= \sigma_3(\psi_2(\psi_1(n))) = \sigma_3(\psi_3(n)).\end{aligned}$$

Finally, $n \in I_1$ implies

$$\begin{aligned}\varphi_3(F_1(n)) &= \varphi_2(\varphi_1(F_1(n))) = \varphi_2(F_2(\psi_1(n)))\\ &= F_3(\psi_2(\psi_1(n))) = F_3(\psi_3(n)).\end{aligned}$$

This proves (a), (b), (c) for φ_3, ψ_3, using the same conditions for φ_1, ψ_1 and φ_2, ψ_2; hence the first system is isomorphic to the third.

(14.2.19) Two systems $(G_1, \mathsf{o}_1, \mathsf{p}_1, H_1, +_1, \times_1)$, $(G_2, \mathsf{o}_2, \mathsf{p}_2, H_2, +_2, \times_2)$ are isomorphic if there exist one-to-one correspondences φ, ψ between G_1 and G_2 and between H_1 and H_2, respectively, such that

(a) $a, b \in G_1$ implies $\varphi(a)\, \mathsf{o}_2\, \varphi(b) = \varphi(a\, \mathsf{o}_1\, b)$;

(b) $a, b \in G_1$ implies $\varphi(a)\, \mathsf{p}_2\, \varphi(b) = \varphi(a\, \mathsf{p}_1\, b)$;

(c) $x, y \in H_1$ implies $\psi(x) +_2 \psi(y) = \psi(x +_1 y)$;

(d) $a \in G_1$, $x \in H_1$ implies $\varphi(a) \times_2 \psi(x) = \psi(a \times_1 x)$.

(14.2.20) Since $(G_1, \circ_1) \sim (G_2, \circ_2)$, there exists a one-to-one correspondence φ between G_1 and G_2 which carries $\circ_1$ into $\circ_2$. Let $a_2, b_2, c_2 \in G_2$. Then define $a_1 \equiv \varphi^*(a_2)$, $b_1 \equiv \varphi^*(b_2)$, $c_1 \equiv \varphi^*(c_2)$. Then

$$\begin{aligned} a_2 \circ_2 (b_2 \circ_2 c_2) &= \varphi(a_1) \circ_2 (\varphi(b_1) \circ_2 \varphi(c_1)) \\ &= \varphi(a_1) \circ_2 (\varphi(b_1 \circ_1 c_1)) \\ &= \varphi(a_1 \circ_1 (b_1 \circ_1 c_1)) \\ &= \varphi((a_1 \circ_1 b_1) \circ_1 c_1). \end{aligned}$$

Similarly $(a_2 \circ_2 b_2) \circ_2 c_2 = \varphi((a_1 \circ_1 b_1) \circ_1 c_1)$. This proves the group axiom I for $(G_2, \circ_2)$. Let $a_2, b_2 \in G_2$. Since $a_1 \equiv \varphi^*(a_2)$, $b_1 \equiv \varphi^*(b_2)$ are in G_1, there exists $x_1 \in G_1$ [by Axiom II] with $a_1 \circ_1 x_1 = b_1$. Hence, if $x_2 \equiv \varphi(x_1)$, $b_2 = \varphi(b_1) = \varphi(a_1 \circ_1 x_1) = \varphi(a_1) \circ_2 \varphi(x_1) = a_2 \circ_2 x_2$, and Axiom II holds for $(G_2, \circ_2)$. Similarly, Axiom III is proved.

(14.2.21) Let $(a_1, a_2), (b_1, b_2), (c_1, c_2) \in G$. Then

$$\begin{aligned} ((a_1, a_2) \circ (b_1, b_2)) \circ (c_1, c_2) &= (a_1 \circ_1 b_1, a_2 \circ_2 b_2) \circ (c_1, c_2) \\ &= ((a_1 \circ_1 b_1) \circ_1 c_1, (a_2 \circ_2 b_2) \circ_2 c_2) \\ &= (a_1 \circ_1 (b_1 \circ_1 c_1), a_2 \circ_2 (b_2 \circ_2 c_2)). \end{aligned}$$

The proof of the group axiom I is now easily completed. To prove Axiom II, let $(a_1, a_2), (b_1, b_2) \in G$. There exist $x_1 \in G_1$, $x_2 \in G_2$ with $a_1 \circ x_1 = b_1$, $a_2 \circ x_2 = b_2$. Hence show that $(a_1, a_2) \circ (x_1, x_2) = (b_1, b_2)$. Axiom III is similarly proved.

(14.3.2) One first verifies the commutativity directly, that $x, y \in G_1$ implies $x \circ_1 y = y \circ_1 x$. There are twelve cases to consider. To prove that $x, y, z \in G$ implies $(x \circ_1 y) \circ_1 z = x \circ_1 (y \circ_1 z)$, first verify this for sixteen cases (if $x = y = z$, commutativity is used):

$$\begin{aligned} (x, y, z) = {} & (a, a, b), (a, a, c), (a, a, d); (b, b, a), (b, b, c), (b, b, d); \\ & (c, c, a), (c, c, b), (c, c, d); (d, d, a), (d, d, b), (d, d, c); \\ & (a, b, c), (a, b, d), (a, c, d), (b, c, d). \end{aligned}$$

The remaining forty-four cases are handled by the device used in this example:

$$\begin{aligned} (d \circ_1 c) \circ_1 a &= (c \circ_1 d) \circ_1 a && \text{[by commutativity]} \\ &= a \circ_1 (c \circ_1 d) && \text{[by commutativity]} \\ &= (a \circ_1 c) \circ_1 d && \text{[by above associativity]} \\ &= d \circ_1 (a \circ_1 c) && \text{[by commutativity]} \\ &= d \circ_1 (c \circ_1 a) && \text{[by commutativity].} \end{aligned}$$

The following equalities, easily proved, together with commutativity, prove Axioms II, III:

$$\begin{array}{lll} a \circ_1 a = a, & b \circ_1 b = c, & c \circ_1 c = a, \\ a \circ_1 b = b, & b \circ_1 c = d, & c \circ_1 d = b, \\ a \circ_1 c = c, & b \circ_1 d = a, & d \circ_1 d = c. \\ a \circ_1 d = d, & & \end{array}$$

(14.3.3) Define $(G_3, \circ_3)$ as in (7.2.1), whence $G_3 = [m, n]$,

$$m \circ_3 m = m, \quad m \circ_3 n = n \circ_3 m = n, \quad n \circ_3 n = m.$$

Define $(G, \circ)$ as the direct product of $(G_3, \circ_3)$ and itself. Then $G = G_3 \times G_3$, and $\circ$ is the operation described by the table [use (14.2.21)]:

	(m, m)	(m, n)	(n, m)	(n, n)
(m, m)	(m, m)	(m, n)	(n, m)	(n, n)
(m, n)	(m, n)	(m, m)	(n, n)	(n, m)
(n, m)	(n, m)	(n, n)	(m, m)	(m, n)
(n, n)	(n, n)	(n, m)	(m, n)	(m, m)

By (14.2.21), $(G, \circ)$ is a group. Now define φ on G_2 to G so that

$$\varphi(a) = (m, m), \quad \varphi(b) = (m, n), \quad \varphi(c) = (n, m), \quad \varphi(d) = (n, n).$$

Direct verification shows that range of $\varphi = G$ and that (10.2.2.b) holds. Finally, one shows easily that φ carries $\circ_2$ into $\circ$. This proves $(G, \circ) \sim (G_2, \circ_2)$, whence $(G_2, \circ_2)$ is a group by (14.2.20). Commutativity is verified directly from the table for $\circ_2$.

(14.3.4) It is to be proved that, if a one-to-one correspondence φ exists between I_1 and I_2, then one exists which carries 1_1 into 1_2. If $\varphi(1_1) = 1_2$, then φ is effective. Suppose $x_2 \equiv \varphi(1_1) \neq 1_2$, and define $x_1 \equiv \varphi^*(1_2)$, whence $x_1 \neq 1_1$. Define ψ on I_1 to I_2 so that $\psi(1_1) = 1_2$, $\psi(x_1) = x_2$, and, for $y \in I_1 - [1_1, x_1]$, $\psi(y) = \varphi(y)$. Then one readily proves that ψ is a one-to-one correspondence between I_1 and I_2 such that ψ carries 1_1 into 1_2. (This result illustrates a case, in contradistinction to groups, in which equivalence of the basic sets is sufficient to secure isomorphism of the systems.)

(14.4.2) Define $H_1 \equiv [k_1 \in I_1; \varphi(k_1) = \psi(k_1)]$. Then $\varphi(1_1) = 1_2 = \psi(1_1)$, and $1_1 \in H$. If $q_1 \in H_1$, then

$$\varphi(\sigma_1(q_1)) = \sigma_2(\varphi(q_1)) = \sigma_2(\psi(q_1)) = \psi(\sigma_1(q_1)),$$

and $\sigma_1(q_1) \in H_1$. (The first and last equalities result from the defining properties of the isomorphisms φ, ψ.)

(14.4.3) It is first shown that φ carries $+_1$ into $+_2$ and $\times_1$ into $\times_2$ [see (14.2.11)]. Let $m_1 \in I_1$; it is to be shown that

(1) $$H_1 \equiv [n_1 \in I_1; \varphi(m_1 +_1 n_1) = \varphi(m_1) +_2 \varphi(n_1)] = I_1.$$

That $1_1 \in H_1$ follows from (14.2.7). Let $q_1 \in H_1$; then

$$\begin{aligned}\varphi(m_1 +_1 q_1 +_1 1_1) &= \varphi(m_1 +_1 q_1) +_2 1_2 = \varphi(m_1) +_2 \varphi(q_1) +_2 1_2 \\ &= \varphi(m_1) +_2 \varphi(q_1 +_1 1_1),\end{aligned}$$

whence $q_1 +_1 1_1 \in H_1$. Hence (1) holds. Now we prove

(2) $$K_1 \equiv [n_1 \in I; \varphi(m_1 \times_1 n_1) = \varphi(m_1) \times_2 \varphi(n_1)] = I_1.$$

Evidently $1_1 \in K_1$. Let $q_1 \in K_1$; then

$$\begin{aligned}\varphi(m_1 \times_1 (q_1 +_1 1_1)) &= \varphi((m_1 \times_1 q_1) +_1 m_1) \\ &= \varphi(m_1 \times_1 q_1) +_2 \varphi(m_1) && \text{[by (1)]} \\ &= \varphi(m_1) \times_2 \varphi(q_1) +_2 \varphi(m_1) \\ &= \varphi(m_1) \times_2 (\varphi(q_1) +_2 1_2) \\ &= \varphi(m_1 \quad \times_2 \varphi(q_1 +_1 1_1) && \text{[by (1)],}\end{aligned}$$

whence $q_1 +_1 1_1 \in K_1$. This proves (2). It is now shown that φ carries $<_1$ into $<_2$ [see (14.2.5)]. If $m_1, n_1 \in I_1$, $m_1 <_1 n_1$, there exists $q_1 \in I_1$ with $m_1 +_1 q_1 = n_1$. Now apply (a) to obtain $\varphi(m_1) +_2 \varphi(q_1) = \varphi(n_1)$, that is, $\varphi(m_1) <_2 \varphi(n_1)$. Conversely, if $\varphi(m_1) +_2 q_2 = \varphi(n_1)$, define $q_1 \equiv \varphi^*(q_2)$. It follows that $\varphi(m_1 +_1 q_1) = \varphi(n_1)$, whence $m_1 +_1 q_1 = n_1$, and $m_1 <_1 n_1$.

(14.5.4)

(a) System: $(I, 1, \sigma)$; subsystem: $(J, 1, \sigma)$, where $J \subset I$, $1 \in J$, and $a \in J$ implies $\sigma(a) \in J$.

(b) System: (I, J); subsystem: (K, J), where $J \subset K \subset I$.

(c) System: (I, R, S); subsystem: (J, R, S), where $J \subset I$. (Note: By our convention, (J, R, S) really means $(J, R \cdot (J \times J), S \cdot (J \times J))$, that is, R and S are "reduced.")

(d) System: $(G, \circ, \mathsf{p})$; subsystem: $(H, \circ, \mathsf{p})$, where $H \subset G$, and a, $b \in H$ implies $a \circ b$, $a \,\mathsf{p}\, b \in H$.

(e) System: (A, B); subsystem: (C, D), where $C \subset A$, $D \subset B$.

(f) System: (C, A, B); subsystem: (D, A, B), where A, $B \subset D \subset C$.

(g) System: $(G, I, 1, \sigma, \circ)$; subsystem: $(H, J, 1, \sigma, \circ)$, where $(H, \circ)$ is a subsystem of $(G, \circ)$, and $(J, 1, \sigma)$ is a subsystem of $(I, 1, \sigma)$.

(h) System: $(S, I, 1, \sigma, F)$; subsystem: $(T, J, 1, \sigma, F)$, where $T \subset S$, $(J, 1, \sigma)$ is a subsystem of $(I, 1, \sigma)$, and $a \in J$ implies $F(a) \in T$.

(14.5.5) Let $(J, 1, \sigma)$ be a subsystem of $(I, 1, \sigma)$, where $J \subset I, 1 \in J$, and $n \in J$ implies $\sigma(n) \in J$. By Axiom III for positive integers, $J = I$.

Chapter 15

(15.1.2) Thirteen relations: all except $[(p_1, p_2), (p_2, p_1)]$, $[(p_1, p_2), (p_2, p_1), (p_1, p_1)]$, $[(p_1, p_2), (p_2, p_1), (p_2, p_2)]$.

(15.2.4) If $(y, x) \in R^*$, then $(x, y) \in R$, whence $(x, y) \in R^*$ (since $R \subset R^*$), and $(y, x) \in R$.

(15.2.5) If R is reflexive, then $x \in A$ implies $x \, R \, x$, whence domain of R = range of $R = A$. This applies then to equivalence relations.

(15.2.6) Suppose $x \, R \, y$. By (a), we have $y \, R \, y$ and $x \, R \, y$. By (b), $y \, R \, x$. This proves (15.2.3.b). Now (15.2.3.c) is immediate. If $R = \Theta$, then (b) holds, while (a) fails. But if domain of $R = A$, then (a) follows from (b). For, if $x \in A$, there exists $y \in A$ with $x\,R\,y$. Now apply (b) with $z = x$, to obtain $x\,R\,x$.

(15.3.7) If $A_R(x) \cdot A_R(y) \neq \Theta$, then $x\,R\,y$ by the contrapositive of (c). Then (b) yields $A_R(x) = A_R(y)$. Reverse the steps to obtain the converse.

(15.3.8) Evidently $E \subset E$, $E^* = E$, whence E is reflexive and symmetric. If $x\,E\,y$, $y\,E\,z$, then $x = y$, $y = z$, so that $x\,E\,z$. Clearly $A \times A$ satisfies (a), (b), (c) of (15.2.3).

$$\mathfrak{A}_E = [[x];\, x \in A]; \quad \mathfrak{A}_{R\times R} = [A].$$

(15.3.9) Clearly domain and range of $(\mathfrak{A}_R;\, R \in \mathcal{E}_A)$ are $\mathcal{E}_A$ and $\mathcal{P}_A$, respectively. To prove (10.2.2.b), let $R_1, R_2 \in \mathcal{E}_A$, $R_1 \neq R_2$. By the uniqueness in (15.3.6), $\mathfrak{A}_{R_1} \neq \mathfrak{A}_{R_2}$.

(15.3.10) Let $A = [p_1, p_2]$. By (5.3.13.d), the only reflexive and symmetric relations are E and $A \times A$. But these are also transitive by (15.1.2). Hence $\mathcal{E}_A = [E, A \times A]$. Also, the only partitions are $[[p_1], [p_2]]$ and $[A]$. In fact,

$$\mathfrak{A}_E = [[p_1], [p_2]], \quad \mathfrak{A}_{A\times A} = [A].$$

Now let $A = [p_1, p_2, p_3]$. Then $\mathcal{E}_A$ is the set consisting of

$$E, \quad E + [(p_1, p_2), (p_2, p_1)], \quad E + [(p_1, p_3), (p_3, p_1)],$$
$$E + [(p_2, p_3), (p_3, p_2)], \quad A \times A.$$

(Note that three other relations are reflexive and symmetric but not transitive.) The set $\mathcal{P}_A$ consists of

$$[[p_1], [p_2], [p_3]], \quad [[p_1, p_2], [p_3]], \quad [[p_1, p_3], [p_2]],$$
$$[[p_2, p_3], [p_1]], [A].$$

(15.4.10) Let $A = [p_1, p_2]$, $R = [(p_1, p_1)]$.

(15.4.11) Let $A = [p_1, p_2, p_3]$, $R = [(p_1, p_2), (p_2, p_1), (p_1, p_3)]$. Clearly Θ is symmetric; (15.4.3.b) is vacuously true.

(15.4.12) To be irreflexive, R must satisfy $R \cdot E = \Theta$. This is obvious since $R = S - E$. To prove that R is asymmetric, suppose there exist $x, y \in A$ with $x\,R\,y$, $y\,R\,x$. Then $x\,S\,y$, $y\,S\,x$, $x \neq y$. This is impossible in view of (15.4.8.c). (Note that (15.4.8.a) is not needed in this proof.)

(15.4.13) If $>$ is a well-ordering, I has a greatest. Hence, by (9.3.8), there exists $m \in I$ such that $I \subset I_m$. But $m + 1 \in I$, so that $m + 1 \in I_m$, which is impossible.

(15.4.14) All linear orderings are also well-orderings. These follow:

$$[(p_1, p_2), (p_2, p_3), (p_1, p_3)],$$
$$[(p_1, p_3), (p_3, p_2), (p_1, p_2)],$$
$$[(p_2, p_3), (p_3, p_1), (p_2, p_1)],$$
$$[(p_2, p_1), (p_1, p_3), (p_2, p_3)],$$
$$[(p_3, p_1), (p_1, p_2), (p_3, p_2)],$$
$$[(p_3, p_2), (p_2, p_1), (p_3, p_1)].$$

Partial orderings are the linear orderings, together with the following:

Θ, $[(p_1, p_2)]$, $[(p_2, p_1)]$, $[(p_1, p_3)]$, $[(p_3, p_1)]$, $[(p_2, p_3)]$, $[(p_3, p_2)]$, $[(p_1, p_2), (p_1, p_3)]$, $[(p_2, p_1), (p_2, p_3)]$, $[(p_3, p_1), (p_3, p_2)]$, $[(p_2, p_1), (p_3, p_1)]$, $[(p_1, p_2), (p_3, p_2)]$, $[(p_1, p_3), (p_2, p_3)]$.

(15.5.5) The relation $>$ is a linear ordering of A by (15.4.6). Hence (15.5.3) applies with $<$ replaced by $>$; the least in $S \subset A$ (with respect to $>$) is in fact a greatest (with respect to $<$).

(15.5.6) If $S \subset A$, $S \neq \Theta$, then S is finite, whence (15.5.3) applies, yielding a least in S. Thus (15.4.7.b) holds.

(15.5.7) Suppose the principle is false. Then there exists $H \subset A$ such that $H \neq A$, and such that, if $x \in A$ such that $y \in H$ for every $y < x$, then $x \in H$. Since $A - H \neq \Theta$, $A - H$ has a least element x. Since x is a least, $y < x$ implies $y \in' A - H$, whence $y \in H$. It follows that $x \in H$, contrary to $x \in A - H$.

(15.5.8)

Proof of (a): If $x \in T^+$, then $x \geqq y$ for every $y \in T$, so that $x \geqq y$ for every $y \in S$. Therefore $x \in S^+$. Similarly $S^- \supset T^-$.

Proof of (b): Let $x \in S$. Now

$$S^{+-} = [z \in A; y \in S^+ \text{ implies } z \leqq y].$$

But $y \in S^+$ implies $y \geqq x$; hence $x \in S^{+-}$. Similarly $S^{-+} \supset S$.

Proof of (c): By (b) applied to S^+, $S^{+-+} \supset S^+$. Since $S^{+-} \supset S$ by (b), we have, by (a), $S^{+-+} \subset S^+$. Therefore $S^{+-+} = S^+$. Similarly $S^{-+-} = S^-$.

Proof of (d): Obvious from (c).

(15.5.9) Define $T \equiv \prod \mathfrak{M}$. Then $S \in \mathfrak{M}$ implies $T \subset S$, so that $T^+ \supset S^+$, and $T^{+-} \subset S^{+-} = S$ by (15.5.8.a). This yields $T^{+-} \subset \prod \mathfrak{M} = T$. But $T^{+-} \supset T$ by (15.5.8.b). Thus $T^{+-} = T$.

(15.5.10) Let S have a least element x. Then $[x] \subset S$ yields $[x]^- \supset S^-$. If y is a lower bound of S, $y \in S^-$, whence $y \in [x]^-$. Hence $y \leqq x$.

But $z \in S$ implies $x \leqq z$, whence $x \in S^-$. This proves that x is a greatest in S^-, that is, $x =$ g.l.b. S. Conversely, if $x =$ g.l.b. $S \in S$, then $x \in S^-$, so that the requirements of a least are met.

Chapter 16

(16.4.10) Put $n = m$ in (16.4.2), so that m/m is the unique $f \in F$ such that $m \odot f = m \odot \boldsymbol{u}$. Since $\boldsymbol{u}$ is effective as f, the result follows.

(16.4.11) By (16.4.2), $f \equiv m_1/n_1$ satisfies $n_1 \odot f = m_1 \odot \boldsymbol{u}$. We prove that $g \equiv m_2/n_2$ satisfies the same equality, so that $f = g$. From $n_2 \odot g = m_2 \odot \boldsymbol{u}$, it follows that

$$\begin{aligned}(n_1 \cdot n_2) \odot g = n_1 \odot (n_2 \odot g) = n_1 \odot (m_2 \odot \boldsymbol{u}) &= (n_1 \cdot m_2) \odot \boldsymbol{u} \\ &= (m_1 \cdot n_2) \odot \boldsymbol{u}.\end{aligned}$$

Hence $n_2 \odot (n_1 \odot g) = n_2 \odot (m_1 \odot \boldsymbol{u})$, and $n_1 \odot g = m_1 \odot \boldsymbol{u}$.

(16.4.12) This follows a pattern similar to that in (14.2.18).

(16.6.8) Let $f = m_1/n_1$, $g = p_1/q_1$, and let m, n, p, q be any positive integers satisfying (a). Then $m_1 \cdot n = n_1 \cdot m$, $p_1 \cdot q = q_1 \cdot p$. Define $h \equiv (m_1 \cdot p_1)/(n_1 \cdot q_1)$. Then

$$\begin{aligned}(m_1 \cdot p_1) \cdot (n \cdot q) &= (m_1 \cdot n) \cdot (p_1 \cdot q) \\ &= (n_1 \cdot m) \cdot (q_1 \cdot p) \\ &= (n_1 \cdot q_1) \cdot (m \cdot p),\end{aligned}$$

whence $h = (m \cdot p)/(n \cdot q)$. Uniqueness is immediate.

(16.6.9) PROOF OF (e): If $f = m/n$, $g = p/q$, $h = r/s$, then

$$\begin{aligned}f \otimes (g \oplus h) &= \frac{m}{n} \otimes \frac{p \cdot s + q \cdot r}{q \cdot s} \\ &= \frac{m \cdot (p \cdot s + q \cdot r)}{n \cdot q \cdot s} \\ &= \frac{m \cdot n \cdot (p \cdot s + q \cdot r)}{(n \cdot q) \cdot (n \cdot s)} \\ &= \frac{(m \cdot p) \cdot (n \cdot s) + (n \cdot q) \cdot (m \cdot r)}{(n \cdot q) \cdot (n \cdot s)} \\ &= \frac{m \cdot p}{n \cdot q} \oplus \frac{m \cdot r}{n \cdot s} \\ &= (f \otimes g) \oplus (f \otimes h).\end{aligned}$$

(16.6.10) We have

$$\frac{m}{p} \oplus \frac{n}{p} = \frac{m \cdot p + p \cdot n}{p \cdot p} = \frac{p \cdot (m + n)}{p \cdot p} = \frac{m + n}{p}.$$

(16.6.11) Let $f = m/n \in F$. Then

$$f \otimes u = \frac{m}{n} \cdot \frac{1}{1} = \frac{m \cdot 1}{n \cdot 1} = \frac{m}{n} = f.$$

Also,

$$\frac{m}{n} \cdot \frac{n}{m} = \frac{m \cdot n}{n \cdot m} = \frac{1}{1} = u.$$

(16.6.12) We have

$$\frac{2}{3} \oplus \frac{1}{2} = \frac{2 \cdot 2 + 3 \cdot 1}{3 \cdot 2} = \frac{4+3}{6} = \frac{7}{6};$$

$$\frac{3}{4} \otimes \frac{5}{6} = \frac{3 \cdot 5}{4 \cdot 6} = \frac{3 \cdot 5}{3 \cdot 4 \cdot 2} = \frac{5}{8};$$

$$\frac{5}{4} \otimes \frac{4}{5} = u = \frac{1}{1} \qquad \text{[by (16.6.11)]}.$$

(16.7.8) Suppose $m \cdot q = n \cdot p$. We have, by (2),

$$\begin{aligned}(n \cdot q) \cdot (m_1 \cdot q_1) = m \cdot n_1 \cdot q \cdot q_1 &= (n_1 \cdot n) \cdot (p \cdot q_1) \\ &= (n \cdot q) \cdot (n_1 \cdot p_1),\end{aligned}$$

so that $m_1 \cdot q_1 = n_1 \cdot p_1$. The converse is similar.

(16.7.9) Let $f = m/n, g = p/q$, and let $g = f \oplus h, h = r/s$. It follows that $m \cdot s \cdot q + n \cdot r \cdot q = n \cdot s \cdot p$. By (9.4.7), $s \mid n \cdot r \cdot q$, whence there exists $k \in I$ such that $n \cdot r \cdot q = k \cdot s$. Thus, by cancellation,

$$m \cdot q + k = n \cdot p,$$

and the conclusion follows.

(16.7.10)

PROOF OF (a): If $f = m/n \oslash f$, then $m \cdot n < n \cdot m$, which is false.

PROOF OF (b): Obvious by (a), (c) and (15.4.4).

PROOF OF (d): Use (16.7.5) and the technique of (9.2.11).

PROOF OF (f): Let $f = m/n$, $g = p/q$. Then $m \cdot q < n \cdot p$ or $m \cdot q = n \cdot p$ or $n \cdot p < m \cdot q$. These cases lead respectively to $f \oslash g$, $f = g$, $g \oslash f$.

PROOF OF (e): Suppose the contrary. Then $f = g$ or $g \oslash f$ by (f). Then apply (d) to obtain a contradiction.

PROOF OF (g): Since $f \oslash g$, there exists, by (16.7.5), $k \in F$ such that $g = f \oplus k$. Hence, by (16.6.4.e),

$$g \otimes h = (f \otimes h) \oplus (k \otimes h),$$

whence the result follows by (16.7.5).

PROOF OF (h): Use (f) as in (e).

PROOF OF (i): If $h = k$, this follows from (g). Otherwise, by (g),

$$f \otimes h \oslash g \otimes h \oslash g \otimes k.$$

(16.7.11) To prove $3 \cdot 5 < 4 \cdot 4$, note that

$$3 \cdot 5 + 1 = 3 \cdot (4 + 1) + 1 = 3 \cdot 4 + 3 + 1 = 3 \cdot 4 + 4 = (3 + 1) \cdot 4 = 4 \cdot 4.$$

(16.8.3) To prove $m_1 \cdot 2 \cdot n_1 \cdot n_2 < n_1 \cdot (m_1 \cdot n_2 + n_1 \cdot m_2)$, note that assumption of the contrary yields

$$m_1 \cdot n_1 \cdot n_2 \geqq n_1 \cdot n_1 \cdot m_2,$$

so that $m_1 \cdot n_2 \geqq n_1 \cdot m_2$, contrary to $f_1 \bigcirc\!\!\!\!< f_2$. Similar argument proves $g \bigcirc\!\!\!\!< f_2$.

(16.8.4) If $f = m/n \in \boldsymbol{F}$, then

$$g \equiv 2 \odot f = \frac{2}{1} \otimes \frac{m}{n} = \frac{2 \cdot m}{n} \bigcirc\!\!\!\!> f,$$

the last statement holding since $m \cdot n < 2 \cdot m \cdot n$. If f is a greatest element, then $g \bigcirc\!\!\!\!> f$ contradicts the property $g \mathrel{\underline{\bigcirc\!\!\!\!<}} f$.

(16.9.6) Existence of m follows from (16.9.1). If $m/1 = n/1$, then $m \cdot 1 = 1 \cdot n$, whence $m = n$. Clearly φ has domain $\boldsymbol{I}$. If $f = m/1 \in \boldsymbol{I}$, then

$$\varphi(f) = \frac{m}{1} \oplus \frac{1}{1} = \frac{m + 1}{1} \in \boldsymbol{I},$$

whence range of $\varphi \subset \boldsymbol{I}$. Obviously $\boldsymbol{u} = 1/1 \in \boldsymbol{I}$.

(16.10.4) We have

$$a \otimes b = \frac{m}{1} \otimes \frac{n}{1} = \frac{m \cdot n}{1} = \psi(m \cdot n) = \psi(m) \otimes_0 \psi(n) = \frac{m}{1} \otimes_0 \frac{n}{1} = a \otimes_0 b;$$

this proves (2). Let $a \bigcirc\!\!\!\!< b$. Then $m < n$, whence $a = \psi(m) \bigcirc\!\!\!\!<_0 \psi(n) = b$. The converse is immediate. This proves (3).

(16.10.5) To prove (1), note that, by (4), (5) and (7), (8), each of $f <_1 g$ and $\psi(f) <_2 \psi(g)$ holds if and only if $m \cdot q < n \cdot p$. The proof of (3) is similar to the proof of (2) given in the text.

(16.10.6) Let $(\boldsymbol{F}_1, \boldsymbol{u}_1, <_1, +_1, \times_1)$ and $(\boldsymbol{F}_2, \boldsymbol{u}_2, <_2, +_2, \times_2)$ be any two algebraic systems of positive rational numbers, and let $(\boldsymbol{F}_1, \boldsymbol{u}_1, \odot_1)$ and $(\boldsymbol{F}_2, \boldsymbol{u}_2, \odot_2)$ be the corresponding basic systems of positive rational numbers. By (16.4.9), there is an isomorphism ψ between $(\boldsymbol{F}_1, \boldsymbol{u}_1, \odot_1)$ and $(\boldsymbol{F}_2, \boldsymbol{u}_2, \odot_2)$. Then, by (16.10.2), ψ is also an isomorphism between $(\boldsymbol{F}_1, \boldsymbol{u}_1, <_1, +_1, \times_1)$ and $(\boldsymbol{F}_2, \boldsymbol{u}_2, <_2, +_2, \times_2)$.

Chapter 17

(17.2.7) Let b, b' be upper endpoints of S. Since $b \in S$, we have $b \leqq b'$; similarly $b' \leqq b$. Hence $b = b'$. This proves (c). Suppose S is open, and let b, b' be endpoints. If $b \neq b'$, then $b < b'$ or $b' < b$. If $b < b'$, then $b \in S$, whence $b > b$, which is false. Similarly, $b' < b$ is impossible. (Note that the hypothesis $S \neq \Theta$ is not required here as in (b).)

(17.2.8) In $(\boldsymbol{F}, <)$, any upper (lower) bound of $\boldsymbol{F}$ must be in $\boldsymbol{F}$ and hence is a greatest (least). Hence, by (16.8.1), (16.8.4), no such bounds exist. The example in (15.5.4) is not a *linearly* ordered system, and so does not answer the question here.

(17.2.9) Let $(I, <)$ be the linearly ordered system, and define $S \equiv [2, 3] = [m \in I; 1 < m, m < 4]$, whence S is an open interval with endpoints 1, 4. But g.l.b. $S = 2$, l.u.b. $S = 3$. However, let $(\boldsymbol{F}, <)$ be the linearly ordered system, let $g, h \in \boldsymbol{F}$, $g < h$, and define

$$S \equiv [f \in \boldsymbol{F}; g < f, f < h].$$

Now let g_1 be a lower bound of S. Since $S \neq \Theta$ by (16.8.2), it follows that $g_1 \leqq g$. (Otherwise $g_1 \in S$, and $g < g_1$ leads to an element $f \in \boldsymbol{F}$ with $g < f, f < g_1$ by (16.8.2), so that g_1 cannot be a lower bound.) Similarly, $h =$ l.u.b. S. Hence the answer to the question is in the negative for some systems and in the affirmative for others. What is needed in the affirmative proof for $(\boldsymbol{F}, <)$ is the "density" (16.8.2).

(17.2.10) The answer is similar to that in (17.2.9). Density yields an affirmative answer, but in $(I, <)$ the answer is again negative, as the sets $I_n - [n]$ show.

(17.4.11) If $J_1 < J_2$ and $J_2 < J_1$, we have $J_1 \subset J_2$, $J_2 \subset J_1$, whence $J_1 = J_2$, contrary to $J_1 < J_2$. If $J_1 < J_2$, $J_2 < J_3$, then $J_1 \subset J_3$ is immediate. But $J_1 = J_3$ yields $J_1 < J_2$, $J_2 < J_1$ contrary to the irreflexive property.

(17.4.12) Clearly $z \in J_3$ implies $z < y$, whence $y \in J_2$ yields $z \in J_2$, since J_2 is a lower set. This proves $J_3 \subset J_2$. Now $y \in J_2$, $y \in' J_3$ implies $J_3 \neq J_2$. Hence $J_3 < J_2$. Now suppose $w \in J_1$. Then $w \neq x$. If $x > w$, then $x \in J_1$, which is false. Hence $w < x$. But then $w < y$, whence $w \in J_3$. This proves $J_1 \subset J_3$. Since $x \in J_3$, $x \in' J_1$ implies $J_1 \neq J_3$. Therefore $J_1 < J_3$.

(17.5.6) Let $p \in S$, whence $k \in T$ implies $k \leqq p$. Thus p is an upper bound of T, so that $p \geqq g$. This proves that g is a lower bound of S. Now let h be a lower bound of S. Then $h \in T$, so that $h \leqq g$. This proves that $g =$ g.l.b. S.

(17.5.7) It is shown that (2) implies that h is an upper bound of S. Let $p \in S$, $n \in I$, $q \in K$ with

$$C_n = [x \in K; p \leqq x, x \leqq q].$$

If $n \leqq m$, then $C_m \subset C_n$, whence $p^* \in C_n$, and $p \leqq p^*$. Then $p \leqq q^* < h$. If $n > m$, $C_n \subset C_m$, whence $p \in C_m$, so that $p \leqq q^* < h$. In all cases, $p < h$.

(17.5.8) Let $n \in I$. Define

$$H \equiv [k \in I; \alpha(n) < \alpha(n + k)].$$

By (3), $1 \in H$. If $q \in H$, then, by (3), $\alpha(n) < \alpha(n + q) < \alpha(n + q + 1)$, so that $q + 1 \in H$. If $m, n \in I$, $m \neq n$, we have $m > n$ or $m < n$. If $m > n$, define $k \equiv m - n$, whence $k \in H$, and $\alpha(n) < \alpha(m)$. Similar argument yields $\alpha(n) > \alpha(m)$ if $m < n$. Hence (4) holds.

(17.5.9) Consider a system $(L, <)$ satisfying I, II, III, (17.5.1). We list the properties of $(L, >)$, that is, we restate I, II, III, (17.5.1), but employ wherever possible the relation $>$. First, I is unchanged. Next, from II we obtain that II* (a) $>$ is irreflexive, (b) $>$ is transitive, (c) a, $b \in K$ implies $a = b$ or $a > b$ or $b > a$. According to III, we have III* for every $a, b \in K$ with $a > b$, there exists $x \in K$ such that $a > x$, $x > b$. Finally, (17.5.1) states that

IV′*. every non-empty subset of K which is bounded "above" has a "least upper" bound,

where "above," "least upper" refer to the relation $>$. Properties I, II*, III*, IV′* state precisely that $(L, >)$ is a one-dimensional continuum. Now Theorem (17.5.1) is proved in the text for *any* one-dimensional continuum; hence it applies to $(L, >)$. This yields

(17.5.1)* every non-empty subset of K which is bounded "below" has a "greatest lower" bound.

(Again "below," "greatest lower" refer to $>$.) But (17.5.1)* restated in terms of $<$ becomes exactly IV. Thus Axioms I, II, III, IV hold.

The proof given was purposely used in place of a direct proof in order to illustrate an "argument by duality." When, as is the case with one-dimensional continua, a "dual" system [here $(L, >)$] derived from the original [here $(L, <)$] possesses the same properties, the theorems proved for the original may be asserted for the derived system to yield additional theorems in the theory of the original. The reader should study the method of proof carefully, since it is a very important tool in the study of such "self-dual" systems.

(17.5.10) Define a sequence $(J_n; n \in I)$ in K so that, for $n \in I$,

$$J_n = \left[x \in F; x < \frac{n+1}{n}\right],$$

and define

$$J_0 \equiv \left[x \in F; x < \frac{1}{1}\right].$$

That $J_0, J_n \in K$ follows from (17.4.3). Define a sequence $(C_n; n \in I)$ of open intervals so that, for every $n \in I$,

$$C_n = [J \in K; J_0 < J, J < J_n].$$

We show that $n \in I$ implies $J_{n+1} < J_n$. If $x \in J_{n+1}$,

$$x < \frac{n+2}{n+1} < \frac{n+1}{n},$$

and $x \in J_n$. By the density (16.8.2), there exists $y \in F$ with $(n+2)/(n+1) < y$, $y < (n+1)/n$, whence $y \in J_n$, $y \in' J_{n+1}$. This proves $J_{n+1} < J_n$. Now if $n \in I$, then $J \in C_{n+1}$ implies $J < J_{n+1}$, whence $J < J_n$, and $J \in C_n$. The sequence $(C_n; n \in I)$ is therefore nested. It is easily proved that $n \in I$ implies $C_n \neq \Theta$.

Suppose J exists such that $J \in C_n$ for every $n \in I$. It follows that $J_0 < J$. There exists $b \in F$ with $b \in J$, $b \in' J_0$. Since J has no greatest element, there exists $b' \in J$ such that $b' > b$. Now $b' \in' J_0$, since otherwise $b \in J_0$. Define

$$J' \equiv [x \in F; x < b'].$$

It follows easily by familiar arguments that

$$J_0 < J', \quad J' < J.$$

Let $b' = p/q$. Evidently $b' > 1/1$, so that $p > q$. Define $n \equiv q + 1$. Then

$$\frac{n+1}{n} = \frac{q+2}{q+1} < \frac{q+1}{q} \leqq \frac{p}{q},$$

so that $J_n \subset J'$. This leads to $J_n < J$ and contradicts $J \in C_n$.

Chapter 18

(18.2.10) We show first that, in the proof of III, if $[f + h; f \in J] \subset J$, then, for every $f \in J$, $t \in I$, it is true that $f + t \cdot h \in J$. Define

$$H \equiv [t \in I; f \in J \text{ implies } f + t \cdot h \in J].$$

Clearly $1 \in H$. Suppose $q \in H$, and let $f \in J$. Then

$$f + (q+1) \cdot h = (f + q \cdot h) + h \in J,$$

since $f + q \cdot h \epsilon J$. Hence $q + 1 \epsilon H$. To prove IV, let $J_1, J_2 \epsilon \mathcal{P}$ with $J_1 \otimes J_2$, and let $m \epsilon I$. Then $m \odot J_1 = [m \cdot h; h \epsilon J_1]$ and $m \odot J_2 = [m \cdot h; h \epsilon J_2]$. Let $k \epsilon m \odot J_1$, so that there exists $h_1 \epsilon J_1$ such that $k = m \cdot h_1$. Since $J_1 \subset J_2$, $h_1 \epsilon J_2$, whence $m \cdot h_1 \epsilon m \odot J_2$. This proves $m \odot J_1 \subset m \odot J_2$. But $J_1 \neq J_2$, whence there exists $h_2 \epsilon J_2$ such that $h_2 \epsilon' J_1$. Then $m \cdot h_2 \epsilon m \odot J_2$ and $m \cdot h_2 \epsilon' m \odot J_1$ (since $m \cdot h_2 = m \cdot h_3$ implies $h_2 = h_3$). Thus $m \odot J_1 \neq m \odot J_2$. This proves IV. To prove V, note that

$$m \odot (n \odot J) = [m \cdot (n \cdot h); h \epsilon J];$$
$$(m \cdot n) \odot J = [(m \cdot n) \cdot h; h \epsilon J].$$

(18.3.11) The set $S \equiv [x \epsilon \mathfrak{F}; a \otimes x, x \otimes b]$ is non-empty by (18.3.7). Suppose S finite. Then, by (15.5.3), there is a least $f \epsilon S$. But, by (18.3.7), there exists $g \epsilon \mathfrak{F}$ with $a \otimes g$, $g \otimes f \otimes b$. Then $g \epsilon S$, contradicting that f is a least.

(18.4.7) Similar to (14.2.18).

(18.4.8) To prove $J_1 = [\varphi^*(x_2); x_2 \epsilon J_2]$ is a lower cut, note first that $J_1 \neq \Theta$ follows from $J_2 \neq \Theta$. Now, by (16.10.2), φ is an isomorphism between the algebraic systems of positive rational numbers associated with $(\mathfrak{F}_1, v_1, \odot_1)$ and $(\mathfrak{F}_2, v_2, \odot_2)$; in particular, if $y_1, z_1 \epsilon \mathfrak{F}_1$, then $y_1 \otimes_1 z_1$ if and only if $\varphi(y_1) \otimes_2 \varphi(z_1)$, and, if $y_2, z_2 \epsilon \mathfrak{F}_2$, then $y_2 \otimes_2 z_2$ if and only if $\varphi^*(y_2) \otimes_1 \varphi^*(z_2)$. From this it is easily seen that, if b is an upper bound of J_2, then $\varphi^*(b)$ is an upper bound of J_1. Also, if J_1 has a greatest c, then $\varphi(c)$ is a greatest in J_2. Finally, let $t_1 \epsilon J_1$ and $s_1 \otimes_1 t_1$. Then $t_1 = \varphi^*(t_2)$, $s_1 = \varphi^*(s_2)$ with $s_2, t_2 \epsilon J_2$ and $s_2 \otimes_2 t_2$. Since J_2 is a lower set, $s_2 \epsilon J_2$, whence $s_1 \epsilon J_1$, and J_1 is a lower set. Hence J_1 is a lower cut. The remainder of the proof is straightforward.

(18.5.9) Define

$$T \equiv [x_1 \cdot x_2; x_1, x_2 \epsilon \mathfrak{F}, x_1 \otimes f_1, x_2 \otimes f_2],$$

so that $f_1 \otimes f_2 = \text{l.u.b. } T$. If $y \epsilon S$, then $y = x_1 \cdot x_2 < f_1 \cdot f_2$, so that $f_1 \cdot f_2$ is an upper bound of T. Let $b \epsilon \mathcal{P}$ be any upper bound of T and suppose $b \otimes f_1 \cdot f_2$. By (18.3.7), there exists $g \epsilon \mathfrak{F}$ such that $b \otimes g < f_1 \cdot f_2$. By (18.5.3.b), there exist $h_1, h_2 \epsilon \mathfrak{F}$ such that $g = h_1 \cdot h_2$, $h_1 < f_1$, $h_2 < f_2$. Then $g \epsilon T$, contradicting that b is an upper bound of T. Hence $f_1 \cdot f_2 \leqq b$, and $f_1 \cdot f_2 = \text{l.u.b. } T$. The proof is complete.

(18.5.10) Define

$$T \equiv [x_1 \cdot x_2; x_1, x_2 \epsilon \mathfrak{F}, x_1 \otimes a_1, x_2 \otimes a_2],$$

and let $f \otimes a_1 \otimes a_2$. Since $a_1 \otimes a_2 = \text{l.u.b. } T$, f is not an upper bound of T, and there exists $y \epsilon T$ with $f < y$. Since $y \epsilon T$, there exist $f_1, f_2 \epsilon \mathfrak{F}$ with $y = f_1 \cdot f_2$, $f_1 \otimes a_1$, $f_2 \otimes a_2$. Since $f < f_1 \cdot f_2$, by (18.5.3.b) there exist $g_1, g_2 \in \mathfrak{F}$ such that $f = g_1 \cdot g_2, g_1 < f_1, g_2 < f_2$. But $g_1 \bigcirc\!\!\!\!< a_1, g_2 \bigcirc\!\!\!\!< a_2$. Hence $f \in T$. Conversely let $f \in T$, so that there exist $g_1, g_2 \in \mathfrak{F}$ such that $f = g_1 \cdot g_2, g_1 \bigcirc\!\!\!\!< a_1, g_2 \bigcirc\!\!\!\!< a_2$. By (18.3.7), there exist $x_1, x_2 \in \mathfrak{F}$ such that $g_1 \bigcirc\!\!\!\!< x_1, x_1 \bigcirc\!\!\!\!< a_1, g_2 \bigcirc\!\!\!\!< x_2, x_2 \bigcirc\!\!\!\!< a_2$. Then $g_1 \cdot g_2 < x_1 \cdot x_2$. But $x_1 \cdot x_2 \in T$, whence $x_1 \cdot x_2 \circledleq a_1 \otimes a_2 = \text{l.u.b. } T$. Hence $f = g_1 \cdot g_2 \bigcirc\!\!\!\!< a_1 \otimes a_2$. This proves (18.5.6.b).

(18.5.11) To prove (a), note that

$$a \oplus b = \text{l.u.b. } [x + y;\, x, y \in \mathfrak{F},\, x \bigcirc\!\!\!\!< a,\, y \bigcirc\!\!\!\!< b];$$
$$b \oplus a = \text{l.u.b. } [y + x;\, x, y \in \mathfrak{F},\, y \bigcirc\!\!\!\!< b,\, x \bigcirc\!\!\!\!< a].$$

To prove (b), define

$$S \equiv [x + y;\, x, y \in \mathfrak{F},\, x \bigcirc\!\!\!\!< (a \oplus b),\, y \bigcirc\!\!\!\!< c];$$
$$T \equiv [r + s;\, r, s \in \mathfrak{F},\, r \bigcirc\!\!\!\!< a,\, s \bigcirc\!\!\!\!< (b \oplus c)].$$

Then $(a \oplus b) \oplus c = \text{l.u.b. } S$ and $a \oplus (b \oplus c) = \text{l.u.b. } T$, and it suffices to prove that $S = T$. Let $z \in S$. Then there exist $x, y \in S$ with $z = x + y, x \bigcirc\!\!\!\!< a \oplus b, y \bigcirc\!\!\!\!< c$. By (18.5.6.a), there exist $f_1, f_2 \in \mathfrak{F}$ such that $x = f_1 + f_2, f_1 \bigcirc\!\!\!\!< a, f_2 \bigcirc\!\!\!\!< b$. But $z = f_1 + f_2 + y$. Define $r \equiv f_1, s \equiv f_2 + y$. Then $z = r + s, r = f_1 \bigcirc\!\!\!\!< a, s = f_2 + y \bigcirc\!\!\!\!< b \oplus c$ by (18.5.6.a). Thus $z \in T$, and we have shown $S \subset T$. Similarly $T \subset S$, and the proof of (b) is complete. The proofs of (c), (d) are parallel to the above with $+$ replaced by $\cdot$ and $\oplus$ by $\otimes$.

(18.5.12) The proof is similar to the proof of (12.2.8) in view of (18.5.7.e).

(18.6.8) Since $a \bigcirc\!\!\!\!< b$, $a \oplus c \bigcirc\!\!\!\!< b \oplus c$ by (18.6.6.a). Similarly, since $c \bigcirc\!\!\!\!< d$, $b \oplus c \bigcirc\!\!\!\!< b \oplus d$. Then $a \oplus c \bigcirc\!\!\!\!< b \oplus d$ by transitivity. The proof of the other half is similar, using (18.6.6.c).

(18.6.9) If $a \bigcirc\!\!\!\!< b$, then $a^2 \bigcirc\!\!\!\!< b^2$ by (18.6.8). Now let $a^2 \bigcirc\!\!\!\!< b^2$. Then, if $b \circledleq a$, we have $b^2 \circledleq a^2$, contrary to $a^2 \bigcirc\!\!\!\!< b^2$.

(18.6.10) Let $a \bigcirc\!\!\!\!< v$ and suppose $a^{-1} \circledleq v$. Then, by **(18.6.8)** or (18.6.6.c), $a \otimes a^{-1} \bigcirc\!\!\!\!< v \otimes v = v$. But $a \otimes a^{-1} = v$, by the definition of an inverse. Thus $v \bigcirc\!\!\!\!< v$, which is a contradiction; this proves $v \bigcirc\!\!\!\!< a^{-1}$. The other half is similar.

(18.6.11) Since $f \bigcirc\!\!\!\!< v$, we have $v \bigcirc\!\!\!\!< f^{-1}$ by (18.6.10). It is easily seen that $f^{-1} \in \mathfrak{F}$. Applying (18.6.1.b) to $a \cdot f^{-1}, f^{-1}$, we have the existence of $g \in \mathfrak{F}$ such that $g \bigcirc\!\!\!\!< a \cdot f^{-1}, a \cdot f^{-1} \bigcirc\!\!\!\!< g \cdot f^{-1}$. Then, by (18.6.6.d), $g \cdot f \bigcirc\!\!\!\!< a, a \bigcirc\!\!\!\!< g$.

(18.6.12) Suppose that $b^n \circledleq a$ for every $n \in I$. Then $S \equiv [b^n;\, n \in I]$ is bounded above and so has a least upper bound $x \in \mathcal{P}$. Since $v \bigcirc\!\!\!\!< b$, by (18.6.1.b) there exists $g \in \mathfrak{F}$ such that $g \mathbin{\textcircled{<}} x$, $x \mathbin{\textcircled{<}} g \cdot b$. Since $g \mathbin{\textcircled{<}} x$, g is not an upper bound of S, and so there exists $m \in I$ such that $g < b^m$. Then $g \cdot b < b^m \cdot b = b^{m+1}$. But $b^{m+1} \in S$ and $x \mathbin{\textcircled{<}} b^{m+1}$. This contradicts that x is an upper bound of S.

(18.6.13) This is similar to (18.6.12) using g.l.b. instead of l.u.b. [see (17.5.1)] and (18.6.11) instead of (18.6.1.b).

(18.7.3) It has been shown that $\mathcal{P} - \mathfrak{F} \neq \Theta$. Let $x \in \mathcal{P} - \mathfrak{F}$. Since $a \mathbin{\textcircled{<}} b$ then, by (18.3.7), there exist $f_1, f_2 \in \mathfrak{F}$ such that $a \mathbin{\textcircled{<}} f_1 < f_2 \mathbin{\textcircled{<}} b$. Since $f_1 < f_2$, there exists $h \in \mathfrak{F}$ such that $f_1 + h = f_2$. By (18.6.1.a), there exists $k \in \mathfrak{F}$ such that $k \mathbin{\textcircled{<}} x \mathbin{\textcircled{<}} k + h$. Consider separately the three cases $f_1 = k$, $f_1 < k$, $k < f_1$. If $f_1 = k$, then $f_1 = k \mathbin{\textcircled{<}} x \mathbin{\textcircled{<}} k + h = f_1 + h = f_2$, and $a \mathbin{\textcircled{<}} x \mathbin{\textcircled{<}} b$. If $f_1 < k$, there exists $g \in \mathfrak{F}$ such that $f_1 + g = k$. But $g < k \mathbin{\textcircled{<}} x$, so that there exists $y \in \mathcal{P}$ such that $y \oplus g = x$. From $f_1 + g = k \mathbin{\textcircled{<}} x = y \oplus g$ it follows that $f_1 \mathbin{\textcircled{<}} y$. Similarly $y \mathbin{\textcircled{<}} f_1 + h = f_2$. Hence $a \mathbin{\textcircled{<}} y \mathbin{\textcircled{<}} b$. But $y \in \mathcal{P} - \mathfrak{F}$. For if $y \in \mathfrak{F}$, then, since $g \in \mathfrak{F}$, $x = y + g \in \mathfrak{F}$, contrary to $x \in \mathcal{P} - \mathfrak{F}$. The remaining case $k < f_1$ is treated similarly.

Chapter 19

(19.4.14) Let $r = \{p, q\}$. Since $s \in \mathsf{P}$, there exists $m \in \mathcal{P}$ such that $s = \{m + v, v\}$. Then $r \oplus s = \{p + m + v, q + v\}$, and $r \mathbin{\textcircled{<}} r \oplus s$ since $p + q + v < q + p + m + v$.

(19.4.15) $\{p, q\} \oplus \{q, p\} = \{p + q, q + p\} = \{v, v\} = 0$.

(19.4.16) This is similar to (14.2.20).

(19.4.17) Let $g, h, p, q, m \in \mathcal{P}$ such that $r = \{g, h\}$, $s = \{p, q\}$, $t = \{m + v, v\}$. Since $r \mathbin{\textcircled{<}} s$, $g + q < h + p$. Now

$$r \otimes t = \{g \cdot m + g + h, h \cdot m + h + g\} = \{g \cdot m, h \cdot m\},$$

and

$$s \otimes t = \{p \cdot m + p + q, q \cdot m + q + p\} = \{p \cdot m, q \cdot m\}.$$

Then $r \otimes t \mathbin{\textcircled{<}} s \otimes t$ follows since $m \cdot g + m \cdot q < m \cdot h + m \cdot p$.

(19.5.9) Let $r = \{p, q\}$, $s = \{m, n\}$. Then $-r = \{q, p\}$, $-s = \{n, m\}$ [see (19.4.15)]. Thus

$$\begin{aligned}(-r) \otimes s &= \{q \cdot m + p \cdot n, q \cdot n + p \cdot m\}\\ &= -\{q \cdot n + p \cdot m, q \cdot m + p \cdot n\}\\ &= -(r \otimes s).\end{aligned}$$

This proves (a). To prove (b), since $\otimes$ is commutative, we have

$$r \otimes (-s) = (-s) \otimes r = -(s \otimes r) = -(r \otimes s).$$

Finally, (c) follows from (a), (b), in view of (19.5.8).

(19.5.10) Begin as in (19.5.9).

(19.7.18) Straightforward.

(19.7.19) By (19.7.10),

$$\begin{aligned}(-a) \otimes (-(a^{-1})) &= -(a \otimes (-(a^{-1}))) \\ &= -(-(a \otimes a^{-1})) = -(-\mathsf{w}) = \mathsf{w}.\end{aligned}$$

(19.7.20) By (19.7.4), from $a \olessthan b$ it follows that $a \otimes b^{-1} \olessthan b \otimes b^{-1} = \mathsf{w}$. Suppose $a^{-1} \oleq b^{-1}$. Then $a \otimes a^{-1} \oleq a \otimes b^{-1}$, whence $\mathsf{w} \olessthan \mathsf{w}$, which is a contradiction.

(19.8.12) First note that no use of Axiom I(c) has been made in any of the proofs in (19.7), (19.8), and so the theorems of these sections can be used. Let $a, b \in \mathsf{P}$ with $a \olessthan b$. Consider the following cases: (1) $a \in \mathsf{P}$, $b \in \mathsf{P}$; (2) $a = 0$, $b \in \mathsf{P}$; (3) $a \in \mathsf{N}$, $b \in \mathsf{P}$; (4) $a \in \mathsf{N}$, $b = 0$; (5) $a \in \mathsf{N}$, $b \in \mathsf{N}$ (since $a \olessthan b$, no other cases are possible). In (1), there exists $x \in \mathsf{P}$ such that $a \olessthan x$, $x \olessthan b$ by (19.8.9). In (2), use the fact that P has no least, whence there exists $x \in \mathsf{P}$ with $x \olessthan b$. Since $x \in \mathsf{P}$, $0 \olessthan x$. In (3), $x = 0$ is effective. In (4), $-a \in \mathsf{P}$, so there exists $x \in \mathsf{P}$ with $0 \olessthan x \olessthan -a$. Then, by (19.7.5), $a \olessthan -x \olessthan 0$. In (5), $-a$, $-b \in \mathsf{P}$ and $-b \olessthan -a$, whence there exists x with $-b \olessthan x \olessthan -a$, and $a \olessthan -x \olessthan b$.

(19.8.13) Compare with (18.5.12).

(19.9) Compare with (18.4.4), (18.4.5).

(19.10.7) R and P are uncountable, since $(\mathsf{R}, <)$ and $(\mathsf{P}, <)$ are one-dimensional continua. Also $\mathsf{N} \sim \mathsf{P}$, whence N is uncountable. Since $(\mathsf{F}, <, 1, \odot)$ is a basic system of positive rational numbers, it follows that F is countable. Also $[-f;\, f \in \mathsf{F}] \sim \mathsf{F}$, whence $[-f;\, f \in \mathsf{F}]$ is countable; $\mathsf{T} = \mathsf{F} + [-f;\, f \in \mathsf{F}] + [0]$ is a finite sum of countable sets and hence is countable. Then $\mathsf{E}\ (\subset \mathsf{T})$ and $\mathsf{I}\ (\subset \mathsf{E})$ are countable.

(19.10.8) Since $1 \in \mathsf{I}$ by (19.10.1.a), it follows that 1 is in each of the sets. It remains to prove that, for each set,

(1) if a and b are in the set, then $a + b$, $a \cdot b$ are in the set.

This follows for I, since, for $m, n \in \mathsf{I}$,

$$\begin{aligned}(m \odot 1) + (n \odot 1) &= (m + n) \odot 1 && \text{[see (12.4.2)]} \\ (m \odot 1) \cdot (n \odot 1) &= m \odot (n \odot 1) = (m \cdot n) \odot 1 && \text{[by (19.8.6)].}\end{aligned}$$

Also, (1) follows for F, since, for $x, y, s, t \in \mathsf{I}$,

$$(x \cdot y^{-1}) + (s \cdot t^{-1}) = ((x \cdot t) + (s \cdot y)) \cdot (t \cdot y)^{-1},$$

as is easily proved, since

$$(x \cdot y^{-1}) \cdot (s \cdot t^{-1}) = (x \cdot s) \cdot (t \cdot y)^{-1},$$

and since $x \cdot t, s \cdot y, t \cdot y, x \cdot s \in \mathsf{I}$. Also, (1) is now evident for $\mathsf{I} + [0]$, $\mathsf{F} + [0]$, $\mathsf{P} + [0]$ in view of (19.7.1), (19.7.9). To prove (1) for E and T, one considers cases, using the fact that $\mathsf{R} = \mathsf{P} + \mathsf{N} + [0]$.

(19.10.9) If $a, b \in \mathsf{T}$ (or E), then $a + x = b$ with $x = b + (-a) \in \mathsf{T}$ (or E). In view of commutativity of $+$ and (19.10.3), $(\mathsf{T}, +)$, $(\mathsf{E}, +)$ are groups. If $a, b \in \mathsf{T} - [0]$, then $a \cdot x = b$ with $x = (a^{-1}) \cdot b$. It is readily shown that $a^{-1} \in \mathsf{T}$, $a^{-1} \neq 0$, whence $x \in \mathsf{T} - [0]$.

(19.10.10) The proof of (19.8.12) may be modified to obtain $x \in \mathsf{F}$ or $x = 0$ or $-x \in \mathsf{F}$, whence $x \in \mathsf{T}$.

Chapter 20

(20.2.3) Direct verification of the eight equalities establishes III [similar to the treatment of (7.2.1)]. To prove VI, verify the eight equalities like

$$(m + n) \cdot m = n \cdot m = m = m + m = m \cdot m + n \cdot m.$$

(20.2.4) Axiom I is obvious; II follows from (7.2.2); III is proved directly by verifying twenty-seven equalities from the table (similar to (7.2.7)); IV is similarly proved (six equalities are verified); proof of VI is similar to that of III. The following prove V, since $p = 0$:

$$q \cdot p = p, \quad q \cdot q = q, \quad q \cdot r = r,$$
$$r \cdot p = p, \quad r \cdot r = q, \quad r \cdot q = r.$$

(20.2.5) The set of real numbers is not equivalent to the set of rational numbers, since the latter is countable and the former is not. Hence the systems are not isomorphic. This proof depends on consistency for the positive integers, while the proof in the text does not.

(20.3.11) The proof of (a) is similar to that of (12.2.8). [See also (18.5.12), (19.8.13).] Proof of (b): If $m \in I_n$ implies $a_m = 0$, then, by (a) and (20.3.3),

$$\sum_{m=1}^{n} a_m = \sum_{m=1}^{n} 0 = \sum_{m=1}^{n} (0 \cdot a_m) = 0 \cdot \sum_{m=1}^{n} a_m = 0.$$

(20.3.12) (a) Isomorphism (one-to-one correspondence) by (20.3.2) and (10.2.2);
(b) isomorphism, since $a, b \in K$ implies

$$F(a + b) = -(a + b) = -a + (-b) = F(a) + F(b)$$

by (20.3.2.d);
(d) isomorphism, since $F(0) = -0 = 0$ by (20.3.2.c).
(c), (f) Since F carries $+$ into $+$, these are equivalent. If $a, b \in K$,

$$F(a \cdot b) = -(a \cdot b);$$
$$F(a) \cdot F(b) = (-a) \cdot (-b).$$

If $a = 0$ or $b = 0$, it follows that $F(a \cdot b) = F(a) \cdot F(b)$. In (20.2.1), $-(n \cdot n) = -n = n = n \cdot n = (-n) \cdot (-n)$, so that F is an isomorphism, since $F(a \cdot b) = F(a) \cdot F(b)$ for every $a, b \in K$. However, in (20.2.2), $(-q) \cdot (-r) = r \cdot q = r$, while $-(q \cdot r) = -r = q$, so that $F(q \cdot r) \neq F(q) \cdot F(r)$. The reader can show that, in the rational or real number system, F is not an isomorphism.

(e) Here again F may be, but need not be, an isomorphism; in (20.2.1), $-1 = 1$, so that the answer is affirmative. But in the other examples, the answer is negative, since $-1 \neq 1$.

(20.3.13) Let F be an isomorphism. Then

$$0 + F(0) = F(0 + 0) = F(0) + F(0),$$

whence $0 = F(0)$ by cancellation. Similarly,

$$1 \cdot F(1) = F(1 \cdot 1) = F(1) \cdot F(1)$$

yields $1 = F(1)$.

(20.3.14) Part (a) follows from (12.4.2), which applies since $+$ is associative. PROOF OF (b): Evidently, by (20.3.11.a), (12.4.4),

$$F(m) \cdot F(n) = F(m) \cdot \sum_{k=1}^{n} 1 = \sum_{k=1}^{n} F(m) = \sum_{k=1}^{n}\left(\sum_{j=1}^{m} 1\right) = \sum_{k=1}^{n \cdot m} 1 = F(m \cdot n).$$

If F is a one-to-one correspondence between I and K_0, then K is infinite. (This is false in (20.2.1), (20.2.2).) In the rational or real number system, F is a one-to-one correspondence. In (20.2.1), $0 \in K_0$, since $F(2) = 1 + 1 = 0$. But, in the rational number system, $0 \in' K_0$.

(20.3.15) The proof is easily made by induction with the help of (12.2.6), (20.3.6).

(20.4.16) In view of III, (12.4.3) and (12.4.5) apply to yield the desired results.

(20.4.17) These are all easy; for example, the analogue of (9.8.5.c) is this: *Let $a, b, c \in K$. Then $b, c \neq 0$ implies $(a/b) \cdot c = a/(b/c)$.*

PROOF: By (20.4.7.c), (20.4.13), (20.4.10), $a/(b/c) = (a/1)/(b/c) = (a/1) \cdot (c/b) = (a \cdot c)/(b \cdot 1) = (a/b) \cdot c$.

(20.4.18) If n is even, there exists $k \in I$ with $n = 2 \cdot k$. Then

$$\begin{aligned}(-a)^n = (-a)^{2 \cdot k} &= ((-a)^2)^k && \text{[by (20.4.16)]}\\ &= (a^2)^k && \text{[by (20.4.2)]}\\ &= a^{2 \cdot k} = a^n.\end{aligned}$$

If n is odd, then let $n = 2 \cdot k + 1$, whence

$$(-a)^n = (-a)^{2 \cdot k} \cdot (-a) = -(a^{2 \cdot k} \cdot a) = -a^{2 \cdot k + 1} = -a^n.$$

Prove the last part by induction.

(20.4.19) Trivial.

(20.4.20) Use the fact that $-a = (-1) \cdot a$ and (20.3.11.a) to obtain the first part. Use induction to prove the second part.

(20.5.8) (c) We have

$$\begin{aligned} (a - b) + c &= c + (a - b) & \\ &= (c + a) - b & \text{[by (a)]} \\ &= (a + c) - b & \\ &= a + (c - b) & \text{[by (a)]} \\ &= a - (b - c) & \text{[by (20.5.3.b)].} \end{aligned}$$

(20.5.9) Referring to (20.3.14), we see, in view of (20.3.11), that, for $(n, a) \in I \times K$

$$n \odot a = F(n) \cdot a.$$

Hence, by (20.3.14), if $m, n \in I$, $a \in K$, then

$$(m + n) \odot a = (m \odot a) + (n \odot a),$$
$$(m \cdot n) \odot a = m \odot (n \odot a).$$

Further properties (let $a, b \in K$, $m, n \in I$):

$$m \odot (a + b) = F(m) \cdot (a + b) = (m \odot a) + (m \odot b);$$
$$m \odot (a \cdot b) = (m \odot a) \cdot b;$$
$$1 \odot a = a;$$
$$n \odot 0 = 0;$$
$$m > n \text{ implies } (m - n) \odot a = (m \odot a) - (n \odot a);$$
$$(m \odot a) \cdot (n \odot b) = (m \cdot n) \odot (a \cdot b);$$
$$n \mid m, n \odot a \neq 0 \text{ implies } (m \odot a)/(n \odot a) = (m \div n) \odot 1.$$

(20.5.10) $(a \cdot b)^n = a^n \cdot b^n$ [use induction]; $(a/b)^n = (a \cdot (b^{-1}))^n = a^n \cdot ((b)^{-1})^n = a^n \cdot (b^n)^{-1} = a^n/b^n$ by (20.4.20) with $a_m = b$.

(20.5.11)

$$(a + b)^1 = a + b;$$
$$(a + b)^2 = a^2 + 2 \odot (a \cdot b) + b^2;$$
$$(a + b)^3 = a^3 + 3 \odot (a^2 \cdot b) + 3 \odot (a \cdot b^2) + b^3;$$
$$(a + b)^4 = a^4 + 4 \odot (a^3 \cdot b) + 6 \odot (a^2 \cdot b^2) + 4 \odot (a \cdot b^3) + b^4;$$
$$(a - b)^3 = a^3 - 3 \odot (a^2 \cdot b) + 3 \odot (a \cdot b^2) - b^3.$$

(20.5.12)

$$\frac{a \cdot b}{a + b} \text{ if } a + b \neq 0; \quad \frac{a \cdot b}{b - a} \text{ if } a \neq b;$$

$$\frac{(a + 1) \cdot b}{(b + 1) \cdot a} \text{ if } b \neq -1.$$

INDEX